TTINGHAM

AWN

RARY

DEP... ... ADULT EDUCATION
(...Joint A... ...asses Committee)

CIRCULATING LIBRARY

Class 102   No 9387   Vol

RC480 . E9

BEHAVIOUR THERAPY
AND
THE NEUROSES

It is a wretched argument that is supported by custom and tradition . . . There are only two ways to arrive at knowledge—experience (through personal experiment) and reason.

ROGER BACON (1214–1286)

BEHAVIOUR THERAPY AND THE NEUROSES

Readings in modern methods of treatment
derived from Learning Theory

EDITED BY

H. J. EYSENCK, Ph.D.

PROFESSOR OF PSYCHOLOGY, UNIVERSITY OF LONDON

DIRECTOR, PSYCHOLOGICAL LABORATORIES,
INSTITUTE OF PSYCHIATRY

PSYCHOLOGIST,
MAUDSLEY AND BETHLEM ROYAL HOSPITALS

UNIVERSITY OF NOTTINGHAM
DEPT. OF EXTRA-MURAL STUDIES

SYMPOSIUM PUBLICATIONS DIVISION

PERGAMON PRESS

OXFORD · LONDON · NEW YORK · PARIS

1960

PERGAMON PRESS LTD.
Headington Hill Hall, Oxford
4 and 5 Fitzroy Square, London W.1

PERGAMON PRESS INC.
122 East 55th Street, New York 22, N.Y.
P.O. Box 47715, Los Angeles, California

PERGAMON PRESS S.A.R.L.
24 Rue des Écoles, Paris Vᵉ

PERGAMON PRESS G.m.b.H.
Kaiserstrasse 75, Frankfurt am Main

Copyright © 1960
Pergamon Press Ltd.

10029783 21

Library of Congress Card No. 60-8296

Printed in Great Britain by Bell and Bain Ltd., Glasgow

TO THE MEMORY OF
J. B. WATSON

CONTENTS

CONTENTS

FOREWORD

DISSATISFACTION with current methods of psychotherapeutical treatment in the field of the neuroses and behaviour disorders is widespread. There appears to have occurred what one critic characterized as " the premature crystallization of spurious orthodoxy "; the unsupported assumptions and theories of psychoanalysis have established a stranglehold upon psychiatric practice, and are now widely accepted in spite of the lack of experimental or clinical evidence in their favour. Psychiatrists in training are now frequently indoctrinated with these mumpsimus beliefs and no critical voices are allowed to reach their ears, nor are they exposed to factual accounts of methods of treatment different from those considered " orthodox." They are not permitted to experience for themselves the truth of Michael Faraday's words: " They reason theoretically, without demonstrating experimentally, and errors are the result."

There have, of course, been many dissenting voices, and a number of ingenious experiments have demonstrated the usefulness of alternative methods of treatment. Hitherto, however, these voices have been isolated and these experiments remained unknown and probably inaccessible to the practising psychiatrist or clinical psychologist. It is the purpose of this book to bring together a number of such accounts and to attempt to show that they can all be unified theoretically under the general heading of " behaviour therapy." This term, as is explained in the first chapter, has been introduced to characterize a large group of methods of treatment, all of which owe their existence and their theoretical justification to modern learning theory; they thus derive from Pavlov, Watson, and Hull, rather than from Freud, Jung, and Adler. It will be argued that behaviour therapy is an *alternative* type of treatment to psychotherapy; that it is a *superior* type of treatment, both from the point of view of theoretical background and practical effectiveness; and that, in so far as psychotherapy is at all effective, it is so in virtue of certain principles which can be *derived from learning theory*. In other words, it will be suggested that psychotherapy itself, when shorn of its inessential and irrelevant parts, can usefully be considered as a minor part of behaviour therapy.

In presenting the various chapters and sections, I have attempted (in a very preliminary way) to organize the different methods used by psychologists and psychiatrists; the final grouping adopted is not necessarily the best—and certainly not the only one which might be used. It may serve, however, to indicate the multiplicity of weapons at our disposal and the necessity of choosing the correct one in each particular case. A proper analysis of the dynamics of each case (using the term here in the sense in which I used it in the title of my book *Dynamics of Anxiety and Hysteria*) still remains an essential preliminary to treatment.

The selection of papers included will indicate to the reader the necessity to make himself thoroughly acquainted with modern psychology and in particular with modern learning theory, before attempting to use or even judge these methods. It cannot be said too plainly that a superficial knowledge of some of Pavlov's writings is not sufficient to undertake behaviour therapy with any reasonable hope of success; there have been considerable developments in learning theory in the last 30 years and a thorough mastery of this field is required for anyone wishing to establish for himself the truth of any claims made for these methods.

Much fundamental work in this field has been done on animals and should perhaps have been included here. Lack of space has prevented any but the briefest mention, except for a special chapter contributed by Mr. Kendrick on recent work dealing with *conditioned inhibition*. This was done because of the theoretical importance of this concept and because much of this material had not previously been published. For other work the reader will have to go to the references given by several writers; or else he may wish to consult the chapter by P. Broadhurst on experimental neurosis in the *Handbook of Abnormal Psychology* (ed. H. J. Eysenck), published by Pitman. In this handbook will also be found much more extensive theoretical and experimental documentation of many points than could be included here.

Most of the contents of this book are reprints of articles published in psychological and psychiatric journals. In a number of cases original material is presented for the first time; thus I am indebted to Mr. Gwynne Jones for his review of the voluminous literature of the conditioning therapy of enuresis, which could not have been covered in any other way. Other colleagues have contributed further follow-up material on cases previously published; I am indebted to Mr. Sylvester, Mr. Gwynne Jones and Mr. Walton in this connection. A number of entirely new cases are reported here for the first time; thanks are due to Dr. Wolpe, Mr. Walton, Dr. Beech, Mr. Bevan and Mrs. Maclaren.

Last but certainly not least, I am indebted to authors and publishers who permitted articles and papers to be reproduced in this book. In looking through the list of contributors as it finally appears, I note that present and former colleagues and students have contributed about half of the contents; among these are A. Yates, V. Meyer, J. Sylvester, D. Walton, H. Gwynne Jones, R. Beech, C. Franks and D. Kendrick. Not represented, although strongly influential through both his writing and teaching, has been Dr. M. Shapiro, who is in charge of the clinical training courses in the department.

All of these have very much influenced my own views through their practical and theoretical work; without them I would never have attempted to put this book together. I am also much indebted to Dr. J. Wolpe, whose fundamental book *Psychotherapy by Reciprocal Inhibition* marks the coming of age of behaviour therapy as an independent and practically applicable discipline; his advice and discussion have been both stimulating and helpful. Professor A. Lewis and several consultants at the Maudsley and Bethlem Royal Hospitals deserve our sincerest thanks for giving permission to have cases under their care treated by means of these new methods; it should not be assumed that they necessarily share the views here expressed. Nor should it be assumed that the editor necessarily shares all the views expressed by contributors; in many cases the complexity of the subject makes alternative theories and points of view equally possible, and only experiment can decide between them.

The growth of behaviour therapy has been uneven, sporadic and unco-ordinated; it is my hope that this book will not only introduce its methods to a wider circle, but will also pull together some of the strands so that by mutual reinforcement they will be able all the more readily to carry the burden imposed on us by the proliferation of neurotic and behaviour disorders.

Institute of Psychiatry,   H. J. EYSENCK
(Maudsley Hospital),
University of London

Part I

THEORETICAL BASES
AND CLASSICAL EXPERIMENTS

INTRODUCTION

THE PAPERS in this section are intended to furnish the reader with some basic theoretical considerations and arguments, and to make accessible to him some early classics, such as the famous cases of " little Albert " and of Peter. The first paper deals with "learning theory and behaviour therapy," and in a way may be regarded as a general introduction to this book. Originally delivered as a lecture, this paper provoked so much discussion and so many requests for reprints (and also so many complaints that the references were inaccessible to most clinical workers !) that the notion of publishing a book of readings in this field may be said to have originated as a response to this reaction. The paper by Yates is included because in dealing with " symptoms and symptom substitution " it goes straight to the heart of the difference between therapy behaviour and psychotherapy. The paper on " psychotherapy as a problem in learning theory " is included both because it contains much basic discussion of theoretical issues and also because it has become a classic as being the first determined attempt to show that in so far as psychotherapy is successful, it is so by virtue of following certain principles of learning theory and not by virtue of the esoteric practices and theories, supererogatory at best, which are superimposed upon this basis by different schools.

As regards the papers by Watson and Rayner, and by Mary Cover Jones, nothing needs to be said in justification of their inclusion. It is the work of these writers, more than anything else, which may be said to have formed the beginnings of " behaviour therapy," and to have laid the theoretical foundations for it; however crude and even naive they may sound at times, these articles have succeeded in doing something which is given to few papers to achieve—they have formed the springboard for a new advance in the scientific treatment of neurosis.

The last paper in this section deals with " modern learning theory " and has been included largely because it may serve to introduce the symbols which some other contributors have used in their writings, and which would not otherwise have been intelligible to readers not familiar with Hull's writings. This paper is extremely short, and should not be regarded as in any sense an introduction to modern learning theory; it merely states in ordinary language certain points which must be thoroughly grasped in order to make understandable some of the arguments to follow.

LEARNING THEORY
AND BEHAVIOUR THERAPY*†

H. J. EYSENCK

Department of Psychology, Institute of Psychiatry, University of London

IT WOULD probably be true to say that the present position in the psychiatric treatment of neurotic disorders is characterized by the following features. (1) With the exception of electroshock, the only method of treatment at all widely used is psychotherapy. (2) In practically all its manifestations, psychotherapy is based on Freudian theories. (3) With the exception of intelligence testing, psychological contributions consist almost entirely in the administration and interpretation of projective tests, usually along psychoanalytic lines. I have argued in the past and quoted numerous experiments in support of these arguments, that there is little evidence for the practical efficacy of psychotherapy,‡ whether strictly Freudian or " eclectic "[7,8]; that Freudian theories are outside the realm of science because of their failure to be consistent, or to generate testable deductions[9]; and that projective tests are so unreliable and lacking in validity that their use, except in research, cannot be defended.[10]§ I shall not here argue these points again; the evidence on which these views are based is quite strong and is growing in strength every year. I shall, instead, try to make a somewhat more constructive contribution by discussing an alternative theory of neurosis, an

* Reprinted by permission of the editor *J. Ment. Sci.*, 1959, **105**, 61–75.
† This paper was delivered on 3 July 1958 to a meeting of the R.M.P.A., and its style inevitably bears traces of the fact that it was originally prepared for verbal presentation. It was followed by another paper, delivered by Mr. Gwynne Jones, giving concrete examples of the application of behaviour therapy from our own experience. Some of these are discussed in his article published in this Journal,[1] and it is suggested that readers interested in the theories here advanced may like to consult this article in order to obtain some notion of the practical methods emanating from these theories. A more detailed discussion of many theoretical points that arise may be found in *Dynamics of Anxiety and Hysteria*,[2] as well as several of my previous books.[3,4,5]
‡ When I first suggested that the literature did not contain any kind of unequivocal proof of the efficacy of psychotherapeutic treatment, this conclusion was widely criticized. Since then however, Dr. Weinstock, Chairman of the Fact-Finding Committee of the Amer. Psychoanalyt. Assoc., has explicitly stated in a lecture delivered at the Maudsley Hospital that his Association made *no claims of therapeutic usefulness for psychoanalytic methods* and in this country Glover[6] has equally explicitly disavowed such claims. On this point, therefore, leading psychoanalysts appear to share my views to a considerable extent.
§ This fact is also beginning to be more widely realized, and it is symptomatic that such well-known departments as that belonging to the New York Psychiatric Hospital, have followed the lead of the Institute of Psychiatry and discontinued the routine use of projective techniques like the Rorschach.

alternative method of treatment and an alternative way of using the know-ledge and competence of psychologists in the attempted curing of neurotic disorders. It need hardly be emphasized that the brief time at my disposal will make it inevitable that what I have to say will sound much more dog-matic than I would like it to be; I have to ask your indulgence in this respect, and request you to bear in mind all the obvious qualifying clauses which, if included in this paper, would swell it to three times its present size.

Few psychiatrists are likely to deny that all behaviour ultimately rests on an inherited basis, but even fewer would be prepared to assert that environ-mental influences played no part in the genesis and modification of behaviour. Once we are agreed that learning and conditioning are instru-mental in determining the different kinds of reaction we may make to environmental stimulation, we will find it very difficult to deny that neurotic reactions, like all others, are *learned* reactions and must obey the laws of learning. Thus, I would like to make my first claim by saying that modern learning theory,[11] and the experimental studies of learning and conditioning carried out by psychologists in their laboratories[12] are extremely relevant to the problems raised by neurotic disorders.[13] If the laws which have been formulated are, not necessarily true, but at least partially correct, then it must follow that we can make deductions from them to cover the type of behaviour represented by neurotic patients, construct a model which will duplicate the important and relevant features of the patient and suggest new and possibly helpful methods of treatment along lines laid down by learning theory. Whether these methods are in fact an improvement over existing methods is, of course, an empirical problem; a few facts are available in this connection and will be mentioned later. It is unfortunate that insistence on empirical proof has not always accompanied the production of theories in the psychiatric field—much needless work, and many heart-breaking failures, could have been avoided if the simple medical practice of clinical trials with proper controls had always been followed in the consideration of such claims.

How, then, does modern learning theory look upon neurosis? In the first place, it would claim that neurotic symptoms are *learned patterns of behaviour* which for some reason or other are *unadaptive*. The paradigm of neurotic symptom formation would be Watson's famous experiment with little Albert, an eleven months old boy who was fond of animals.[14] By a simple process of classical Pavlovian conditioning, Watson created a phobia for white rats in this boy by standing behind him and making a very loud noise by banging an iron bar with a hammer whenever Albert reached for the animal. The rat was the conditioned stimulus in the experiment, the loud fear-producing noise was the unconditioned stimulus. As predicted, the unconditioned response (fear) became conditioned to the C.S. (the rat), and Albert developed a phobia for white rats, and indeed for all furry

animals. This latter feature of the conditioning process is of course familiar
to all students as the generalization gradient[12]; an animal or a person
conditioned to one stimulus also responds, although less and less strongly,
to other stimuli further and further removed from the original one along
some continuum.

The fear of the rat thus conditioned is unadaptive (because white rats
are not in fact dangerous) and hence is considered to be a neurotic symptom;
a similarly conditioned fear of snakes would be regarded as adaptive, and
hence not as neurotic. Yet the mechanism of acquisition is identical in both
cases. This suggests that chance and environmental hazards are likely to
play an important part in the acquisition of neurotic responses. If a rat
happens to be present when the child hears a loud noise, a phobia results;
when it is a snake that is present, a useful habit is built up!

The second claim which modern learning theory would make is this.
People and animals differ in the speed and firmness with which conditioned
responses are built up.[15] Those in whom they are built up particularly
quickly and strongly are more likely to develop phobias and other anxiety
and fear reactions than are people who are relatively difficult to condition.[2]
Watson was lucky in his choice of subject; others have banged away with
hammers on metal bars in an attempt to condition infants, but not always
with the same success. Individual differences must be taken into account
in considering the consequences of any course of attempted conditioning.
Nor is the degree of conditionability the only kind of individual variability
with which we are concerned. Learning theory tells us that the amount of
reinforcement following any action determines in part the amount of
conditioning that takes place.[16] Thus the louder the noise, the greater the
fright of the infant, and the greater the fright, the stronger the phobia.
But different children have different types of autonomic system, and the same
amount of noise produces quite unequal amounts of autonomic upheaval
in different children. Consequently, autonomic reactivity must also be
considered; the more labile or reactive the child, the more likely he is to
produce strongly conditioned fear reactions, anxieties and phobias. The
individual differences in autonomic reactivity and in conditionability have
been conceptualized as giving rise to two dimensions of personality, namely
neuroticism and introversion respectively.[5] The more autonomically reactive,
the more prone will the individual be to neurotic disorders. The more easily
he forms conditioned responses, the more introverted will his behaviour be.
Combine introversion and neuroticism, and you get the dysthymic individual,
the person almost predestined to suffer from anxieties, conditioned fears and
phobias, compulsions and obsessions, reactive depressions and so forth.

But this is only part of the story. Many conditioned responses are
unadaptive, and consequently may embarrass the individual and even drive
him into a mental hospital if sufficiently intense. Yet other conditioned

responses are obviously necessary and desirable; indeed, many of them are indispensable for survival. It has been argued very strongly that the whole process of socialization is built up on the principle of conditioning[17]; the overt display of aggressive and sexual tendencies is severely punished in the child, thus producing conditioned fear and pain responses (anxiety) to situations in which the individual is likely to display such tendencies. He consequently refrains from acting in the forbidden manner, not because of some conscious calculus of hedonic pleasure which attempts to equate the immediate pleasure to be gained from indulgence with the remote probability of later punishment, but because only by not indulging, and by physically removing himself can he relieve the very painful conditioned anxiety responses to the whole situation. Anxiety thus acts as a mediating drive, a drive which may be exceedingly powerful by virtue of its combination of central, autonomic, skeletal, and hormonal reactions. This mediating role of anxiety, and its capacity to function as an acquired drive, have been subjected to many well conceived experimental studies, and the consensus of opinion appears to leave little doubt about the great value and predictive capacity of this conception.[18]

Let us now consider an individual who is deficient in his capacity to form quick and strong conditioned responses. He will be all the less likely to be subject to phobias and other anxieties, but he will also be less likely to form useful conditioned responses, or to become a thoroughly socialized individual. When this lack of socialization is combined with strong autonomic drive reactions (high neuroticism), such an individual is likely to show the neurotic symptomatology of the psychopath or the hysteric, and indeed, in our experimental work we have found that, as predicted, dysthymic patients, and normal introverts, are characterized by the quick and strong formation of conditioned responses, while psychopaths and normal extraverts are characterized by the weak and slow formation of conditioned responses.[19,20,2] Thus the deviation from the average in either direction may prove disastrous—too strong conditioning easily leads to dysthymic reactions, too weak conditioning easily leads to psychopathic and hysterical reactions. The logic of this whole approach leads me to postulate two great classes of neurotic symptoms which between them exhaust in principle all the possible abnormal reactions with which you are all familiar. On the one hand we have *surplus conditioned reactions*, i.e. reactions acquired along the lines I have adumbrated, and where the reaction is unadaptive, even though originally it may have been well suited to circumstances. On the other hand we have *deficient conditioned reactions*, i.e. reactions normally acquired by most individuals in society which are adaptive, but which because of defective conditioning powers have not been acquired by a particular person. It is necessary to emphasize that surplus conditioned reactions and deficient conditioned reactions are due to an interplay between such individual factors as conditionability and autonomic lability, on the one hand, and environmental conditions on the other. There will be no socialization for an individual who cannot form conditioned responses at all, but conversely, there will be no socialization for a person growing up on a desert island, however powerful his conditioning mechanism may happen to be. In this paper I have no time to deal with differences in the conditioning forces of the environment, and their relation to such factors as social class, but they should certainly not be forgotten.

Many other testable deductions, apart from the differential conditionability of dysthymics and hysterics, follow from such a formulation. Some of these deductions can be tested in the laboratory, and examples have been given in my book, *Dynamics of Anxiety and Hysteria*.[2] But others can be tested clinically, and for the sake of an example I shall give just one of these. I have shown how psychopathic reactions originate because of the inability of the psychopath, due to his low level of conditionability, to acquire the proper socialized responses. But this failure is not absolute; he conditions much less quickly and strongly than others, but he does condition. Thus, where the normal person may need 50 pairings of the conditioned and the unconditioned stimulus and where the dysthymic may need 10, the psychopath may require 100. But presumably in due course the 100 pairings will be forthcoming, although probably much later in life than the 10 of the dysthymic, or the 50 of the normal person, and then he will finally achieve a reasonable level of socialization. If this chain of reasoning is correct, it would lead us to expect that the diagnosis " psychopath " would by and large be confined to relatively young people, say under thirty years of age; after thirty the course of life should have brought forth the required 100 pairings and thus produced the needed amount of socialization. As far as I can ascertain, clinical psychiatric opinion is in agreement with this prediction.

How does our theory compare with the psychoanalytic one? In the formation of neurotic symptoms, Freud emphasizes the traumatic nature of the events leading up to the neurosis, as well as their roots in early childhood. Learning theory can accommodate with equal ease traumatic single-trial learning, for which there is good experimental evidence,[21] but it can also deal with repeated sub-traumatic pain and fear responses which build up the conditioned reaction rather more gradually.[22] As regards the importance of childhood, the Freudian stress appears to be rather misplaced in allocating the origins of *all* neurosis to this period. It is possible that many neurotic symptoms find their origin in this period, but there is no reason at all to assume that neurotic symptoms cannot equally easily be generated at a later period provided conditions are arranged so as to favour their emergence.

The point, however, on which the theory here advocated breaks decisively with psychoanalytic thought of any description is in this. Freudian theory regards neurotic symptoms as adaptive mechanisms which are evidence of repression; they are " the visible upshot of unconscious causes."[23] Learning theory does not postulate any such " unconscious causes," but regards neurotic symptoms as simple learned habits; there is no neurosis underlying the symptom, but merely the symptom itself. *Get rid of the symptom and you have eliminated the neurosis.* This notion of purely symptomatic treatment is so alien to psychoanalysis that it may be considered the crucial part of the theory here proposed. I would like to explore its implications a little further later on.

From the point of view of learning theory, treatment is in essence a very simple process. In the case of surplus conditioned responses, treatment should consist in the extinction of these responses; in the case of deficient conditioned responses, treatment should consist in the building up of the missing stimulus-response connections. Yet this apparent simplicity should not mislead us into thinking that the treatment of neurotic disorders offers no further problems. It is often found in scientific research that the solution of the problems posed by applied science is as complex and difficult as is the solution of the problems posed by pure science; even after Faraday and Maxwell had successfully laid the foundations of modern theories of electricity it needed fifty years and the genius of Edison to make possible the actual application of these advances to the solution of practical problems. Similarly here: a solution in principle, even if correct, still needs much concentrated and high-powered research in the field of application before it can be used practically in the fields of cure, amelioration, and prophylaxis.

What are the methods of cure suggested by learning theory? I shall give two brief examples only, to illustrate certain principles; others have been given by G. Jones.[1] One method of extinguishing the neurotic response X to a given stimulus S is to condition another response R to S, provided that R and X are mutually incompatible. This method, called " reciprocal inhibition " by Wolpe,[24] harks back to Sherrington[25] of course, and may be illustrated by returning to our rat-phobic little boy. Essentially, what Watson had done was to condition a strong sympathetic reaction to the sight of the rat. If we could now succeed in establishing a strong parasympathetic reaction to the sight of the rat, this might succeed in overcoming and eliminating the sympathetic response. The practical difficulty arises that, to begin with at least, the already established conditioned response is of necessity stronger than the to-be-conditioned parasympathetic response. To overcome this difficulty, we make use of the concept of stimulus gradient already mentioned. The rat close by produces a strong conditioned fear reaction; the rat way out in the distance produces a much weaker reaction. If we now feed the infant chocolate while the rat is being introduced in the far distance the strong parasympathetic response produced by the chocolate-munching extinguishes the weak sympathetic response produced by the rat.

As the conditioned parasympathetic response grows in strength, so we can bring the rat nearer and nearer, until finally even close proximity does not produce sympathetic reactions. The sympathetic reaction has been extinguished; the phobia has been cured. This is in fact the method which was used experimentally to get rid of the experimentally induced fear,[26] and it has been used successfully by several workers in the field of child psychiatry. More recently Herzberg[27] in his system of active psychotherapy, and more particularly, Wolpe[24] in his psychotherapy by reciprocal inhibition, have shown that these principles can be applied with equal success to the severe neuroses of adult men and women—substituting other methods, of course, for the chocolate-munching, which is more effective with children than with adults.

As an example of the cure of deficient conditioned responses, let me merely mention *enuresis nocturna*, where clearly the usual conditioned response of waking to the conditioned stimulus of bladder extension has not been properly built up. A simple course of training, in which a bell rings loudly whenever the child begins to urinate, thus activating an electric circuit embedded in his bedclothes, soon establishes the previously missing connection, and the extremely impressive list of successes achieved with this method, as compared with the very modest success of psychotherapeutic methods, speaks strongly for the correctness of the theoretical point of view which gave rise to this conception.[28]

We thus have here, I would suggest, an alternative theory to the Freudian, a theory which claims to account for the facts at least as satisfactorily as does psychoanalysis, and which in addition puts forward quite specific suggestions about methods of treatment. I have called these methods " behaviour therapy " to contrast them with methods of psychotherapy.*
This contrast of terms is meant to indicate two things. According to psychoanalytic doctrine, there is a psychological complex, situated in the unconscious mind, underlying all the manifest symptoms of neurotic disorder. Hence

---

* The growth of the theoretical concepts and practical methods of treatment subsumed in the term " behaviour therapy " owes much to a large number of people. Apart from Pavlov and Hull, who originated the main tenets of modern learning theory, most credit is probably due to Watson, who was among the first to see the usefulness of the conditioned paradigm for the explanation of neurotic disorders; to Miller and Mowrer, who have done so much to bring together learning theory and abnormal human behaviour; to Spence, whose important contributions include the detailed analysis of the relation between anxiety and learning; and to Wolpe, who was the first to apply explicitly some of the laws of learning theory to the large-scale treatment of severe neurotics. If there is any novelty in my own treatment of these issues it lies primarily: (1) in the pulling together of numerous original contributions into a general theory and (2) in the introduction into this system of the concepts of neuroticism and extraversion–introversion as essential parameters in the description and prediction of behaviour. I would like to emphasize, however, that this contribution could not have been made had the ground work not been well and truly laid by the writers quoted above and by many more, only some of whom are quoted in the bibliography.

the necessity of therapy for the psyche. According to learning theory, we are dealing with unadaptive behaviour conditioned to certain classes of stimuli; no reference is made to any underlying disorders or complexes in the psyche. Following on this analysis, it is not surprising that psychoanalysts show a preoccupation with psychological methods involving mainly *speech*, while behaviour therapy concentrates on actual *behaviour* as most likely to lead to the extinction of the unadaptive conditioned responses. The two terms express rather concisely the opposing viewpoints of the two schools. Below, in summary form, is a tabulation of the most important differences between psychotherapy and behaviour therapy.

TABLE 1

Psychotherapy	Behaviour therapy
1. Based on inconsistent theory never properly formulated in postulate form.	Based on consistent, properly formulated theory leading to testable deductions.
2. Derived from clinical observations made without necessary control observations or experiments.	Derived from experimental studies specifically designed to test basic theory and deductions made therefrom.
3. Considers symptoms the visible upshot of unconscious causes (" complexes ").	Considers symptoms as unadaptive conditioned responses.
4. Regards symptoms as evidence of *repression*.	Regards symptoms as evidence of faulty learning.
5. Believes that symptomatology is determined by defence mechanisms.	Believes that symptomatology is determined by individual differences in conditionability and autonomic lability, as well as accidental environmental circumstances.
6. All treatment of neurotic disorders must be *historically* based.	All treatment of neurotic disorders is concerned with habits existing at *present*; their historical development is largely irrelevant.
7. Cures are achieved by handling the underlying (unconscious) dynamics, not by treating the symptom itself.	Cures are achieved by treating the symptom itself, i.e. by extinguishing unadaptive C.Rs and establishing desirable C.Rs.
8. Interpretation of symptoms, dreams, acts, etc. is an important element of treatment.	Interpretation, even if not completely subjective and erroneous, is irrelevant.
9. Symptomatic treatment leads to the elaboration of new symptoms.	Symptomatic treatment leads to permanent recovery provided autonomic as well as skeletal surplus C.Rs are extinguished.
10. Transference relations are essential for cures of neurotic disorders.	Personal relations are not essential for cures of neurotic disorder, although they may be useful in certain circumstances.

What kind of answer would we expect from the Freudians? I think their main points would be these. They would claim, in the first place, that conditioning therapy has frequently been tried, but with very poor results; aversion therapies of alcoholism are often mentioned in this connection. They would go on to say that even where symptomatic treatments of this kind are apparently successful, as in enuresis, the symptom is likely to return, or be supplanted by some other symptom, or by an increase in anxiety. Finally, they would claim that even if in some cases the therapies suggested might be successful, yet in the great majority of cases psychoanalysis would be the only method to produce lasting cures. Let me deal with these points one by one.

There is no doubt that conditioning treatment of alcoholism has often been tried, and that it has often failed. I have no wish to take refuge in a *tu quoque* argument by pointing out that alcoholism has been particularly difficult to treat by any method whatever, and that psychoanalytic methods also have been largely unsuccessful. I would rather point out that learning theory is an exact science, which has elaborated quite definite rules about the establishment of conditioned reflexes; it is only when these rules are properly applied by psychologists with knowledge and experience in this field that the question of success or failure arises. Thus it is quite elementary knowledge that the conditioned stimulus must precede the unconditioned stimulus if conditioning is to take place; backward conditioning, if it occurs at all, is at best very weak. Yet some workers in the field of alcoholism have used a method in which the unconditioned stimulus regularly preceded the conditioned stimulus; under these conditions learning theory would in fact predict the complete failure of the experiment actually reported! Again, the time relation between the application of the conditioned stimulus and the unconditioned stimulus is a very important one; it is controlled to very fine limits of hundredths of a sec in psychological experimentation and it has been universally reported that conditioning in which any but the optimal time relation is chosen is relatively ineffective. Taking eye-blink conditioning as an example: it is found that a time interval of about $\frac{1}{2}$ sec is optimal and that with intervals of $2\frac{1}{2}$ sec no conditioning at all takes place.[29],[30] No attention seems to have been paid to these points by most workers on alcoholism, who apply the conditioned and unconditioned stimuli in such a vague way that it is often impossible to find out what the actual time relations were. This lack of rigour makes it quite impossible to adduce these so-called experiments as evidence either in favour or against conditioning therapy.[31]

How about the return of symptoms? I have made a thorough search of the literature dealing with behaviour therapy with this particular point in view. Many psychoanalytically trained therapists using these methods have been specially on the outlook for the return of symptoms, or the emergence of alternative ones; yet neither they nor any of the other practitioners have found anything of this kind to happen except in the most rare and unusual cases.[17] Enuresis, once cured by conditioning therapy, remains cured as a general rule; relapses occur, as indeed one would expect in terms of learning theory under certain circumstances, but they quickly yield to repeat treatment. So certain of success are the commercial operators of this method that they work on a " money back if unsuccessful " policy;

their financial solvency is an adequate answer to the psychoanalytic claim. Nor would it be true that alternative symptoms emerge; quite the contrary happens. The disappearance of the very annoying symptom promotes peace in the home, allays anxieties, and leads to an all-round improvement in character and behaviour. Similar results are reported in the case of major applications of behaviour therapy to adults suffering from severe neurotic disorders; abolition of the symptom does not leave behind some mysterious complex seeking outlet in alternative symptoms.[17] Once the symptom is removed, the patient is cured; when there are multiple symptoms, as there usually are, removal of one symptom facilitates removal of the others, and removal of all the symptoms complete the cure.[24]

There is one apparent exception to this rule which should be carefully noted because it may be responsible for some of the beliefs so widely held. Surplus conditioned reactions may themselves be divided into two kinds, autonomic and motor. Anxiety reactions are typical of the autonomic type of surplus conditioned reactions, whereas tics, compulsive movements, etc. are typical of motor conditioned reactions. What has been said about the complete disappearance of the symptom producing a complete disappearance of the neurosis is true only as far as the autonomic conditioned reactions are concerned. Motor reactions are frequently activated by their drive reducing properties *vis a vis* the historically earlier conditioned autonomic responses[17]; the extinction of the motor response without the simultaneous extinction of the conditioned autonomic response would only be a very partial cure and could not be recommended as being sufficient. As pointed out at the end of the previous paragraph, " removal of *all* the symptoms completes the cure," and clearly removal of the motor conditioned response by itself, without the removal of the autonomic conditioned response is only a very partial kind of treatment. Behaviour therapy requires the extinction of all non-adaptive conditioned responses complained of by the patient, or causally related to these symptoms.

But how frequently does this type of treatment result in cures? Again I have made a thorough search of the literature, with the following outcome. GP treatment, not making use of psychotherapy in any of its usual forms, results in a recovery of about two seriously ill neurotics out of three.[32] Eclectic psychotherapy results in a recovery of about two seriously ill neurotics out of three.[7] Psychotherapy by means of psychoanalysis fares slightly worse, but results are at a comparable level.[8] Results of behaviour therapy of seriously ill neurotics, as reported by Wolpe, are distinctly superior to this, over 90 per cent recovering.[24] This difference is highly significant statistically and it should be borne in mind that the number of sessions required by behaviour therapy is distinctly smaller than that required by psychotherapy, whether eclectic or psychoanalytic. (Wolpe reports an average of about 30 sittings for his cases.)

These results are encouraging, but of course, they must not be taken too seriously. Actuarial comparisons of this kind suffer severely from the difficulty of equating the seriousness of disorders treated by different practitioners, the equally obvious difficulty of arriving at an agreed scale for the measurement of " recovery," and the impossibility of excluding the myriad chance factors which may affect gross behaviour changes of the kind we are here considering. I would not like to be understood as saying that behaviour therapy has been *proved* superior to psychotherapy; nothing could be further from my intention. What I am claiming is simply that as far as they go—which is not very far—available *data* do not support in any sense the Freudian belief that behaviour therapy is doomed to failure, and that only psychoanalysis or some kindred type of treatment is adequate to relieve neurotic disorders. This Freudian belief is precisely this—a belief; it has no empirical or rational foundation. I have no wish to set up a counter-belief, equally unsupported, to the effect that psychotherapy is doomed to failure and that only behaviour therapy is adequate to relieve neurotic disorders. What I would like to suggest is simply that a good case can be made out, both on the theoretical and the empirical level, for the proposition that behaviour therapy is an effective, relatively quick, and probably lasting method of cure of some neurotic disorders. This case is so strong that clinical trials would appear to be in order now to establish the relative value of this method as compared with other available methods, such as psychoanalysis, or electroshock treatment. Even more important, I think the evidence would justify psychiatrists in experimenting with the method, or rather set of methods, involved, in order to come to some preliminary estimate of their efficiency. I have noted with some surprise that many psychotherapists have refused to use such methods as conditioning therapy in enuresis, not on empirical grounds, but on *a priori* grounds, claiming that such mechanical methods simply could not work, and disregarding the large body of evidence available. Even in long established sciences *a priori* considerations carry little weight; in such a young discipline as psychology they are quite out of place. Only actual use can show the value of one method of treatment as opposed to another.

There is one point I would like to emphasize. Freud developed his psychological theories on the basis of his study of neurotic disorders and their treatment. Behaviour therapy, on the contrary, began with the thorough experimental study of the laws of learning and conditioning in normal people and in animals; these well-established principles were then applied to neurotic disorders. It seems to me that this latter method is in principle superior to the former; scientific advance has nearly always taken the form of making fundamental discoveries and then applying these in practice, and I can see no valid reason why this process should be inverted in connection with neurosis. It may be objected that learning theorists are not always in agreement with each other[11] and that it is difficult to apply principles about which there is still so much argument. This is only very partially true; those points about which argument rages are usually of academic interest rather than of practical importance. Thus, reinforcement theorists and contiguity theorists have strong differences of view about the necessity of reinforcement during learning and different reinforcement theorists have different theories about the nature of reinforcement. Yet there would be general agreement in any particular case about the optimum methods of achieving a quick rate of conditioning, or extinction; these are questions of fact and it is only with the interpretation of some of these facts that disagreements arise. Even when the disputes about the corpuscular or wavular nature of light were at their height, there was sufficient common ground between contestants regarding the facts of the case to make possible the practical application of available knowledge; the same is true of learning theory. The 10 per cent which is in dispute should not blind us to the 90 per cent which is not—disagreements and disputes naturally attract more attention, but agreements on facts and principles are actually much more common. Greater familiarity with the large and rapidly growing literature will quickly substantiate this statement.[12]

It is sometimes said that the model offered here differs from the psychoanalytic model only in the terminology used and that in fact the two models are very similar. Such a statement would be both true and untrue. There undoubtedly are certain similarities, as Mowrer[17] and Miller and Dollard[33] have been at pains to point out. The motivating role of anxiety in the Freudian system is obviously very similar in conception to the drive-producing conditioned autonomic responses of learning theory, and the relief from anxiety produced by hysterical and obsessional symptoms in Freudian terminology is very similar to the conditioned drive-reducing properties of motor movements. Similarly, a case could be made out in favour of regarding the undersocialized, non-conditionable psychopathic individual as being Id-dominated, and the dysthymic, over-conditionable individual as being Super-Ego dominated. Many other similarities will occur to the reader in going through these pages and indeed the writer would be the first to acknowledge the tremendous service that Freud has done in elucidating for the first time some of these dynamic relationships and in particular in stressing the motivating role of anxiety.

Nevertheless, there are two main reasons for not regarding the present formulation as simply an alternative differing from the psychoanalytic one only in the terminology used. In the first place, the formulation here given differs from the Freudian in several essential features, as can be seen most clearly by studying Table 1. Perhaps these differences are most apparent with respect to the deductions made from the two theories as to treatment. Psychoanalytic theory distrusts purely symptomatic treatment

and insists on the removal of the underlying complexes. Behaviour theory
on the other hand stresses the purely symptomatological side of treatment
and is unconvinced of the very existence of " complexes." It might, of
course, be suggested that there is some similarity between the Freudian
" complex " and the " conditioned surplus autonomic reaction " posited
by behaviour theory. That there is some similarity cannot be denied, but
no one familiar with psychoanalytic writings would agree that the Freudian
complex was not in essence a very different conception from the conditioned
autonomic response, both from the point of view of its origins, as well as
from the point of view of the appropriate method of extinction.

This brings me to the second great difference between the two models.
What the Freudian model lacks above all, is an intelligible objectively
testable *modus operandi* which can be experimentally studied in the
laboratory, which can be precisely quantified and which can then be subjected to the formulation of strict scientific laws. The stress on such a
mechanism, namely that of conditioning, is the most noteworthy feature
of the model here advocated. It is entirely due to the great body of research
which has been done in connection with the elaboration of laws of modern
learning theory, that we are enabled to make fairly precise deductions
resulting in different methods of treatment for patients suffering from
neurotic disorders and it is with respect to this feature of the model that
the relevant case histories and accounts of treatment should be read.[34,35,36]

It has sometimes been suggested that the criticisms which I have levelled
against the psychotherapeutic schools because of their failure to provide
adequate control groups to validate their claims regarding the curative
properties of their methods, could justifiably be levelled against the accounts
given by those who have used behaviour therapy and reported upon the
effects achieved. Such a criticism would not be justified for two reasons.
In the first place, the cases quoted are *illustrative of methods*, not *proofs
of psychotherapeutic efficacy*; the only case in which claims regarding
relative efficacy have been made contains a statistical comparison with the
effects of psychoanalytic treatment of similar cases.[24] In the second place,
the concept of " control " in scientific experiments is somewhat more than
simply the provision of a control *group*; the control in an experiment may be
internal. As an example, consider the experiment reported by Yates[36] on
the extinction of 4 tics in a female patient by means of a rather novel and
unusual method, namely that of repeated voluntary repetition of the tic by
massed practice. Precise predictions were made as to the effects that should
follow and these predictions were studied by using the fate of some of the
tics as compared to the fate of other tics submitted to dissimilar treatment.
Thus, practice for 2 tics might be discontinued for a fortnight, while practice
on the other two would go on. By showing that the predictions made could
thus be verified and the *rate of extinction* of the tics varied at will—in

accordance with the experimental manipulation for such variables as massing of practice—a degree of control was achieved far superior to the simple assessment of significance produced in the comparison of two random groups submitted to different treatments. It is by its insistence on such experimental precision and the incorporation of experimental tests of the hypotheses employed, even during the treatment, that behaviour theory differs from psychotherapy.

There is one further method of pointing up the differences between the two theories and of deciding between them; I mention this matter with some hesitation because to many psychiatrists it seems almost sacrilegious to use animal experimentation in the consideration of human neurosis. However, Fenichel himself [37, p.19] has quoted " experimental neuroses " as support for the Freudian conception of neurotic disorders and it is with respect to these experiments that the contrast between the psychoanalytic and our own model may be worked our most explicitly. Fenichel maintains that the model of psychoneurosis " is represented by the artificial neuroses that have been inflicted upon animals by experimental psychologists. Some stimulus which had represented pleasant instinctual experiences or which had served as a signal that some action would now procure gratification is suddenly connected by the experimenter with frustrating or threatening experiences, or the experimenter decreases the difference between stimuli which the animal had been trained to associate with instinct gratification and threat respectively; the animal then gets into a state of irritation which is very similar to that of a traumatic neurosis. He feels contradictory impulses; the conflict makes it impossible for him to give in to the impulses in the accustomed way; the discharge is blocked, and this decrease in discharge works in the same way as an increase in influx: it brings the organism into a state of tension and calls for emergency discharges.

" In psychoneuroses some impulses have been blocked; the consequence is a state of tension and eventually some ' emergency discharges.' These consist partly in unspecific restlessness and its elaborations and partly in much more specific phenomena which represent the distorted involuntary discharges of those very instinctual drives for which a normal discharge has been interdicted. Thus we have in psychoneuroses, first a defense of the ego against an instinct, then a conflict between the instinct striving for discharge and the defensive forces of the ego, then a state of damming up and finally the neurotic symptoms which are distorted discharges as a consequence of the state of damming up—a compromise between the opposing forces. The symptom is the only step in this development that becomes manifest; the conflict, its history, and the significance of the symptoms are unconscious."

Hebb[38] has laid down certain requirements for attempting to demonstrate that experimental neurosis occurs in animals and Broadhurst[39, 40] has examined the literature, and particularly that referred to by Fenichel, from this point of view. Here is his summary. " How does the large body of American work stand up to such an assessment? For the purposes of a recent review,[40] the available literature was examined in the light of Hebb's criteria. Noteworthy among this is the work of the group headed by Liddell,[41] one of the pioneers of conditioning methodology in the United States, who has used principally the sheep as his experimental subject; of Gantt,[42] whose long term study of the dog ' Nick ' is well known; and of Masserman,[43] who has done extensive work using cats. This is not the place to enter into the details of this evaluation, which is reported elsewhere,[40] but the overall conclusion which was reached was that there are few instances in all this work of any cases of experimentally induced abnormalities of animal behaviour which meet all of Hebb's criteria. Let us take, for example, the work of Masserman, whose theoretical interpretation of abnormal behaviour need not concern us here except to note that it was the basis upon which he designed his experiments to produce ' conflict ' between one drive and another. What he did was this. He trained hungry cats to respond to a sensory signal by opening a food box to obtain food. Then he subjected them to a noxious stimulus, a blast of air, or electric shock, just at the moment of feeding. The resulting changes in behaviour—the animals showed fear of the situation and of the experimenter, and refused to feed further—he identified as experimental neurosis. But the behaviour observed fails to fulfil more than one or two of Hebb's criteria and, moreover, certain deficiencies in the design of his experiments make it impossible to draw any satisfactory conclusions from them. Thus Wolpe[44] repeated part of Masserman's work using the essential control group which Masserman had omitted—that is, he gave the cats the noxious stimulus alone, without any ' conflict ' between the fear motivation thus induced, and the hunger which, in Masserman's animals, operated as well—and found that the same behaviour occurred. It hardly needs to be said that a fear response to a threatening stimulus is not abnormal and cannot be regarded as an experimental neurosis."

It is clear from the studies cited that Fenichel is quite wrong in claiming that " experimental neurosis " is in any way analogous to the Freudian model of human neurosis. It appears, therefore, that in so far as these studies are relevant at all they can be regarded as demonstrating nothing but simple conditioned fear responses of the kind called for by our theory. It is perhaps worthy of note that the failure of psychoanalysis to use control groups in the human field has extended to their work with animals, as in the case of Masserman quoted above. Fenichel's easy acceptance of data congruent with his hypothesis is paralleled by his failure to mention data contrary to the psychoanalytic viewpoint. By taking into account all the data it seems more likely that a correct conclusion will be reached.

I would now like to return to some of the points which I raised at the beginning of this paper. I argued then, that the special knowledge and competence of psychologists in mental hospitals was largely wasted because of concentration on and preoccupation with Freudian theories and projective types of test. I would now like to make a more positive suggestion and maintain that by virtue of their training and experience psychologists are (or should be) experts in the fields of conditioning and learning theory, laboratory procedures and research design. In suitable cases, surely their help would be invaluable in diagnostic problems, such as ascertaining a given patient's speed of conditioning, in the theoretical problem of constructing a model of his personality dynamics and in the practical problem of designing a suitable course of behaviour therapy which would take into account all the available information about the case.* I am not suggesting that psychologists should themselves necessarily carry out this course of treatment; it would appear relatively immaterial whether the therapy is carried out by one person or another, by psychologist or psychiatrist. Both types of procedure have been experimented with and both have shown equally promising results. Indeed, certain aspects of the therapy can obviously be carried out by less senior and experienced personnel, provided the course of treatment is reviewed periodically by the person in charge. Psychoanalysis lays much stress on what is sometimes called " transference," a devil conjured up only to be sent back to his usual habitat with much expenditure of time and energy.[37] Behaviour therapy has no need of this adjunct, nor does it admit that the evidence for its existence is remotely adequate at the present time. However that may be, relinquishing the personal relationship supposed to be indispensable for the " transference " relation allows us to use relatively unqualified help in many of the more time-consuming and routine parts of behaviour therapy. In certain cases, of course, personal relationships may be required in order to provide a necessary step on the generalization gradient; but this is not always true.†

* It will be clear that the function here sketched out for the psychologist demands that he be furnished with the necessary tools of his trade, such as sound-proof rooms, conditioning apparatus and all the other techniques for delivering stimuli and measuring responses on a strictly quantified basis.[45] It is equally clear that such facilities do not exist in the majority of our mental hospitals. Until they do, the handicaps under which the clinical psychologists work at such institutions will be all but insurmountable, and no reasonable estimate of their potential usefulness can be formed. One might just as well employ an electroencephalographer and refuse to pay for the machine which he has been trained to use! It would be better to have a few, properly equipped departments than a large number of small, ill-equipped ones as at present. Even in the United States the position is bad; in this country it is worse. A relatively small capital investment would be likely to bear considerable fruit.

† As an example of this we may quote a case reported by Graham White. This concerns a child who became anorexic after the death of her father. The therapist adopted the father's role in a variety of circumstances, ranging in order from play with dolls' teasets to the actual eating situation, and reinforced those reactions which were considered desirable. The theoretical rationale was that the father had become a conditioned stimulus on which eating depended.

From a limited experience with this kind of work, carried out by various members of my department, I can with confidence say two things. The direct application of psychological theories to the practical problem of effecting a cure in a particular person, here and now, acts as a very powerful challenge to the psychologist concerned, and makes him more aware than almost anything else of the strengths and weaknesses of the formulations of modern learning theory. And the successful discharge of this self-chosen duty serves more than almost anything else to convince his psychiatric colleagues that psychology can successfully emerge from its academic retreat and take a hand in the day-to-day struggle with the hundred-and-one problems facing the psychiatrist. It seems to me that the tragic fratricidal struggle between psychiatrists and psychologists, which has so exacerbated relations between them in the United States, could easily be avoided here by recognizing the special competence of the psychologist in this particular corner of the field, while acknowledging the necessity of keeping the general medical care of the patient in the hands of the psychiatrist. I believe that most psychiatrists are too well aware of the precarious state of our knowledge in the field of the neurotic disorders to do anything but welcome the help which the application of learning theory in the hands of a competent psychologist may be able to bring.

REFERENCES

1. JONES, H. G. (1958). Neurosis and experimental psychology. *J. Ment. Sci.*, **104**, 55-62.
2. EYSENCK, H. J. (1957). *Dynamics of Anxiety and Hysteria*. Routledge & Kegan Paul, London.
3. EYSENCK, H. J. (1947). *Dimensions of Personality*. Routledge & Kegan Paul, London.
4. EYSENCK, H. J. (1952). *The Scientific Study of Personality*. Routledge & Kegan Paul, London.
5. EYSENCK, H. J. (1953). *The Structure of Human Personality*. Methuen, London.
6. GLOVER, E. (1955). *The Technique of Psychoanalysis*. Bailliere, London.
7. EYSENCK, H. J. (1952). The effects of psychotherapy: an evaluation. *J. Cons. Psychol.*, **16**, 319-324.
8. EYSENCK, H. J. (1960). The effects of psychotherapy. In *Handbook of Abnormal Psychology*. Ed. by H. J. Eysenck. Pitman, London.
9. EYSENCK, H. J. (1953). *Uses and Abuses of Psychology*. Pelican, London.
10. EYSENCK, H. J. (1958). Personality tests: 1950–1955. In *Recent Progress in Psychiatry*. Ed. by G. W. T. W. Fleming. J. & A. Churchill, London.
11. HILGARD, G. A. (1956). *Theories of Learning*. Appleton–Century, New York.
12. OSGOOD, C. E. (1953). *Method and Theory in Experimental Psychology*. Oxford Univ. Press, London.
13. SHOBEN, E. J. (1949). Psychotherapy as a problem in learning theory. *Psychol. Bull.*, **46**, 366-392.
14. WATSON, J. B. and RAYNER, R. (1920). Conditioned emotional reaction. *J. Exp. Psychol.*, **3**, 1-4.
15. PAVLOV, I. P. (1927). *Conditioned Reflexes*. Oxford Univ. Press, London.
16. SPENCE, K. G., HAGGARD, P. F. and Ross, L. G. (1958). UCS intensity and the associated (habit) strength of the eyelid CR. *J. Exp. Psychol.*, **95**, 404-411.
17. MOWRER, O. H. (1950). *Learning Theory and Personality Dynamics*. Ronald Press, New York.

18. MILLER, V. G. (1951). Learnable drives and rewards. *Handbook of Experimental Psychology.* Ed. by S. S. Spencer. Wiley, New York.
19. EYSENCK, H. J. (1954). Zur Theorie der Personlichkeitsmessung. *Z. Diag. Psychol. Personlichkeitsforsch.*, **2**, 87-101, 171-187.
20. EYSENCK, H. J. (1957). Los principios del condicionamiento y la teoria de la personalidad. *Riv. Psicol.*, **12**, 655-667.
21. HUDSON, B. B. (1950). One-trial learning in the domestic rat. *Genet. Psychol. Monogr.*, **41**, 94-146.
22. SOLOMON, R. L., KAMIN, L. J. and WYNNE, L. C. (1953). Traumatic avoidance learning. *J. Abnorm. (Soc.) Psychol.*, **48**, 291-302.
23. MUNROE, R. L. (1955). *Schools of Psychoanalytic Thought.* Dryden Press, New York.
24. WOLPE, J. (1958). *Psychotherapy by Reciprocal Inhibition.* Stanford Univ. Press.
25. SHERRINGTON, C. S. (1926). *The Integrative Action of the Central Nervous System.* Oxford Univ. Press, London.
26. JERSILD, A. T. and HOLMES, F. B. (1935). Methods of overcoming children's fears. *J. Psychol.*, **1**, 25-83.
27. HERZBERG, A. (1941). Short treatment of neuroses by graduated tasks. *Brit. J. Med. Psychol.*, **19**, 36-51.
28. MOWRER, O. H. and MORER, W. A. (1938). Enuresis. A method for its study and treatment. *Amer. J. Orthopsychiat.*, **8**, 436-447.
29. MCALLISTER, W. R. (1953). Eyelid conditioning as a function of the CS–UCS interval. *J. Exp. Psychol.*, **45**, 412-422.
30. MCALLISTER, W. R. (1953). The effect on eyelid conditioning of shifting the CS–UCS interval. *J. Exp. Psychol.*, **45**, 423-428.
31. FRANKS, C. M. (1958). Alcohol, alcoholics and conditioning: a review of the literature and some theoretical considerations. *J. Ment. Sci.*, **104**, 14-33.
32. DENKER, P. G. (1946). Results of treatment of psychoneuroses by the general practitioner. A follow-up study of 500 cases. *N.Y. State J. Med.*, **46**, 2164-2166.
33. DOLLARD, J. and MILLER, V. G. (1950). *Personality and Psychotherapy.* McGraw-Hill, New York.
34. JONES, H. G. (1956). The application of conditioning and learning techniques to the treatment of a psychiatric patient. *J. Abnorm. (Soc.) Psychol.*, **52**, 414-420.
35. MEYER, V. (1957). The treatment of two phobic patients on the basis of learning principles. *J. Abnorm. (Soc.) Psychol.*, **55**, 261-266.
36. YATES, A. (1958). The application of learning theory to the treatment of tics. *J. Abnorm. (Soc.) Psychol.*, **56**, 175-182.
37. FENICHEL, O. (1945). *The Psychoanalytic Theory of Neurosis.* Kegan Paul, London.
38. HEBB, D. O. (1947). Spontaneous neurosis in chimpanzees: theoretical relations with clinical and experimental phenomena. *Psychosom. Med.*, **9**, 3-16.
39. BROADHURST, P. L. (1958). The contribution of animal psychology to the concept of psychological normality–abnormality. *Proc. XIII Internat. Congr. Appl. Psychol.*
40. BROADHURST, P. L. (1960). Abnormal animal behaviour. In *Handbook of Abnormal Psychology.* Ed. by H. J. Eysenck. Pitman, London.
41. ANDERSON, O. P. and PARMENTER, A. (1941). A long-term study of the experimental neurosis in the sheep and dog. *Psychosom. Med. Monogr.*, **2**, Nos. 3 and 4, 1-150.
42. GANTT, W. H. (1944). Experimental basis for neurotic behaviour. *Psychosom. Med. Monogr.*, **3**, 1-211.
43. MASSERMAN, J. K. (1943). *Behavior and Neurosis.* Univ. Press, Chicago.
44. WOLPE, J. (1952). Experimental neurosis as learned behaviour. *Brit. J. Psychol.*, **43**, 243-268.
45. EYSENCK, H. J. (1955). *Psychology and the Foundation of Psychiatry.* H. K. Lewis, London.
46. ESTES, W. K. *et al* (1954). *Modern Learning Theory.* Appleton–Century, New York.
47. HILGARD, E. A. and MARQUIS, D. G. (1940). *Conditioning and Learning.* Appleton–Century, New York.

SYMPTOMS
AND SYMPTOM SUBSTITUTION*

AUBREY J. YATES

University of New England, Australia

IN RECENT years there has been a number of attempts to derive rational methods of symptomatic treatment of the behavioral disorders, based mainly on learning theory[1,2,3,4,5,6] and information theory.[7] Nevertheless, symptomatic treatment has not been favorably considered by most clinical psychologists and the failure to appreciate its possibilities is perhaps best shown by the almost total neglect of Dunlap's classic work[8] on habit-formation and the remedial treatment of undesirable habits. The object of this paper is to point out some misconceptions on which objections to symptomatic treatment are based, and to show that such treatment can in fact be firmly founded on modern learning theory.

The argument that symptomatic treatment is a waste of time has had as its strongest proponent the psychoanalytic school, which has insisted that symptoms are but the surface indicators of underlying conflicts, anxieties, etc. This argument has been accepted by most " dynamic " psychologists, who concluded that removing the symptom without also effectively treating the anxiety or conflict underlying it would lead to symptom substitution. For example, even if tics could be treated directly and extinguished, the patient would quickly develop either new tics or some other form of symptomatic response. Even orthodox psychiatrists who have little patience with Freudian psychodynamics have accepted this point of view. Thus Kanner writes that " symptomatic therapy which does not care what the complaint is a ' symptom ' of is rarely successful and leads to unwarranted pessimism."[9,p.244] Mowrer has summed up the position neatly and abusively: " the behavioral manifestations which we now call ' symptoms ' are not the essence of neurosis and . . . the modes of treatment that are aimed at their direct alleviation are as ill-considered theoretically as they are futile practically."[10,p.620]

This point of view has become so widely accepted that until recently almost no symptomatic treatment was carried out, except in the educational field of remedial teaching and speech therapy. However, the distinction

* Reprinted by permission of the author and the Amer. Psychol. Ass. from the (1958) *Psychol. Rev.*, **65**, 371-374.

between a " fundamental " underlying anxiety and a " superficial " surface symptom is open to a number of objections.

(1) The term " symptom " has been employed very loosely in psychology. In general medicine a clear distinction is made " between symptoms, that is disorders described by the patient, and physical signs or the deviations from the normal revealed by examination."[11,p.1] In other words, a symptom is a subjectively experienced abnormality, a sign is an objective indication of abnormality. In many cases the symptom may, of course, also be a sign.

Mowrer, having accepted, as we have seen, Freud's conclusion with regard to the meaning and function of symptoms, was considerably embarrassed by his own empirical finding that " symptomatic " treatment of enuresis was not only 100 per cent successful with regard to the symptoms, but was not followed by symptom substitution in a single case! Instead, however, of rejecting Freud's hypothesis Mowrer took the extraordinary step of denying that enuresis was a symptom in any of the cases he treated. He distinguished between habits which were also symptoms, and habits which were not. Thus: " ' symptoms ' differ from ordinary ' habits ' primarily in that the former are motivated by and are perpetuated because they lessen the drive of anxiety, whereas ' normal ' habits are motivated by and are perpetuated because they lessen other drives, such as hunger, thirst, cold, fatigue, sex, fear, etc."[10,p.546]

Now the above distinction is clearly a meaningful and possibly a valid one. As far as the author is aware, however, Mowrer has not presented any evidence that the distinction can be sustained in the form in which he has put it, and his own experimental results seem strongly to contraindicate the validity of any such distinction. Mowrer's acrobatics in this regard are as good an example as any of an *a priori* clinical bias being allowed to outweigh cogent experimental evidence.*

It is clear that, as used by Freud,[12] Mowrer,[10] and other " dynamic " psychologists, the symptom is regarded as a response to some hidden, basic conflict or anxiety. It will be suggested that this " vertical," dualistic approach is unnecessary and should be replaced by a " horizontal," monistic approach, as described below.

(2) The " dynamic " approach ignores the distinction between neuroticism and neurosis.[13] Neuroticism may be conceptualized as an innate predisposition to develop a neurosis under certain specifiable conditions. This conceptualization is at least as plausible as the alternative outlined above. But, if such a predisposition exists, then it follows that a neurosis *is* symptoms and nothing else, i.e., that a particular neurosis consists of a

---

* Mowrer admits that is is impossible to " know from the incontinence alone that it is a symptom rather than simply a reflection of pedagogical inadequacy."[10,p.414] Presumably, therefore, decision as to whether the incontinence is a symptom or a habit can be determined only by carrying out " symptomatic " treatment and seeing what happens.

particular set of learned responses; and that treatment on psychological grounds can only be symptomatic, since treatment of the predisposition must ultimately be by genetic or chemical means.

(3) Finally, it should be noted that belief in symptom substitution seems to be based largely on clinical experience. Considering the significant role such a distinction has played in clinical psychology, experimental demonstration of its existence is singularly lacking. We conclude, therefore, that the reasons generally given for rejecting symptomatic treatment in favor of " dynamic " treatment are not soundly based. Nevertheless, the definition of a neurosis as a system of learned responses is not in itself incompatible with the notion of symptom substitution. We must now turn to the question whether there are any theoretical reasons to suppose that symptom substitution would take place, if symptomatic treatment were to be undertaken. It will be maintained that learning theory suggests both that symptomatic treatment is a rational procedure and that symptom substitution would not be expected except under certain specifiable conditions.

This may perhaps be most easily shown by reference to some recent work on the symptomatic treatment of tics.[6] A model was constructed to account for the genesis of some tics in terms of two-factor learning theory. It was hypothesized that the tic is a conditioned avoidance response to anxiety, the latter being also a learned response (the conditioned form of the original fear response). A method of treatment was derived in terms of the Hullian concepts of I_R and sI_R, making use of massed practice.* With regard to this theory, the following points are specifically relevant to this discussion:

(a) Both the anxiety and the tic are learned responses. Now it would be a logical error to suppose that the fact that the tic is a response *to* the anxiety necessarily means that the anxiety must therefore be more fundamental or that it must receive prior treatment. It seems more reasonable to regard the situation simply as one in which two sets of responses (anxiety and the response to anxiety) are learned over time. This may be termed the " horizontal " approach, as opposed to the dualistic " vertical " approach rejected above.

(b) From this point of view it does not much matter which aspect of behavior (anxiety or tic) is treated first. The fact is, however, that in our present state of knowledge it is easier to treat the tic than the anxiety. The former is more readily manipulated and measured, and, since it usually involves motor behavior, is easily dealt with in relation to the concepts of learning theory. It turns out, however, that in treating the symptoms we

---

* In this study[6] it was found convenient to use the concepts of I_R and sI_R in deriving a method of treatment. This aspect could also, however, have been conceptualized in terms of two-factor learning theory, as Mowrer has shown in connection with studies in the field of general motor behavior.[10,p.169, footnote 4.]

are also treating the anxiety. For suppose the symptom is destroyed; then the anxiety, instead of being reduced by it, will persist. But since in fact no traumatic event occurs if the anxiety is allowed to persist, the latter, being itself a learned response, will begin to extinguish. This is what in fact seems to happen, though the principle of partial irreversibility of traumatic anxiety,[14] if valid, suggests that extinction of the anxiety would never be complete.*

This formulation is, of course, derived directly from Mowrer's two-factor theory of learning. That removal of the symptom will affect the learned anxiety is hinted at by Mowrer, when he explains why a symptom " is at one and the same time both self-perpetuating and self-defeating. It is self-perpetuating because it is reinforced by the satisfaction provided through the resultant anxiety reduction; and it is self-destructive in that *it prevents the individual from experiencing the full force of his anxiety and being modified by it in such a direction as to eliminate the occasion for the anxiety,*"[10, p.535] footnotes; italics not in original.

Supposing, therefore, both the symptom and the anxiety to be alleviated, we would be left with a basically neurotic person without a current behavior disorder. But, in terms of learning theory, there would be no reason to suppose that this person would develop new anxieties or symptoms unless put into a new traumatic situation. This would, of course, involve knowledge of what situations would be likely to be traumatic for a particular patient.†

Such empirical evidence as there is supports the position outlined above. Symptom substitution has not been found in those instances where a single patient has been subjected to intensive investigation and symptomatic treatment;[16,2,6] nor in those few instances where large-scale follow-up has been carried out on groups of subjects. For example, two recent investigations[17,18] of the results of symptomatic (*pace* Mowrer) treatment of enuresis indicate 70–80 per cent success, and a failure to find symptom substitution over periods up to two years. Mowrer himself,[3] reported 100 per cent success. The critical point seems to be that we are faced in such cases with a vicious circle (as Mowrer has indeed pointed out): the tic, for example, is a response to anxiety, but performance of the tic increases the general level of drive (irritability, annoyance, etc.), which increases the rate of responding, and so on. The important factor seems to be the breaking of this vicious circle; it does not much matter whether this is accomplished by treating the anxiety or the symptom, since both react upon each other. Thus, in the

---

* The nature of traumatic avoidance learning is a very complex problem, which has been greatly oversimplified here. The reader is referred to recent papers by Solomon and Brush[15] and by Solomon and Wynne[14] for comprehensive discussions of the current position.
† In the case of the patient treated by the author, for example, any situation involving anaesthesia (such as dental or medical operations) would be potentially traumatic.

shadowing method described by Cherry and Sayers[7] for the treatment of stammering, the mere fact of demonstrating to the patient that he can speak normally (even though under special conditions and before treatment has started) usually has a very striking effect on the patient's general well-being. In many instances it seems that the symptom itself generates a good deal of anxiety, which can be alleviated by a direct attack on the symptom.

The seriousness of the present situation is clearly demonstrated by Eysenck's recent contention[19,p.271] that, in spite of the experimental validation of symptomatic treatment of enuresis, this technique is not used in any child guidance clinic in Great Britain. It is obvious that a re-orientation is highly desirable, in which the " vertical " approach is abandoned, the use of the term " symptom " dropped altogether, and the patient considered as an individual who has developed a series of learned responses to certain situations. Clinical psychologists may then perhaps begin to apply that large body of knowledge and theory to be found in general psychology in which they are specially trained, and apply the principles of behavior to the abnormal field as well as to the normal.

REFERENCES

1. LIVERSEDGE, L. A. and SYLVESTER, J. D. (1955). Conditioning techniques in the treatment of writer's cramp. *Lancet*, **2**, 1147-1159.
2. MEYER, V. (1957). The treatment of two phobic patients on the basis of learning principles. *J. Abnorm. (Soc.) Psychol.*, **55**, 261-266.
3. MOWRER, O. H. (1938). Enuresis: A method for its study and treatment. *Amer. J. Orthopsychiat.*, **8**, 436-459.
4. RAYMOND, M. J. (1956). Case of fetishism treated by aversion therapy. *Brit. Med. J.*, **2**, 854-857.
5. WOLPE, J. (1952). Experimental neuroses as learned behaviour. *Brit. J. Psychol.*, **43**, 243-268.
6. YATES, A. J. (1958), The application of learning theory to the treatment of tics. *J. Abnorm. (Soc.) Psychol.*, **56**, 175-182.
7. CHERRY, C. and SAYERS, M. McA. (1956). Experiments upon the total inhibition of stammering by external control and some clinical results. *J. Psychosom. Res.*, **1**, 233-246.
8. DUNLAP, K. (1932). *Habits. Their Making and Unmaking.* Liveright, New York.
9. KANNER, L. (1935). *Child Psychiatry.* Charles C. Thomas, Springfield, Ill.
10. MOWRER, O. H. (1950). *Learning Theory and Personality Dynamics.* Ronald Press, New York.
11. HOLMES, G. (1946). *Introduction to Clinical Neurology.* Livingstone, Edinburgh.
12. FREUD, S. (1936). *The Problem of Anxiety.* Norton, New York.
13. EYSENCK, H. J. (1952). *The Scientific Study of Personality.* Routledge & Kegan Paul, London.
14. SOLOMON, R. L. and WYNNE, L. C. (1954). Traumatic avoidance learning: The principles of anxiety conservation and partial irreversibility. *Psychol. Rev.*, **61**, 353-385.
15. SOLOMON, R. L. and BRUSH, E. S. (1956). Experimentally derived conceptions of anxiety and aversion. In *Nebraska Symposium on Motivation*. Ed. by M. R. Jones. Pages 212-305. Univ. Nebraska Press, Lincoln.
16. JONES, H. G. (1956). The application of conditioning and learning techniques to the treatment of a psychiatric patient. *J. Abnorm. (Soc.) Psychol.*, **52**, 414-419.

17. BALLER, W. and SCHALOCK, H. (1956). Conditioned response treatment of enuresis. *Except. Child*, **22**, 233-236.
18. MARTIN, B. and KUBLY, D. (1955). Results of treatment of enuresis by a conditioned response method. *J. Consult. Psychol.*, **19**, 71-73.
19. EYSENCK, H. J. (1957). *Dynamics of Anxiety and Hysteria*. Routledge & Kegan Paul, London.

CONDITIONED EMOTIONAL REACTIONS*

JOHN B. WATSON and ROSALIE RAYNER

IN RECENT literature various speculations have been entered into concerning the possibility of conditioning various types of emotional response, but direct experimental evidence in support of such a view has been lacking. If the theory advanced by Watson and Morgan[1] to the effect that in infancy the original emotional reaction patterns are few, consisting so far as observed of fear, rage and love, then there must be some simple method by means of which the range of stimuli which can call out these emotions and their compounds is greatly increased. Otherwise, complexity in adult response could not be accounted for. These authors without adequate experimental evidence advanced the view that this range was increased by means of conditioned reflex factors. It was suggested there that the early home life of the child furnishes a laboratory situation for establishing conditioned emotional responses. The present authors have recently put the whole matter to an experimental test.

Experimental work has been done so far on only one child, Albert B. This infant was reared almost from birth in a hospital environment; his mother was a wet nurse in the Harriet Lane Home for Invalid Children. Albert's life was normal: he was healthy from birth and one of the best developed youngsters ever brought to the hospital, weighing 21 lbs at 9 months of age. He was on the whole stolid and unemotional. His stability was one of the principal reasons for using him as a subject in this test. We felt that we could do him relatively little harm by carrying out such experiments as those outlined below.

At approximately 9 months of age we ran him through the emotional tests that have become a part of our regular routine in determining whether fear reactions can be called out by other stimuli than sharp noises and the sudden removal of support. Tests of this type have been described by the senior author in another place.[2] In brief, the infant was confronted suddenly and for the first time successively with a white rat, a rabbit, a dog, a monkey, with masks with and without hair, cotton wool, burning newspapers, etc. A permanent record of Albert's reactions to these objects and situations has been preserved in a motion picture study. Manipulation was the most usual reaction called out. *At no time did this infant ever show fear in any situation.* These experimental records were confirmed by the casual

* Reprinted by permission of the Amer. Psychol. Ass. from (1920) *J. Exp. Psychol.*, 3, 1-14.

observations of the mother and hospital attendants. No one had ever seen him in a state of fear and rage. The infant practically never cried.

Up to approximately 9 months of age we had not tested him with loud sounds. The test to determine whether a fear reaction could be called out by a loud sound was made when he was 8 months, 26 days of age. The sound was that made by striking a hammer upon a suspended steel bar, 4 ft in length and $\frac{3}{4}$ in. in diameter. The laboratory notes are as follows: " One of the 2 experimenters caused the child to turn its head and fixate her moving hand; the other, stationed back of the child, struck the steel bar a sharp blow. The child started violently, his breathing was checked and the arms were raised in a characteristic manner. On the 2nd stimulation the same thing occurred, and in addition the lips began to pucker and tremble. On the 3rd stimulation the child broke into a sudden crying fit. This is the first time an emotional situation in the laboratory has produced any fear or even crying in Albert."

We had expected just these results on account of our work with other infants brought up under similar conditions. It is worth while to call attention to the fact that removal of support (dropping and jerking the blanket upon which the infant was lying) was tried exhaustively upon this infant on the same occasion. It was not effective in producing the fear response. This stimulus is effective in younger children. At what age such stimuli lose their potency in producing fear is not known. Nor is it known whether less placid children ever lose their fear of them. This probably depends upon the training the child gets. It is well known that children eagerly run to be tossed into the air and caught. On the other hand it is equally well known that in the adult fear responses are called out quite clearly by the sudden removal of support, if the individual is walking across a bridge, walking out upon a beam, etc. There is a wide field of study here which is aside from our present point.

The sound stimulus, thus, at 9 months of age, gives us the means of testing several important factors. (I) Can we condition fear of an animal, e.g., a white rat, by visually presenting it and simultaneously striking a steel bar? (II) If such a conditioned emotional response can be established, will there be a transfer to other animals or other objects? (III) What is the effect of time upon such conditioned emotional responses? (IV) If after a reasonable period such emotional responses have not died out, what laboratory methods can be devised for their removal?

(I) *The Establishment of Conditioned Emotional Responses*

At first there was considerable hesitation upon our part in making the attempt to set up fear reactions experimentally. A certain responsibility attaches to such a procedure. We decided finally to make the attempt, comforting ourselves by the reflection that such attachments would arise anyway as soon as the child left the sheltered environment of the nursery for the rough and tumble of the home. We did not begin this work until Albert was 11 months, 3 days of age. Before attempting to set up a conditioned response we, as before, put him through all of the regular emotional tests. *Not the slightest sign of fear response was obtained in any situation.*

The steps taken to condition emotional responses are shown in our laboratory notes.

11 months, 3 days—(1) White rat suddenly taken from the basket and presented to Albert. He began to reach for rat with left hand. Just as his hand touched the animal the bar was struck immediately behind his head. The infant jumped violently and fell forward, burying his face in the mattress. He did not cry, however.

(2) Just as the right hand touched the rat the bar was again struck. Again the infant jumped violently, fell forward and began to whimper.

In order not to disturb the child too seriously no further tests were given for 1 week.

11 months, 10 days—(1) Rat presented suddenly without sound. There was steady fixation but no tendency at first to reach for it. The rat was then placed nearer, whereupon tentative reaching movements began with the right hand. When the rat nosed the infant's left hand, the hand was immediately withdrawn. He started to reach for the head of the animal with the forefinger of the left hand, but withdrew it suddenly before contact. It is thus seen that the two joint stimulations given the previous week were not without effect. He was tested with his blocks immediately afterwards to see if they shared in the process of conditioning. He began immediately to pick them up, dropping them, pounding them, etc. In the remainder of the tests the blocks were given frequently to quiet him and to test his general emotional state. They were always removed from sight when the process of conditioning was under way.

(2) Joint stimulation with rat and sound. Started, then fell over immediately to right side. No crying.

(3) Joint stimulation. Fell to right side and rested upon hands, with head turned away from rat. No crying.

(4) Joint stimulation. Same reaction.

(5) Rat suddenly presented alone. Puckered face, whimpered and withdrew body sharply to the left.

(6) Joint stimulation. Fell over immediately to right side and began to whimper.

(7) Joint stimulation. Started violently and cried, but did not fall over.

(8) Rat alone. *The instant the rat was shown the baby began to cry. Almost instantly he turned sharply to the left, fell over on left side, raised himself on all fours and began to crawl away so rapidly that he was caught with difficulty before reaching the edge of the table.*

This was as convincing a case of a completely conditioned fear response as could have been theoretically pictured. In all seven joint stimulations were given to bring about the complete reaction. It is not unlikely had the sound been of greater intensity or of a more complex clang character that the number of joint stimulations might have been materially reduced. Experiments designed to define the nature of the sounds that will serve best as emotional stimuli are under way.

(II) *When a Conditioned Emotional Response has been Established for one Object, is there a Transfer?*

Five days later Albert was again brought back into the laboratory and tested as follows:

11 months, 15 days—(1) Tested first with blocks. He reached readily for them, playing with them as usual. This shows that there has been no general transfer to the room, table, blocks, etc.

(2) Rat alone. Whimpered immediately, withdrew right hand and turned head and trunk away.

(3) Blocks again offered. Played readily with them, smiling and gurgling.

(4) Rat alone. Leaned over to the left side as far away from the rat as possible, then fell over, getting up on all fours and scurrying away as rapidly as possible.

(5) Blocks again offered. Reached immediately for them, smiling and laughing as before.

The above preliminary test shows that the conditioned response to the rat had carried over completely for the 5 days in which no tests were given. The question as to whether or not there is a transfer was next taken up.

(6) Rabbit alone. The rabbit was suddenly placed on the mattress in front of him. The reaction was pronounced. Negative responses began at once. He leaned as far away from the animal as possible, whimpered, then burst into tears. When the rabbit was placed in contact with him he buried his face in the mattress, then got up on all fours and crawled away, crying as he went. This was a most convincing test.

(7) The blocks were next given him, after an interval. He played with them as before. It was observed by 4 people that he played far more energetically with them than ever before. The blocks were raised high over his head and slammed down with a great deal of force.

(8) Dog alone. The dog did not produce as violent a reaction as the rabbit. The moment fixation occurred the child shrank back and as the animal came nearer he attempted to get on all fours but did not cry at first. As soon as the dog passed out of his range of vision he became quiet. The dog was then made to approach the infant's head (he was lying down at the moment). Albert straightened up immediately, fell over to the opposite side and turned his head away. He then began to cry.

(9) The blocks were again presented. He began immediately to play with them.

(10) Fur coat (seal). Withdrew immediately to the left side and began to fret. Coat put close to him on the left side, he turned immediately, began to cry and tried to crawl away on all fours.

(11) Cotton wool. The wool was presented in a paper package. At the end the cotton was not covered by the paper. It was placed first on his feet. He kicked it away but did not touch it with his hands. When his hand was laid on the wool he immediately withdrew it but did not show the shock that the animals or fur coat produced in him. He then began to play with the paper, avoiding contact with the wool itself. He finally, under the impulse of the manipulative instinct, lost some of his negativism to the wool.

(12) Just in play W. put his head down to see if Albert would play with his hair. Albert was completely negative. Two other observers did the same thing. He began immediately to play with their hair. W. then brought the Santa Claus mask and presented it to Albert. He was again pronouncedly negative.

11 months, 20 days—(1) Blocks alone. Played with them as usual.

(2) Rat alone. Withdrawal of the whole body, bending over to left side, no crying. Fixation and following with eyes. The response was much less marked than on first presentation the previous week. It was thought best to freshen up the reaction by another joint stimulation.

(3) Just as the rat was placed on his hand the rod was struck. Reaction violent.

(4) Rat alone. Fell over at once to left side. Reaction practically as strong as on former occasion but no crying.

(5) Rat alone. Fell over to left side, got up on all fours and started to crawl away. On this occasion there was no crying, but strange to say, as he started away he began to gurgle and coo, even while leaning far over to the left side to avoid the rat.

(6) Rabbit alone. Leaned over to left side as far as possible. Did not fall over. Began to whimper but reaction not so violent as on former occasions.

(7) Blocks again offered. He reached for them immediately and began to play.

All of the tests so far discussed were carried out upon a table supplied with a mattress, located in a small, well-lighted dark-room. We wished to test next whether conditioned fear responses so set up would appear if the situation were markedly altered. We thought it best before making this test to freshen the reaction both to the rabbit and to the dog by showing them at the moment the steel bar was struck. It will be recalled that this was the first time any effort had been made to directly condition response to the dog and rabbit. The experimental notes are as follows:

(8) The rabbit at first was given alone. The reaction was exactly as given in test (6) above. When the rabbit was left on Albert's knees for a long time he began tentatively to reach out and manipulate its fur with forefingers. While doing this the steel rod was struck. A violent fear reaction resulted.

(9) Rabbit alone. Reaction wholly similar to that on trial (6) above.

(10) Rabbit alone. Started immediately to whimper, holding hands far up, but did not cry. Conflicting tendency to manipulate very evident.

(11) Dog alone. Began to whimper, shaking head from side to side, holding hands as far away from the animal as possible.

(12) Dog and sound. The rod was struck just as the animal touched him. A violent negative reaction appeared. He began to whimper, turned to one side, fell over and started to get up on all fours.

(13) Blocks. Played with them immediately and readily.

On this same day and immediately after the above experiment Albert was taken into the large well-lighted lecture room belonging to the laboratory. He was placed on a table in the center of the room immediately under the skylight. Four people were present. The situation was thus very different from that which obtained in the small dark room.

(1) Rat alone. No sudden fear reaction appeared at first. The hands, however, were held up and away from the animal. No positive manipulatory reactions appeared.

(2) Rabbit alone. Fear reaction slight. Turned to left and kept face away from the animal but the reaction was never pronounced.

(3) Dog alone. Turned away but did not fall over. Cried. Hands moved as far away from the animal as possible. Whimpered as long as the dog was present.

(4) Rat alone. Slight negative reaction.

(5) Rat and sound. It was thought best to freshen the reaction to the rat. The sound was given just as the rat was presented. Albert jumped violently but did not cry.

(6) Rat alone. At first he did not show any negative reaction. When rat was placed nearer he began to show negative reaction by drawing back his body, raising his hands, whimpering, etc.

(7) Blocks. Played with them immediately.

(8) Rat alone. Pronounced withdrawal of body and whimpering.

(9) Blocks. Played with them as before.

(10) Rabbit alone. Pronounced reaction. Whimpered with arms held high, fell over backward and had to be caught.

(11) Dog alone. At first the dog did not produce the pronounced reaction. The hands were held high over the head, breathing was checked, but there was no crying. Just at this moment the dog, which had not barked before, barked 3 times loudly when only about 6 in. from the baby's face. Albert

immediately fell over and broke into a wail that continued until the dog was removed. The sudden barking of the hitherto quiet dog produced a marked fear response in the adult observers!

From the above results it would seem that emotional transfers do take place. Furthermore it would seem that the number of transfers resulting from an experimentally produced conditioned emotional reaction may be very large. In our observations we had no means of testing the complete number of transfers which may have resulted.

(III) *The Effect of Time upon Conditioned Emotional Responses*

We have already shown that the conditioned emotional response will continue for a period of 1 week. It was desired to make the time test longer. In view of the imminence of Albert's departure from the hospital we could not make the interval longer than 1 month. Accordingly no further emotional experimentation was entered into for 31 days after the above test. During the month, however, Albert was brought weekly to the laboratory for tests upon right- and left-handedness, imitation, general development, etc. No emotional tests whatever were given and during the whole month his regular nursery routine was maintained in the Harriet Lane Home. The notes on the test given at the end of this period are as follows:

1 year, 21 days—(1) Santa Claus mask. Withdrawal, gurgling, then slapped at it without touching. When his hand was forced to touch it, he whimpered and cried. His hand was forced to touch it two more times. He whimpered and cried on both tests. He finally cried at the mere visual stimulus of the mask.

(2) Fur coat. Wrinkled his nose and withdrew both hands, drew back his whole body and began to whimper as the coat was put nearer. Again there was the strife between withdrawal and the tendency to manipulate. Reached tentatively with left hand but drew back before contact had been made. In moving his body to one side his hand accidentally touched the coat. He began to cry at once, nodding his head in a very peculiar manner (this reaction was an entirely new one). Both hands were withdrawn as far as possible from the coat. The coat was then laid on his lap and he continued nodding his head and whimpering, withdrawing his body as far as possible, pushing the while at the coat with his feet but never touching it with his hands.

(3) Fur coat. The coat was taken out of his sight and presented again at the end of a minute. He began immediately to fret, withdrawing his body and nodding his head as before.

(4) Blocks. He began to play with them as usual.

(5) The rat. He allowed the rat to crawl towards him without withdrawing. He sat very still and fixated it intently. Rat then touched his hand. Albert withdrew it immediately, then leaned back as far as possible but did not cry. When the rat was placed on his arm he withdrew his body and began to

fret, nodding his head. The rat was then allowed to crawl against his chest. He first began to fret and then covered his eyes with both hands.

(6) Blocks. Reaction normal.

(7) The rabbit. The animal was placed directly in front of him. It was very quiet. Albert showed no avoiding reactions at first. After a few seconds he puckered up his face, began to nod his head and to look intently at the experimenter. He next began to push the rabbit away with his feet, withdrawing his body at the same time. Then as the rabbit came nearer he began pulling his feet away, nodding his head, and wailing " da da." After about a minute he reached out tentatively and slowly and touched the rabbit's ear with his right hand, finally manipulating it. The rabbit was again placed in his lap. Again he began to fret and withdrew his hands. He reached out tentatively with his left hand and touched the animal, shuddered and withdrew the whole body. The experimenter then took hold of his left hand and laid it on the rabbit's back. Albert immediately withdrew his hand and began to suck his thumb. Again the rabbit was laid in his lap. He began to cry, covering his face with both hands.

(8) Dog. The dog was very active. Albert fixated it intensely for a few seconds, sitting very still. He began to cry but did not fall over backwards as on his last contact with the dog. When the dog was pushed closer to him he at first sat motionless, then began to cry, putting both hands over his face.

These experiments would seem to show conclusively that directly conditioned emotional responses as well as those conditioned by transfer persist, although with a certain loss in the intensity of the reaction, for a longer period than one month. Our view is that they persist and modify personality throughout life. It should be recalled again that Albert was of an extremely phlegmatic type. Had he been emotionally unstable probably both the directly conditioned response and those transferred would have persisted throughout the month unchanged in form.

(IV) " Detachment " or Removal of Conditioned Emotional Responses

Unfortunately Albert was taken from the hospital the day the above tests were made. Hence the opportunity of building up an experimental technique by means of which we could remove the conditioned emotional responses was denied us. Our own view, expressed above, which is possibly not very well grounded, is that these responses in the home environment are likely to persist indefinitely, unless an accidental method for removing them is hit upon. The importance of establishing some method must be apparent to all. Had the opportunity been at hand we should have tried out several methods, some of which we may mention. (1) Constantly confronting the child with those stimuli which called out the responses in the hopes that habituation would come in corresponding to " fatigue " of reflex when differential reactions are to be set up. (2) By trying to " recondition " by showing objects calling out fear responses (visual) and simultaneously stimulating the erogenous zones (tactual). We should try first the lips, then the nipples and as a final resort the sex organs. (3) By trying to " recondition " by feeding the subject candy or other food just as the animal is shown. This method calls for the food control of the subject. (4) By building up " constructive " activities around the object by imitation and by putting the hand through the motions of manipulation. At this age imitation of overt motor activity is strong, as our present but unpublished experimentation has shown.

INCIDENTAL OBSERVATIONS

(a) *Thumb sucking as a compensatory device for blocking fear and noxious stimuli*—During the course of these experiments, especially in the final test, it was noticed that whenever Albert was on the verge of tears or emotionally upset generally he would continually thrust his thumb into his mouth. The moment the hand reached the mouth he became impervious to the stimuli producing fear. Again and again while the motion pictures were being made at the end of the 30-day rest period, we had to remove the thumb from his mouth before the conditioned response could be obtained. This method of blocking noxious and emotional stimuli (fear and rage) through erogenous stimulation seems to persist from birth onward. Very often in our experiments upon the work adders with infants under 10 days of age the same reaction appeared. When at work upon the adders both of the infants' arms are under slight restraint. Often rage appears. They begin to cry, thrashing their arms and legs about. If the finger gets into the mouth crying ceases at once. The organism, thus apparently from birth, when under the influence of love stimuli, is blocked to all others.* This resort to sex stimulation when under the influence of noxious and emotional situations, or when the individual is restless and idle, persists throughout adolescent and adult life. Albert, at any rate, did not resort to thumb sucking except in the presence of such stimuli. Thumb sucking could immediately be checked by offering him his blocks. These invariably called out active manipulation instincts. It is worth while here to call attention to the fact that Freud's conception of the stimulation of erogenous zones as being the expression of an original " pleasure " seeking principle may be turned about and possibly better described as a compensatory (and often conditioned) device for the blockage of noxious and fear and rage producing stimuli.

* The stimulus to love in infants according to our view is stroking of the skin, lips, nipples and sex organs, patting and rocking, picking up, etc. Patting and rocking (when not conditioned) are probably equivalent to actual stimulation of the sex organs. In adults of course, as every lover knows, vision, audition and olfaction soon become conditioned by joint stimulation with contact and kinaesthetic stimuli.

(b) *Equal primacy of fear, love and possibly rage*—While in general the results of our experiment offer no particular points of conflict with Freudian concepts, one fact out of harmony with them should be emphasized. According to proper Freudians, sex (or in our terminology, love) is the principal emotion in which conditioned responses arise which later limit and distort personality. We wish to take sharp issue with this view on the basis of the experimental evidence we have gathered. Fear is as primal a factor as love in influencing personality. Fear does not gather its potency in any derived manner from love. It belongs to the original and inherited nature of man. Probably the same may be true of rage although at present we are not so sure of this.

The Freudians 20 years from now, unless their hypotheses change, when they come to analyze Albert's fear of a seal skin coat—assuming that he comes to analysis at that age—will probably tease from him the recital of a dream which upon their analysis will show that Albert at 3 years of age attempted to play with the pubic hair of the mother and was scolded violently for it. (We are by no means denying that this might in some other case condition it.) If the analyst has sufficiently prepared Albert to accept such a dream when found as an explanation of his avoiding tendencies, and if the analyst has the authority and personality to put it over, Albert may be fully convinced that the dream was a true revealer of the factors which brought about the fear.

It is probable that many of the phobias in psychopathology are true conditioned emotional reactions either of the direct or the transferred type. One may possibly have to believe that such persistence of early conditioned responses will be found only in persons who are constitutionally inferior. Our argument is meant to be constructive. Emotional disturbances in adults cannot be traced back to sex alone. They must be retraced along at least three collateral lines—to conditioned and transferred responses set up in infancy and early youth in all three of the fundamental human emotions.

REFERENCES

1. WATSON, J. B. and MORGAN. (April, 1917). Emotional reactions and psychological experimentation. *Amer. J. Psychol.*, **28**, 163-174.
2. WATSON, J. B. *Psychology from the Standpoint of a Behaviourist*, p. 202.

THE ELIMINATION OF CHILDREN'S FEARS*

MARY COVER JONES

Institute of Educational Research, Teachers College, Columbia University

THE INVESTIGATION of children's fears leads directly to a number of important problems in the genetic study of emotion. At the Johns Hopkins laboratory[1] Dr. John B. Watson has analyzed the process by which fears are acquired in infancy, and has shown that the conditioned reflex formula may apply to the transfer of emotional reactions from original stimuli (pain, loud noises, or loss of bodily support) to various substitute fear objects in the child's environment. This process has been further demonstrated by the author in the case of children from 1 to 4 years of age.[2] A study of how children's fears may be reduced or eradicated would seem to be the next point for an experimental attack. Such a study should include an attempt to evaluate, objectively, the various possible methods which laboratory experience has suggested.

The present research, an approach to this problem, was conducted with the advice of Dr. Watson, by means of a subvention granted by the Laura Spelman Rockefeller Memorial to the Institute of Educational Research of Teachers College.

The subjects, 70 children from 3 months to 7 years of age, were maintained in an institution for the temporary care of children. Admission to this institution depended as a rule upon conditions which made it difficult or impossible to keep the children at home: a case of illness in the family, the separation of father and mother, or an occupation which kept the mother away from home for a part of the day. As there was a charge for weekly care, those homes which were in actual poverty were not represented; the economic and social status of the parents, as well as the results of our intelligence tests (Kuhlmann and Terman) would indicate that this group of children was normal, and superior to the average for orphan asylums and similar institutions. As the danger of contagion is great in a group so constantly changing, a very thorough medical examination eliminated all those with symptoms of infection, and even those decidedly below normal in nutrition or general development. Our laboratory could not determine the admission and discharge of children, nor interfere in the prescribed

* Reprinted by permission of the author and the Amer. Psychol. Assoc. from (1924) *J. Exp. Psychol.*, **7**, 383-390.

routine of eating, sleeping and play. It was possible however for the experimenter to live in the building with the children in order to become acquainted with them in their usual environment, to observe them continuously for days at a time, and to take them daily, or oftener if desirable, to the laboratory where observations could be made under specifically controlled conditions.

In our selection of children from this group, we attempted to find those who would show a marked degree of fear under conditions normally evoking positive (pleasant) or mildly negative (unpleasant) responses. A wide range of situations was presented in a fairly standardized way to all of the children: such as being left alone, being in a dark room, being with other children who showed fear, the sudden presentation of a snake, a white rat, a rabbit, a frog, false faces, loud sounds, etc. This procedure served to expose fear trends if they were already present; it was not designed as a conditioning process, but merely as a method of revealing prior conditionings. In the majority of the children tested, our standard situations failed to arouse observable negative responses. This survey of children's fears is reported in another article.

When specific fears were demonstrated, our next step was to attempt their removal. By what devices could we eliminate these harmful reactions, which in many cases were subject to diffusion, and were interfering with the formation of useful attitudes and necessary habits? Our method or combination of methods depended upon the type of case presented and the manner in which treatment was received, as well as upon such external circumstances as quarantines, and the length of time the child was likely to remain in the institution.

THE METHOD OF ELIMINATION THROUGH DISUSE

A common assumption with regard to children's fears is that they will die out if left alone, i.e., if the child is carefully shielded from stimuli which would tend to re-arouse the fear. "Elimination through disuse" is the name given to this process. The following cases from our records provide suggestive material:

CASE 1—Rose D. Age 21 months. General situation: sitting in play-pen with other children, none of whom showed specific fears. A rabbit was introduced from behind a screen.

19th Jan. At sight of the rabbit, Rose burst into tears, her crying lessened when the experimenter picked up the rabbit, but again increased when the rabbit was put back on the floor. At the removal of the rabbit she quieted down, accepted a cracker, and presently returned to her blocks.

5th Feb. After 2 weeks the situation was repeated. She cried and trembled upon seeing the rabbit. E. (the experimenter) sat on the floor between Rose and the rabbit; she continued to cry for several minutes. E. tried to divert her attention with the peg-board; she finally stopped crying, but continued to watch the rabbit and would not attempt to play.

Case 8—Bobby G. Age 30 months.

6th Dec. Bobby showed a slight fear response when a rat was presented in a box. He looked at it from a distance of several feet, drew back and cried. A 3-day period of training followed bringing Bobby to the point where he tolerated a rat in the open pen in which he was playing, and even touched it without overt fear indications. No further stimulation with the rat occurred until:

30th Jan. After nearly 2 months of no experience with the specific stimulus, Bobby was again brought into the laboratory. While he was playing in the pen, E. appeared, with a rat held in her hand. Bobby jumped up, ran outside the pen, and cried. The rat having been returned to its box, Bobby ran to E., held her hand, and showed marked disturbance.

Case 33—Eleanor J. Age 21 months.

17th Jan. While playing in the pen, a frog was introduced from behind her. She watched, came nearer, and finally touched it. The frog jumped. She withdrew and when later presented with the frog, shook her head and pushed the experimenter's hand away violently.

26th March. After 2 months of no further experience with animals, Eleanor was taken to the laboratory and offered the frog. When the frog hopped she drew back, ran from the pen and cried.

These and similar cases show that an interval of " disuse," extending over a period of weeks or months, may not result in eliminating a fear response, and that when other conditions are approximately constant there may be no diminution in the degree of fear manifested. From our experience, it would appear to be an unsafe method to attempt the cure of a fear trend by ignoring it.

THE METHOD OF VERBAL APPEAL

As most of our subjects were under 4 years of age, the possibilities of verbal analysis and control were very limited. We attempted to find how much we could accomplish toward breaking down a negative reaction by merely talking about the fear-object, endeavoring to keep it in the child's attention, and connecting it verbally with pleasant experiences. This method showed no applicability except in the case of one subject, Jean E., a girl in her 5th year. At the initial presentation of the rabbit a marked fear response was registered. This was followed by 10 minutes daily conversation about the rabbit; to hold her interest the experimenter introduced such devices as the picture book of " Peter Rabbit," toy rabbits and rabbits drawn or modelled from Plasticene. Brief stories were used, and there was always a reference to the " real " rabbit as well. On such occasions she would say, " Where is your rabbit? " or " Show me your rabbit," or once " I touched your rabbit, and stroked it, and it never cried." (This latter was pure make-believe, and an interesting example of projection.) However, when the rabbit was actually presented again, at the end of a week, her reaction was practically the same as at the first encounter. She jumped up from her play and retreated; when coaxed, she reluctantly touched the rabbit while the experimenter held it; when the animal was put down on the floor she sobbed, " Put it away," " Take it," and ran about the room frightened and distracted. She had learned to speak freely of rabbits, but this altered verbalization apparently was not accompanied by any change in her response to the rabbit itself. The experiment was interrupted after another three days of the same procedure, at the end of which time Jean left the institution with her initial fear patterns intact, so far as we could tell. It seems likely that many hours of training in the toleration of symbols may have little or no modifying effect on a mass reaction to the primary stimulus.

THE METHOD OF NEGATIVE ADAPTATION

This method is based on the theory that familiarity breeds indifference: if the stimulation is repeated often enough, monotonously, the subject finally becomes used to it and tempers his response accordingly.

CASE 17—Godfried W. Age 3 years.
A white rat was introduced from behind a screen. Godfried sat quietly for a few minutes, watching the rat with close attention. He then began to cry, made avertive movements with his hands and feet, and finally withdrew as far as possible from the animal. At the next presentation of the rat, Godfried did not cry; he advanced cautiously, making quick startled withdrawals whenever the animal moved.
A few days later when the same situation was presented, Godfried smiled and said, " Put it down on the floor." After 3 hours the rat was again brought in and allowed to run free in the pen. It scurried about and occasionally came very near him, but Godfried made no attempt to withdraw even when the animal advanced and touched him.

In this case, with practically no re-educative measures except repeated stimulation, Godfried conquered his specific fear. The experiment was not carried to the point where he showed a distinct positive reaction to rats, but he had developed a socially satisfactory attitude. As a strictly non-verbal approach, the method of negative adaptation is undoubtedly useful with infants and animals. In actual practice, however, we find very few fears in children of the pre-language period, and with the older children it is inefficient to eliminate the degree of control, however slight, which language may afford.

Furthermore, with all but a few of our fear-objects the aim was not indifference, which negative adaptation implies, but something farther along the scale toward an acceptance reaction.

From our experience in general, it would appear that the repeated presentation of a feared object, with no auxiliary attempt to eliminate the fear, is more likely to produce a summation effect than an adaptation. With Godfried (the case just quoted) the loss of his resistance was possibly due to the fact that he had been afraid the animal would bite him. This fear, unrealized, was gradually overcome.

THE METHOD OF REPRESSION

In the home, as well as in the school and playground, social repression is perhaps the simplest and most common method of dealing with fear symptoms—a method, which, we may commonly note, often fails to remove the roots of the fear. As there are already too many examples of the maladaptive results of repression, we shall not attempt to add to their number. In our laboratory we used no repressive punishment, but within a group of children the familiar situations of ridicule, social teasing and scolding frequently appeared. Because of shame, a child might try to contain his fears without overt expression, but after a certain point had been reached, the reaction appeared notwithstanding.

CASE 41—Arthur G. Age 4 years.
Arthur was shown the frogs in an aquarium, no other children being present. He cried, said " they bite," and ran out of the play-pen. Later, however, he was brought into the room with four other boys; he swaggered up to the aquarium, pressing ahead of the others who were with him. When one of his companions picked up a frog and turned to him with it, he screamed and fled; at this he was chased and made fun of, but with naturally no lessening of the fear on this particular occasion.

Three boys standing around the aquarium each cried " Give me one," holding out their hands for a frog. But when the frog was offered they all precipitously withdrew. When two girls (4 years old) sang out to Sidney (age 3) " Sidney is afraid, Sidney is afraid," Sidney nodded his head in assent . . . illustrating what often happens in the use of social ridicule: the emotion is re-suggested and entrenched, rather than stamped out.

THE METHOD OF DISTRACTION

A convenient method, used frequently and with fair results, involves offering the subject a substitute activity. In order to capture a safety pin from the baby's hand and still preserve peace, its attention may be distracted with another toy, while you steal away the pin. Such a device, known to every mother, may be applied to the problem of eliminating fear responses. Arthur, whose fear of frogs had received some attention from us, wished to play with a set of crayons kept in the laboratory. We placed the crayons close to a frog on the table. Arthur stepped forward cautiously; keeping his gaze on the frog, he grabbed paper and crayons and showed alacrity in darting out of the danger zone. The experience, however, seemed to reassure him. " I ran over there and got it," he told us, " He didn't bite me. To-morrow I'll put it in a little box and bring it home." At one stage of his fear of the rabbit, Sidney would whine whenever the rabbit was brought near, but he could readily be diverted by conversation about the rabbit's name, or some inocuous detail. For verbal distraction the constant presence of a grown-up is of course necessary; this introduces factors which are not always advantageous (such as reliance upon adult protection). Essentially, distraction soothes a fear response by inducing the child temporarily to forget the fear-object. (Substitution of an alternate stimulus-response system.) This may fail to result in any permanent reduction of the fear trend. Where the situation is properly managed, however, distraction passes over into a method which we have found distinctly useful, and which will now be described.

THE METHOD OF DIRECT CONDITIONING

It is probable that each of our methods involves conditioning in one form or another. Under this heading, however, we include all specific attempts to associate with the fear-object a definite stimulus, capable of arousing a positive (pleasant) reaction. The hunger motive appears to be the most effective for use in this connection. During a period of craving for food, the child is placed in a high chair and given something to eat. The fear-object is brought in, starting a negative response. It is then moved away gradually until it is at a sufficient distance not to interfere with the child's eating. The relative strength of the fear impulse and the hunger impulse may be gauged by the distance to which it is necessary to remove the fear-object. While the child is eating, the object is slowly brought nearer to the table, then placed upon the table, and finally as the tolerance increases it is brought close enough to be touched. Since we could not interfere with the regular schedule of meals, we chose the time of the mid-morning lunch for the experiment. This usually assured some degree of interest in the food, and corresponding success in our treatment. The effectiveness of this method increases greatly as the hunger grows, at least up to a certain point. The case of Peter (reported in detail elsewhere) illustrates our procedure; one of our most serious problem cases, he was treated by the method daily or twice daily for a period of 2 months. The laboratory notes for the first and the last days of the training period show an improvement which we were able to attribute specifically to the training measures used.

CASE 30—Peter. Age 2 years, 10 months.
10th March, 10.15 A.M. Peter sitting in high chair, eating candy. Experimenter entered room with a rabbit in an open meshed wire cage. The rabbit was placed on the table 4 ft from Peter who immediately began to cry, insisting that the rabbit be taken away. Continued crying until the rabbit was put down 20 ft away. He then started again on the candy, but continued to fuss, " I want you to put Bunny outside." After 3 minutes he once more burst into tears; the rabbit was removed.
29th April, 9.55 A.M. Peter standing in high chair, looking out of the window. He inquired, " Where is the rabbit? " The rabbit was put down on the chair at Peter's feet. Peter patted him, tried to pick him up, but finding the rabbit too heavy asked the experimenter to help in lifting him to the window sill, where he played with him for several minutes.

This method obviously requires delicate handling. Two response systems are being dealt with: food leading to a positive reaction, and fear-object leading to a negative reaction. The desired conditioning should result in transforming the fear-object into a source of positive response (substitute stimulus). But a careless manipulator could readily produce the reverse result, attaching a fear reaction to the sight of food.

THE METHOD OF SOCIAL IMITATION

We have used this method extensively, as it was one of the first to show signs of yielding results.

CASE 8—Bobby G. Age 30 months.

Bobby was playing in the pen with Mary and Laurel. The rabbit was introduced in a basket. Bobby cried, " No, no," and motioned for the experimenter to remove it. The 2 girls, however, ran up readily enough, looked in at the rabbit and talked excitedly. Bobby became promptly interested, said " What? Me see," and ran forward, his curiosity and assertiveness in the social situation overmastering other impulses.

CASE 54—Vincent W. Age 21 months.

19th Jan. Vincent showed no fear of the rabbit, even when it was pushed against his hands or face. His only response was to laugh and reach for the rabbit's fur. On the same day he was taken into the pen with Rose, who cried at the sight of the rabbit. Vincent immediately developed a fear response; in the ordinary playroom situation he would pay no attention to her crying, but in connection with the rabbit, her distress had a marked suggestion value. The fear transferred in this way persisted for over 2 weeks.

6th Feb. Eli and Herbert were in the play-pen with the rabbit. When Vincent was brought in, he remained cautiously standing at some distance. Eli led Vincent over to the rabbit, and induced him to touch the animal. Vincent laughed.

The second case illustrated a fear socially induced (this is perhaps the most common source of maladjustive fear trends) and the later removal of the fear by social suggestion. Many of the fears we studied pointed to an origin in a specific traumatic experience; it would probably have been a valuable aid in our procedure, had we been able to trace the developmental history of each of these fears. It was usually impossible to do this, however, in view of the institutional life of our subjects, and the fact that parents, even when they could be reached and consulted, were as a rule ignorant of their children's emotional mishaps.

SUMMARY

In our study of methods for removing fear responses, we found unqualified success with only two. By the method of direct conditioning, we associated the fear-object with a craving-object, and replaced the fear by a positive response. By the method of social imitation we allowed the subject to share, under controlled conditions, the social activity of a group of children especially chosen with a view to prestige effect. Verbal appeal, elimination through disuse, negative adaptation, " repression," and " distraction " were methods which proved sometimes effective but were not to be relied upon unless used in combination with other methods. It should be remarked that apart from laboratory analysis we have rarely used any of the above procedures in pure form. Our aim has been to cure the fear, by the group of devices most appropriate at any given stage of treatment.

REFERENCES

1. WATSON, J. B. and RAYNER (Dec., 1921). Studies in infant psychology. *Sci. Mon.*, N.Y.
2. JONES, M. C. (1924). *Conditioned Fear in Children.*

A LABORATORY STUDY OF FEAR*:
THE CASE OF PETER

MARY COVER JONES

Institute of Educational Research, Teachers College, Columbia University

As PART of a genetic study of emotions,† a number of children were observed in order to determine the most effective methods of removing fear responses.

The case of Peter illustrates how a fear may be removed under laboratory conditions. His case was selected from a number of others for the following reasons:

(1) Progress in combating the fear reactions was so marked that many of the details of the process could be observed easily.

(2) It was possible to continue the study over a period of more than three months.

(3) The notes of a running diary show the characteristics of a healthy, normal, interesting child, well adjusted, except for his exaggerated fear reactions. A few descriptive notes show something of his personality: " Remarkably active, easily interested, capable of prolonged endeavour . . . A favorite with the children as well as with the nurses and matrons . . . Peter has a healthy passion for possessions. Everything that he lays his hands on is his. As this is frequently disputed by some other child, there are occasional violent scenes of protest. These disturbances are not more frequent than might be expected in a three-year-old, in view of the fact that he is continually forced to adjust to a large group of children, nor are they more marked in Peter's case than in others of his age. Peter's I.Q. at the age of 2 years and 10 months was 102 on the Kuhlmann Revision of the Binet. At the same time he passed 5 of the 3 year tests on the Stanford Revision. In initiative and constructive ability, however, he is superior to his companions of the same mental age."

(4) This case is a sequel to one recently contributed by Dr. Watson and furnished supplementary material of interest in a genetic study of emotions. Dr. Watson's case illustrated how a fear could be produced experimentally under laboratory conditions.[1] A brief review follows: Albert, 11 months of age, was an infant with a phlegmatic disposition, afraid of " nothing

* Reprinted by permission of the author and the editor of (1924) *Pedagogical Sem.*, **31**, 308-315.
† The research was conducted with the advice of Dr. John B. Watson, by means of a subvention granted by the Laura Spelman Rockefeller Memorial to the Institute of Educational Research of Teachers College.

under the sun " except a loud sound made by striking a steel bar. This made him cry. By striking the bar at the same time that Albert touched a white rat, the fear was transferred to the white rat. After seven combined stimulations, rat and sound, Albert not only became greatly disturbed at the sight of a rat, but this fear had spread to include a white rabbit, cotton wool, a fur coat and the experimenter's hair. It did not transfer to his wooden blocks and other objects very dissimilar to the rat.

In referring to this case, Dr. Watson says, " We have shown experimentally that when you condition a child to show fear of an animal, this fear transfers or spreads in such a way that without separate conditioning he becomes afraid of many animals. If you take any one of these objects producing fear and uncondition, will fear of the other objects in the series disappear at the same time? That is, will the unconditioning spread without further training to other stimuli? "

Dr. Watson intended to continue the study of Albert in an attempt to answer this question, but Albert was removed from the hospital and the series of observations was discontinued.

About 3 years later this case, which seemed almost to be Albert grown a bit older, was discovered in our laboratory.

Peter was 2 years and 10 months old when we began to study him. He was afraid of a white rat, and this fear extended to a rabbit, a fur coat, a feather, cotton wool, etc., but not to wooden blocks and similar toys. An abridgment of the first laboratory notes on Peter reads as follows: " Peter was put in a crib in a play-room and immediately became absorbed in his toys. A white rat was introduced into the crib from behind. (The experimenter was behind a screen.) At sight of the rat, Peter screamed and fell flat on his back in a paroxysm of fear. The stimulus was removed, and Peter was taken out of the crib and put into a chair. Barbara was brought to the crib and the white rat introduced as before. She exhibited no fear but picked the rat up in her hand. Peter sat quietly watching Barbara and the rat. A string of beads belonging to Peter had been left in the crib. Whenever the rat touched a part of the string he would say ' my beads ' in a complaining voice, although he made no objections when Barbara touched them. Invited to get down from the chair, he shook his head, fear not yet subsided. Twenty-five minutes elapsed before he was ready to play about freely." The next day his reactions to the following situations and objects were noted:

Play-room and crib - - - -	Selected toys, got into crib without protest.
White ball rolled in - - -	Picked it up and held it.
Fur rug hung over crib - -	Cried until it was removed.
Fur coat hung over crib - -	Cried until it was removed.
Cotton - - - - -	Whimpered, withdrew, cried.
Hat with feathers - - -	Cried.
Blue woolly sweater - -	Looked, turned away, no fear.
White toy rabbit of rough cloth -	No interest, no fear.
Wooden doll - - - -	No interest, no fear.

This case made it possible for the experiment to continue where Dr. Watson had left off. The first problem was that of "unconditioning" a fear response to an animal, and the second, that of determining whether unconditioning to one stimulus spreads without further training to other stimuli.

From the test situations which were used to reveal fears, it was found that Peter showed even more marked fear responses to the rabbit than to the rat. It was decided to use the rabbit for unconditioning and to proceed as follows: Each day Peter and three other children were brought to the laboratory for a play period. The other children were selected carefully because of their entirely fearless attitude toward the rabbit and because of their satisfactory adjustments in general. The rabbit was always present during a part of the play period. From time to time Peter was brought in alone so that his reactions could be observed and progress noted.

From reading over the notes for each session it was apparent that there had been improvement by more or less regular steps from almost complete terror at sight of the rabbit to a completely positive response with no signs of disturbance. New situations requiring closer contact with the rabbit had been gradually introduced and the degree to which these situations were avoided, tolerated, or welcomed, at each experimental session, gave the measure of improvement. Analysis of the notes on Peter's reactions indicated the following progressive steps in his degrees of toleration:

(A) Rabbit anywhere in the room in a cage causes fear reactions.
(B)   ,,   12 ft away in cage tolerated.
(C)   ,,   4 ft away in cage tolerated.
(D)   ,,   3 ft away in cage tolerated.
(E)   ,,   close in cage tolerated.
(F)   ,,   free in room tolerated.
(G)   ,,   touched when experimenter holds it.
(H)   ,,   touched when free in room.
(I)   ,,   defied by spitting at it, throwing things at it, imitating it.
(J)   ,,   allowed on tray of high chair.
(K) Squats in defenseless position beside rabbit.
(L) Helps experimenter to carry rabbit to its cage.
(M) Holds rabbit on lap.
(N) Stays alone in room with rabbit.
(O) Allows rabbit in play-pen with him.
(P) Fondles rabbit affectionately.
(Q) Lets rabbit nibble his fingers.

These "degrees of toleration" merely represented the stages in which improvement occurred. They did not give any indications of the intervals between steps, nor of the plateaus, relapses and sudden gains which were actually evident. To show these features a curve was drawn by using the 17 steps given above as the Y axis of a chart and the experimental sessions as the X axis. The units are not equal on either axis, as the "degrees of toleration" have merely been set down as they appeared from consideration of the laboratory notes with no attempt to evaluate the steps. Likewise the experimental sessions were not equi-distant in time. Peter was seen twice daily for a period and thence only once a day. At one point illness and quarantine interrupted the experiments for 2 months. There is no indication of these irregularities on the chart. For example, along the X axis, 1 represents the date, 4 December, when the observations began. 11 and 12 represent the dates, 10 March A.M. and P.M. (from 17 December to 7 March, Peter was not available for study).

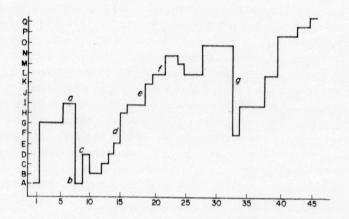

The question arose as to whether or not the points on the Y axis which indicated progress to the experimenter represented real advance and not merely idiosyncratic reactions of the subject. The " tolerance series " as indicated by the experimenter was presented in random order to 6 graduate students and instructors in psychology to be arranged so as to indicate increase in tolerance, in their judgment. An average correlation of ·70 with the experimenter's arrangement was found for the 6 ratings. This indicates that the experimenter was justified from an *a priori* point of view in designating the steps to be progressive stages.

The first 7 periods show how Peter progressed from a great fear of the rabbit to a tranquil indifference and even a voluntary pat on the rabbit's back when others were setting the example. The notes for the 7th period (see (*a*) on chart) read: " Laurel, Mary, Arthur, Peter playing together in the laboratory. Experimenter put rabbit down on floor. Arthur said, ' Peter doesn't cry when he sees the rabbit come out.' Peter, ' No.' He was a little concerned as to whether or not the rabbit would eat his kiddie car. Laurel and Mary stroked the rabbit and chattered away excitedly. Peter walked over, touched the rabbit on the back, exulting, ' I touched him on the end.'" At this period Peter was taken to the hospital with scarlet fever. He did not return for 2 months.

By referring to the chart at (*b*), it will be noted that the line shows a decided drop to the early level of fear reaction when he returned. This was easily explained by the nurse who brought Peter from the hospital. As they were entering a taxi at the door of the hospital, a large dog, running past, jumped at them. Both Peter and the nurse were very much frightened, Peter so much that he lay back in the taxi pale and quiet, and the nurse debated whether or not to return him to the hospital. This seemed reason enough for his precipitate descent back to the original fear level. Being threatened by a large dog when ill, and in a strange place and being with an adult who also showed fear, was a terrifying situation against which our training could not have fortified him.

At this point (*b*) we began another method of treatment, that of " direct conditioning." Peter was seated in a high chair and given food which he liked. The experimenter brought the rabbit in a wire cage as close as she could without arousing a response which would interfere with the eating. Through the presence of the pleasant stimulus (food) whenever the rabbit was shown, the fear was eliminated gradually in favor of a positive response. Occasionally also, other children were brought in to help with the " unconditioning." These facts are of interest in following the charted progress. The first decided rise at (*c*) was due to the presence of another child who influenced Peter's reaction. The notes for this day read: " Lawrence and Peter sitting near together in their high chairs eating candy. Rabbit in cage put down 12 ft away. Peter began to cry. Lawrence said, ' Oh, rabbit.' Clambered down, ran over and looked in the cage at him. Peter followed close and watched." The next two decided rises at (*d*) and (*e*) occurred on the day when a student assistant, Dr. S., was present. Peter was very fond of Dr. S. whom he insisted was his " papa." Although Dr. S. did not directly influence Peter by any overt suggestions, it may be that having him there contributed to Peter's general feeling of well-being and thus indirectly affected his reactions. The fourth rise on the chart at (*f*) was, like the first, due to the influence of another child. Notes for the 21st session read: " Peter with candy in high chair. Experimenter brought rabbit and sat down in front of the tray with it. Peter cried out, ' I don't want him,' and withdrew. Rabbit was given to another child sitting near to hold. His holding the rabbit served as a powerful suggestion; Peter wanted the rabbit on his lap, and held it for an instant." The decided drop at (*g*) was caused by a slight scratch when Peter was helping to carry the rabbit to his cage. The rapid ascent following shows how quickly he regained lost ground.

In one of our last sessions, Peter showed no fear although another child was present who showed marked disturbance at sight of the rabbit.

An attempt was made from time to time to see what verbal organization accompanied this process of " unconditioning." Upon Peter's return from hospital, the following conversation took place:

E. (experimenter): " What do you do upstairs, Peter?" (The laboratory was upstairs.)
P.: " I see my brother. Take me up to see my brother."
E.: " What else will you see?"
P.: " Blocks."

Peter's reference to blocks indicated a definite memory as he played with blocks only in the laboratory. No further response of any significance could be elicited. In the laboratory 2 days later (he had seen the rabbit once in the meantime), he said suddenly, " Beads can't bite me, beads can only look at me." Toward the end of the training an occasional " I like the rabbit," was all the language he had to parallel the changed emotional organization.

Early in the experiment an attempt was made to get some measure of the visceral changes accompanying Peter's fear reactions. On one occasion Dr. S. determined Peter's blood pressure outside the laboratory and again later, in the laboratory while he was in a state of much anxiety caused by the rabbit's being held close to him by the experimenter. The diastolic blood pressure changed from 65 to 80 on this occasion. Peter was taken to the infirmary the next day for the routine physical examination and developed there a suspicion of medical instruments which made it inadvisable to proceed with this phase of the work.

Peter has gone home to a difficult environment but the experimenter is still in touch with him. He showed in the last interview, as on the later portions of the chart, a genuine fondness for the rabbit. What has happened to the fear of the other objects? The fear of the cotton, the fur coat, feathers, was entirely absent at our last interview. He looked at them, handled them, and immediately turned to something which interested him more. The reaction to the rats and the fur rug with the stuffed head was greatly modified and improved. While he did not show the fondness for these that was apparent with the rabbit, he had made a fair adjustment. For example, Peter would pick up the tin box containing frogs or rats and carry it around the room. When requested, he picked up the fur rug and carried it to the experimenter.

What would Peter do if confronted by a strange animal? At the last interview the experimenter presented a mouse and a tangled mass of angle-worms. At first sight, Peter showed slight distress reactions and moved away, but before the period was over he was carrying the worms about and watching the mouse with undisturbed interest. By " unconditioning " Peter to the rabbit, he has apparently been helped to overcome many superfluous fears, some completely, some to a less degree. His tolerance of strange animals and unfamiliar situations has apparently increased.

The study is still incomplete. Peter's fear of the animals which were shown him was probably not a directly conditioned fear. It is unlikely that he had ever had any experience with white rats, for example. Where the fear originated and with what stimulus, is not known. Nor is it known what Peter would do if he were again confronted with the original fear situation. All of the fears which were " unconditioned " were transferred fears, and it has not yet been learned whether or not the primary fear can be eliminated by training the transfers.

Another matter which must be left to speculation is the future welfare of the subject. His " home " consists of one furnished room which is occupied by his mother and father, a brother of 9 years and himself. Since the death of an older sister, he is the recipient of most of the unwise affection of his parents. His brother appears to bear him a grudge because of this favoritism, as might be expected. Peter hears continually, " Ben is so bad and so dumb, but Peter is so good and so smart! " His mother is a highly emotional individual who cannot get through an interview, however brief, without a display of tears. She is totally incapable of providing a home on the $25 a week which her husband steadily earns. In an attempt to control Peter she resorts to frequent fear suggestions. " Come in Peter, some one wants to steal you." To her erratic resorts to discipline, Peter reacts with temper tantrums. He was denied a summer in the country because his father " forgets he's tired when he has Peter around." Surely a discouraging outlook for Peter.

But the recent development of psychological studies of young children and the growing tendency to carry the knowledge gained in the psychological laboratories into the home and school induce us to predict a more wholesome treatment of a future generation of Peters.

REFERENCE

1. WATSON, J. B. and RAYNER, R. (Dec., 1921). Studies in infant psychology. *Sci. Mon.*, N.Y.

PSYCHOTHERAPY AS A PROBLEM
IN LEARNING THEORY*†

EDWARD JOSEPH SHOBEN, Jr.

IT HAS become increasingly apparent that clinical psychologists are more and more drawing psychotherapy into their compass of activities. If this enlargement of scope is to be something more than a trading of one's psychological birthright for a share of psychiatric pottage, it would seem imperative that the therapeutic functions of the psychologist would be regarded from the point of view of research as well as from that of practice. As Sanford[1] puts it, " What should be of great help to us here is our training in scientific method and our tradition of research-mindedness. It would be hard to name an area in which research is more needed than it is in therapy, or an area in which what is being done lags further behind what might be done. . . . And one might say, furthermore, that it is primarily up to the psychologist to perform this needed research."

The difficulties in the way of such inquiry, however, are enormous, as is well attested to by the paucity of investigations of the therapeutic process in terms of the problems, techniques and concepts common to general psychology. The nature of some of these barriers to psychological research on a matter of such importance probably merits some brief attention.

In the first place, there are situational deterrents to research in psychotherapy. Counseling‡ usually takes place in a " service " setting and is consequently seldom subject to the kinds of exact manipulation required by rigorous experimentation. Often, attempts to control various factors in the therapeutic set-up give rise to serious ethical problems concerning the relationship of the therapist and his agency to their clients and certainly the pressure of the demand for counseling services frequently conflicts with the

---

* Reprinted by permission of the author and Amer. Psychol. Assoc. from (1949) *Psychol. Bull.*, **46**, 366-392.

† This article represents a revision and extension of an earlier attempt[2] to conceptualize psychotherapy in terms of systematic behavior theory. Acknowledgment must be made to a number of people, foremost among whom is Dr. O. H. Mowrer, who, though he may recognize some of his ideas in the ensuing pages, must not be held responsible either for their form or for the uses to which they are put. Others are Dr. Kenneth Spence and Dr. I. E. Farber, of the University of Iowa, who have been invaluable sources of stimulation and instruction but who are absolved from any responsibility for what is here said.

‡ The terms counseling and psychotherapy are here used interchangeably without regard for any of the distinctions they are sometimes employed to convey.

requirements of a research program. Secondly, the problem of complexity gives one pause. Psychotherapy is a form of social interaction, an active social situation, in which many subtle, difficult-to-isolate aspects of the personalities of *both* patient and counselor must be taken into consideration. The therapist is not merely the wielder of some supposedly meliorative technique but is deeply involved as a personality in the counseling process. Thus, the psychology of the psychologist, as well as the psychology of the patient and the nature of the therapeutic method, enters into the determination of the therapeutic end product. Third, there are personnel problems militating against effective research in psychotherapy. Psychologists most familiar with the therapeutic process are seldom well schooled in the experimental and conceptual skills basic to fruitful investigations in general psychology, whereas those who are best equipped technically and conceptually as research workers are generally rather untutored in therapeutic techniques, are unfamiliar with clinical material and are frequently repelled by the admittedly gross and somewhat nebulous notions clinicians use in their efforts to conceptualize the complete phenomena with which they work. In sum, the situational lack of amenability of psychotherapy to experimental inquiry, the enormous complexity of the factors entering into the counseling process and the differences in training and interest between clinical and laboratory workers all tend to impede a *rapprochement* between psychotherapy and the research functions characteristic of general psychology.

In spite of these difficulties, there is one slender lead that might be profitably followed in the attempt to provide a basis for the conceptualization and investigation of psychotherapy as a problem in general psychology. This is the widespread recognition that psychotherapy is essentially a learning process and should be subject to study as such.

This point of view is not only in harmony with the general conception of counseling as a conversation or series of conversations between two persons, therapist and patient, the goal of which is to resolve the conflicts, reduce the anxiety, or somehow modify the behavior of the latter—a conception which clearly implies learning; it has been more or less clearly so verbalized by a number of clinical workers. Cameron[3] sees the *desideratum* of counseling as the patient's " acquisition of normal biosocial behavior," a statement which definitely implies the learning of new ways of reacting as a function of the therapeutic process. Alexander and French[4] advance as a basic therapeutic principle the re-exposure of the client, within the favorable circumstances of psychotherapy, to emotional situations with which he was unable to deal in the past. Presumably, the justification for such a re-exposure rests on the hypothesis that its occurrence " under more favorable conditions " in some way permits the patient to learn more adequate ways of coping with such experiences. Rogers[5] describes the therapeutic process as a freeing of the " growth capacities " of the individual which permits him to acquire " more mature " ways of reacting. If " growth " in this context means (as it must) something more than physiological maturation and if it is not to be lumped with the old and rather mystic homeopathic notion of the *vis medicatrix maturae*, it must refer to the client's acquisition of new modes of response. Such new modes of response are " more mature " because for a given patient they are less fraught with anxiety or conflict. Thus, Rogers is actually talking about psychotherapy as a learning process. White[6] insists that, " Psychotherapy is designed to bring about learning . . . "; and Darley[7] argues that unless the process of learning in counseling is demonstrated, it is not legitimate to infer that the modifications of behavior that may occur during or following therapy are necessarily outcomes of therapy.

In spite of this widespread acknowledgment of psychotherapy as a learning process, there have been few attempts[8,9,10,11] systematically to formulate therapy in terms of learning theory. This paper represents a tentative, apologetically offered effort to construct a learning-theory interpretation of counseling that will help to narrow the gap between practitioner and researcher, clinician and experimentalist, and to encourage some much needed investigation.

COMMON FACTORS IN SCHOOLS OF PSYCHOTHERAPY

When one surveys the various theories and practices of psychotherapy in an effort to find those common factors which a learning-theory interpretation of the counseling process must cover, it appears possible to make four summarizing general statements:

(1) All schools of psychotherapy can with some justice claim cures.[12] Notable successes seem to be the common property of virtually all forms of counseling from moral suasion through non-directive therapy to psychoanalysis.

(2) Clinical patients,* in spite of their enormous differences, tend to present a similar problem in that one of their primary motivations is anxiety and much of their non-integrative or " symptomatic " behavior is maintained on the basis of anxiety reduction.

(3) The goal common to most psychotherapies is the modification of the client's underlying anxiety. This is related to the hypothesis that once his motivation is altered, the overt habit structures of the patient will change.

(4) Finally, all types of counseling employ the techniques of the *therapeutic relationship*, the unique social situation that is formed when therapist and patient meet to discuss the problems of the latter, and of *conversational*

---

* The " clinical patients " spoken of in this paper include only those classifiable as neurotic or " maladjusted." Nothing said here is meant to apply to psychotics, psychopaths, or behavior problems associated with endocrine disturbances or lesions of the central or autonomic nervous systems.

content, that is, of talking about certain things within the therapeutic setting rather than others.

A word must be said about each of these four factors which seem to be common to the various forms of counseling, regardless of the doctrinal banners flown.

All schools report cures—If it is true that the proponents of various theories of psychotherapy all seem able to claim successes and if it is true— as has often been pointed out—that successes are no proof of therapeutic theory, then it would seem to follow that an understanding of the counseling process would be furthered by giving more attention to the conditions under which the patient's learning of new modes of reaction takes place within the general clinical setting. If this is a fair notion, based as it is on the conception of therapy as a learning situation, it might be instructive to explore the points in common among the different approaches to counseling in terms of (*a*) the similarity of patients' problems, (*b*) the agreement among clinicians as to goals, and (*c*) the techniques common to nearly all therapeutic enterprises. Such an exploration might lead to a formulation of the learning process in counseling in terms of these three sets of information.

Similarities in clinical cases—While from the practical standpoint of dealing therapeutically with patients it is necessary to consider each case in all its uniqueness, from a theoretical point of view it is instructive to look for similarities. This amounts to asking the rather ambitious questions of (*a*) What constitutes the core of " neurosis " or " maladjustment "? and (*b*) What are the common problems faced by therapists in their contacts with patients? While no definitive answer can be given here, it is important to consider these issues as bearing on the goals and techniques employed by counselors of different theoretical persuasions and as factors to be accounted for in attempting to formulate a learning-theory interpretation of the therapeutic process.

A point on which there seems to be widespread agreement is, in Horney's[13] phrase, that " one essential factor common to all neuroses . . . is anxieties and the defenses built up against them." The phenomena clinically identified as feelings of insecurity, feelings of inadequacy and guilt feelings are all variants of anxiety, in the sense that they involve debilitating expectations of future punishment. Likewise, it would seem that the " phenomenological self-concept " of Combs[14] and Rogers[5] refers to little more than a patient's level of anxiety, guilt, or inadequacy, together with his verbalizations, accurate or otherwise, of his defenses against them.

To conceptualize anxiety usefully, it is necessary to discriminate between anxiety and fear or, as Freud[15,16,17] did, between neurotic anxiety and objective anxiety. Fear may be thought of as an affective reaction proportionate to some external danger. Anxiety, on the other hand, differs from fear in at least two ways. First, if one asks a " neurotic " patient what he is afraid of, he will admit to being afraid but will generally have no idea of what the source of the possible danger might be. Anxiety may be aptly termed either a fear of " nothing " or a fear of something which is objectively irrelevant. Second, while both fear and anxiety are anticipatory states involving some kind of premonition of danger, the signal to which anxiety is a reaction is usually internal, some impulse to act in a way that has been forbidden. An illustrative case may clarify this point.

E. B., a 24-year-old male undergraduate veteran, despite slightly better than average academic ability, is making poor grades and is in danger of being dismissed from his university. He complains of being " unable " to study, feelings of inferiority in social groups and serious doubts as to both his intellectual and social adequacy. He has some guilt feelings about having transferred from a pre-medical curriculum to English, because his parents are quite eager for him to become a physician. His father is a farmer who has been quite successful financially and in community politics, and who has been highly ambitious for his son. He has imposed very high standards of attainment on the boy, has been quite strict and stern with him and has had a number of set ideas which he felt that the youngster should accept and act upon " for his own good." Any deviation on the part of the patient from the parentally prescribed ways of doing was met with severe punishment, the verbal part of which usually consisted in a variety of changes rung on the theme of the boy's worthlessness and a series of predictions that he would come to no good end. In short, any self-initiated activity—behavior which the parents themselves did not lay out—was fraught with danger. When the boy began counseling, he was squarely on the horns of a dilemma: unable to meet parental demands for a variety of reasons, he was also unable to initiate any divergent plans of his own without experiencing a flood of anxiety, i.e. anticipations of parental punishment.

This, if it is acceptable, leads to a general formulation of non-integrative or neurotic behavior. Anxiety has repeatedly been shown to have drive properties,[18],[19] and on the basis of the anxiety drive, individuals who are maladjusted seem to develop various overt reaction patterns that become stable according to the degree to which they reduce the anxiety. This statement in terms of contemporary reinforcement theory[20] is quite in keeping with Freud's[15] idea of the interchangeability of anxiety and symptom, by which he means that through the formation of symptoms the patient protects himself from anxiety attacks. Anxiety is allayed by some anxiety-reducing symptom; if the symptomatic behavior is somehow eliminated, the anxiety returns. On the basis of this notion it is possible to define a neurosis or a maladjustment in terms of behavior which serves to reduce anxiety directly *without altering the conditions which produce the anxiety*. Freud consistently refers to anxiety as a signal of impending danger; the maladjusted person is one who either consciously or unconsciously engages in acts which eliminate or neutralize the signal while leaving the objective danger unaffected. He is in the position of the motorist who shuts his eyes to warnings of dangerous curves, thus protecting himself from worry but leaving himself liable to serious accidents.

Such a conception permits an explanation of the curious observation that non-integrative behavior is at the same time self-defeating and self-perpetuating. It is self-defeating in that such behavior leads inevitably to further punishment: the motorist has accidents; the illustrative case suffers academic failures and social disarticulation through his avoidance of study to protect himself from the anxiety engendered by self-initiated activity and his withdrawal from social affairs to hide his " worthlessness." It is self-perpetuating because of the immediate reinforcement derived from anxiety reduction. Since the occurrence of a reinforcing state of affairs lies on the temporal gradient of reinforcement in greater proximity to the anxiety-reducing behavior than does the more remote punishment, the connection between the external and internal cues of anxiety and the non-integrative response tends to be strengthened.[21]

A necessary concept in a theory of anxiety is that of repression. This notion refers to the exclusion from communicability (consciousness) of an impulse to act which has led to punishment. When a parent punishes a child severely for some tabooed act, the impulse to commit such an act becomes, through its association with the punishment, a stimulus for anxiety. One way by which the anxiety may be avoided is through repression—the exclusion from awareness of the impulse. If the repression is complete, there is a thorough-going allaying of anxiety and the forbidden impulse no longer constitutes a problem.

Difficulty arises because repression is seldom if ever complete. The individual is constantly threatened by " a return of the repressed "[17] which touches off anxiety without the patient's being able to verbalize the cues for it. In short, the repressed impulse, although excluded from communicability, is still operative at subliminal levels. Why this should be true is something of a psychological mystery, although some light is shed upon it by investigations of punishment. Estes,[22] for example, by a series of experiments has shown that punishment does not extinguish a response which has been positively reinforced. He concludes, " . . . a response cannot be eliminated from an organism's repertoire more rapidly with the aid of punishment than without it. In fact, severe punishment may have precisely the opposite effect. . . . The punished response continues to exist in the organism's repertoire with most of its original latent strength. While it is suppressed, the response is not only protected from extinction, but it also may become a source of conflict. An emotional state, such as ' anxiety ' or ' dread,' which has become conditioned to the incipient movements of making the response, will be aroused by any stimuli which formerly acted as occasions for the occurrence of the response." This provides a neat parallel to what is implied in the concept of repression.

In summary, then, one might say that clinical cases share in common (a) anxiety touched off by (b) unverbalized, unsuccessfully repressed impulses to act in ways that have met with punishment, and (c) persistent non-integrative behavior of many kinds, which reduces the anxiety but does nothing about eliminating its objective causes.

Common goals in psychotherapy—In spite of its non-integrative nature, overt neurotic behavior acquires remarkable persistence through anxiety-avoidance. This persistence is probably the factor most responsible for the failure and consequent elimination of clinical techniques aimed at the elimination of symptoms. Such a goal, in effect, defined psychotherapy as a process of robbing the patient of his defenses against anxiety without alleviating the unbearable state of dread. Since such an end is impossible of realization, advice, persuasion, exhortation, and suggestion have largely gone by the board in favor of methods which focus on the client's anxiety itself.

In other words, the goal of most modern psychotherapies is the modification of the emotional determinants of neurotic behavior. Thus, Alexander and French[4] speak of therapy as " a corrective emotional experience," which presumably results in a diminution of anxiety and a consequent elimination of persistent non-integrative behavior from the patient's repertoire. Likewise, White[6] points out that " Psychotherapy does not take place primarily in the sphere of intellect. . . . Its sphere of operation is the patient's feelings." The kind of learning with which counseling is concerned has to do chiefly with the alteration of motives and affective drives. This does not mean, of course, that the therapist is uninterested in his client's overt behavior ; on the contrary, it is his job to help the patient alter it and achieve a repertoire of more integrative habits. But since this goal does not seem attainable through any kind of direct manipulation, the counselor generally works on the elimination of the basic anxieties, implicity hypothesizing that once the drive conditions are changed, the neurotic behavior will show less strength.

Common tools in psychotherapy—From the standpoint of technique, there are two main aspects of the counseling process, common to all schools of psychotherapy. One is the unique *relationship* that develops between therapist and patient; the other is the *conversational content*, what they talk about during their sessions together. The proponents of different theories of counseling may emphasize one or the other of these factors, but both figure in their final formulations of therapeutic procedure. Thus, Williamson[23] and Kraines[24] stress the therapist's obtaining personal information from the client so that the counselor may guide him somehow to a higher level of adjustment. In spite of this emphasis, both these clinicians devote a good deal of attention to the necessity of establishing and maintaining rapport or winning and retaining the patient's confidence. On the other hand, therapists like Taft,[25] Allen[26] and Rogers[27] play up the quality of the counselor–client relationship and are concerned only secondarily with the conversational content aspect of therapeutic interviews. Nonetheless, they are quite insistent that the proper content of counseling contacts is the " feelings " of the patient rather than his overt behavior or his intellectualized beliefs.

What is this content factor in counseling? What are the areas of discussion between counselor and counselee? In line with the foregoing (although at variance with a widespread belief among laymen), therapeutic conversations are concerned with the patient's overt behavior only in so far as it bears on his covert reactions—the anxieties from which he suffers and against which he so non-integratively defends himself.

The client's anxiety (guilt feelings, feelings of inferiority or inadequacy), then, constitutes the central topic of concern in psychotherapeutic interviews. But clinicians are also interested in the occurrences that engender anxiety. Especially are they interested in the formative past experiences* which have been associated with anxiety, and they encourage patients to discuss such events and their reactions to them rather fully. Emphasis throughout seems to be more on the way the client feels about his experience rather than on the objective accuracy of his reportage.

Thus, the conversational content of counseling consists chiefly in the discussion of the patient's anxieties and the conditions which either currently evoke them or seem to be casually linked in some historical sense to them.

The relationship aspect of therapeutic procedure has been recently most vigorously expounded by Rogers,[27] Snyder[28] and other members[29,14] of the so-called non-directive or client-centered school. Such a notion is, of course, by no means new to counseling technique. Freud[16] in stressing the idea of transference was talking about essentially the same thing: the basic role in psychotherapy of the affective bonds uniting client to counselor. In the case of orthodox psychoanalysis, transference refers to the displacement of childish attitudes from the analysand's past to the analyst, who becomes a substitute for the important previous objects of his patient's loves and hates. That such things do take place in psychotherapy is not questioned but whether they *must* occur in just such a form for counseling to be successful may be doubted. For present purposes, it is merely necessary to establish the point that the relationship factor is inherent in the psychoanalytic approach to therapy. Cameron,[3] writing from a point of view strongly influenced by Adolph Meyer, says: " . . . the acquisition of normal biosocial behavior may be greatly facilitated by the organization of a permissive situation, in which the patient has maximal opportunity to work through his attitudes and responses overtly in the presence of a skilled therapist. . . . The immediate goal of treatment in the behavior disorders is that of establishing a biosocial interrelationship . . . in which patient and therapist participate.

---

* Even therapists like Rogers, who verbally disclaim any interest in personal history *data*, hardly prevent their patients' discussing past experiences. It would be revealing to go systematically through a series of electrically recorded non-directive interviews to see if the *data* collected fall very far short of affording a relatively complete case history. In a preliminary trial by the writer, using material collected from 12 sessions with 1 case, the greater part of a typical anamnestic form could be filled out from the transcriptions of the recordings.

The ultimate goal is that of making this interrelationship unnecessary and terminating it with benefit to the patient" (pp. 576–577). Dejerine and Gauckler[30] warn, " If . . . you have not been able to awaken a reciprocal sympathy in your patient, and if you have not succeeded in gaining his confidence, it is useless to go any further. The result that you will obtain will be worthless. . . . " Sullivan[31] stresses the concept of parataxis and speaks of the psychiatrist's " participating helpfully in the life of the patient."

While there may be some important differences among the various points of view just touched on, it may be pointed out that there is virtually universal agreement among clinicians on the *importance* of the relationship; there is also high agreement on certain of its characteristics.

The most underscored aspect of the therapeutic relationship seems to be its warmth, permissiveness and complete freedom from moralistic and judgmental attitudes on the part of the counselor. Far from being a coldly objective consideration of the patient's troubles, therapy necessarily involves a highly personal form of interaction in which the counselor is highly acceptant of the client's behavior, both overt and covert, within clearly defined limits.

Just what " acceptance " means has become somewhat clouded, and a word of clarification may throw some light on the dynamics of the counseling relationship generally. As Sullivan[31] points out, anything a patient feels, says, or does constitutes the data of the therapeutic enterprise. As is the case with *data* of any kind, one's first job is to understand; it is not to condemn, ignore, reject, or judge. Among such *data* are the feelings and attitudes that the counselee may develop toward the therapist and which, according to most clinical workers of whatever theoretical orientation, are intimately related to the success or failure of therapy. Here again an atmosphere free from censure or judgment but pervaded by sympathetic understanding is provided by the counselor. On the other hand, acceptance does not imply approval of the client's feelings, attitudes, or overt behavior. This is not surprising, since most clinical cases hardly approve of themselves and their self-disapproval provides one of the most important aspects of the discomfort that brings them into therapy.

As can be inferred from the foregoing, the counseling relationship differs importantly from other forms of human interaction. In the first place, it is essentially one-sided in the sense that the therapist ordinarily says little about himself and that the changes effected within the context of the relationship are centered in the client rather than being a mutual modification. The exchange between counselor and patient, then, does not resemble that between friends in spite of the friendliness that generally permeates the relationship. Secondly, it is sharply limited in that the therapist's expressed interest in his client does not extend beyond the confines of the clinic. The two do not mingle socially, the clinician does not usually intercede for the patient in times of stress, and he generally does not become embroiled in attempts to manipulate the patient's environment. The therapist's office is designated as a place where one can come in perfect safety, free from threats and blame, to " think about " one's problems; but it is not a place where dispensations are sold or intercessions granted. Finally, there is a tacit agreement between therapist and patient that their connection is to be severed as soon as the patient feels free to go about his business without the counselor's support. In other words, the interest, acceptance and " affection " of the therapist is there for the client to make capital of so long as he wishes. Unlike non-clinical situations, there is no pressure on him to maintain the relationship out of politeness or any of the other social rules that more or less govern intimate relationships in society at large.

All this may be recapitulated by saying that the methods common to the various forms of psychotherapy involve (a) the formation of a special kind of personal relationship and (b) a conversation with the patient about his anxieties and the events which tend to produce them. As Finesinger[32] puts it, " Communication . . . and the physician-patient relation are the tools that must be adapted to the goals of psychotherapy."

The argument thus far, then, runs something like this: The common problem characterizing clinical patients is anxiety and the behavioral defenses built up against it. The goal of psychotherapy, regardless of the therapist's theoretical leanings, is to eliminate the anxiety and thereby to do away with the symptomatic persistent non-integrative behavior. To accomplish this goal, all therapists use the devices of conversing with the patient about his anxiety and the situations calling it forth both currently and historically, and forming a unique therapeutic relationship. Since all psychotherapies seem to have successes to their credit and since psychotherapy seems to be a process whereby a patient learns to modify his emotional reactions and his overt behavior, it is hypothesized that therapy may be conceptualized from the point of view of general psychology as a problem in learning theory. Such a conceptualization must account for the changes that occur in counselees in terms of these factors that are apparently common to all forms of counseling. Before attempting such a conceptualization, it is necessary briefly to review the situation in learning theory.

MAJOR THEORIES OF LEARNING

One of the major issues with which learning theorists are concerned has to do with the conditions which are necessary if learning is to occur. Two points of view have gained the widest currency with respect to this question.

Reinforcement theory—The first is that of Clark Hull.[20] Within Hull's system, learning is thought to proceed somewhat in this manner: When a motivated organism is subjected to stimulation—from either or both the stimuli associated with the motivating conditions themselves, as in hunger or pain, and those acting on it from the external environment—it tends to respond in a trial-and-error way. If, in the course of its trial-and-error behavior, the organism performs a response which is associated with the reduction of motivation, the probability of that response's occurring again under similar stimulus conditions is increased, or—to put it somewhat differently—the connection between the present stimuli and the response is strengthened. The central emphasis here is on the occurrence of drive reduction or a satisfying state of affairs, variously designated as the law of effect or the principle of reinforcement. As Miller and Dollard[33] succinctly sum it up: To learn, an organism must want something (be motivated in some way), notice something (be acted upon by stimulus cues from the external or internal environment), do something (perform a response or response sequence) and get something (experience a reduction in motivation).

Contiguity theory—Opposed to a reinforcement theory of learning is a point of view which holds that the basic condition necessary for learning is that of contiguity in experience. Tolman and Guthrie are perhaps the outstanding proponents of this theory, although they differ markedly in their conceptions of the nature of learning.

Tolman,[34] taking his point of departure essentially from *Gestalt-theorie*, conceives of learning as the acquisition of information or cognitions about the environment. Variously referred to as " sign-gestalt expectations," "sign-significate relations " and " hypotheses," these cognitions presumably have reference to knowledge which the organism acquires to the effect that a given stimulus or sign, if reacted to in a given way by the organism, will lead to a spatially or temporally more remote stimulus or significate. The necessary condition for the acquisition of such " cognitive maps," as Tolman[35] has called them, is contiguity, the spatial and temporal patterning of stimulus events from sign to significate in the organism's experience. Aided by such secondary principles as recency, emphasis and belongingness, the law of association by contiguity, governs *learning*; learning—i.e., the acquired cognitive maps—together with the organism's needs and skills governs *performance*.

For Guthrie,[36] learning is conceived as the acquisition of stimulus-response bonds as is the case with Hull. Unlike Hull, however, he holds that the occurrence of reinforcement is not a necessary condition for learning. Instead, he states that the principle governing learning is associated by contiguity: " A stimulus pattern that is acting at the time of a response will, if it recurs, tend to produce that response." Simultaneity of stimulus cues and response is all that is required for the formulation of new S–R bonds. Drive states or the existence of unconditioned stimuli are important only as " forcers " of the response to be learned, not as the basis of reinforcement in the Hullian sense.

The behavior with which the various proponents of these points of view have been concerned in their experimentation has consisted for the most part of skeletal muscle acts—maze running, problem-box solutions, conditioned leg flexions, etc. With this fact kept in mind, it seems fair to conclude that the reinforcement point of view seems to have something of an edge in predictive and explanatory utility over contiguity theory. O'Connor[37] has argued rather devastatingly against Guthrie's position by showing that it cannot accommodate the facts of delayed-reward learning. Likewise, Spence and Lippitt,[38] Spence and Kendler,[39] and Kendler and Menchei[40] have thrown serious doubt on the adequacy of Tolman's notion of contiguity in experience of sign, significate and response as the essential and sufficient condition for learning.

Reinforcement theory, on the other hand, has demonstrated its utility in a variety of ways. Whiting[41] has conceptualized the socialization process in terms of Hull's notions. Miller and Dollard[33] have made some fruitful incidental remarks on cultural diffusion. Miller[42] has shown the adequacy of the scheme for explaining certain psychopathological phenomena. Loucks[43] and Loucks and Gantt[44] have supplied evidence that strongly supports Hull's contention that the classical conditioning of skeletal muscle responses is merely a special case of learning according to the principle of reinforcement.

It is precisely at this point, however—in the conditioning of defense reactions—that the law of effect runs into difficulties. Hull[45] pointed out this problem as early as 1929, referring to it as " the dilemma of the conditioned defense reaction." He then wrote: " For a defense reaction to be wholly successful, it should take place so early that the organism will completely escape injury, i.e., the impact of the nocuous (unconditioned) stimulus. But in case the unconditioned stimulus fails to impinge upon the organism, there will be no reinforcement of the conditioned tendency, which means one would expect that experimental extinction will set in at once. This will rapidly render the conditioned reflex impotent, which, in turn, will expose the organism to the original injury. This will initiate a second cycle substantially like the first, which will be followed by another and another indefinitely, a series of successful escapes (from all contact with the noxious stimulus) always alternating with a series of injuries. From a biological point of view, the picture emerging from the above theoretical considerations is decidedly not an attractive one.

" There is thus presented a kind of biological dilemma. . . ." (p. 511).

In other words, reinforcement theory finds it hard to explain how an organism can learn to avoid painful stimulation entirely, because if the painful stimuli do not act upon the organism's receptors, no drive is aroused to act as a basis for maintaining the defense reaction.

Mowrer and Lamoreaux,[46] concerning themselves with this problem, resolved the dilemma by positing a conditioned fear reaction to the conditioned stimulus. According to their formulation, the conditioned stimulus has signal value, signifying to the organism an approaching danger and arousing in it those anticipations of punishment known as the secondary (acquired) drive of fear (anxiety). On the basis of this secondary drive, trial-and-error behavior occurs, out of which is differentiated, according to the principle of reinforcement, a response which reduces the fear and permits the organism to avoid or to minimize the painful unconditioned stimulus.

Such a resolution of the dilemma of the conditioned defense reaction, however, gives rise to another difficulty of comparable magnitude: How is the fear learned? If one holds to a thoroughly monistic reinforcement position, one is forced to say that the drive state of fear or anxiety is somehow " satisfying " or motivation reducing. Baldly, the reinforcement theorist is forced to hold that secondary drive arousal occurs on the basis of drive reduction That this is certainly contrary to any kind of common sense consideration is immediately apparent and it is difficult to see how an exchange of one drive for another—the situation which would obtain were the law of effect rigidly adhered to—could be of any biological benefit. This is particularly true when one recalls that many fears, especially neurotic anxiety, are much more debilitating than the objective conditions which generate them—witness the many people who cannot bear to have dental work done or who refuse to see doctors.

Thus, a kind of *impasse* is reached. Reinforcement theory seems to account rather adequately for the acquisition of striped muscle acts; but at least in the conditioned defense situation—most germane to the clinical problems here under scrutiny—its adequacy is dependent on the operation of secondary motivational states, for the acquisition of which it is hard put to it to explain.

Two-factor theory—A number of writers have attempted to overcome this obstacle to efficient theorizing by formulating *two principles* to explain *two different kinds of learning*. Schlosberg[47] in 1937 expressed himself, on the basis of a long series of studies in his laboratory, as believing that there were two types of learning. One had to do with the acquisition of " diffuse, preparatory responses," by which he meant such things as changes in breathing, pulse rate, electrical skin resistance, body volume, voice pitch, and tonicity, which proceeds by " simple conditioning " or according to the principle of association by sheer contiguity. It will be recognized that these reactions are essentially those autonomically mediated viscero-vascular reactions usually thought of as the basic physiological concomitants of emotion. The other type of learning, which he felt it necessary to distinguish, referred to the acquisition of more " precise, adaptive responses," withdrawal, flexion, or more generally defensive reactions which are governed by the principle of " success " or reinforcement. These, of course, are the skeletal muscle acts which Hull's kind of theorizing seems to account for so admirably, whether the experimental situation be of the classical or instrumental kind of conditioning.

Skinner[48] in his 1938 volume made explicit a point of view at which he had hinted earlier.[49] He distinguished between Type S conditioning as preparatory and Type R as consummatory, holding that the fundamental distinction rested on the event with which the unconditioned stimulus was correlated. In Type S the unconditioned stimulus is correlated with the conditioned stimulus, whereas in Type R it is correlated with the response. Skinner further says: " Most of the experiments upon skeletal behavior which have been offered as paralleling Pavlov's work are capable of interpretation as discriminated operants of Type R. . . . It is quite possible on the existing evidence that a strict topographical separation of types following the skeletal-autonomic distinction may be made."[48,p.112]

In this formulation, the same classification as that suggested by Schlosberg is implied. Autonomically mediated " emotional " reactions are learned on the basis of contiguity, whereas mediated skeletal muscle responses are learned on the basis of reinforcement.

Razran[50] in 1939 offered a somewhat similar formulation, classifying learning according to what he called " quantitative " and " qualitative " conditioning, corresponding to learning without reinforcement and law-of-effect learning. He reports no evidence for the so-called qualitative conditioning of autonomic reactions, but does not say explicitly that quantitative conditioning applies exclusively to the acquisition of viscero-vascular reactions. He does raise the issue of the differential importance of two events, the *application* or onset of the unconditioned stimulus and the *termination* of the unconditioned stimulus, for the conceptualization of types of learning.

More recently, Mowrer[51] has vigorously exploited the idea of a two-factor theory of learning to account not only for the learning of skeletal muscle responses but for the acquisition of secondary drives like fear and anxiety. He fully accepts the notion that striped muscle acts, mediated by the central nervous system, are learned, according to the principle of reinforcement, by virtue of their association with the *termination* of the noxious stimulation identified as motivational states. This is not only fully in keeping with Hull's position but is quite in line with Mowrer's own previous enthusiastic experimentation and theorizing as a monistic member of the reinforcement school.[52] His new point of view, however, holds that smooth muscle and glandular " emotional " reactions, autonomically mediated, are acquired through their association with the *onset* of the paired unconditioned stimulus of pain and conditioned stimulus or signal. In other words, fear refers to the viscero-vascular components of the pain response, conditioned to a substitute stimulus through the latter's contiguity with the *onset* of the action of a noxious adequate stimulus. He prefers to restrict the term *conditioning* to the learning of " emotional " reactions by contiguity and to use *problem-solving* to designate the learning of skeletal responses which " solve " the " problems " created by drives and which are acquired according to the reinforcement principle.

One of the points which must be made immediately with respect to two-factor theories such as these is aimed at the scotching of the criticism often (and fairly) leveled against attempts to account for learning in terms of multiple principles. Such attempts frequently permit the theorist to invoke whichever notion happens most easily to explain his *data*; he can explain everything but predict nothing. With the possible exception of Razran's, the two-factor formulations just reviewed are not liable to such an attack. While two principles are postulated, contiguity and reinforcement, two learning processes, one involving the viscero-vascular system and the other the skeletal muscular system, are also suggested. The principle that governs one process may not be invoked to explain what occurs in the other. For either process, the theory is monistic and parsimonious and presumably subject to an *experimentem crucis*.*

Direct experimental tests of the two-factor theory are as yet few. One study having an immediate bearing on the issue is that of Mowrer and Suter.[53] These researchers argue that if the drive-termination theory of acquiring " conditioned " responses is valid, the response should become more readily connected with those stimuli present at the time of drive-reduction. If, on the other hand, the drive-onset interpretation is correct, there should be no difference in the resulting learning curves. The rationale on which this deduction is based, of course, is that a conditioned stimulus (warning signal) *must* coincide with or approximate to the turning on of the noxious unconditioned stimulus. If this contiguity with the *onset* of drive is all that is necessary for " conditioning " to occur, it should make no difference whether the conditioned stimulus overlaps with the *termination* of the unconditioned stimulus or not. Using an arbitrary running response as an index of fear and as their criterion of conditioning, Mowrer and Suter obtained experimental results confirmatory of their prediction: there was no difference in the curves of response acquisition between a group of rats trained under conditions where the conditioned stimulus overlapped and terminated with the turning off of the unconditioned stimulus of shock and a group of animals where the conditioned stimulus was turned off at the time of the unconditioned stimulus's onset.

The interpretation of these results is that the animals learned to *fear* the conditioned stimulus by virtue of its contiguity with the onset of pain. This anticipation of pain gave rise to trial-and-error behavior out of which was

* The two-factor theories reviewed here may be contrasted with those of Stephens[54] and Maier and Schnierla.[55] For a careful and trenchant critique of these points of view, see Kendler and Underwood.[56]

differentiated the running response, which was reinforced by fear reduction or the avoidance of pain. The acquisition of the fear reaction was not furthered, as reinforcement theory would predict, by having the warning signal overlap and end in contiguity with the reinforcing state of affairs provided by the termination of the shock.

The more crucial experiment, yet to be done, would involve the testing of the hypothesis that some autonomically mediated reaction, taken as an index of fear, will be attached to some conditioned stimulus by virtue of its association by contiguity with the onset of noxious stimulation, whereas it will not become attached any more effectively under conditions of reinforcement.

Experimentation with viscero-vascular reactions presents many problems, however, and there is little in the literature that can be brought directly to bear on this issue. Indirect evidence is presented in the cited publications of Schlosberg and Skinner and is thoroughly reviewed by Mowrer.[51]

While such interpretations are not crucial, much recent experimentation on secondary drives is readily assimilable into two-factor theory. Miller,[18] for example, reports having trained rats by means of strong shock to escape from a white compartment with a grid floor through an open door into a black compartment without a grid. Subsequently, the animals, without shock or noxious stimulation of any kind, learned a new habit—rotating a little wheel to open the door, which had been closed, in order to escape from the white compartment to the black one. This was interpreted to mean that the secondary drive of fear had been acquired and that its termination could be used as reinforcement for striped muscle responses. In terms of the two-factor formulation, the rats learned to run into the black box by virtue of the reinforcement provided by pain reduction. At the same time, however, fear or the visceral component of pain became conditioned to the cues of " whiteness and grid floor " associated with *onset* of shock. The conditioned fear then served as the drive on the basis of which the wheel rotating habit was learned without benefit of further primary drive arousal through shock.

It would seem, then, that in spite of its present tentative status, a two-factor theory of learning—holding that adaptive, striped muscle habits are built up according to the principle of reinforcement whereas anticipatory, " emotional " reactions, probably viscero-vascular in nature and having drive properties, are acquired according to the principle of contiguity—has the greatest explanatory and predictive power at the moment.

LEARNING THEORY AND PSYCHOTHERAPY

How can such a conception of learning be applied to psychotherapy to cover the elements of the psychotherapeutic process common to all forms of counseling? It will be recalled that the problem of therapy is essentially that of somethow ridding the patient of neurotic anxiety, which supports his persistent non-integrative defenses and accounts in large measure for his " unhappiness." The tools used by all therapists to accomplish this job are those of conversational content and the therapeutic relationship.

Therapy as the acquisition of symbolic controls—Shaffer[10] suggests that psychotherapy be conceptualized in terms of the patient's acquisition of language symbols by which he can more effectively control his non-integrative behavior. The rationale of this approach is based on the observation than an outstanding characteristic of the maladjusted is their inability to control their own acts; in their own terms, " I know I should (or shouldn't) do this, but I just can't (or must)." Since " normal " people seem to control their behavior by means of symbols—including subvocal and gestural symbols—Shaffer's notion seems at first blush to follow readily.

Such an idea is also more or less explicit in Shaw's[11] analysis of repression and insight. He argues from Mowrer and Ullman's[21] point that: " The common denominator in all . . . forms of non-integrative behavior seems to be the inability to use symbols appropriately as a means of bringing remote as well as immediate consequences into the present in such a manner that they may exert an influence proportional to their objective importance " (p. 81).

Shaw moves from here to the contention that therapy is a process by which non-integrative behavior is eliminated by the making available of symbols, holding that the symbols become cues for the more remote punishing consequences of neurotic defenses.

It is not quite clear, however, according to either Shaffer or Shaw, what the symbolization at which therapy aims might be. If it is the symbolizing of acts which have been repressed, there is no indication of how such a procedure would accomplish anything more than the release of a flood of anxiety heretofore held in check—albeit imperfectly—by the repression mechanism. On the other hand, if the symbols made available by therapy amount only to accurate predictions of the consequences of the client's non-integrative behavior, their utility is questionable on several grounds: (1) Most clinical patients are only too sharply aware of the self-defeating nature of their activity; their complaint is that they don't know why they engage in it and at the same time seem unable to avoid it. (2) Some cases (especially those who have been formally psychoanalyzed) demonstrate a remarkable glibness—sometimes quite accurate—about their own defenses and yet are anxiety ridden on the one hand and socially somewhat abnoxious on the other. It is probably these instances which gave rise to H. M. Johnson's[57] rather oversevere recent strictures on psychoanalysis as therapy and as rationale. (3) There is a question as to whether or not simply making available symbols—which can arouse at an earlier point in the temporal sequence the anxiety that accrues from future punishment—amounts to anything more than a more effective punishment of the already non-integrative response. In this case, there may be the danger of the repression of one mechanism while another, equally self-defeating, is developed as a defense against a compounded neurotic anxiety, now attached not only to the ineffectively repressed impulses which existed prior to " therapy," but also to those incipient tendencies connected with the defense mechanism which has undergone the " punishment " of having its hurtful ultimate consequences symbolically brought into the psychological present. Thus, if a clinician is dealing with a patient whose anxiety has its origin in the faulty repression of aggressive tendencies and defends himself against it by social withdrawal, the anxiety may be compounded by making the damaging effects of the mechanism more apparent through the providing of symbols within the therapeutic context. All this is not to be construed as an attack on the Shaw–Shaffer hypothesis; as a matter of fact, it seems to describe quite adequately one segment of the therapeutic process. It is merely an effort to point out that such an hypothesis does not seem quite to account for *everything* that happens in psychotherapy.

A somewhat different suggestion, here proposed, is this: If neurotic anxiety is produced by the repression of some unextinguished response, it should follow that the anxiety can be dissipated in one of two ways—either by the elicitation of unreinforced occurrences of the response, thus leading to extinction, or by the connecting of a different affect to response tendencies which have undergone repression. With respect to the illustrative case mentioned above, anxiety could be dispelled either through eliciting self-initiated behavior and failing to reinforce it until extinction occurred, or through forming a bond between the tendencies to self-initiated behavior and some non-anxious visceral reaction which will supplant the connection between anxiety and the repressed activity. In either case, the Shaw–Shaffer notion holds as the first step in therapy, the bringing into communicability (consciousness) of the tendency that has undergone repression.

This lifting of repression is what is usually known as insight. When the patient is able to verbalize the repressed tendencies fundamentally associated with his anxiety, he " sees " or demonstrates insight. It is difficult to understand, however, why this should be equated with cure, regardless of how important it is as a step toward psychological recovery. Merely being able to talk about the cues for anxiety does not make them any less terrifying. Extinction or counter-conditioning is still necessary.

Whether the extinction or the counter-conditioning technique is preferable depends in part on the desirability of the repressed behavior. In the case of self-initiated activity, the question seems rather clear. Socialization has been defined[58] as the process of developing from a dependent infant into an independent and dependable adult. The extinction of tendencies toward self-initiated " responsible " behavior would mean the continuation of dependence and infantilism. It seems probable that few clinicians would look upon this as a suitable therapeutic goal. The same thing might well be said of most of the impulses which typically undergo repression, sexuality being a case in point. The frigid wife, raised under conditions of puritanical restrictiveness, might well find some immediate relief from anxiety by having her repressed sexual impulses extinguished (if this is possible); but it is doubtful that such a procedure would be helpful in her marriage.

The counter-conditioning hypothesis — The hypothesis of counter-conditioning is suggested as somewhat more tenable. It involves the following set of notions: The conversational content aspect of counseling consists in the symbolic reinstatement of the stimuli which produce and have produced the patient's anxiety. Through his words to the therapist, the client, on a symbolic level, again " lives through " the stimulus situations which were painful to him, in which he underwent punishment, and which initiated the repression sequence. This constitutes the lifting of repression, the introduction into communicability of the repressed tendencies, the development of insight. This proceeds essentially by the therapist's reinforcing, by his acceptance of and his sympathetic participation in the patient's self-revelatory behavior. At the same time, the discussion of the client's anxiety is being carried on within the context of the unique patient-therapist relationship. This is conceived as an unconditioned stimulus for feelings of pleasure, acceptance, security—non-anxious affective reactions. The therapeutic process consists in the establishment of a bond between the symbolically reproduced stimuli which evoke and have evoked anxiety—chiefly the cues associated with the incipient movements toward performing some repressed activity—and the non-anxiety, i.e., comfort and confidence, reactions made to the counseling relationship.

Such a formulation goes somewhat beyond the bounds of " emotional " learning as accounted for by the two-factor theories briefly discussed above. They are chiefly concerned with the learning of fear or anxiety, basic secondary drives. While the idea presented here may be an extension of the theory that its protagonists would find acceptable, there seems to be no reason why the principle of contiguity should not apply to viscero-vascular reactions that are " pleasant " as well as to those which are " unpleasant "; as a matter of fact, such an application seems to be demanded if the learning of affects is governed by a single principle. The conceptualization proceeds in this wise: Affects possessing drive value—fear, anxiety, and anger*— are learned by virtue of the association by contiguity of the visceral aspects of some primary drive with concurrent external stimuli. The so-called " positive " or " pleasurable " affects are learned by virtue of the association by contiguity of proprioceptive cues set up at the onset of drive *reduction*

---

* The inclusion of anger in this list of secondary drives is somewhat cavalier. Virtually nothing is known of the conditions under which the learning of anger takes place, and it is certainly not assured that it derives from pain.

with concurrent external stimuli. It is quite possible that Murray's[59] scheme for conceptualizing motivation in terms of goals is analyzable on some such basis as this latter motion.

Hull[20] seems to use a similar idea when he defines secondary reinforcement in terms of a stimulus situation which has been closely and consistently associated with the occurrence of need reduction. Experimental animals thus develop " needs " for poker chips, tones of given frequency, black compartments rather than white, etc. Likewise, the judgmental theory of affections, as proposed by Carr[60] and expanded upon and experimentally verified by Peters,[61,62] is fully consonant with the suggestion here proposed as fundamental in therapy. According to these writers, the pleasantness or unpleasantness of objects is a function of their association with " satisfying " or " unsatisfying " events in experience. Integrating this with the aspect of two-factor theory that deals with the learning of affects, " satisfying " events in experience are those correlated with drive reduction; " unsatisfying " events in experience are those correlated with drive onset.* To return to the counter-conditioning hypothesis in psychotherapy, a rather striking analogy may be pointed out between this formulation and the now famous experiment of Mary Cover Jones† with the boy Peter. It will be remembered that Peter was a three-year-old with a number of acquired fears of various objects, including small white furry animals. In an effort to eliminate these fears, Dr. Jones attempted a counter-conditioning procedure. At lunchtime, just as the child began to eat a meal which included his favorite dishes, a white rabbit was introduced in a wire cage at the end of the room, far enough away not to disturb the boy's eating. Each day the animal was brought a little closer until finally Peter could eat with one hand while stroking the rabbit with the other. Further tests showed that the newly conditioned " comfort " reaction to the rabbit had generalized to a large number of other, formerly fear-evoking stimuli such as rats, frogs, cotton and fur rugs.

The meaning of these results is that a new connection was formed between the stimuli (rabbit) which produced a fear reaction and the comfort reaction made to the stimulus of the lunch with all its various cues. The necessary condition for the formation of this new connection was contiguity of the noxious stimulus and the comfort reaction aroused by the unconditioned luncheon stimulus situation. The problem of how to pair the stimuli so that those connected with the mean did not come to evoke fear does not affect the fundamental point of contiguity as the basis for the establishment of the new bond, but is merely a matter of the spatial and temporal patterning of

---

* It is interesting to speculate as to whether or not this is the mechanism underlying the acquisition of aesthetic tastes, preferences, and other " likes " and " dislikes." The implications for a psychological approach to valuative behavior are obvious.

† A complete account of which is included in this book, p. 45, Part I, 5.

stimuli common to most experimentation under the conditions of classical conditioning.

The main objection to this analogy probably rests on the point that Peter was troubled by a fear rather than an anxiety—that is, an affective reaction, uncomplicated by repression, made to external stimuli rather than to some impulse to behave in a tabooed way. The objection is certainly granted and actually implies the basis for the first step in therapy, the uncovering by use of the conversational content of therapeutic interviews of the repressed impulses. Before counter-conditioning can occur, the stimuli connected with anxiety must be brought into communicability, where they can be symbolically reinstated at the appropriate times. Insight is a prior condition of counter-conditioning.

A second objection that can be raised to the counter-conditioning notion is this: If therapy is simply a matter of connecting anxiety-provoking stimuli with some comfort reaction, why is it not therapeutically effective to think of one's troubles while lying in a comfortably warm tub?* There seem to be three answers to this. First, to a degree it *is* effective. The widespread method of combatting the " blues " by means of a shower is directly in point, as is the use of continuous baths and warm packs in mental hospitals. The real problem is: Why is such a procedure less effective than psychotherapy? This gives rise to the second answer, which is that thinking of one's troubles while lying in a comfortably warm tub is usually of little help in creating insight, symbolically re-introducing the relevant anxiety-producing stimuli. The bath is of little assistance in bringing forbidden impulses into communicability, hence the " therapeutic effects " of the bath are of short duration. The third reply to such an objection is based on the fact that neurotic anxiety is primarily social in its inception. Sullivan[63] insists that this " interpersonal induction of anxiety, and the exclusively interpersonal origin of every instance of its manifestations, is the unique characteristic of anxiety and of the congeries of more complex tensions . . . to which it contributes." This squares perfectly, of course, with the concept of repression and the role it plays in anxiety theory. If neurotic anxiety is an anticipation of punishment for the performance of some tabooed act, it follows that the taboo must have been laid down and enforced through some kind of social medium. Consequently, one would expect in the light of such social origins that the elimination of anxiety would be facilitated by the presence of certain social factors in therapy—provided in this case by the patient-therapist relationship.

This last point also bears on the function of catharsis in psychotherapy. It is a commonplace experience among clinicians to have clients say, after a period of vigorous abreaction, " I've thought about that a lot, but I've

---

* This point was raised in a very helpful personal communication from Dr. John P. Seward. The replies offered to the objection, however, are not chargeable to him.

never said it to anybody before. I feel a bit better now." This poses something of a conceptual difficulty, since it is hard to understand how the expression of an affect should dissipate an affect unless the expression has some effect on the maintaining stimulus conditions. Such an environmental modification certainly does not occur in counseling; and yet catharsis in the social situation of therapy (and possiby in other social situations) seems to bring some relief, whereas catharsis subvocally or made without the presence of a therapist or therapist-surrogate apparently does not. According to the formulation here offered, *catharsis will be effective when it involves* (a) *the symbolic reinstatement of the repressed cues for anxiety*, (b) *within the context of a warm, permissive, non-judgmental social relationship*. Under these conditions the situation is ripe for counter-conditioning to take place, whereby the patient learns to react non-anxiously to the original stimuli.

The counter-conditioning hypothesis likewise bears on the problems of technique inherent in the directive-non-directive controversy. This argument can perhaps be more profitably stated this way: How much and what can the therapist do to help reinstate symbolically the anxiety-arousing stimuli acting on the patient without endangering the relationship (i.e. weakening the relationship-comfort bond)? Asked in these terms, the question bears on the first step in counseling, that of lifting repressions or developing insight and becomes the purely empirical matter of determining the categories of counselor response that most effectively further the bringing into communicability of repressed impulses. On somewhat dangerous *a priori* grounds it would seem that interpretation, probing and other more active procedures would be useful unless introduced too pre-emptorily or too early into therapy, thereby destroying the patient-therapist relationship. That this occurs is not denied, but to attack such techniques as being of no value because they are sometimes misused seems somewhat absurd. The situation is analogous to bringing the rabbit too far into Peter's lunchroom too early and connecting the fear reaction to the animal to the stimulus complex of food, room, high chair and so forth. It seems somewhat nonsensical to argue that the baby should be thrown out with the bath water simply because it is still a bit grimy. One wonders if Peter would have overcome his fear of rabbits had he only been thoroughly " accepted " without ever having any help in re-encountering the noxious stimulus in a secure and " pleasant " situation.

The directive-non-directive controversy may well reduce to a consideration of the types of case for which each is best suited. It can be hypothesized that more non-directive approaches will be more likely to succeed with those clients who have few and relatively unsevere repressions, some insight into the sources of their anxiety, and a capacity to relate easily to the therapist. These are cases which do not require much help in *discovering* the anxiety-producing stimuli; they do need assurance from a counselor that they may talk about them in his presence with complete impunity. Conversely, more interpretative methods by hypothesis will be of greater effectiveness with cases characterized by higher defenses, greater repression, and less initial insight. It must be emphasized, however, that all this is a matter of the empirical determination of what techniques work best for given cases so far as the lifting of repressions is concerned. The hypothesis of counter-conditioning is still the means of explaining the diminution of anxiety after insight has been developed.

If this formulation is correct, how can various failures of counter-conditioning methods in psychological treatment be answered? Voegtlin's[64] work with alcoholics is typical. This clinician attempted to cure his patients of drinking by having them take whiskey so heavily dosed with a powerful emetic that vomiting to the point of pain was immediately induced. Results were disappointing. Most of his cases did not build up more than momentary conditioned aversions to alcohol. Of those few who became conditioned against liquor over a period of time, several showed symptom substitutions, e.g., the development of psychosomatic symptoms or neurotic syndromes instead of alcohol addiction.

The first objection to such a procedure is that it consists in a direct attack on the symptomatic mechanism rather than on the underlying anxiety. If the anxiety reduction occurring from drinking were greater than the pain of the treatment, the treatment would have very nearly as little effect as strongly advising the patient " to get on the wagon." The ineffectiveness of " hangovers " is relevant in this connection. Second, if the alcohol addiction were wiped out by virtue of the conditioning procedure, the underlying anxiety would be unaffected, and one would therefore expect that the patient would develop some other persistently non-integrative way of reducing it. Third, the treatment situation contains too many elements of attempting to eliminate a response by merely punishing it. The inefficacy of such methods has already been discussed. Thus, an objection based on such therapeutic experience fails to carry much weight.

Re-education in psychotherapy—Does the point of view developed here overlook this notion in the therapeutic armamentarium? On the contrary, it fully includes it as an important third aspect of counseling, along with the lifting of repression and the counter-conditioning of anxiety. Following the development of insight, as anxiety is dissipated through conditioning, the patient typically begins to plan. His first tentative steps in this direction may take the form of asking, " What shall I do? " Or it may be a more vigorous exploration of the possible consequences of projected steps. Here the therapist may be of assistance in helping his client to formulate goals clearly and to consider realistically the various behavioral methods he might employ to reach them. This constitutes a law-of-effect learning situation in which reinforcement is produced through the patient's own verbal self-approval or self-disapproval, based in part on the predictions of consequences which the counselor can help him arrive at. In a sense, this constitutes the " rational " exercise of symbolically mediated self-control of which Shaw and Shaffer may be speaking. It is rational in so far as the behavior selected is founded on some consideration of its probable remote outcomes rather than on its immediate value as an anxiety-reducing agent, and it is " responsible " in so far as it is chosen* in terms of the patient's own values as of the moment of choice. The counselor does not direct; he merely helps the client work out relatively accurate estimates of the consequences. If a particular behavior pattern is rejected, it merely undergoes a voluntary suppression or is extinguished through failure of reinforcement without being forced into incommunicability and becoming a stimulus for anxiety, as is the case in the repression of punished tendencies. Through this symbolic trial and error, then, the patient develops, according to the principle of reinforcement, a tentative plan of integrative behavior based on rational considerations to supplant his former pattern of persistent non-integrative behavior based on the immediate necessity of reducing anxiety regardless of the ultimate cost.

SUMMARY

A learning theory interpretation of psychotherapy must take into account (a) the fact that all forms of psychotherapy are able to claim cures, (b) the similarity of clinical cases in terms of neurotic anxiety and its defenses, (c) the common goal of psychotherapies of the diminution of anxiety and (d) the fact that all clinicians employ as their chief techniques conversational content and the therapeutic relationship.

It is here proposed that psychotherapy occurs through three interrelated processes: first, the lifting of repression and development of insight through the symbolic reinstating of the stimuli for anxiety; second, the diminution of anxiety by counter-conditioning through the attachment of the stimuli for anxiety to the comfort reaction made to the therapeutic relationship; and third, the process of re-education through the therapist's helping the patient to formulate rational goals and behavioral methods for attaining them.

Such a scheme seems to harmonize most effectively with a two-factor learning theory of the type most recently developed by Mowrer.[51] Such a theory conceives of skeletal muscle responses as being acquired through the principle of reinforcement, whereas viscero-vascular, " emotional " reactions are acquired according to the principle of contiguity.

This formulation is certainly not to be regarded as anything final. It leans rather too much on plausible but inadequately tested hypotheses and on

---

* Lest the language used here seem flavored too heavily with free will, reference is made to Hall's[65] paper, in which the problem of choice within a deterministic philosophy is discussed.

scientifically tenuous analogies. It is offered only as a preliminary attempt to effect a *rapprochement* between psychotherapy and general psychology, and to organize some of the phenomena of clinical practice within the framework of systematic behavior theory.

REFERENCES

1. SANFORD, R. N. (1948). Psychotherapy and counseling: Introduction. *J. Consult. Psychol.*, **12**, 65-67.
2. SHOBEN, E. J., Jr. (1948). A learning-theory interpretation of psychotherapy. *Harvard Educ. Rev.*, **18**, 129-145.
3. CAMERON, N. (1947). *The Psychology of the Behavior Disorders*. Houghton Mifflin, Boston.
4. ALEXANDER, F. and FRENCH, T. (1946). *Psychoanalytic Therapy*. Ronald Press, New York.
5. ROGERS, C. (1947). Some observations on the organization of personality. *Amer. Psychologist*, **2**, 358-368.
6. WHITE, R. (1948). *The Abnormal Personality*. Ronald Press, New York.
7. DARLEY, J. (1943). Review of *Counseling and Psychotherapy*. *J. Abnorm. (Soc.) Psychol.*, **38**, 199-201.
8. FRENCH, T. (1933). Interrelations between psychoanalysis and the experimental work of Pavlov. *Amer. J. Psychiat.*, **12**, 1165-1203.
9. KUBIE, L. S. (1934). Relation of the conditioned reflex to psychoanalytic technique. *Arch. Neurol. Psychiat.*, **32**, 1137-1142.
10. SHAFFER, L. (1947). The problem of psychotherapy. *Amer. Psychologist*, **2**, 459-467.
11. SHAW, F. (1946). A stimulus-response analysis of repression and insight in psychotherapy. *Psychol. Rev.*, **53**, 36-42.
12. ROSENZWEIG, S. (1936). Some implicit common factors in diverse methods of psychotherapy. *Amer. J. Orthopsychiat.*, **6**, 412-415.
13. HORNEY, K. (1937). *The Neurotic Personality of our Time*. Norton, New York.
14. COMBS, A. W. (1948). Phenomenological concepts in non-directive therapy. *J. Consult. Psychol.*, **12**, 197-208.
15. FREUD, S. (1933). *New Introductory Lectures on Psychoanalysis*. Norton, New York.
16. FREUD, S. (1935). *A General Introduction to Psychoanalysis*. Liveright, New York.
17. FREUD, S. (1936). *The Problem of Anxiety*. Norton, New York.
18. MILLER, N. E. (1948). Studies of fear as an acquirable drive. I. Fear as motivation and fear-reduction as reinforcement in the learning of new responses. *J. Exp. Psychol.*, **38**, 89-101.
19. MOWRER, O. H. (1948). The law of effect and ego psychology. *Psychol. Rev.*, **53**, 321-334.
20. HULL, C. (1943). *Principles of Behavior*. Appleton–Century, New York.
21. MOWRER, O. H. and ULLMAN, A. D. (1945). Time as a determinant in integrative learning. *Psychol. Rev.*, **52**, 61-90.
22. ESTES, W. K. (1944). An experimental study of punishment. *Psychol. Monogr.*, **57**, No. 3, 37-38.
23. WILLIAMSON, E. G. (1939). *How to Counsel Students*. McGraw–Hill, New York.
24. KRAINES, S. (1943). *Treatment of the Neuroses and Psychoses* (second edition). Lea & Feabiger, Philadelphia.
25. TAFT, Jessie (1933). *The Dynamics of Therapy*. Macmillan, New York.
26. ALLEN, F. (1942). *Psychotherapy with Children*. Norton, New York.
27. ROGERS, C. (1942). *Counseling and Psychotherapy*. Houghton Mifflin, Boston.
28. SNYDER, W. U. (1945). An investigation of the nature of non-directive counseling. *J. Gen. Psychol.*, **33**, 193-224.
29. AXLINE, V. (1947). *Play Therapy*. Houghton Mifflin, Boston.
30. DEJERINE, J. and GAUCKLER, E. (1913). *The Psychoneuroses and their Treatment by Psychotherapy*. Lippincott, Philadelphia.

31. SULLIVAN, H. S. (1947). *Conceptions of Modern Psychiatry.* The William Alanson White Memorial Foundation, Washington.
32. FINESINGER, J. E. (1948). Psychiatric interviewing. *Amer. J. Psychiat.*, **105**, 187-195.
33. MILLER, N. E. and DOLLARD, J. (1941). *Social Learning and Imitation.* Yale Univ. Press, New Haven.
34. TOLMAN, E. C. (1938). The determiners of behavior at the choice point. *Psychol. Rev.*, **45**, 1-41.
35. TOLMAN, E. C. (1948). Cognitive maps in rats and men. *Psychol. Rev.*, **55**, 189-208.
36. GUTHRIE, E. R. (1942). A theory of learning in terms of stimulus, response and association. *National Society for the Study of Education*, 41st Yearbook, pp.17-60. Public School Publ. Co., Bloomington.
37. O'CONNOR, F. J. (1946). Recency or effect? A critical analysis of Guthrie's theory of learning. *Harvard Educ. Rev.*, **16**, 194-206.
38. SPENCE, K. W. and LIPPITT, R. (1946). An experimental test of the sign-gestalt theory of trial-and-error learning. *J. Exp. Psychol.*, **36**, 491-502.
39. SPENCE, K. W. and KENDLER, H. H. (1948). The speculations of Leeper with respect to the Iowa tests of the sign-gestalt theory of learning. *J. Exp. Psychol.*, **38**, 106-109.
40. KENDLER, H. H. and MENCHER, H. C. (1948). The ability of rats to learn the location of food when motivated by thirst—an experimental reply to Leeper. *J. Exp. Psychol.*, **38**, 82-88.
41. WHITING, J. W. M. (1941). *Becoming a Kwoma.* Yale Univ. Press, New Haven.
42. MILLER, N. E. (1948). Theory and experiment relating psychoanalytic displacement to stimulus-response generalization. *J. Abnorm. (Soc.) Psychol.*, **43**, 155-178.
43. LOUCKS, R. B. (1935). The experimental delimitation of neural structures necessary for learning: the attempt to condition striped muscle responses with faradization of the sigmoid gyri. *J. Psychol.*, **1**, 5-44.
44. LOUCKS, R. B. and GANTT, W. H. (1938). The conditioning of striped muscle responses based on faradic stimulation of dorsal roots and dorsal columns of the spinal cord. *J. Comp. Psychol.*, **25**, 415-426.
45. HULL, C. (1929). A functional interpretation of the conditioned reflex. *Psychol. Rev.*, **36**, 498-511.
46. MOWRER, O. H. and LAMOREAUX, R. R. (1946). Fear as an intervening variable in avoidance conditioning. *J. Comp. Psychol.*, **39**, 29-50.
47. SCHLOSBERG, H. (1937). The relationship between success and the laws of conditioning. *Psychol. Rev.*, **44**, 379-394.
48. SKINNER, B. F. (1938). *The Behavior of Organisms.* Appleton–Century, New York.
49. SKINNER, B. F. (1935). Two types of conditioned reflex and a pseudo-type. *J. Gen. Psychol.*, **12**, 66-77.
50. RAZRAN, G. S. (1939). The law of effect or the law of qualitative conditioning? *Psychol. Rev.*, **46**, 445-463.
51. MOWRER, O. H. (1947). On the dual nature of learning—A reinterpretation of " conditioning " and " problem-solving." *Harvard Educ. Rev.*, **17**, 102-148.
52. MOWRER, O. H. (1939). A stimulus-response analysis of anxiety and its role as a reinforcing agent. *Psychol. Rev.*, **46**, 553-565.
53. MOWRER, O. H. and SUTER, J. Further evidence for a two-factor theory of learning. Unpublished study.
54. STEPHENS, J. M. (1942). Expectancy vs. effect-substitution as a general principle of reinforcement. *Psychol. Rev.*, **49**, 102-116.
55. MAIER, N. R. F. and SCHNIERLA, T. C. (1942). Mechanisms in conditioning. *Psychol. Rev.*, **49**, 117-134.
56. KENDLER, H. H. and UNDERWOOD, B. J. (1948). The role of reward in conditioning theory. *Psychol. Rev.*, **55**, 209-215.
57. JOHNSON, H. M. (1948). Psychoanalytic therapy versus psychoanalytic rationale. *Amer. Psychologist*, **3**, 337.
58. MOWRER, O. H. and KLUCKHOHN, C. (1943). A dynamic theory of personality. *Personality and the Behavior Disorders*, pp. 69-135. Ed. by J. McV. Hunt. Ronald Press, New York.

59. Murray, H. (1938). *Explorations in Personality*. Oxford Univ. Press, New York.
60. Carr, H. (1925). *Psychology*. Longmans Green, New York.
61. Peters, H. N. (1935). The judgmental theory of pleasantness and unpleasantness. *Psychol. Rev.*, **42**, 354-386.
62. Peters, H. N. (1938). Experimental studies of the judgmental theory of feeling: (I) Learning of positive and negative reactions as a determinant of affective judgments. *J. Exp. Psychol.*, **23**, 1-25.
63. Sullivan, H. S. (1948). The meaning of anxiety in psychiatry and in life. *Psychiatry*, **11**, 1-13.
64. Voegtlin, W. L. (1940). The treatment of alcoholism by establishing a conditioned reflex. *Amer. J. Med. Sci.*, **109**, 102.
65. Hall, E. W. (1943). An ethics for to-day. *Amer. J. Econ. Sociol.*, **2**, 444-446.

MODERN LEARNING THEORY*

H. J. EYSENCK

Institute of Psychiatry, Maudsley Hospital, London

IF IT is agreed that the modification of the central nervous system through experience which we call " learning " is the basis of most, if not all, human and animal behaviour patterns, then it will be clear why modern learning theory occupies such a prominent part in psychology. Most influential in this connexion has been the work of Clark L. Hull, whose *Principles of Behavior* has become the classic text.[1] The model of learning which he elaborated is a combination and formalization of two streams of thought, both of which are of considerable antiquity. One component is that of hedonism, or motivation by pain and pleasure. This was formalized and subjected to experimental study by Thorndike as the " law of effect," and now emerges under the name of " reinforcement " or " drive reduction." The other component is that of associationism; this was brought under experimental control by Pavlov and Bechtereff, in the form of conditioning or habit formation.

Hull joined these components in an impressive theoretical structure, the formal character of which makes possible large numbers of experimental predictions, many of which have been verified. This approach, it should be stressed, is a purely *molar* one; the concepts used are what psychologists call " intervening variables " or " hypothetical constructs " for which no neurological or physiological equivalent is necessarily postulated, although most psychologists would probably expect to encounter such equivalents, if only neurology and physiology were more advanced than they are.[2]

The most important aspect of the Hullian theory is the dissociation of performance (symbolized by Hull as $_sE_R$) from habit (symbolized as $_sH_R$). The letters S and R here denote stimulus and response respectively. Habit is conceived as the relatively permanent modification of the nervous system which mediates learning; the locus of this modification lies between the cortical representation of the stimulus and the cortical innervation causally preceding the response. Habits as so conceived are not directly visible or measurable; they can be indexed in terms of performance only under very special conditions. To equate habit and performance, as is often done by experimenters lacking psychological sophistication, is to invite disaster.

* Reprinted by permission of the editor from (1956) *Proc. Roy. Soc. Med.*, **49**, 1024-1026, with some additions.

A very important part of Hull's work has been the elaboration of a
formula linking the concepts of habit and performance. He does this by
invoking another concept, namely that of drive (D). Drives in his system
are the result of physiological needs such as hunger, thirst, sex, etc.; Hull
takes great care in his definition of the concept of drive to avoid the many
difficulties which have bedevilled the related concept of instinct.

The fundamental formula then, which links performance, habit and drive,
is as follows:

$$_sE_R = {_sH_R} \times D$$

In other words, performance is a multiplicative function of habit and drive,
and we can only use performance as a measure of habit if we keep drive
constant. When drive is zero there is no performance, however strong the
habit may be; we have many habits, but these are only translated into
performance when sparked off by a suitable drive. Much experimental work
has been done on the conditions determining the growth of $_sH_R$. Among
those found to be relevant are the number of reinforcements given, the
nature and amount of the reinforcing agent, and the delay in reinforcement.
In the studies sorting out the influence of these variables, no distinction is
made between trial and error learning of the traditional kind, and classical
conditioning as introduced by Pavlov; the theory is claimed to be universally
applicable to all the phenomena of learning. It will be noted that among the
variables determining the growth of habit, drive is not included. This is not
an accidental oversight, but a part of the theoretical structure. For Hull, the
amount of drive present during learning is irrelevant. This somewhat
paradoxical position has been criticized, and recent experimental evidence
suggests that Hull was mistaken in his neglect of drive as determining the
growth of $_sH_R$.[2]

Further concepts are necessary to make this formula applicable to the
majority of experimental studies. In particular, we must add the concepts
of reactive inhibition (I_R) and of conditioned inhibition $(_sI_R)$. According
to the theory, all learning, that is, all formation of stimulus-response
connexions, produces some degree of inhibition or fatigue in the mediating
structures; this fatigue acts as a negative drive and tends to dissipate with
time during periods of rest. Such dissipation acts as a reinforcement for
the prevailing state of affairs, namely, the state of rest, so that we obtain a
negative habit, that is, a habit of not responding to the stimulus.

Hull regarded I_R as a (negative) drive, while $_sI_R$ was regarded as a
habit. In combining these concepts into one formula with the others
mentioned above, he was inconsistent, writing:

$$_sE_R = (D \times {_sH_R}) - (I_R + {_sI_R})$$

In other words, he adds a habit $(_sI_R)$ and a drive (I_R), instead of multiplying them, as he should in terms of his general principles. Gwynne Jones[3] has provided the proper correction to this formula, and has shown that this new formulation is superior to the original one in accounting for well-known phenomena. His formula reads:

$$_sE_R = (D - I_R) \times (_sH_R - _sI_R)$$

This point is mentioned in some detail because these formulations generate different predictions, and several papers have used arguments based upon such predictions in justification of therapeutic procedures, notably in relation to " negative practice " and conditioned inhibition.

Hull's general formula for performance $(_sE_R)$ needs to be complicated by the addition to several other concepts, but these have played little part in therapeutic practice, and their discussion would enlarge this brief account unduly. A short and non-technical discussion of the whole matter has been given by Eysenck.[4]

There are other systems which also attempt to provide a formal theory for the phenomena of mammalian learning, all of which differ from Hull's in important respects. None of these, however, has been worked out in sufficient detail to generate the vast amount of detailed and precise predictions which can be made from Hull's principles. It is small wonder, therefore, that it has recently been found that no other book is quoted as frequently by psychologists in their writings as is *Principles of Behavior*. Similarly, no other system has given rise to so many experimental attempts to test its predictions, or to modify its hypotheses. While undoubtedly such experimental work will extensively modify the system, and has indeed already shown up considerable deficiencies in it, yet there seems to be no doubt that Hull has made a very great contribution indeed to psychology and has enabled us to transcend the purely empirical type of work which was so common in the first decades of this century.

The application of Hullian learning theory to the complex phenomena of social learning and psychiatry can be made in two ways. We can conceive of the symptoms shown by mentally ill people as the products of the learning process obeying the laws which Hull has laid down. A typically early example of such an application was Watson's famous demonstration of the experimental induction of a phobia in an 11-months-old boy by means of a conditioning technique. Equally, we would then think of a therapy as the removal of such symptoms and habits, also by the application of the laws of modern learning theory. Again, the success in removing the phobia induced by means of experimental excitation may be cited as a very early example of this approach. Among psychiatrists, Wolpe[5,6] of South Africa is a prominent exponent of these techniques, and his own work is in impressive confirmation of the possibilities opened up by this new approach. Here, it would seem, we have the beginning of what no other theory has ever been able to give us in the psychiatric field, namely, a *rational method of treatment based on well-known and experimentally demonstrated scientific principles*.[7] Few people who have given serious consideration to this approach doubt that in due course it will oust the so-called psychotherapeutic approaches, which not only fail to be based on independently demonstrable and experimentally established general psychological laws, but which also, in spite of 50 years of extensive application, have signally failed to present any evidence of therapeutic effectiveness.[8]

Another mode of application of the principles of learning theory was adumbrated by Pavlov, who suggested on the basis of systematic observations of hospitalized psychiatric patients that hysteria was due to exaggeratedly strong inhibition, while psychasthenia was due to an exaggeratedly strong excitation. As hysteria is strongly linked with extraversion and psychasthenia with introversion, this hypothesis gives us the possible basis for a typology soundly based on experimental findings. Large numbers of experiments have been done recently in an effort to investigate some of the consequences of this theory, which have been formalized and generalized by the present writer. Results have throughout been strongly favourable, leading one to the conclusion that Pavlov's long-neglected observation shows a considerable degree of insight and opens up a whole new chapter in the history of personality research.[9,10]

These two applications of learning theory to psychiatry are not, of course, mutually exclusive. In line with Pavlov's hypothesis, Franks[11] has shown that introverted neurotics, i.e. those suffering from anxiety, reactive depression and obsessional compulsive disorders, tend to condition very easily; while extroverted neurotics, i.e. those suffering from hysterical and psychopathic disorders, conditioned only with great difficulty. This typological and purely descriptive approach can be used in discovering the correct method of re-training a particular patient and eliminating the symptoms or habits of which he complains. (It is obvious that psychiatric symptoms in learning theory are to be classed as habits, i.e. come under the heading of $_sH_R$; thus learning theory contrasts strongly with Freud's theory, which tends to regard symptoms as symbolic activities characteristic of some purely hypothetical and ill-conceived unconscious conflict. The fact that so-called symptomatic cures can be achieved which are long-lasting and do not produce alternative symptoms argues strongly against the Freudian hypothesis.) Enuresis, tics, writer's cramp, stammer, and a variety of obscure autonomic dysfunctions have been treated very successfully by conditioning procedures, even when the patient had been treated unsuccessfully by psychotherapeutic methods for many years, but it does appear that such re-training methods are more effective in introverted people, i.e. those who condition easily, than in extraverts, i.e. those who condition less easily. In this way therapy becomes properly related to diagnosis (it is well known that in orthodox psychiatry as well as in psycho-analysis there is a very tenuous relationship between diagnosis and treatment); thus modern learning theory provides us not only with a rational method of treatment, but also with a rational method of diagnosis.

It will be obvious to the reader that, in view of the very recent development of learning theory, its application to psychiatric problems must be in its infancy. The fact that so many promising results have already been achieved in such a short period of time, and on the basis of a very imperfect type of theory, leads us to the confident expectation that an improvement in the theory, and further research into the application of that theory to psychiatrically ill patients, will provide the great upsurge in therapeutic effectiveness which psychoanalysis originally promised to give but failed to provide.

REFERENCES

1. HULL, C. L. (1943). *Principles of Behavior.* Appleton–Century, New York.
2. OSGOOD, C. E. (1953). *Method and Theory in Experimental Psychology.* Oxford Univ. Press, London.
3. JONES, H. GWYNNE (1958). *Psychol. Rev.*, **65**, 179.
4. EYSENCK, H. J. (1957). *Dynamics of Anxiety and Hysteria.* Routledge & Kegan Paul, London.
5. WOLPE, J. (1952). *S. Afr. Med. J.*, **26**, 825.
6. WOLPE, J. (1954). *Arch. Neurol. Psychiat.*, **72**, 205. Chicago.
7. EYSENCK, H. J. (1956). *Quart. Bull. Brit. Psychol. Soc.*, **30**, 27.
8. EYSENCK, H. J. (1952). *J. Cons. Psychol.*, **16**, 319.
9. EYSENCK, H. J. (1955a). *J. Ment. Sci.*, **101**, 28.
10. EYSENCK, H. J. (1955b). *J. Abnorm. (Soc.) Psychol.*, **52**, 95.
11. FRANKS, C. M. (1956). *J. Abnorm. (Soc.) Psychol.*, **52**, 143.

PART II

RECIPROCAL INHIBITION THEORY

INTRODUCTION

THIS section appropriately enough opens with a paper by J. Wolpe on " reciprocal inhibition as the basis of psychotherapeutic effects." Of all the methods here introduced, this is probably the most fundamental and the most important; of all the authors represented in this book, Wolpe is almost certainly the one best qualified in terms both of psychological knowledge and experimental achievement, on the one hand, and medical knowledge and therapeutic achievement, on the other, to speak for and to both sides. His book on *Psychotherapy by Reciprocal Inhibition* marks a milestone in the development of rational methods of treatment, and should certainly be familiar to every practitioner as well as to every research worker. Because of this, his representation in this book is probably less than it should be; it has been thought wiser to give space to papers by others (many of them his pupils and followers) in order to demonstrate that the success of the method is not confined, as is too often the case, to the original proponent, but can be duplicated by those willing to become acquainted with the method itself, and its theoretical basis.

It should be noted that Wolpe has laid a sound experimental basis for his procedures by his animal experiments and if space had permitted, an extensive account of these would have been included. They are discussed in detail in his book, and the interested reader will no doubt follow up the brief mention of them in his paper by referring to the longer account. This bringing together of animal experimentation and behaviour therapy in one united whole represents a very considerable achievement which had always eluded research workers in the field of " experimental neurosis "—largely because, starting with preconceived ideas about the correctness of psychoanalytic notions, they failed to take the results of the animal experiments seriously enough to run the necessary control experiments. This use of animal work to *illustrate*, rather than to establish, principles and conclusions has already been mentioned in the first paper in this book; its methodological weaknesses cannot be overemphasized.

The only point on which Wolpe's original treatment was perhaps open to criticism was his failure to recognize the importance of individual differences and diagnostic procedures; this point is brought out particularly in the paper by V. Meyer and in some of the contributions of D. Walton. It appears that on this point also there is now no difference of opinion any longer.

RECIPROCAL INHIBITION
AS THE MAIN BASIS
OF PSYCHOTHERAPEUTIC EFFECTS*

JOSEPH WOLPE, M.D., B.CH.

Department of Psychiatry, University of Witwatersrand, South Africa

THE AIM of this paper is to show that when fundamental psychotherapeutic effects are obtained in neuroses—no matter by what therapist—these effects are nearly always really a consequence of the occurrence of reciprocal inhibition of neurotic anxiety responses, i.e. the complete or partial suppression of the anxiety responses as a consequence of the simultaneous evocation of other responses physiologically antagonistic to anxiety. Several new psychotherapeutic techniques are described that have been derived directly from the reciprocal inhibition principle and have turned out to be of value.

In previous writings[2,3,4] I presented evidence in support of the view that neurotic behavior is persistent unadaptive learned behavior in which anxiety is almost always prominent and which is acquired in anxiety-generating situations. By " anxiety " is meant the autonomic response pattern or patterns that are characteristically part of the given organism's response to noxious stimulation and the term is applied irrespective of the duration of the autonomic responses or of what has led to them. An anxiety response is unadaptive when it is evoked in circumstances in which there is objectively no threat.

Successful therapy of experimental neuroses[5,6,2,4] seems to depend on obtaining reciprocal inhibition of neurotic responses,[2,4] for conditioned (learned) inhibition of these responses evidently develops on the basis of their repeated reciprocal inhibition. The mechanisms presumed to be concerned in this process have been discussed in some detail in another connection.[7] Taking a cue from the experimental findings, it was decided to investigate the effects on human neuroses of measures designed specifically to bring about reciprocal inhibition of neurotic responses. Favorable early experiences[3] encouraged the use and further development of these measures, and in 1952 a series of 70 cases was reported,[8] in 86 per cent of which the

---

* This paper is an amplified version of an article originally published under the same title in (1954) *A.M.A. Arch. Neurol. Psychiat.*, 72, 205-226. The same thesis has been more fully presented in a recent book.[1]

condition had been either apparently cured or much improved after an average of 25 interviews. A short account of the techniques employed was included in that report. In the present paper these techniques, including new ones, are described in more detail, and the results of treatment of 52 additional cases are set forth.

EXPERIMENTAL BACKGROUND OF PSYCHOTHERAPY BASED ON THE PRINCIPLE OF RECIPROCAL INHIBITION

In the course of experiments during the years 1947 to 1948,[2,4] I found that cats could be made neurotic merely by placing them in a small cage and then, immediately after presenting an auditory stimulus, subjecting them to a small number of high-voltage, low-amperage shocks from an induction coil. (Previous workers[9,6] had mistakenly thought that neurosis would ensue only if the reaction to the shock was in conflict with a previously conditioned food-approach response.) The animals all reacted violently to the shock, showing various combinations of rushing to and fro; clawing at the roof, floor and sides of the experimental cage; crouching, trembling, howling and spitting, mydriasis, tachypnea, piloerection, and, in some cases, urination or defecation. After a variable number of shocks these reactions would become stabilized, and it would then be found that if the animal was replaced in the experimental cage on a later occasion it would manifest a reaction pattern similar to that observed at the time of the shock. Confinement in the cage for several hours did not diminish the reactions, nor did they show remission when the animals were put in the cage day after day without ever again being shocked. The disturbance was such that an animal starved for 24–72 hr would not eat meat dropped in front of him in the cage. Months of absence from the experimental cage did not weaken the reactions evocable there.

It was thus clear that the usual means by which ineffectual responses are eliminated—experimental extinction, which depends upon a process associated with fatigue of the response[10,7]—was ineffective as far as the anxiety responses were concerned. It seemed for a time as though these responses would have to be regarded as permanent and irreversible, but in our considering possible methods by which they might be eliminated, it seemed reasonable to try causing some other response to occur in the experimental situation that might be expected to be incompatible with the anxiety responses. The obvious response to try was feeding. Neurotic animals were placed inside the experimental cage after having been starved for 48 or 72 hr, and pellets of meat were tossed in front of them. As usual, no eating occurred. Now, since in their living cages the animals were accustomed to having food conveyed to them by the human hand, it was presumed that the hand had become a conditioned food-approach stimulus and it was hoped that, added to the food-approach tendencies aroused by the sight and smell of the meat, the presentation of the human hand might lead to the overcoming of the inhibition of the feeding response. Accordingly, meat pellets were offered to the animals on an ebony rod held in the hand. Some of the animals ate the food after various periods of hesitation and then took subsequent offerings with increasing readiness.

In those animals that were not induced to eat by the above technique a method was tried that proved to be very instructive. In addition to their reactions in the experimental cage, the animals also reacted with anxiety anywhere in the experimental laboratory and also in each of a series of rooms that had varying degrees of resemblance to the experimental laboratory. They were offered meat pellets in each of these places, starting with the rooms that more closely resembled the laboratory. In the case of each cat a place was eventually found where the evocation of anxiety responses was not great enough to inhibit the feeding response. The animal would be fed about 20 pellets in this place and on the next day would usually be found to accept food in the room next closest in resemblance to the laboratory—as it would not have done previously. From day to day further advances were made, until the animal would eat in the laboratory and eventually, through several stages, in the experimental cage itself. There it would be given numerous pellets of meat on successive days and at last would move about in the cage freely, without any signs of anxiety.

But at this stage the anxiety responses could again be evoked by presenting the auditory stimulus that had preceded the neurosis-producing shocks. The effects of this stimulus could be eliminated in a manner parallel to that applied to the visual stimuli—by feeding the animal first at a considerable distance from the continuously sounding stimulus and then gradually coming nearer day by day. Meanwhile, the auditory stimulus would incidentally have become linked to a food-seeking response; but extinction of this by repeated nonreward did not lead to a recurrence of anxiety in any animal.

These experiments seemed clearly to confirm the expectation of a reciprocal antagonism between the anxiety responses and the feeding responses. As long as, in a given situation, the anxiety was strong enough to inhibit feeding, anxiety would continue to be dominant, and would even increase or spread, as certain supplementary experiments[2],[3(p.615)],[11] showed. But if conditions were so changed that the feeding tendency was relatively stronger and feeding could occur in the face of some measure of anxiety, the strength of the tendency to respond by anxiety to the stimuli concerned was gradually weakened.

RECIPROCAL INHIBITION IN PSYCHOTHERAPY

The above findings led to the framing of the general hypothesis that if a response incompatible with anxiety can be made to occur in the presence of anxiety-evoking stimuli it will weaken the bond between these stimuli and the anxiety responses. Responses incompatible with anxiety can be produced in human subjects in a number of different ways. It is not surprising that this should be so, for although Sherringtonian reciprocal inhibition associated with spinal reflex activity is apparently rather specific, at higher levels of organization reciprocal inhibition is clearly often diffuse within the functional " modality " concerned—for example, accompanying the articulation of any word there is ordinarily an automatic inhibition of all simultaneous tendencies to pronounce other words.

The first requirement in a planned attack on neurotic anxieties on the principle of reciprocal inhibition is to determine in what circumstances anxieties are aroused in the patient. Sometimes, usually when the patient has been available for only a small number of interviews, it has been possible to obtain satisfactory results with the therapist knowing only the general character of the situations producing anxiety and without his precisely identifying the disturbing elements. But it is always desirable and nearly always possible, to examine the situations carefully and to determine in detail to what stimuli the patient reacts with anxiety. To this end, it has been found helpful in some cases to make use of the psychogalvanic response (PGR). *A careful history of the patient's life and background is, of course, an essential preliminary to the foregoing.*

Under the headings that follow it is explained how various responses incompatible with anxiety have their therapeutic effects. Sections 1–4 discuss, in the main, techniques that have emerged directly from the reciprocal inhibition principle, and Sections 5–8 show how the effects of a number of procedures widely used in the treatment of neuroses are understandable in terms of reciprocal inhibition.

(1) *Assertive Responses*

These responses are mainly employed in situations that occur spontaneously in the normal course of the patient's life. Great prominence has been given to their use by Salter,[12] who, having been led to them by a different theory, seems to apply them almost universally. I have found them of use only for overcoming unadaptive anxieties aroused in the patient by other people during his direct dealings with them. In these circumstances assertive responses are extremely effective. To take a common example, a patient feels hurt when members of his family criticize him and responds by trying to defend himself, by sulking, or by an outburst of petulant rage. Such responses are expressive of anxiety and helplessness. But some measure of resentment is, understandably, almost invariably present at the same time. The patient is unable to express this resentment because, for example, through previous training, the idea of talking back to his elders produces anxiety.

Now, just because this anxiety inhibits the expression of the resentment, it might be expected that if the patient could be motivated to express the resentment, the latter would, in turn, be reciprocally inhibitory to the anxiety and would thus suppress it, to some extent at least. The therapist provides this motivation by pointing out the emptiness of the patient's fears, emphasizing how his fearful patterns of behavior have incapacitated him and placed him at the mercy of others, and informing him that, though expression of resentment may be difficult at first, it becomes progressively easier with practice. It usually does not take long for patients to begin to perform the required behavior, although some need much initial exhortation and repeated promptings. Gradually the patient becomes able to behave assertively in progressively more exacting circumstances and reports a growing feeling of ease in all relevant situations. A conditioned inhibition of the anxiety responses is clearly developing, presumably on the basis of their repeated reciprocal inhibition—a process in all respects parallel to that involved in the overcoming of animal neuroses, as described above. Cases 3, 4 and 5 illustrate this technique.

Obviously, in advising assertive behavior, the therapist must be discreet. He should advise it only when the anxiety evoked in the patient by the other person concerned is unadaptive—in other words, it is an anxiety that occurs even though no unpleasant repercussions can reasonably be expected to follow from making a stand. For nothing can be gained and sensitivity may even be increased, if the patient's assertiveness should meet with a swift and sharp punishment. For example, however much a person may resent his boss's surly manner, it would in most cases be foolhardy to give frank expression to this resentment. But it is quite frequently possible to express aggression indirectly, through gaining control of an interpersonal relationship by means subtler than overt assertiveness.

Occasionally, when there is unusual difficulty in the expression of aggression in the life situation, it is helpful to initiate the patient by means of a kind of " psycho-drama " in the consulting-room in which the therapist takes the role of some person who in life evokes anxiety in the patient.

(2) Sexual Responses

These responses, of course, are mainly of use when anxiety responses have been conditioned to various aspects of sexual situations. When very high degrees of anxiety conditioning have been accompanied by a complete inhibition of sexual responsiveness, other measures, described below, have to be employed. But very often the sexual inhibition is partial and varies according to variations in definable properties of the relevant situations. The patient is told that he must on no account perform sexually unless he has an unmistakable positive desire to do so, for otherwise he may very well consolidate, or even extend, his sexual inhibitions. He is instructed to wait for or to seek out situations in which pleasurable sexual feelings are aroused and in these he must " let himself go " as freely as possible. If he is able to act according to plan, he experiences a gradual increase in sexual responsiveness to the kind of situation of which he has made use, with varying degrees of generalization to sexual situations of other kinds. Case 10 illustrates the employment of this principle in a case of impotence.

Such favorable consequences occur, it seems, because each time a positive sexual feeling occurs and is intensified by a sexual approach there is reciprocal inhibition of whatever anxieties are also being evoked by the situation, and the strength of the anxiety-evocation tendency is each time slightly weakened. There is no apparent basic difference at all between this process and that which occurred in our cats, in which anxieties were overcome through appropriate manipulations with feeding reactions.

(3) Relaxation Responses

(a) *Relaxation responses in life situations*—Jacobson's work has shown[13] that intense muscle relaxation is accompanied by autonomic effects that are antagonistic to the characteristic effects of anxiety. I have repeatedly found clinical confirmation of this in the rapid drop of a pulse rate from 120 to 80 or in the equally rapid drying of profusely sweating palms in a patient who is practiced in relaxation.

Relaxation can be used with lasting good effects in the great majority of cases of neurosis, in my experience. Jacobson himself obtained impressive results by training patients in " progressive relaxation " and then urging them to be as relaxed as possible all the time. It would appear that the improvement in a patient who follows this program may be explained as follows: Persistent relaxation implies some measure of reciprocal inhibition of the effects of any anxiety-producing stimuli that happen to appear and the occurrence of repeated temporary inhibitions of this kind enables conditioned inhibition of the anxiety responses gradually to develop.

I have sometimes obtained highly gratifying results in patients placed on Jacobson's regime (Case 6), but oftener than not its value is limited, seemingly because the patient is unable to relax at short notice sufficiently deeply to counter the high degree of anxiety produced by the relevant stimulus situations. In a few patients this difficulty has been overcome when the subject has learned how to anticipate such situations and to relax deeply in preparation for them. The following technique, in which the therapist has a good deal of detailed control, has proved to have far wider application.

(b) *Systematic desensitization based on relaxation**—This method of systematic desensitization to anxiety-producing stimuli is carried out in the consulting room.

* This technique, which is of outstanding importance, is discussed at length in *Psychotherapy by Reciprocal Inhibition*.[1]

The patient is given training in progressive relaxation in the course of several interviews. Preliminary experiments on his responses to hypnotic techniques are meanwhile conducted and during the same interviews steps are taken toward the construction of what is called an " anxiety hierarchy." This is a list of stimuli to which the patient reacts with unadaptive anxiety. The most disturbing items are placed at the top and the least disturbing at the bottom. The arrangement is usually derived solely from the patient's answers to questioning. Very occasionally, when he has had difficulty in assessing the relative effects of different stimuli, it has been necessary to base the hierarchy, or parts of it, on the psychogalvanic response (PGR). Multiple hierarchies are very often obtained.

In the session after the preliminaries have been completed, the patient is hypnotized and given powerful relaxation suggestions. (A good relaxer can do almost as well without hypnosis, just closing his eyes.) He is then asked to imagine a scene embodying the feeblest member of the anxiety hierarchy. Sometimes it is advisable to start even more mildly, causing the name of the feared object to be visualized. The patient is instructed to signal if at any time he feels more than the slightest disturbance. Usually, 2–4 items from the hierarchies are presented at each session, the speed of progression depending on how much disturbance is shown or afterward reported. An item may be presented several times during a session until the reaction aroused by it entirely disappears. (It is always preferable to advance too slowly rather than too fast. During early experiments with the method I produced serious setbacks in two patients by the premature presentation of stimuli with a high anxiety-evoking potential.) It usually takes between 10 and 30 desensitization sessions before the highest items in the hierarchies can be accepted by the patient without disturbance.

It is natural to ask: Does it follow that because a patient can imagine a scene calmly, he will also be calm when he comes upon a similar scene in reality? Experience shows the answer to be in the affirmative. A very striking example is afforded by Case 7. Sometimes there is a tendency for the real-life improvement to lag behind somewhat, but even then it eventually catches up. The one proviso for success, given the ability to relax, is that the imagined stimulus must at the outset be able to evoke anxiety. A small minority of patients experience no anxiety when they imagine situations that in actuality are anxiety-producing, and in them desensitization is not accomplished by the above procedure. It is interesting to note that recently a patient who repeatedly failed to respond emotionally to images aroused by verbal cues from the therapist has shown considerable disturbance on verbalizing the same situations himself.

The above procedure, originally confined to " simple " phobias, has in the past year been applied to a wide variety of disturbing situations (Case 8), often of a social nature. Sometimes there are multiple distinct, though usually interrelated, hierarchies. These may exist in parallel, or may be, so to speak " layered." For example in a dentist, phobic reactions to a variety of work situations were found after a time to depend on fears of criticism, which were, in their turn, partly based on a claustrophobic system. A separate hierarchy was derived from each of these three areas.

(4) Conditioned Avoidance Responses

(a) *Conditioned inhibition of anxiety through a dominating motor response—* In 1948 Mowrer and Viek[14] performed an interesting experiment in which they showed that when rats are repeatedly exposed to a continuous mild electric shock, those animals who are enabled to learn a definite motor response in relation to the termination of the shock develop very little anxiety when placed in the experimental situation minus the shock; and, in contrast to these, much greater anxiety is shown by animals who have no opportunity to learn such a motor response. I have elsewhere[11] given reasons for rejecting Mowrer and Viek's own interpretation of their experiment and have argued that the less anxiety of the first-mentioned group of animals could be attributed to a gradual weakening of the autonomic anxiety responses due to their repeated reciprocal inhibition by the musculo-skeletal response that regular reinforcement makes dominant.

It was reasonable to suppose that this experiment might have a therapeutic application. It was postulated that if in the presence of a stimulus evoking neurotic anxiety a mild noxious stimulus were to be applied on repeated occasions, and if this noxious stimulus were at the same time conditioned to produce a well-defined motor response, the neurotic anxiety would gradually be weakened. So far I have found only one case that has lent itself to the use of this method, and in which at the same time the response to other measures was poor enough to warrant the great expenditure of effort and time demanded.

CASE 1—The patient was a 23-year-old university graduate. She had been unbelievably over-protected during her childhood and adolescence. Three years previously she had had two fairly violent falls in the street within a few weeks and thereafter had been apprehensive of walking outside unaccompanied lest she should fall. As is apt to happen in such cases, her range of activity had then gradually become more and more circumscribed. At one stage she would walk in the street only if her mother held her arm; later she entirely refused to leave the house, and by the time I first saw her, she was practically bedridden, apart from very tense wall-hugging journeys between her bed and a couch in the drawing room. After a year of interviews at approximately weekly intervals, she was feeling more confident and had greatly improved her handling of other people, but was only slightly more freely mobile. Her central fear—of falling—was undiminished, the hypnotic desensitization technique described above having turned out to be inapplicable to her case.

Then the following procedure, based on Mowrer and Viek's experiment, was adopted. Silver electrodes were attached to the patient's left hand and forearm. She was instructed to close her eyes and imagine a relatively easy (though, to her, slightly disturbing) fall and to signal at the commencement of the imagined movement. At this signal a mild electric shock (secondary of inductorium at 8·0 cm with 6-volt dry cell in primary) was passed into her forearm, being stopped only upon the occurrence of a brisk flexion of the forearm, which the patient had been directed to make. This movement soon became the instant response to the shock. When the whole sequence had been repeated a number of times, the patient reported that imagining the fall was becoming less unpleasant and disturbing, and, after further repetitions, that she could imagine it with ease. Thereafter, she was able to attempt this particular fall in actuality, and after practicing it a good many times a day, she could do it easily after a few days. Then she was ready for a slightly more difficult fall. Standing at increasing distances from chairs and other supports was later accomplished in similar fashion. The procedure was repeated at intervals of approximately 5 days, and as she became capable of falling farther and harder and, later, of standing farther from a support, she was able to walk and move around with increasing freedom. (It is intended to publish separately a detailed account of this case.)*

(b) *Conditioning of "anxiety-relief" responses*—The possibility that "anxiety-relief" responses might be directly conditioned to convenient stimuli and subsequently used to counter anxiety was suggested by an observation in a recent experiment by Zbrozyna.[15] This observation was that if a stimulus is repeatedly presented to an eating animal just before withdrawing the food, that stimulus acquires the property of inhibiting feeding even when the animal is in the middle of a meal. By analogy with this, it seemed reasonable to expect that if an uncomfortable induction shock were administered to a human subject for several seconds and were then made to cease immediately after a signal, that signal would become connected to such bodily responses as would follow cessation of the shock, and, furthermore, that these responses would be the negative of the anxiety that had been produced by the shock. This, it was hoped, would imply the acquisition of an additional means of inhibiting anxiety due to other stimuli.

This idea has been put into practice in 8 patients, with marked effects in 2 and slight in 4. With the inductorium set at about 7·5 cm (but varying according to the subject's reaction) and a primary inflow of 6V, a continuous shock is administered to the subject's left forearm. He is told to bear it until the desire to have it removed becomes very strong, then to say aloud the word "calm." As soon as he says the word, the current is switched off. This is repeated 10–20 times in a session. Most subjects report a feeling of relief at the cessation of shock that seems profoundly out of proportion to the disturbing effect of the shock and find, after 1–3 sessions, that using the word in disturbing situations decreases the disturbed feeling. In one case the word "calm" did not become the effective conditioned stimulus to the relief reaction but the subject reported that she found herself automatically picturing the inductorium against the background of the consulting room whenever she experienced anxiety rising within her. This would bring on "surges of relief," under which the anxiety would melt away. Gradually, according to prediction on the reciprocal inhibition principle, with repeated occurrences of this experience the amount of anxiety produced by the

---

* Such an account appears in *Psychotherapy by Reciprocal Inhibition*.[1] Recovery was eventually complete and has now (March, 1959) been maintained for 3 years.

relevant stimuli became less and less. (It should be noted that this technique has in no case been the sole method of treatment.)

(c) *Avoidance conditioning of obsessions*—In the production of reactions of avoidance to obsessional stimuli, we have an instance of the application of the reciprocal inhibition principle to a response other than anxiety, for here it is an intense and excessive approach response that is being overcome. The essence of the method is to subject the patient to a very unpleasant electric shock in the presence of the obsessional object. It seems that the first to report the use of such a method was Kantorovich,[16] who employed it in the treatment of alcoholics—with considerable success. The technique was first applied to an obsessional patient by Max[17] a good many years ago and was then apparently ignored. Max administered to his patient an unusually severe induction shock in the presence of a fetishistic object. By doing this repeatedly and then reinforcing at intervals when required, he produced a persistent avoidance reaction to this object, which alone, it seems, very greatly ameliorated the patient's emotionally disturbed state.

CASE 2—I have used a modification of Max's method in the treatment of a food obsession of 16 years' standing, which previously had completely resisted almost every current mode of therapy, from ECT to psychoanalysis. The patient was a very intelligent woman of 36 who had long suffered from cardiac insufficiency and was on a restricted diet. Besides the obsession, she had other exceptionally severe and distressing neurotic reactions, which had improved considerably on the more usual reciprocal inhibition techniques. But the obsession was still present almost always and was worse when the patient was reacting to any persistent anxiety-producing stimulus. She would have visions of various items of delectable food and would be tortured by a conflict as to whether to eat or not. If she did eat, she soon felt a rising guilt (anxiety about something done) which would lead back to the obsession. Thus, a vicious circle of eating and anxiety would be started, which, within a few days, would leave her in a desperately helpless and exhausted state.

Avoidance conditioning was carried out as follows: The electrodes having been attached to her left forearm, the patient was told to raise her right hand as soon as she had formed a clear imaginary picture of some desirable foodstuff. An almost unbearable current from the inductorium at 7·0 cm (6V) was then instantly delivered and continued until she lowered her right hand as a signal that the shock could no longer be borne, as she usually did after a second or two. About 10 reinforcements were given at each session, and 2–3 days were allowed to elapse between sessions. After the first session the "nagging" of the obsession was already markedly reduced. It was further reduced in 4 more sessions, which implicated the whole range of items of "delectable food." The patient reported that on imagining any such food she immediately had a feeling of fear and revulsion, accompanied by an image of the shock situation. (At an earlier stage this feeling was occasionally preceded by a momentary feeling of pleasure.) Within a few seconds she was able to return her attention to whatever she had been doing before the food image came up—a tremendous gain as contrasted with the old misery of hours spent debating, "Should I eat; should I not?" After her fifth and last session, she stated that her tendency to think of food was also diminishing. Unfortunately, but not unexpectedly, there was also some generalization of the avoidance to permitted foods, i.e., nonfattening sodium-free foods eaten only at mealtime. This was a very considerable difficulty, but the patient regarded it as trivial in comparison with her obsession. The over-all lightening of the burden made it much easier to return to the usual procedures for overcoming the anxiety reactions. Gratifying progress was made, only to be brought to an end by the patient's sudden death from ventricular fibrillation due to chronic rheumatic heart disease.

(5) Feeding Responses

I have not employed feeding responses to obtain reciprocal inhibition of anxiety in human subjects, but Jones[18] has done so successfully in young children. There is no reason why feeding should not be effective in overcoming fears in adults under certain circumstances. What is required is that in the presence of the anxiety-evoking stimulus food must be given under so intense a hunger drive that in the act of eating there will be an inhibition of anxiety. Probably, it is precisely this that is the explanation of the beneficial effects on neuroses of subcoma doses of insulin[19,20]; and it is worth noting that the effects of this method have been greatest when the patient has eaten substantially more than usual and has put on weight. Presumably, in eating voraciously because of heightened hunger drive, the patient obtains a reciprocal inhibition of any anxiety responses that happen to be occurring within him at that particular time. This explanation, with its close parallel in animal experiments, gains credence when one takes into account the haziness of the explanations that have been offered in terms of gross physiology. However, from the results of a controlled experiment by Teitelbaum and associates,[21] as reviewed by Sargant and Slater,[22] it is clear that only a small percentage of patients are favorably affected by subcoma insulin. This finding is not surprising, because any effects depend on the fortuitous occurrence of anxiety-producing stimuli at the time of the eating (this implies, of course, that the patients who should respond best are those that have a good deal of so-called free-floating anxiety, i.e. secondary conditionings of anxiety to commonplace stimuli, such as room walls or voices).

(6) Respiratory Responses

In 1947 Meduna[23] reported the very interesting discovery that in many patients neurotic reactions can be ameliorated, and sometimes even overcome, by inhalations of high concentrations of carbon dioxide. His usual technique has been to make the patient breathe a mixture of 30 per cent CO_2 and 70 per cent O_2 until consciousness is lost. More recently, La Verne[24] has claimed equally good or better results from single full-capacity inhalations of 70 per cent CO_2 and 30 per cent O_2, usually producing no more than stupor. Meduna and his followers have assumed that the effects of this kind of treatment are due to the depressing action of CO_2 on nerve structures. Gellhorn[25,p.462] has criticized Meduna's theory and has gone on to suggest another explanation of these effects, also in terms of gross physiology. But from a psychological point of view any such theory is untenable, because the treatment apparently affects only neurotic anxiety responses. If the effects of CO_2 were due to its action on some chemical factor in certain nerve cells, all cells containing this factor would be influenced; and since the relevant cells are those that in one way or another subserve anxiety responses, all anxieties, even those aroused in response to real threats, would be similarly diminished by the treatment. Neither Meduna's case histories nor my own personal experience reveals any indication of this happening. Anxiety responses, as such, are by no means removed from the repertoire of the patient, who continues to have and display normal anxieties. It is therefore to be concluded that a specific unlearning of the connection between certain stimuli and the anxiety responses has occurred. It is reasonable to suspect that the unlearning occurs by a process of reciprocal inhibition in this instance, too. Neurotic anxiety-producing stimuli are brought forth during the dreamy or confused stage of the treatment, or are already present if there is " free-floating " anxiety. Processes antagonistic to anxiety can be found both in the excitation that goes with intense respiratory stimulation and in association with the complete muscle relaxation that high concentrations of carbon dioxide produce.[25, p.459]

I have occasionally treated patients with carbon dioxide, employing La Verne's method because, in contrast to Meduna's, it arouses little or no anxiety. Of 5 patients, 1 was completely unaffected, 2 felt sedated afterward for the rest of each treatment day, 1 showed slight but definite lasting improvement, and one obtained very marked benefit. The last-mentioned had a war neurosis of 10 years' standing. He displayed, almost continuously, a high degree of " free-floating " anxiety and had a special sensitivity to all situations involving explosions or low-pitched rumblings. Desensitization under hypnosis could not even be started because when asked to imagine a scene the patient could never visualize anything but irregular black and white blotches. He had 3 treatments, each consisting of 2 full inhalations of the mixture of 70 per cent CO_2 and 30 per cent O_2. There was a week between treatments, and he felt persistently better after each. After the third treatment he said he felt perfectly well. Three months later he was still well and reported that thunderstorms had left him quite undisturbed, in contrast with the past.*

(7) Interview-Induced Emotional Responses

Cures of neuroses seem to be obtained by all kinds of therapists, even though, owing to their different theories, they devote the interview period to procedures that differ in a large variety of ways. Such studies as have compared the success of various kinds of interviews have shown no important differences either in the percentage of cures or in their quality.[26, 27] Wilder,[27] for example, found that the psychotherapeutic results achieved by hospitals,

---

* Later studies, reported in *Psychotherapy by Reciprocal Inhibition*,[1] indicate that this method usually produces dramatic and, under certain circumstances, lasting relief from pervasive (" free-floating ") anxiety. Its possibilities with *specific* anxieties might be investigated by presenting anxiety-arousing stimuli at different stages of the sequences of responses to the gas.

mental hygiene clinics, psychoanalytic institutes, private psychoanalysts, and private psychotherapists were much the same. This finding strongly suggests that the various special points of procedure that the different therapists regarded as crucial to success were not crucial at all and that the effective factor must have been something that all the therapeutic situations generated in common.

The only feature common to all the therapies seems to be that there is a private interview in which the patient confidentially reveals and talks about his difficulties to a person he believes to have the knowledge, skill, and desire to help him. This kind of situation undoubtedly excites emotional responses in patients, and both the character and the strength of these responses vary as functions of many factors, of which the personality and attitude of the therapist and the individual reactive potentialities of the patient are presumably the most important. If, in a patient, the emotional response evoked by the interview situation is (a) antagonistic to anxiety and (b) of sufficient strength, it may be supposed that it will reciprocally inhibit the anxiety responses that are almost certain to be evoked by some of the subject matter of the interview.

This hypothesis requires systematic testing, but it is my clinical impression that those patients who display strong emotions other than anxiety during the early anamnestic interviews are the ones who are likely to show improvement before special methods for obtaining reciprocal inhibition of anxiety responses are applied.

(8)   *Abreaction*

Abreaction may be defined as the emotional re-evocation of a fearful past experience. It is a special case of the interview-induced emotional reactions considered under the previous heading. It may occur under thiopental (Pentothal), hypnosis, or deep relaxation, or even in the course of an ordinary interview. The emotion is of considerable intensity and beneficial effects seem, by and large, to be positively correlated with its intensity. But, as Grinker and Spiegel[28,p.81] have pointed out, if unrelieved terror is the only emotional component of the abreaction, the patient makes no progress. It is only when the patient can feel the impact of the therapeutic situation, e.g. the therapist's sympathetic acceptance of him, that beneficial abreaction can occur. This is emphasized by Grinker and Spiegel's observation[29,p.392] that "abreactions that occur spontaneously under alcohol are nontherapeutic." In the case of abreaction, too, then, benefit depends on the evocation of other emotional responses in association with the fearful situation, so that, presumably, reciprocal inhibition of anxiety occurs. The specially dramatic changes sometimes produced by abreaction are in line with the experimental finding that modifications of response are likely to be more marked when there is a higher level of drive to be reduced.[10,30]

If the above interpretation is correct, it would follow that the uprooting of " repressed memories " is not essential to the therapeutic effects of abreaction, although the ventilation of forgotten material often provides the subject matter. Many of Grinker and Spiegel's patients[28,p.83-84] were improved by abreactions in which the battle experiences concerned were well-remembered ones. The case that follows demonstrates how irrelevant to a patient's recovery the restoration of forgotten memories can be.

CASE 3—A 37-year-old miner was seen in a state of intense anxiety. He had had a very marked tremor and total amnesia for the previous 4 days. He gave a story that his wife, on whom he was greatly dependent, had cunningly got him to agree to " temporary divorce " 6 months before and was now going to marry a friend of his. No attempt was made at this juncture to recall the lost memories. The patient was made to realize how ineffectual his previous attitudes had been and how he had been deceived. As a result, he angrily " had it out " with his wife (and a few others, incidentally); anxiety rapidly decreased, and he soon felt strongly motivated to organize his whole life differently. At his fifth interview (10 days after treatment began), he said that he felt " a hundred per cent," and looked it, and he was full of plans for the future. Yet, he had still recalled nothing whatever of the forgotten 4 days.

Since the possible effects of restoring the memories at this stage were obviously a matter of great interest, the patient was then deeply hypnotized and told to recount the story of the 4 days. He narrated in detail how he had traveled 300 miles to his rival, meaning to strangle him; how he had been fobbed off and how, returning, and at last hearing from his wife's own lips that she was in love with the rival, he had staggered out

TABLE 1

Classification of cases

Category:	Number		
	1952 series	Present series	Total
Anxiety states	39	33	72
Hysteria	6	3	9
Reactive depression	7	3	10
Obsessions and compulsions	5	6	11
Neurasthenia	3	0	3
Mixed and unclassifiable	10	7	17
Totals	70	52	122

of the house, made his way to his sister's house and there collapsed. He told all this quietly, with little emotion, except where he described meeting his rival. Then he moved his hands as if about to throttle someone. He was given the posthypnotic suggestion that he would remember the whole story on waking. When he woke, he told it again briefly, expressing slight amusement at it and surprise at having remembered. There were no important consequences. A few months later he married another woman and was apparently very well adjusted generally. After 4 years there has been no evidence of relapse.

RESULTS

In 1952 the results were reported of the treatment of 70 patients by the reciprocal inhibition techniques that were then available.[8] In the 52 additional cases now presented, these were the techniques that were again chiefly employed; but, in addition, the three induction coil methods described above and La Verne's method of CO_2 therapy were occasionally used.

Both series include only patients whose treatment has ceased after they have been afforded a reasonable opportunity for the application of the available methods; i.e. they have had as a minimum both a course of instruction on the changing of behavior in the life situation and a proper initiation of a course of relaxation-desensitization. This minimum takes up to about 15 interviews, including the anamnestic interviews and no patient who has had 15 or more interviews has been omitted from the series. Almost invariably, when a patient has experienced some early improvement, he continues until improvement is very marked, and then, oftener than not, breaks off treatment, even though I am not quite ready to discharge him.

The degree of response to treatment has been estimated by reference to Knight's 5 criteria[31]—symptomatic improvement, increased productiveness, improved adjustment and pleasure in sex, improved interpersonal relationships and ability to handle ordinary psychological conflicts and reasonable reality stresses. In addition, if available, the patient's score on Willoughby's questionnaire[32,33] is compared with his score at the beginning of treatment, and no patient is regarded as greatly benefited unless his

TABLE 2

Results of reciprocal inhibition-based psychotherapy

	No. of cases	Apparently cured	Much improved	Slightly to moderately improved	Unim- proved
1952 series	70	34	26	7	3
Present series	52	20	30	1	1
Totals	122	54 (44%)	56 (46%)	8 (7%)	4 (3%)

TABLE 3

Distribution of interviews

No. of interviews	Up to 10	11–20	21–30	31–40	Over 40	Total
No. of patients	12	17	12	3	8	52

Mean number of interviews per patient 26·1

TABLE 4

Comparative results

Series	No. of cases	Apparently cured or much improved	Improvement moderate, slight, or nil
Berlin Psychoanalytic Institute[31]	263–402*	163* (62–40·5%)	100–239* (38–59·5%)
New York Hospital[34]	100	53 (53%)	47 (47%)
Combined reciprocal inhibition series	122	110 (90%)	12 (10%)

score has dropped markedly, preferably to 20 or less. On the basis of these criteria, results are grouped under the headings used by Knight: (1) apparently cured; (2) much improved; (3) moderately to slightly improved; and (4) unimproved.

In Table 1 the cases are grouped according to the " type " of neurosis. This grouping has little value from any clinical angle,† for almost all neuroses are really " mixed," and the compartment into which a case falls is no guide to its tractability.

Table 2 shows the results of reciprocal inhibition-based psychotherapy in our two series. It will be noticed that in the present series the percentage of good results has risen slightly, but a more rigorous standard has been applied for " cure." Systematic long-term follow-up studies have not been done, but information has been received from 14 patients of the 1952 series. Not one of these has relapsed, and all but one have reported continuing progress 2–5 years after the end of therapy.

Table 3 subdivides the present 52 cases according to the number of interviews given. Four-fifths of the patients had 30 interviews or less. The mean is 26·1, as compared with a mean of 24·9 in the earlier series. It may be noted that in the two series there was a total of 13 patients who had previously been psychoanalyzed, and these had an average of 51·7 interviews. Part of the reason for this high average was that some of these patients were exceedingly verbose and found difficulty in participating in treatment by objective techniques. Nevertheless, 10 of the 13 patients were either apparently cured or much improved. It is interesting to note that 2 psychoanalyzed patients, while repeatedly expressing skepticism regarding the present methods during their early interviews, nevertheless agreed to follow out instructions, and both did very well—one being apparently cured

* See text.
† I no longer hold this view. See *Psychotherapy by Reciprocal Inhibition.*

after 14 interviews and the other much improved after 16. Another such skeptic, however, was the only patient in the present series who made no improvement at all.

Table 4 compares the total results of our 2 series with those of Hamilton and Wall's New York Hospital series[35] and those of the largest reported psychoanalytically treated series[31]—from the Berlin Psychoanalytic Institute. In the case of the last series, two figures are given for both the total number of cases and the percentages. The larger total includes those patients who had less than 6 months' psychoanalysis. But for the purposes of our comparison the smaller, and more favorable, total is taken. The χ^2 test for significance yields a value of 44 when our results are compared with those of the New York Hospital series, and a value of 31 when they are compared with those of the psychoanalytic series. Thus, both comparisons indicate that the probability that the higher proportion of successes in the present series is due to chance is negligible.

The crucial point of the comparative figures in Table 4 is that 90 per cent of the patients in our 2 series were either apparently cured or much improved, and only about 60 per cent of the cases in the other two series. If the favorable results of the present series are, to the extent of 60 per cent, regarded as due to the nonspecific reciprocal inhibition that would occur in any kind of interview situation, the additional 30 per cent of good results appears to be attributable to the special measures for obtaining reciprocal inhibition described above. Furthermore, the small average number of interviews needed suggests that the use of these special measures early in treatment greatly accelerates the improvement of those patients who would have responded to the nonspecific factors alone.

COMMENTS ON OTHER THEORIES OF THE PSYCHOTHERAPEUTIC PROCESS

In reciprocal inhibition we have a single principle that can explain (a) the effectiveness of measures used to overcome animal neuroses, (b) the similar success of various, often widely different, interview techniques, and (c) the effectiveness of certain special measures—subcoma insulin and carbon dioxide therapy. At the same time, the principle has led directly to the development of effective new psychotherapeutic techniques, as described above.

It is necessary at this point to examine some other current theories to see whether any of them can, with equal ease, cover the same range of facts. The theories will not be considered in relation to all the facts. If any theory is found to contradict even one major fact, that finding is sufficient to challenge the validity of that theory. It will be seen in what follows that on this basis there is cause to doubt each of the more or less influential theories considered.

(1) *Psychoanalytic Types of Theory*

(a) *Pure psychoanalytic theory*—The essential features of this type of theory have been described in great detail by Fenichel.[36] Neurotic symptoms are regarded as due to " distorted discharges " that come from the damming up of the energies of repressed memories and the essential aim of psychoanalytic psychotherapy is to remove the repressions and so let the memories be reintegrated into the patient's conscious life. In Fenichel's words,[36,p.570] " The therapeutic task, then, is to reunite with the conscious ego the contents (both unconscious anxieties of the ego and instinctual impulses of the id) which have been withheld from consciousness by counter-cathexis." Now, the accomplishment of this " therapeutic task " cannot really be the essence of psychotherapy, because other methods which do nothing to lift repressions produce individual cures as impressive as any that psychoanalysis can claim, as often and at least as rapidly (in the present series apparently oftener and certainly more rapidly). Fenichel[36,p.555] is well aware that methods other than psychoanalysis have psychotherapeutic effects; but, on the basis of his theoretical presuppositions and without empirical support, he discards these effects as being limited in comparison with those of psychoanalysis. Meanwhile, the findings of Landis[26] and Wilder,[27] mentioned above, are contrary to Fenichel's presumption, as are the results of the treatment recorded here, with its high proportion of cases fully satisfying all of Knight's criteria.

Unfortunately, there is little likelihood that psychoanalysts in general will take the above considerations into account, any more than they have in the past taken account of facts or arguments unfavorable to their theories. It is not easy even for a strict scientist to give up a favorite hypothesis when the evidence fails to support it; but psychoanalysts seem especially liable to acquire habits of thought that do not conform to the requirements of science, as Ellis' recent monograph clearly shows.[37] Perhaps it is this that explains why such serious criticisms of the psychoanalytic position as those of Wohlgemuth,[38] Johnson,[39] Salter,[40] and Eysenck[41] are glossed over or ignored.

(b) *A behavioristic translation of a psychoanalytic theory of psychotherapy*— In an interesting book, Dollard and Miller[42] have tried to interpret the psychotherapeutic process in terms of the Hullian theory of learning.[10,43] They accept as fact the psychoanalytic account of what happens. For instance, they say,[42,p.301] " The patient is sick just because his mind is lamed by repression, and he cannot use it freely to solve his problems," and imply[42,p.322] that in a severe neurosis a therapist who is not concerned to remove repressions is unlikely to achieve " a complete cure." We have seen above that in view of the failure of psychoanalysis to obtain superior results there is no justification for this opinion. It is interesting, also, to note that, although the book is largely built around an account of a successfully treated case, that of Mrs. A, there is no point at which Mrs. A can clearly be seen to be benefiting from the lifting of repressions in the sense defined by the authors.

However, leaving repression aside, Dollard and Miller have given a very detailed and absorbing account of many of the occurrences that may be observed during psychotherapy. But on the matter of interpretation one must again quarrel with them. They regard extinction, i.e. conditioned inhibition based on reactive inhibition,[10(pp.277-287)],[7] as the main mechanism subserving elimination of neurotic habits.[42,pp.230-232] Now, while it cannot be denied that fear can undergo extinction, this process is usually very long and difficult, as Dollard and Miller themselves remark.[42,pp.71-73] For example, Miller found[44] that a fear-motivated motor habit required hundreds of trials to be extinguished. Thus, when fear responses are eliminated rather rapidly, either experimentaly or clinically, it must be presumed that some mechanism other than extinction is at work—and reasons are given above for believing that reciprocal inhibition is the basis of this mechanism. Dollard and Miller do actually give consideration to the therapeutic effects of responses incompatible with neurotic responses,[42,pp.74,387,388] but apparently regard these effects as having only minor importance. Yet, in most of the therapeutically effective events they describe in the case of Mrs. A it is possible to see how the anxiety is inhibited by antagonistic emotions arising either directly from the therapeutic relationship or as a consequence of the therapist's intervention. The following is an example: At a certain stage[42,p.316] the therapist points out to Mrs. A that now that she is an adult she will not be punished if she acts independently. Dollard and Miller state that this suggestion had two important effects—to inhibit fear of taking necessary actions and to create hope of a way out. But the mere realization that she would not be punished could not be expected to have much fear-inhibiting effect. Patients are very often fully aware that their fears are unreasonable and yet go on having them. What the therapist really seems to have done is to motivate Mrs. A to take action, and it is the taking of this action which is " anti-anxiety " in effect and of far more potency in diminishing anxieties than talking or " realizing " could ever be.

(2) Conditioned Reflex Theories

(a) Pavlovian theory—Pavlov's theory of psychotherapeutic effects follows directly from his theory of the basis of neurosis. According to Pavlov, normal cortical function requires a balance between excitatory and inhibitory processes. If at a given locus of the cortex excitation and inhibition come into conflict with each other at high intensity, the neural elements concerned may be unable to bear the strain and so undergo a pathological change by which the balance is overthrown; and then the animal presents neurotic symptoms.[45,pp.292-293] In accordance with this hypothesis, the essence of therapy would be to restore the balance, as Pavlov essayed to do by administering bromides, with the idea of strengthening the inhibitory process, and in many cases he succeeded in curing the neurosis. He later obtained better results from a combination of bromides and caffeine.[46,pp.95-97,181] It has been shown elsewhere[2] that the curative effect of bromides could be due to the fact that they have a selectively greater depressing action on anxiety responses, favoring their reciprocal inhibition by any antagonistic responses that happen to occur. Pavlov's theory, on the other hand, would be hard put to it to explain how *lesions* in the nervous system could be healed either by a drug that depresses nervous activity or by retraining procedures that involve nothing more than the formation or undoing of specific neural connections.

(b) *Salter's excitation theory*—Salter[12] has recently offered a theory of psychotherapy which is broadly based on Pavlovian psychology but which apparently derives its special form from the clinical experience that if neurotic patients are encouraged to express their habitually inhibited nonanxious feelings, they often gradually overcome their neuroses. He holds that a person with a neurosis suffers from an excess of inhibition and it is therefore through the arousal of excitation that this expression of feelings overcomes a neurosis. For Salter, it is on the basis of excitation alone that a neurosis can be cured.

There are several reasons for rejecting this theory. It may be noted that Pavlov himself did not regard an animal as neurotic just because its temperament was a highly inhibitory one but found that both excitatory and inhibitory animals could develop neuroses. The following criticisms are more directly relevant: First, even though it is true that in association with the anxiety many other responses are inhibited, the anxiety responses themselves, especially clearly in acute anxiety states, are quite evidently excitatory. Second, relaxation techniques, involving a negation of excitation, are, as described above, very effective in the treatment of neuroses. Third, electroconvulsive therapy, whose effects on the nervous system are eminently excitatory,[25,pp.438-442] is not of great value in treating neuroses, with the exception of some depressions.[47] Even the most favorable series[48] give no better results than would be obtained from nonspecific interview-induced psychotherapeutic effects and such effects would doubtless occur even when shock therapy is what the therapist is using.

Further Cases Illustrating Psychotherapy Based on Reciprocal Inhibition

CASE 4—A married woman of 24 was first seen on 14th April, 1951, complaining of chronic anxiety and a feeling of inadequacy in most of her social relationships, of which the most distressing was that with her mother-in-law. She had special phobic reactions to certain men, which turned out to depend on the degree of their resemblance to her father, and she also reacted with fear to the ringing of the front doorbell or the sound of footsteps up the garden path. All these reactions were tied up with the early behavior of her father, who was extremely sadistic and had terrorized her in her childhood in a great variety of ways. When she was 14, he removed her from school to work in one of his shops without pay. He would frequently creep up silently and pounce on her for not working hard enough. At 17 she ran away to Johannesburg from her family in Cape Town, and at 21 married a motor mechanic, with whom she was generally happy.

The patient had 65 therapeutic interviews, unevenly distributed over 27 months. The greater part of the time was devoted to discussions of how to gain control of her inter-personal relationships and stand up for herself. She had considerable difficulty with this at first, even though it had early become emotionally important to her to please the therapist. But she gradually mastered the assertive behavior required of her, overcame her anxieties and became exceedingly self-reliant in all interpersonal dealings, including those with her mother-in-law. Finally, she deliberately made a trip to Cape Town to pit herself against her father. She experienced initial nervousness at their first meeting but after that was in complete control, during a 3 weeks' stay.

At the conclusion of therapy, in June, 1953, she was adjudged a very well-adjusted and competent person and early in 1954 reported that she was still going from strength to strength.

CASE 5*—An attractive woman of 28 came for treatment because she was in acute distress as a result of her lovers' casual treatment of her. Every one of very numerous love affairs had followed a similar pattern—first she would attract the man, then she would offer herself on a platter. He would soon treat her with contempt and after a time leave her.

In general she lacked assurance, was very dependent, and was practically never free from feelings of tension and anxiety. Her Willoughby score was 45, reflecting very considerable neuroticism.

At her fifth interview the unadaptiveness of her anxieties and the rationale of the reciprocal inhibition principle were explained to her, and she left feeling optimistic. At the next interview she was told how to behave with firmness and take independent courses of action with her lover. She performed well according to prescription and was able to terminate her relationship with him with dignity and with relatively little disturbance, and, indeed, with a certain feeling of triumph. Meanwhile, she was shown how to counter-attack her nagging mother and to deal with her boss and other people who easily upset her. Through action she gradually developed a feeling of mastery, both at home and work.

Soon she found that she was beginning to hold the reins in a variety of minor sexual situations. After her 13th interview, she went on holiday and returned 6 weeks later to say that she had made continued efforts to control interpersonal situations and was feeling much more stable emotionally. She was much better poised and had been a social success for the first time in her life. About this time she met a man who attracted her, and now her feelings had an adult, independent character. After handling many difficulties admirably, she married him 3 months later. Her Willoughby score had dropped to 17. She had 14 interviews in all, and a year later was reported to be well and happy.

CASE 6—Early in 1951 a divorcee of 39 stated that from as far back as she could remember she had been nervous and hypersensitive and perpetually worried about the future. Many ordinary situations, such as overhearing others quarrel, constituted stresses for her, made her anxious and left her fatigued, and sometimes produced epigastric pain. For 7 years she had persistently suffered from fibrositic backaches. Her symptoms had improved somewhat after her divorce, 2 years previously.

She was encouraged to be more assertive and less subservient to the wishes of her friends. But her severest tensions arose from situations in which no direct action was possible, e.g. having visitors for dinner. Thus, from her seventh interview onward she was given lessons in relaxation. Her response was excellent. She became able to relax and to calm herself in an increasing range of situations, the anxiety-evoking power of which waned and eventually disappeared. The patient had 13 interviews over 4 months, during which she entirely overcame her neurotic nervousness and was functioning well in

---

* The account of this case has been somewhat abbreviated. A fuller version, including a 2½-year follow-up, is to be found in *Psychotherapy by Reciprocal Inhibition.*[1]

all areas. Her fibrositis disappeared completely after the first month. In a 3-year follow-up there has been no recurrence but, instead, continued strengthening.*

CASE 7—A 23-year-old divorced tram driver entered the consulting room in a state of acute anxiety. Eight hours before a woman had walked into his slowly moving tram. She had been "knocked out and her head was bleeding." Although a doctor had told him that the woman's injury was not serious, he had become increasingly shaky and had developed severe epigastric pain. He had recovered from previous accidents in an hour or two, but in these no human injury had been involved.

The significance of the statement that no human injury was involved is that when the patient was 13 his father had died after an accident and since then he had had a fear of human blood. Even the tiny bead of blood that might appear on his face during shaving gave him an uncomfortable feeling. He was quite indifferent to animal blood—had seen oxen killed and had himself cut the throats of fowls. It was clear that his grossly excessive reaction to the present accident was due to his phobia for human blood, and to overcome this phobia was the central aim of therapy.

The first five interviews, which occurred over 6 days, were confined to obtaining an understanding of the patient's personality and background and to overcoming his immediate disturbed state by intense, hypnotically induced relaxation. At the fifth interview he reported feeling very well. He was told to drive a tram again for a short distance, which he did later that day, without any ill-effect.

At the sixth interview various situations involving human blood were arranged in ascending order of their disturbing effect. From this time onward, at each interview, while the patient was in a state of hypnotic relaxation, he was made to visualize "blood situations." The feeblest was a slightly blood-tinged bandage lying in a basket. When this failed to disturb his relaxation, he was presented with a tiny drop of blood on his own face while shaving. In this way, with the presentation of 2 or 3 images at each session, it was possible gradually to work up to a stage at which the patient could visualize a casualty ward full of carnage and not be disturbed by it.

The significance of this method for real-life situations was revealed in this case in a most dramatic way. Two days before his last interview the patient saw a man knocked over by a motorcycle. The victim was seriously injured and was bleeding profusely. The patient was absolutely unaffected by the blood and, when the ambulance arrived, helped to load the victim on to it.

CASE 8—A married woman of 32 came for treatment on 23rd March, 1953. She had been nervous and timid as long as she could remember. Rheumatic fever before puberty had been followed by chorea, which had improved very slowly at first, but not at all since the age of 16, and she had been left with persistently troublesome choreiform movements, which were worse during any emotional upset. In December, 1952, she had been injured in a motor accident and had spent 3 weeks in the hospital. There, as the pain of her injuries lessened, she noticed that she was very tense, that her twitchings were much worse, and that she had great difficulty in concentrating. These symptoms had been unremittingly present ever since. After her discharge from the hospital she had been specially anxious when in a car. This had improved a little through repeatedly forcing herself to go into cars and be driven around. But she still reacted with panic to every minor "threat" of an accident, e.g. if a driver 100 yards ahead were to fail to obey a "stop" sign, or if her husband took a bend in "a swerving way."

Treatment consisted, in the first place, in teaching her progressive relaxation. Her control of personal relations was also given attention, in particular the handling of her small son, which soon improved markedly. After a month's treatment (11 interviews) she was much better and had only occasional choreiform movements. But she was still reacting badly to motorcar situations. Hypnotic desensitization was then begun, and after 12 sessions of this, by the end of June she reported being completely unperturbed by all normal driving experiences. Her choreiform movements had almost stopped, and she said that never at any time, even in childhood, had she felt so well. On being interviewed in February, 1954, she stated that she had, if anything, continued to improve.

* This case has now successfully survived an 8-year follow-up.

CASE 9—A 47-year-old married male nurse, employed in an industrial first-aid room, was sent for psychiatric treatment by the medical officer who had observed him during the previous 4 years. For 17 years he had never been free from an uncontrollable impulse to mimic any rhythmic movements he saw, e.g. waving of arms and dancing. He would also automatically obey any command, no matter from whom. A command, though, could not stop a rhythmic movement. The workmen frequently exploited his compulsion to amuse themselves, often exhausting him and distressing him sometimes so much that he was left trembling.

No anxiety component could be observed in this compulsive behavior, but it was resolved to employ hypnosis to try to break the compulsion by attaching to the cues to its occurrence new and incompatible behavior. The patient was a good hypnotic subject, and 6 inductions were done in the course of 3 interviews. Two were done at the first interview. At the first induction he was made to recall the first occasions of compulsive mimicry and obedience, and was then given the direct suggestion that he would stop imitating. At the second he was simply hypnotized and wakened, as a control experiment. No change followed either of these trances.

At the second interview the posthypnotic suggestion was made that after waking he would copy only alternate movements of the therapist's right arm; but on being wakened, he still copied every movement, as before. He was then hypnotized again and told that on waking he would find that he would move only his hand when the therapist moved his whole arm rhythmically. This posthypnotic suggestion was obeyed. A third trance was induced in that session and the posthypnotic suggestion given that he would decrease his movement as the therapist continued to wave his arm rhythmically, and also a general suggestion that he would move only his right hand when impulses to mimic anybody arose. When he woke, his impulses did lessen.

At his third interview, 2 days later, the patient reported that he had entirely stopped being affected by other people's movements or commands. He showed no reaction at all to the therapist's beating his fist on the desk. He said that he was sleeping much better and was no longer startled at being awakened, and his fear of the dark had vanished. He was hypnotized again and told he would continue to be unaffected by people's movements or commands. During this trance, at the therapist's instigation, he told how the onset had followed a violent wakening by a nurse early one morning when he was in hospital with pneumonia.

Eighteen months later the patient was perfectly well and had not relapsed in any respect.*

CASE 10†—Mr. S., a 40-year-old accountant, was sent to me for the treatment of impotence by a psychoanalyst whom he had told that he could not wait the 2 years estimated to be necessary for psychoanalytic treatment. He said that his relationship with the woman he loved " could not be kept on ice for so long."

At puberty the patient had masturbated a good deal, and at some stage had been told that among other ill effects this might lead to impotence. At 22 he had a regular girl friend with whom he indulged in frequent petting which usually culminated in non-copulatory orgasms for both of them. After a time he noticed with perturbation that he was ejaculating increasingly quickly. An uncle whom he consulted about this upset him further by telling him that this was " a partial impotence." Eventually, he decided to take the risk of persuading his girl friend to submit to coitus; but the attempt ended in emission before penetration. Soon after, she broke off the relationship, leaving him in despair.

After a sexual affair lasting many months and characterized by very premature ejaculations, the patient married at the age of 29. The marriage relationship was erratic and usually disharmonious, with frequent storms in many areas. In coitus, premature ejaculation was almost invariable. After 9 years they were divorced.

Mr. S. felt much happier after the divorce, and had a physically satisfactory sexual affair with a married woman. During the 4th month of this he had an attack of influenza, at the end of which his mistress came to visit him. To his horror he found himself for the

* This patient has now been well for 6½ years.
† This case is published for the first time in this book.

first time without desire and without erection. From that time onward, for several years, his efforts at coitus with many women were consistently bedevilled by erectile failure or premature ejaculations.

About a year before coming for treatment Mr. S. had fallen progressively more deeply in love with a girl of 24 called May who worked in his office. She was responsive to him and one day, despite ejaculating prematurely he managed to deflorate her. Finding that he had made a good impression in this act he used all sorts of excuses to avoid further intercourse. After 6 months, when May was about to go on holiday, he felt obliged to make another attempt but ejaculated before entry. During May's absence, Mr. S. tried to seduce two other women but was thwarted by failure of erection. He then saw a psychiatrist who gave him massive injections of testosterone. He was still receiving the hormone when May returned but his performance was worse than ever, for he could not even muster an erection. May began to show signs of coolness towards Mr. S. when later coital attempts were also unsuccessful. It was for this reason that Mr. S. was anxious to find a quick resolution of his sexual difficulties.

Taking the patient's complete life history occupied 9 interviews over 12 days. In subsequent interviews the reciprocal inhibition principle was explained to Mr. S. and he was given lessons in progressive relaxation and instructed to adopt a relaxed attitude in the sexual situation. He was not to attempt coitus unless he had a strong erection beforehand and after intromission was not to aim at any set level of performance but just to let himself go.*

The simplicity of the treatment described will be surprising to many. Details, of course, vary with the case. A. A. Lazarus and the present writer have to date (March, 1959) treated about 15 cases of impotence on these principles without a failure.

At the twelfth interview Mr. S. was made to relax as deeply as possible under hypnosis and then asked to imagine himself in a bedroom with May.

At the fourteenth interview Mr. S. stated that he had twice had successful intercourse— slightly premature on the first occasion but very prolonged on the second. He was much encouraged—to the extent that he had married May by special licence! Two days later he reported that they had had simultaneous orgasms on 2 successive nights.

In the course of the next 6 weeks Mr. S. consolidated the pattern of normal sexual performance although he again ejaculated prematurely on an occasion when he was persuaded to have intercourse against his inclination. He was warned to avoid this mistake in the future. Treatment was terminated at the twenty-third interview, exactly 3 months after its inception as the patient regarded his sex life as entirely satisfactory. Follow-up reports 10 months, 18 months and $5\frac{1}{2}$ years later, testified to maintained excellence of sexual performance.

SUMMARY

The case is presented that conditioned inhibition founded on reciprocal inhibition is the basis of most fundamental psychotherapeutic effects. This principle is shown to explain a large number of widely used therapeutic methods and has led to some new methods, which are described. Of 122 patients treated by these methods, 110 were apparently cured or much improved. It is shown that certain other current theories are unable to account for the same range of facts as that subsumed by the reciprocal inhibition hypothesis.

* These instructions are based on the rationale that since penile erection is a parasympathetic function and ejaculation a sympathetic function, the predominantly sympathetic discharges of anxiety will tend both to inhibit erection and to precipitate ejaculation prematurely. If the anxiety can be brought down to a low level, the sexual responses will reciprocally inhibit it.

REFERENCES

1. WOLPE, J. (1958). *Psychotherapy by Reciprocal Inhibition.* Oxford Univ. Press, London.
2. WOLPE, J. (1948). *An Approach to the Problem of Neurosis Based on the Conditioned Response, Dissertation.* University of the Witwatersrand.
3. WOLPE, J. (1950). Genesis of neurosis: An objective account. *S. Afr. Med. J.*, **24**, 613.
4. WOLPE, J. (1952). Experimental neuroses as learned behavior. *Brit. J. Psychol.*, *Gen. Sect.*, **43**, 243.
5. FARBER, I. E. (1948). Response fixation under anxiety and non-anxiety conditions. *J. Exp. Psychol.*, **38**, 111.
6. MASSERMAN, J. H. (1943). *Behavior and Neurosis.* University of Chicago Press, Chicago.
7. WOLPE, J. (1952). Formation of negative habits: A neurophysiological view. *Psychol. Rev.*, **59**, 290.
8. WOLPE, J. (1952). Objective psychotherapy of the neuroses. *S. Afr. Med. J.*, **26**, 825.
9. DIMMICK, F. L., LUDLOW, N. and WHITEMAN, A. (1939). Study of " experimental neurosis " in cats. *J. Comp., Psychol.*, **28**, 39.
10. HULL, C. L. (1943). *Principles of Behavior.* Appleton–Century, New York.
11. WOLPE, J. (1953). Learning theory and " abnormal fixations." *Psychol. Rev.*, **60**, 111.
12. SALTER, A. (1950). *Conditioned Reflex Therapy.* Creative Age Press, New York.
13. JACOBSON, E. (1938). *Progressive Relaxation.* University of Chicago Press, Chicago.
14. MOWRER, O. H. and VIEK, P. (1948). Experimental analogue of fear from a sense of helplessness. *J. Abnorm. (Soc.) Psychol.*, **43**, 193.
15. ZBROZYNA, A. W. (1953). Phenomenon of non-identification of a stimulus operating against different physiological backgrounds in dogs. *Lodz. Towar. Nauk.*, **3**, No. 26 (in Polish with English summary).
16. KANTOROVICH, N. V. (1929). An attempt at curing alcoholism by associated reflexes, *Nov. Reflex. Nerv. Sist.*, **3**, 436; cited by G. H. S. RAZRAN: Conditional withdrawal responses with shock as the conditioning stimulus in adult human subjects. *Psychol. Bull.*, **31**, 111 (1934).
17. MAX, L. W. (1935). Breaking up a homosexual fixation by the conditioned reaction technique: A case study. *Psychol. Bull.*, **32**, 734.
18. JONES, M. C. (1924). Elimination of children's fears. *J. Exp. Psychol.*, **7**, 382.
19. MARTIN, G. L. (1949). Sedative insulin treatment of anxiety in the anxiety neurosis. *J. Nerv. Ment. Dis.*, **109**, 347.
20. SARGANT, W. and CRASKE, N. (1941). Modified insulin therapy in war neuroses. *Lancet*, **2**, 212.
21. TEITELBAUM, H. A., HOEKSTRA, C. S., GOLDSTEIN, D. N., HARRIS, I. D., WOODS, R. M. and COHEN, D. (1946). Treatment of psychiatric disorders due to combat by means of a group therapy program and insulin in sub-shock doses. *J. Nerv. Ment. Dis.*, **104**, 123.
22. SARGANT, W. and SLATER, E. (1947). Treatment by insulin in sub-shock doses. *J. Nerv. Ment. Dis.*, **105**, 493.
23. MEDUNA, L. J. (1950). *Carbon Dioxide Therapy.* C. Thomas, Springfield, Ill.
24. LA VERNE, A. A. (1953). Rapid coma technique of carbon dioxide inhalation therapy. *Dis. Nerv. System*, **14**, 141.
25. GELLHORN, E. (1953). *Physiological Foundations of Neurology and Psychiatry.* University of Minnesota Press, Minneapolis.
26. LANDIS, C. (1937). A statistical evaluation of psychotherapeutic methods. In HINSIE, L. E. *Concepts and Problems of Psychotherapy.* Columbia University Press, New York.
27. WILDER, J. (1945). Facts and figures on psychotherapy. *J. Clin. Psychopath.*, **7**, 311.
28. GRINKER, R. R. and SPIEGEL, J. P. (1945). *War Neuroses.* The Blakiston Co., Philadelphia.
29. GRINKER, R. R. and SPIEGEL, J. P. (1945). *Men Under Stress.* Churchill, London.

30. WOLPE, J. (1950). Need-reduction, drive-reduction and reinforcement: A neuro-physiological view. *Psychol. Rev.*, **57**, 19.
31. KNIGHT, R. P. (1941). Evaluation of the results of psychoanalytic therapy. *Amer. J. Psychiat.*, **98**, 434.
32. WILLOUGHBY, R. R. (1932). Some properties of the Thurstone personality schedule and a suggested revision. *J. Social Psychol.*, **3**, 401.
33. WILLOUGHBY, R. R. (1934). Norms for the Clark–Thurstone inventory. *J. Social Psychol.*, **5**, 91.
34. WOLPE, J. *Further Notes on Experimental Neuroses.* To be published.
35. HAMILTON, D. M. and WALL, J. H. (1941). Hospital treatment of patients with psychoneurotic disorders. *Amer. J. Psychiat.*, **98**, 551.
36. FENICHEL, O. (1945). *Psychoanalytic Theory of Neurosis.* Norton, New York.
37. ELLIS, A. (1950). *Introduction to the Principles of Scientific Psychoanalysis*, Genetic Psychology Monograph 41. The Journal Press, Provincetoun, Mass.
38. WOHLGEMUTH, A. (1923). *Critical Examination of Psycho-Analysis.* George Allen & Unwin, London.
39. JOHNSON, H. K. (1948). Psychoanalysis: A critique. *Psychiatric Quart.*, **22**, 321.
40. SALTER, A. (1953). *The Case Against Psychoanalysis.* Henry Holt, New York.
41. EYSENCK, H. J. (1953). *Uses and Abuses of Psychology.* Penguin Books.
42. DOLLARD, J. and MILLER, N. E. (1950). *Personality and Psychotherapy.* McGraw–Hill, New York.
43. MILLER, N. E. and DOLLARD, J. (1945). *Social Learning and Imitation.* Routledge & Kegan Paul, Trench, Trubner, London.
44. MILLER, N. E. (1950). Learnable drives and rewards. Ed. by S. Stevens : In *Handbook of Experimental Psychology.* John Wiley & Sons, New York.
45. PAVLOV, I. P. (1927). *Conditioned Reflexes.* Translated and edited by G. V. Anrep. Oxford University Press, London.
46. PAVLOV, I. P. (1941). *Conditioned Reflexes and Psychiatry.* Translated and edited by W. H. Gantt. International Publishers Co. Inc., New York.
47. KALINOWSKY, L. B. and HOCH, P. H. (1946). *Shock Treatments.* William Heinemann, London.
48. MARTIN, C. A. and LEMIEUX, L. H. (1949). Electro-choc et psychoneuroses. *Laval Med.*, **14**, 579; *Psychol. Abst.*, **25**, 467 (1951).

THE ELIMINATION OF CHILDREN'S PHOBIAS BY DECONDITIONING*

A. A. LAZARUS, M.A.(RAND)

Johannesburg

THE THERAPEUTIC properties of direct deconditioning were first demonstrated by M. C. Jones[1] in 1924. Jones eliminated fear-reactions in young children by coupling the feared objects with pleasant stimuli. She writes: " The hunger motive appears to be the most effective for use in this connection. During a period of craving for food, the child is placed in a high chair and given something to eat. The fear-object is brought in, starting a negative response. It is then moved away gradually until it is at a sufficient distance not to interfere with the child's eating . . . . While the child is eating, the object is slowly brought nearer to the table, then placed upon the table and finally, as the tolerance increases it is brought close enough to be touched."

Until recently, the comprehensive psychotherapeutic value of deconditioning procedures remained relatively unexplored. Sears and Cohen,[2] Guthrie,[3] Max,[4] Mowrer and Mowrer,[5] and Voegtlin[6] were among the first to provide evidence of therapeutic potentials based on this pattern. Most psychotherapists, however, have remained impervious to these and other investigations of the efficacy of techniques which stem directly from the conditioned response. The majority of clinicians appear to view conditioning techniques with suspicion and disfavour and maintain that " symptom removal " exposes the patient to the dangers of alternative symptoms, greater degrees of anxiety, and numerous other undesirable manifestations of the unresolved " underlying complex." Many writers, however, notably Eysenck[7,8,9] and Wolpe[10-13] have cited widespread clinical evidence which runs counter to this general viewpoint. Eysenck[8] for instance, states that " there is no evidence for these putative complexes and symptomatic treatment is all that is required."

In a previous article[14] we endeavoured to demonstrate that neo-behaviouristic psychotherapy is not mechanistic or " symptom centered " in the manner of Watsonian behaviourism but that full cognizance is taken of the interpersonal dynamics of the patient as a functioning member of society. But as Meehl[15] points out, " we find therapeutic results, sometimes very striking and persistent ones, condemned as ' superficial ' or ' purely

* Reprinted with some additional material from (1959) *Medical Proceedings,* South Africa, by permission of the editor.

symptomatic.' . . . I have actually heard a ' dynamic ' (magic word!) clinician loftily shrug off a dramatic 3-year cure in the case of a patient who had nearly ruined his life by drinking, on the grounds that the therapeutic procedure had ' merely (*sic!*) kept him dry ' but had not worked through his defences. In the light of the notably feeble impact of professional uncovering psychotherapy upon alcoholics, this is a remarkable comment . . ."

Eysenck's[8] lucid distinction between these opposing theories is phrased as follows: " According to Freud, there is a ' disease ' which produces symptoms; cure the disease and the symptoms will vanish. According to the alternative view, there is no ' disease,' there are merely wrong habits which have been learned and must be unlearned. If such ' unlearning ' and ' relearning ' is efficacious, and there is no evidence of any ' disease,' then surely we must dismiss this additional concept as superfluous."

Follow-up studies[16-19] on cases treated by a variety of methods which did not concern themselves with the uncovering of repressed material have uniformly revealed little or no tendency to relapse. These studies are directly contrary to the psychoanalytic assumption that neurotic disorders can only be resolved by delving into " unconscious, infantile, repressed material." The significance of these findings has been summed up by Wolpe[13] as follows: " If repression were the essence of neurosis, apparently successful measures that leave ' the repressed ' untouched would be followed before long by relapse, i.e. the emergence of new symptoms or the recurrence of old ones. If, on the other hand, neurotic symptoms are nothing but con-ditioned responses, ' deconditioning ' measures . . . will be all that is needed to eliminate the symptoms permanently; and after thorough extinction of the neurotic responses relapse will not be expected." Employing methods of treatment based on the hypothesis that neurotic responses can be eliminated by deconditioning, Wolpe has reported a 90 per cent level of apparent cures or marked improvements in over 200 cases. Follow-up studies on 45 patients, 2–7 years after the end of treatment, revealed that only 1 patient had suffered a moderate relapse after about a year.

Wolpe[13] defines a neurosis as " any persistent habit of unadaptive behaviour acquired by learning in a physiologically normal organism." He has shown that neuroses are acquired in anxiety-generating situations and that anxiety is usually the central constituent of neurotic behaviour.[20],[21] Wolpe's elaborate therapeutic system is based on the following principle:

" If a response antagonistic to anxiety can be made to occur in the presence of anxiety-evoking stimuli so that it is accompanied by a complete or partial suppression of the anxiety responses, the bond between these stimuli and the anxiety responses will be weakened."

Successful therapy of the neuroses, therefore, would depend on the reciprocal inhibition of neurotic anxiety responses, i.e. the suppression of the anxiety responses as a consequence of the simultaneous evocation of other responses which are physiologically incompatible with anxiety. Independent corroboration of Wolpe's findings on adult patients have been presented elsewhere.[14,22] The present paper is concerned with the application of Wolpe's methods to the field of child therapy. We have already discussed how M. C. Jones employed feeding responses in overcoming neurotic anxieties in children. Wolpe has shown that there are numerous responses (apart from feeding) that are capable of inhibiting anxiety. In the main, our own child therapy programmes have made use of feeding responses, relaxation responses, conditioned avoidance responses and drugs in deconditioning. We shall illustrate these techniques by reference to actual case histories. The examples which follow have been selected from our case records of 18 phobic children who were treated by these specific deconditioning techniques.

DECONDITIONING BASED ON FEEDING RESPONSES

John D., 8 years of age, developed a fear of moving vehicles 2 years after he and his parents had been involved in a motor car accident. He refused to enter any vehicle and on one occasion when his father had unwisely forced him into his car, the child became panic-stricken and hysterical. Therapy consisted of first talking to John about trains, aeroplanes, buses, etc. Even this " mild exposure to the stimulus " tended to evoke anxiety in the child, but whenever he volunteered a " positive " comment, he was casually offered his favourite chocolate. During the third interview, John willingly spoke at length about all types of moving vehicles and there was no longer any evidence of overt anxiety. A series of deliberate " accidents " with toy motor cars constituted the next phase of the treatment project. The child evidenced a fairly high level of initial anxiety. After each " accident " he was given chocolate. His anxiety was soon dissipated and he entered into the full spirit of the game. The next step in the therapy programme consisted of sitting with the child in a stationary motor car while discussing the accident in which he had been involved. He was provided with liberal helpings of chocolate throughout this discussion. Thereafter the child was taken in a car for short distances. At the 17th session (less than 6 weeks after therapy had commenced) he willingly entered a car and accompanied by a complete stranger, he set off for a shop 1½ miles away where he bought chocolate. At first, he refused to go motoring with his parents unless he was given chocolate, but he soon began to enjoy motoring for pleasure.

SYSTEMATIC DESENSITIZATION BASED ON
RELAXATION

Carol M., 9½ years of age, had been an apparently healthy and well-adjusted child until approximately 2 months after her ninth birthday when she became enuretic, afraid of the dark and displayed a variety of symptoms ranging from night terrors to what her doctor had labelled " psychosomatic ailments." While at school she invariably developed violent abdominal pains so that her teacher had to excuse her from class and would eventually have to send for her mother.

Immediately prior to the onset of her anxieties, Carol had been exposed to three successive traumatic incidents in the span of a few weeks. A school friend had fallen into a pond and drowned; her next door playmate contracted meningitis and died; she had witnessed a motor car accident in which a man was killed.

During an interview with Carol's mother, Mrs. M. stated that she had read an article which stressed that one should refrain from giving a 9-year-old child any overt demonstrations of love and affection (such as hugging or kissing the child) since these practises supposedly hindered the development of " personality and maturity." The therapist vehemently condemned this contention and provided " handling instructions " which emphasized the necessity for deliberate and overt love and warmth.

A month later, Mrs. M. telephoned the therapist and reported that the family had been away on vacation for over 3 weeks during which time Carol's behaviour had been " perfectly normal." Since their return, however, Carol bedwetted each night and had become hysterical when taken to school. " She's worse than ever," Mrs. M. declared. " The child won't let me out of her sight."

When Carol returned for therapy she insisted that her mother should be present during the interviews. Her condition had deteriorated considerably. She was extremely agitated and tense and anxiously clung to her mother.

During the diagnostic interviews, it became apparent that the child's central fear was the possibility of losing her mother through death. Projective testing also suggested that she was in fact not afraid to go to school, but she was afraid that her mother might die before she returned home from school. Similarly, she was not afraid to sleep alone, but she feared that her mother might die before the night was over. Whereas psychoanalysts might have interpreted this in terms of a " death wish," we found it unnecessary to account for the child's behaviour in terms of inferred constructs and simply regarded the child's neurotic reactions as having been precipitated by her sudden and harsh exposure to the traumatic realities of death. Since Carol's premature awareness of the finality of death had coincided with her mother's misinformed attitude to displays of love and affection, the child's consequent feelings of rejection finally culminated in a genuine fear of permanent maternal deprivation (i.e. death). Thus, even a brief period of separation from her mother aggravated Carol's anxieties. Our therapeutic approach involved a planned and deliberate attack on this specific area of unadaptive anxiety by means of systematic desensitization (see below).

Wolpe's method of systematic desensitization based on relaxation makes use of Jacobson's[23] finding that muscular relaxation inhibits anxiety and that their concurrent expression is physiologically impossible. Details of the theoretical rationale and clinical application of this technique are presented elsewhere.[12,13,22] Briefly, the patient is given progressive training in relaxation in the course of several interviews and during the same interviews an "anxiety hierarchy" is constructed, i.e. a graded list of stimuli to which the patient reacts with unadaptive anxiety. The following anxiety hierarchy was constructed for Carol M.

Separation from the mother for 1 week.
Separation from the mother for 2 days.
Separation from the mother for 1 day.
Separation from the mother for $\frac{1}{2}$ day.
Separation from the mother for 1 hour.
Separation from the mother for 15 minutes.
Separation from the mother for 5 minutes.

The patient, while fully relaxed, is asked to imagine the individual items of the anxiety hierarchy, starting with the least noxious situation (" Imagine that you are not going to see your mother for 5 minutes ") until eventually, the most " difficult " item is presented (" Imagine that your mother is leaving you for one whole week"). Repeated reciprocal inhibition in this manner eventually leads to the development of conditioned inhibition.[13,24]

It took 5 sessions spaced over 10 consecutive days to desensitize Carol completely to the subjective threat of maternal deprivation. Therapy had commenced on a Tuesday. On the following Friday, Carol willingly went to school. This was followed by an immediate dissipation of all her other neurotic conditions. A 15-month follow-up enquiry revealed that apart from very occasional enuretic incidents, she had maintained an eminently satisfactory level of adjustment.

THE USE OF DRUGS IN DECONDITIONING

Douglas G., aged $3\frac{1}{2}$ years, had displayed severe phobic reactions to dogs ever since one had bitten him nearly 5 months previously. His parents subsequently had obtained a puppy in the hopes that this would enable him to overcome his fears. Unfortunately the child only became hysterical whenever he saw the animal, so that his parents were forced to dispose of it. Douglas soon displayed similar phobic reactions to cats and birds so that eventually he became afraid to venture out of doors. The child was excessively active and distracted, but a detailed medical and neurological examination revealed no organic pathology. His activity level precluded the application of relaxation techniques. Consequently, he was given small doses of amobarbital and phenaglycodol (under medical cover) for 3 days until a satisfactory level of sedation had been achieved. He was then gradually introduced to a variety of animals without displaying any anxiety. Administration of these drugs was gradually reduced over a period of 5 weeks. A follow-up was conducted almost a year later and revealed that the child had not relapsed in any respect.

DECONDITIONING OBTAINED BY
CONDITIONED AVOIDANCE RESPONSES

Ever since he had learned to walk, Brian E., aged 10 years, had made a habit of waking up and going to his mother's bed in the very early hours of the morning. An assortment of punishments, threats, bribes and rewards had each failed to modify his behaviour. The child " automatically " awoke between 1 a.m. and 2 a.m. and would immediately go to his mother's bed. On one occasion, Mrs. E. had decided that if she adamantly refused to have him in her bed he might eventually sleep in his own bed. The result was that Brian spent nearly 4 hours crying outside her bedroom door and she was finally forced to allow the child into her bed.

Professional advice was sought when Mrs. E. broke her ankle and found it acutely uncomfortable to share her bed. Furthermore, at this stage Brian's behaviour was seriously disrupting the interpersonal relationships in the home. When questioned about his behaviour, Brian indicated that he was highly motivated to sleep in his own bed but that when he awoke, anxiety would mount within him and he would become panic-stricken unless he went to his mother's bed. Although the security of his mother's bed constituted a potent source of anxiety-relief, we endeavoured to remedy the situation by means of simple avoidance conditioning.

L. W. Max[4] was the first to show that an unpleasant electric shock in the presence of an obsessional object tends to produce a persistent avoidance reaction to the object. Conversely, it has been shown that approach responses are conditioned to a stimulus repeatedly presented at the moment of termination of an electric shock.[25-28] Consequently, the following technique was employed: Zinc electrodes were attached to the child's left forearm and were connected to the secondary circuit of an induction coil whose primary was wired to a 6V dry battery. The patient was asked to imagine* himself in his mother's bed and to say the words " mother's bed " as soon as he had a clear image of the situation. A mild electric shock (at an inductorium setting of 9 cm) was then passed into his forearm. When he could no longer tolerate the shock (average duration of shock 3·2 sec) he was instructed to say " my bed " at which point the current was immediately switched off. This procedure was repeated 14 times over a period of about 10 min.

Brian was seen again a week later and he announced with great pride that he had slept in his own bed every night. He stated that although he

* Wolpe[13] has shown that it is not necessary to present the actual objects or situations.

had awakened as usual for the first 5 nights, he had merely " turned over and gone back to sleep." He had slept right through the sixth night, however. At the time of writing, he has slept in his own bed for over 6 months.

This case affords a clear illustration of the fact that " symptom removal " *per se* is not a static or isolated process but results in a dynamic redistribution of—to use Lewin's[29] term—the relevant " field forces." Brian's new-found ability to sleep in his own bed has completely altered numerous adverse environmental pressures. His relationship with his father, for instance, had been most casual and restrained. As soon as Brian had shown that " he had the makings of a man," Mr. E's attitude towards him underwent a remarkable change. He began displaying an active interest in his son's activities and whereas previously he had forbidden Brian to keep any pets, he unexpectedly brought home a dog one night. Sibling tensions have also eased considerably. In short, as Mrs. E. expressed it, " the difference in the home is nothing short of fantastic."

It might be surprising to some that the removal of a unitary maladaptive symptom should have had such diverse and important implications. However, this is not difficult to explain. Once the improvement occurred the dynamics of Brian's situation altered markedly in directions which served to consolidate the gain. But there is no doubt that the conditioning procedure provided a strikingly rapid initiation of change. The crucial point, however, is that techniques that reciprocably inhibit neurotic anxieties appear to have widespread and positive repercussions on diverse areas of the individual's personality.

DISCUSSION

We have applied Wolpe's methods of direct deconditioning, based on the principle of reciprocal inhibition,[13] to the field of child psychotherapy. At present, a total of 18 phobic cases ranging in age from $3\frac{1}{2}$ years to 12 years have been treated by these techniques with gratifying results. The cases had all either recovered or were much improved according to Knight's[30] criteria and follow-up studies conducted over periods of 6 months to $2\frac{1}{2}$ years revealed that none of the children had relapsed in any respect. Compared with other forms of psychotherapy, the duration of treatment has been exceedingly short (mean number of sessions 9·4).

A number of non-behaviouristic therapists have tended to explain away these (to our mind) promising results in terms of " transference cures," " strengthening of the ego," and so forth. It was even suggested that our successes may simply be explained in terms of our subjective confidence in the methods employed and that the methods themselves are suspect. (Does this imply that other psychotherapists have little confidence in their own methods?) It is obvious that the therapeutic atmosphere of empathy and acceptance must in itself reciprocally inhibit neurotic anxieties. Since the deliberate deconditioning techniques were applied within the context of therapeutic warmth, the final explanation of our therapeutic successes must necessarily incorporate elements of (a) non-specific reciprocal inhibition via the interpersonal relationship between patient and therapist (common to all types of psychotherapy) and (b) the deliberate and specific reciprocal inhibition of neurotic anxieties as outlined above.

Wolpe's method of systematic desensitization based on relaxation[13,22] has proved especially valuable in our treatment of childhood phobias. In some cases, modifications of this approach were necessary. For instance, we have found that very disturbed children and cases with poor " visual imagery " respond more readily to graded presentations of the actual feared objects after the child has been given posthypnotic suggestions of calmness and relaxation.

In this connection we might also mention that we have conducted preliminary experiments utilizing pleasurable responses to music in order to reciprocally inhibit neurotic anxieties. The child's favourite music would be played while presenting him with the relevant anxiety-generating stimuli. It is still premature to report on the efficacy of this technique.

SUMMARY

We have applied Wolpe's psychotherapeutic methods based on the principle of reciprocal inhibition to a preliminary group of 18 phobic children. Our gratifying results indicate that these methods are eminently effective in the management of childhood phobias. Follow-up enquiries after 6 months to $2\frac{1}{2}$ years have shown no evidence of relapse in any form.

REFERENCES

1. JONES, M. C. (1924). *J. Exp. Psychol.*, **7**, 382.
2. SEARS, R. R. and COHEN, L. H. (1933). *Arch. Neurol. Psychiat.*, **29**, 260.
3. GUTHRIE, E. R. (1935). *The Psychology of Learning.* Harper, New York.
4. MAX, L. W. (1935). *Psychol. Bull.*, **32**, 734.
5. MOWRER, O. H. and MOWRER, W. M. (1938). *Amer. J. Orthopsychiat.*, **8**, 436.
6. VOEGTLIN, W. L. (1940). *Amer. J. Med. Sc.*, **199**, 802.
7. EYSENCK, H. J. (1953). *Uses and Abuses of Psychology.* Pelican, London.
8. EYSENCK, H. J. (1957). *Dynamics of Anxiety and Hysteria.* Routledge & Kegan Paul, London.
9. EYSENCK, H. J. (1957). *Med. World*, **86**, 333.
10. WOLPE, J. (1950). *S. Afr. Med. J.*, **24**, 613.
11. WOLPE, J. (1952). *S. Afr. Med. J.*, **26**, 825.
12. WOLPE, J. (1954). *Arch. Neurol. Psychiat.*, **72**, 205.
13. WOLPE, J. (1958). *Psychotherapy by Reciprocal Inhibition.* Stanford University Press and Witwatersrand University Press.
14. LAZARUS, A. A. (1958). *S. Afr. Med. J.*, **32**, 660.
15. MEEHL, P. E. (1956). In a foreword to E. L. Phillips. *Psychotherapy: A Modern Theory and Practice.* Staples Press Ltd., London.
16. LUFF, M. C. and GARROD, M. (1935). *Brit. Med. J.*, **2**, 54.
17. HAMILTON, D. M. and WALL, S. H. (1941). *Amer. J. Psychiat.*, **98**, 551.

18. SALTER, A. (1952). *Conditioned Reflex Therapy.* George Allen & Unwin Ltd., London.
19. PHILLIPS, E. L. (1956). *Psychotherapy: A Modern Theory and Practice.* Staples Press Ltd., London.
20. WOLPE, J. (1948). *An Approach to the Problem of Neurosis Based on the Conditioned Response.* M.D. Thesis, Witwatersrand University.
21. WOLPE, J. (1952). *Brit. J. Psychol., Gen. Sect.,* **43,** 243.
22. LAZARUS, A. A. and RACHMAN, S. (1957). *S. Afr. Med. J.,* **31,** 934.
23. JACOBSON, E. (1938). *Progressive Relaxation.* University of Chicago Press, Chicago.
24. WOLPE, J. (1952). *Psychol. Rev.,* **59,** 192.
25. BARLOW, J. A. (1955). *Psychol. Rev.,* **63,** 406.
26. COPPOCK, H. W. (1951). *Amer. Psychologist,* **6,** 277.
27. GOODSON, F. A. and BROWNSTEIN, A. (1953). *J. Comp. Physiol. Psychol.,* **48,** 381.
28. SMITH, M. P. and BUCHANAN, G. (1954). *J. Exper. Psychol.,* **48,** 123.
29. LEWIN, K. (1931). Ed. by C. Murchinson. *A Handbook of Child Psychology,* pp. 590-625. Clark University Press, Worcester, Massachusetts.
30. KNIGHT, R. P. (1941). *Amer. J. Psychiat.,* **98,** 434.

THE APPLICATION OF LEARNING THEORY
TO THE TREATMENT OF STAMMERING*†

D. WALTON, B.A., DIP.PSYCH.(LOND.) and D. A. BLACK, M.A.

Rainhill Hospital, near Liverpool; Rainhill Hospital, near Liverpool, and Winwick Hospital, Warrington

IF WE regard psychiatric symptoms as products of learning processes, obeying certain laws as laid down principally by Hull (1943),[1] then it will become apparent why modern learning theory together with subsequent theoretical refinement, can offer much in its therapeutic application to the treatment of psychiatrically-ill patients.[2,3,4,5,6]

The present paper is an attempt to derive from learning theory a method of eliminating an abnormal reaction, on the part of a patient, which had failed to respond to other therapeutic means; to apply this method in an individual case; to relate the procedure adopted to a theoretical rationale; and finally to enquire into the possible limitations of this theoretical model.

SUMMARY OF THE CASE HISTORY

The patient, a young man of 32 years, was admitted to hospital for the investigation and treatment of a chronic stammer. In ordinary conversation his stammer was slight, but when he was forced to use the telephone it became much more severe.

Stammering first occurred at the age of eight or nine. The cause was unknown. It was less acute at home and his parents did not apparently appreciate its full effects. At school however he was ashamed of his affliction, feeling it was regarded as a weakness. To counteract this impression he indulged in acts of extreme bravado and daredevilry. To avoid stammering in class he pretended not to know the answers to questions put to him. Ambition and intelligence, however, repeatedly led him into situations where the stammer would be noticed, and at grammar school no good was to be served in not answering questions if he was to get on and rise above the poor background from which he had come. He discovered numerous " dodges " whereby stammering was minimized, for instance for most stammer-provoking words there were alternatives with the same meaning. But as school work became more technical, requiring use of specific terms, he abandoned ideas of trying for college and left school to take up an electrical apprenticeship.

In the army he continued his trade and also matriculated. The fact that promotion eluded him he attributes to the stammer. Despite further indications of his academic potentiality evidenced in his army career he nevertheless still saw his stammer as too big a handicap and on leaving the army became a draughtsman. He studied electrical engineering at night school and rapidly obtained his H.N.C. By now he was in the design office of the Atomic Energy Authority surrounded by colleagues who were college trained and whom

* The authors are grateful to Dr. B. Finkleman, Medical Superintendent, Rainhill Hospital, for permission to publish the present study. Our thanks are due also to Dr. C. Heller whose assistance made this study possible.

† Reprinted from (1958) *J. Psychosomatic Res.*, 3, 170–179, by permission of the authors and the editor of *J. Psychosomatic Res.*

he noticed were no more competent than himself. Again ambition for a post of leadership and responsibility seemed realizable but for the need to keep his stammer hidden. The telephone, an integral part of an engineer's working life, now became the stumbling block. Ability to speak clearly was all it called for but this he could not do. As a youth using the 'phone in private, speaking to someone he knew well, the stammer was controllable. But now, in a large office, full of people, speaking to complete strangers, on topics requiring specific terminology, without the assistance of personal appearance, facial expression or gesture, his stammer was revealed in its worst form. Although he knew he was ideally qualified for promotion the prospect of increased use of the telephone prevented him applying for promotion and he watched less able men by-pass him. With his wife and family, as with his parents, the stammer was minimized, but in the telephone situation it was aggravated and he had been running away from his stammer too long to face up to it now.

Although there appeared to be a satisfactory rationale and theoretical explanation (next section) of his inability to use the telephone without stammering it was possible that factors other than those of stimulus generalization were creating or exacerbating his difficulties. The most obvious of these was that he might be ill-equipped to cope with the increasing intellectual demands of his job or that he did not possess the other abilities relevant to his position.

The General Aptitude Test Battery,[7] the Wechsler–Bellevue Intelligence Scale, Form 1[8] and the Kuder Vocational Interest Test[9] results were not significantly different from those returned by people successful in engineering and designing occupations.

Both the Minnesota[10] and the Maudsley Personality Inventories[11] returned abnormal scores. The high scores on the hypomania and extraversion scales would be consistent with the intense drive state mentioned previously, whilst the high " neuroticism " score might be in accordance with his early history of a low stress threshold.

All in all the psychological test results are not inconsistent with the development of his stammer in terms of the theoretical model proposed below.

Suggested Development of the Stammer
in Terms of Learning Theory

There is experimental evidence to suggest that the stronger the habit strength, the closer must be the excitatory stimuli to the original stimulus aggregate. It follows that a considerable number of stimuli are able in varying degrees to evoke the same reaction. This spreading of learning to other stimuli has been called by Hull " primary stimulus generalization."

Those circumstances which precipitated the stammer in its acute form, and therefore presumably approaching most closely the original stimulus aggregate were those in which he was required to provide an answer in class or to answer a roll call. The common denominators of these appeared to be the presence of other people and the necessity to make an independent contribution.

The stammering could, therefore, be regarded as a drive-reducing conditioned avoidance response, evoked originally in a traumatic situation. In such a situation intense anxiety would have been generated and the evocation of stammering would have resulted in a reduction or cessation of the anxiety-inducing stimulus. The reaction potential of the stammer would have developed as the product of the habit strength and the fluctuating drive strength (anxiety). The habit strength of the stammer would have increased as a simple negatively accelerated positive growth function, eventually reaching an asymptote or saturation point beyond which similar excitatory stimuli would not have increased the habit strength.

If the stammer is regarded as a conditioned avoidance response arising from the anxiety and the anxiety as a conditioned response to a stress situation, then in similar stress situations anxiety should develop. The patient whose case we are here considering reports that he avoided the direct use of his voice in many situations, e.g. at a tube station by buying tickets from the machines and when taking a girl to the cinema by having bought the tickets earlier in the day. Thus the anxiety which would have normally developed in such situations gradually dissipated, and since the anxiety resulted in stammering, the stammering would also diminish. Similarly, in other situations, by suppressing the conditioned avoidance response with alcohol, or capitalizing on his personal appearance, a reduction of anxiety would again be produced and again in turn cause a decline in stammering. This pattern, reproduced over the years, is given further emphasis by another feature, namely, his failure to stammer when in the company of his wife and family. Here the effects of stimulus generalization as described earlier would appear important in that his wife and family had little in common with the original stimulus aggregate; anxiety was, therefore, not developed; and since the stammer is a conditioned avoidance response arising from the anxiety, the stammer tends not to occur.

In addition, stimuli which become associated with the drive state assume secondary motivating values, whilst stimuli associated with the reinforcement of drive reduction acquire secondary reinforcing values. In other words there develops a conditioned drive for success and praise, both of these values acquiring secondary motivating characteristics. At the same time the stimuli in which these secondary motivating characteristics occur would acquire secondary reinforcing values. Through a process of discrimination these secondary mechanisms would either be retained or extinguished according to their effect. Since presumably this patient's stress threshold is lower than normal, a greater zone of stimuli would be extinguished than retained and he would be left with a continually reinforced drive state limited to a few selected conditions.

Thus the conditioned drive for success and praise forced him into those situations which, because of stimulus generalization, were the most traumatic and anxiety-inducing. The use of the telephone was one of these.

Symptomatic Treatment of the Stammering

(a) *Theoretical considerations*

Hull's fundamental formula linking performance, habit and drive is:

$$_sE_R = {_sH_R} \times D$$

where performance is symbolized by $_sE_R$ and habit by $_sH_R$. In other words performance is a multiplicative function of both habit and drive. If there is no drive there is no performance, although the habit may be a strong one. If the drive remains constant the suggested approach would be to develop a negative habit, a " habit of not responding to the stimulus." The reaction tendency of stammering should then decrease as a negative growth function of the frequency of occurrence of closely associated and successively unreinforced evocations, i.e. the number of times the telephone is used and stammering does not occur.

The work of Cherry et al.[12,13,14] on the treatment of stammering provided a method of minimizing the stammering whilst using the telephone. Their work indicated that stammering was a perceptual rather than a motor abnormality and, as such, amenable to training and conditioning. Their method was to interfere with the speaker's auditory perceptions of his own voice. Their initial experiments used a " speech shadowing " technique, a means whereby part of the speaker's auditory perception is taken away from his own voice and transferred to that of another speaker. The experimenter reads from a book and the patient shadows him, without seeing the text, following one or two words behind.

The development of the habit strength, i.e. of not responding to the telephone with a stammer would proceed as a function of the following seven considerations:

(1) The number of reinforcements. Repetition is of itself of little value in strengthening habits but merely provides the opportunity for learning. The main variable is reinforcement.

(2) The importance of the reinforcing agent (i.e. of not stammering).

(3) The interval between S–R. There should be an immediate reward with no delay between the S–R.

(4) Massing of reinforcements. The closer the massing of the reinforcements, the greater will be the extent of the reminiscence effects.[15,16,17]

(5) The reaction threshold. This will determine the speed with which the response is evoked. Franks[18,19] has shown, for example, that the speed of conditioning tends to vary with the degree of introversion–extraversion.

(6) Further Hullian concepts. It is necessary to introduce two further Hullian concepts, namely those of reactive inhibition (I_R) and conditioned inhibition $(_sI_R)$. According to Hullian theory learning, or the formation of stimulus-response connexions, results in varying degrees of fatigue or inhibition (I_R), though the value of this inhibitory potential diminishes with rest. Stimuli which are closely associated with the acquisition of inhibitory potential (I_R) become conditioned to it. This is known as conditioned inhibitory potential $(_sI_R)$ and tends to be much less affected by rest. Both the reactive and the conditioned inhibition summate functionally to produce the total inhibitory potential (I_R). The reaction potential of the stammer

(i.e. the ability of the subject to stammer) will therefore be determined by the following equation:

$$_sE_R = (_sH_R \times D) - (I_R + _sI_R)$$

As the $_sI_R$ increases so should the $_sE_R$ decrease, providing there is no increase in drive level (D). A point will eventually be reached when the excitatory and inhibitory potentials of the equation are the same and behavourial extinction of the stammering will have been achieved.

(7) A graded re-education programme. This is designed for the purpose of substituting a normal reaction in place of the original anxiety reaction in the context of other people being present when he uses the telephone.

(b) *Deduction of Method of Treatment*

The above theoretical considerations are intended to show that certain cases of stammering can be conceived as specific types of learning or drive reducing conditioned avoidance responses. According to this model the stammer can be regarded as a simple learned habit which has reached maximum habit strength and which can be extinguished by building up a negative habit of not performing the stammer. This could be attempted in the following way. If the patient were asked to shadow the experimenter's voice and at the same time to speak into the telephone, then, according to the above theory just such a negative habit should develop. The habit of not stammering would then be associated with drive-reduction, because of the importance of this improvement to the subject, and so would be reinforced. Repeated massed practice would build up a negative habit and oppose the positive habit of stammering. The simultaneous use of the telephone and " shadowing " would demonstrate to the subject that the telephone does not necessarily result in stammering. There will then be a corresponding decrease in the anxiety. As a result of the stress situation not resulting in the conditioned avoidance response and because the stammering is itself influenced by the anxiety, there will be a still further reduction in this avoident response.

A further decrease in excitatory potential should be achieved by the complementary effects produced by the graded retraining programme. The presence of people well known to him would constitute a weak excitatory stimulus, in contrast to the intense anxiety producing stimulus constituted by people at his place of employment. Since the weak stimuli are less likely to evoke an anxiety reaction the motivation towards achieving an alternative normal reaction is maximized. As the experiment progresses people less well known to him are introduced. Thus by increasing the differential stimuli intensity until a normal reaction supersedes the original anxiety reaction, involved in the original conditioning, a normal response is gradually achieved.

It is difficult to isolate the respective effects of the use of the telephone, " shadowing," the conditioned inhibitory potential and the graded re-education programme. It appears that the excitatory potential of the equation will decrease and the inhibitory potential will tend to increase because of the gradual development of a negative habit and because of the decrease in anxiety associated with the re-education programme. The respective decrease and increase in excitatory and inhibitory potentials should eventually result in the extinction of the stammering. It is important to appreciate that as the decrease in excitatory potential becomes more marked the rate of growth of the inhibitory potential should become less. This is because less effort and difficulty will be experienced as the development of the habit of not stammering proceeds. The result should be a more regular and even level of performance as the experiment progresses.

(c) *Treatment Procedure*

The internal telephone system of a neuropsychiatric unit was used. This made possible the simultaneous use of two internal telephones, so approximating the working environment of the patient.

Before the experiment began the technique of shadowing was demonstrated to the patient. One psychologist read from a book, the other shadowed, following one or two words behind. Following this demonstration 3 practice sessions were carried out in which one psychologist read from a book, the patient " shadowed " him, and the other psychologist recorded any errors incurred by the patient during shadowing. An error was regarded as the inclusion of any word not in the original text or the omission of words from this text. During both the 3 practice trials and the subsequent trials the patient did not face the examiner.

After 3 trials the telephone was introduced. From trial 4 to trial 10 one psychologist rang the patient's telephone number, the patient answered and the psychologist proceeded to read the text to the patient. The second psychologist was in the same room as the patient and recorded any errors in the patient's shadowing. The patient listened to the first psychologist on the telephone then repeated by " shadowing " what he had heard to the other psychologist.

Following the 10 introductory sessions there was a reversal of procedure in that the psychologist read the text as before but this time to the patient in the same room. The patient " shadowed " this material, repeating it directly into the telephone to the second psychologist in another room who immediately recorded the errors and hence the progress made.

In subsequent trials attempts were made to alternate the psychologist who was reading the text or recording the patient's progress. From trial No. 15 two other people were introduced into the experiment, one a member of the technical staff, the other a patient, and from then on one or other was invariably present during trials and whichever of these two people were present listened to and recorded the patient's progress. Both were well known to the subject. In later sessions two other people took part in the experiment. Neither of these people was known to the patient though they were introduced to him as relatives of one of the experimenters. Thus a graded re-education programme was devised based on a theoretical formulation proposed by Guthrie[20] and successfully executed in clinical trials by Wolpe.[21,22] The original anxiety reaction to the stimulus of other people being present is replaced by normal reaction. By gradually decreasing the familiarity of the people in the experiment, though making sure that the initial stimuli are of a greatly reduced intensity the accustomed anxiety response is less likely to be evoked. As suggested by Jones,[2] " . . . the presentation of a stimulus qualitatively remote from the original, but occupying a position on the generalization curve of the latter, would operate in the same way as a reduction in stimulus intensity."

RESULTS

Figure 1 shows the changes in frequency of stammering from the beginning to the end of the experiment. It will be seen that the introduction of the telephone in trial 4 resulted in an immediate increase in stammering, hesitations and inaccurate perceptions. This declined very rapidly only to rise again when the patient was asked to shadow directly into the telephone. This increase was very short lived. It was followed by a consistent improvement in telephone performance which is reflected by the downward trend in the graph.

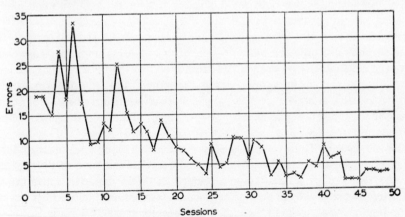

FIG. 1. Telephone performance measured by average number of errors (stammers, hesitations, misinterpretations) per page of text shadowed.

Each figure quoted in the graph represents the mean number of stammers, hesitations and other errors per page of presented text. Sessions numbers

11–39 were 20 min in length, whilst trials 40–49 were 45 min massed-practice sessions. In a general way there appears no significant difference between the 20 and 45 min sessions, though it is not possible to establish this with any certainty because of the limited number of trials which were possible.* The results, however, are in accord with predictions and offer support for both the theoretical model proposed to explain the genesis of his stammering and the deductions for a rational method of treatment made possible from this theory. As a further check on the validity of the theoretical proposals and the methods of treatment following on directly from these, two additional criteria were required. First, it was necessary to see how well the patient performed on the telephone without the assistance of "shadowing" and under conditions approximating to his working environment. In other words to see how well he had developed the negative habit or habit of not responding to the telephone by stammering; and the second criterion of success was whether or not the patient reported that he felt no apprehension with regard to the use of the telephone.

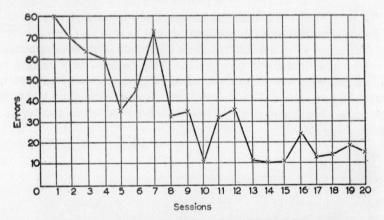

Fig. 2. Telephone conversation performance, without shadowing, measured by total number of errors (stammers and hesitations) per 10 min session.

During the patient's final week in hospital there were 20 additional 10 min sessions. These consisted of one of the two psychologists ringing the patient's telephone and discussing with him subject-matter directly relevant to his job. The patient did not have the help of shadowing. His conversation was scored for stammers and hesitations. Conversations included discourses on uranium, and other elements important to atomic energy; isotopes; power; transformers; electrical relays; drawings; schedules; materials; and radiation effects.

* The experiment was started knowing the patient was due to emigrate to Canada, though sufficient time was available to test the general validity of the theory.

During these 10 min conversations it was difficult to obtain a strictly objective score as the patient talked for varying amounts in each session. As far as possible he was required to talk for the majority of the 10 min. The psychologist merely asked short relevant questions designed to keep the subject talking.

Figure 2 shows the number of stammers and hesitations per 10 min session over 20 trials. The graph reflects a striking decline in frequency as the experiment progressed. During the final trials of this series the stammers and hesitations were very infrequent. In fact the final 10 trials with no shadowing showed an improvement over even the final 10 trials with shadowing.

The day the patient was leaving hospital he was asked to write a frank account of his response to treatment. He reported, " When I came into hospital I was extremely sceptical of success, having tried so many methods of treatment. In contrast to this, on discharge I am quite convinced that I have got into a healthier and better method of speech and am certain that my general speaking level has been maintained at its peak. Under treatment I have not had a bad patch (11 weeks). Prior to hospital I had a regular cycle of stammering during which 1 week in 4 was very bad, though at no time had I confidence in the telephone and I had fear of it irrespective of the week. Since the experiment I have had no such cycle and my level of general conversation has been consistently equivalent to my best week in the cycle. As regards the telephone I am still apprehensive towards it but I no longer consider it an insurmountable difficulty. I am convinced I can get over it and that my telephone conversation can be brought up to my conversational level. The shadowing may have been responsible for maintaining this high level but I have responded most I feel to the use of, and length of time using, the telephone."

DISCUSSION

During the course of the treatments described, considerable improvement in the patient's major dysfunction was evidenced. The results would tend to support both the validity of the theory put forward to explain the genesis and specificity of his stammer, and the deductions for a rational method of treatment made possible from this theory.

It is not possible to state with absolute confidence that such improvement resulted from the treatment employed. Further controlled studies using similar methods of treatment would have to be carried out to determine this. One can say, nevertheless, that the present paper and those of several others[2,6,23] demonstrate that it is possible to devise rational symptomatic methods of treatment for psychiatric symptoms, whether physical or emotional, that these symptomatic cures do not produce alternative symptoms (which should happen according to Freudian theory), that they are in fact long-lasting,[2,5] and have been achieved when the patient has failed to respond to other psychotherapeutic methods over several years.

Several major problems have been presented by the present investigation. Although a satisfactory therapeutic result appears to have been achieved it was not possible in such an exploratory-experimental investigation to control and relate the different variables to specific therapeutic effects. Certain tentative conclusions can be made with regard to suggested optimum conditions of treatment.

First, the experiment would undoubtedly have benefited by a larger number of trials and reinforcements—" the increments from successive reinforcements summate in a manner that yields a combined habit strength $(_sH_R)$ which is a simple positive growth function of the number of reinforcements."[1]

Secondly it is possible that the experiment would have been further enhanced by longer lessons. The sudden introduction of massed practice following a series of shorter trials should then increase the inhibitory potential of the equation. At the same time the " elation " effect, produced by success on the telephone over such a long period, would minimize the anxiety and so both decrease the excitatory potential and contribute to the development of the negative habit.

It might also be more rapid therapeutically to concentrate first on only two treatment variables, viz.: the decrease of the excitatory potential through shadowing and use of the telephone, and the increase of the inhibitory potential through massed practice. Thus one might leave the graded re-education programme until after the rate of experimental extinction had greatly decreased.

The patient for his part reported that he considered the continued use of the telephone therapeutically more helpful than the use of shadowing. One cannot decide, on the basis of the available evidence, whether this is so, though it would not appear to be the case, especially since inevitable and frequent use of the telephone in his present position has been his main difficulty. Experimental evidence outside the present work similarly suggests that repetition alone does not develop a habit either positive or negative but merely provides the opportunity for learning if a suitable reinforcement is present.[1] The mere use of the telephone without shadowing would produce some extra degree of reactive and conditioned inhibition because of his difficulty and so reinforce the habit of not wanting to use the telephone. This would be expected to generate further anxiety which would in turn affect subsequent attempts to use the telephone. The simultaneous use of shadowing, however, prevents or minimizes the development of the anxiety since the previously learned response of stammering is less likely to occur. The use of the telephone alone, therefore, is likely to result only in an increase in inhibition and anxiety with little or no difference to the resultant of the excitatory minus the inhibitory potentials of the equation.

Finally it may be possible to integrate more closely learning theory, personality theory, incentives and stimulant-depressant drugs in their application to similar therapeutic problems. It will be remembered that Franks[18] has shown that introverted neurotics tend to condition far more easily than extroverted neurotics and that the latter group condition only with difficulty. In line with this formulation are the recent attempts by Eysenck *et al.*[24-28] to relate the application of a stimulant drug (dexedrine) to more rapid learning by decreasing cortical inhibition (Pavlov) or reactive inhibition (Hull) and so producing an introverted behavior pattern. It would appear reasonable to suppose that an initial series of shorter trials during which no drugs are applied, followed by a sudden increase in massed practice trials with dexedrine would approximate to the effects produced in Crespi's experiment.[29] It may of course be better to sacrifice speed of learning by not using drugs, particularly if the patient feels that his symptoms have been removed artificially.

SUMMARY

The present paper attempts to formulate a theoretical model according to which the patient's stammer is regarded as a conditioned avoidance response; this response was originally evoked in an unknown traumatic situation and was drive-reducing.

A method of treatment was derived from this model. It was predicted that three major experimental conditions would build up the negative habit of not stammering when using the telephone. These were to decrease the excitatory potential, through the simultaneous use of the telephone and " shadowing "; to increase the inhibitory potential through massed practice trials; and finally to substitute by means of a graded re-education programme a normal reaction for the original anxiety reaction to the telephone.

The results of the experiment tend to support the validity of the proposed model. The patient achieved a satisfactory level of performance on the telephone when unassisted by " shadowing." Furthermore, in a frank assessment of the effects of treatment, he himself reported considerable clinical improvement.

Various suggestions are made for the optimum growth of the negative habit. The proposals attempt to integrate recent experimental findings in learning theory, personality theory, incentives and in the use of stimulant-depressant drugs.

REFERENCES

1. HULL, C. L. (1943). *Principles of Behavior*. Appleton–Century, New York.
2. JONES, H. G. (1956). The application of conditioning and learning techniques to the treatment of a psychiatric patient. *J. Abnorm. (Soc.) Psychol*, **52**, 414-419.

3. MOWRER, O. H. (1950). *Learning Theory and Personality Dynamics.* The Ronald Press, New York.
4. RAYMOND, M. J. (1956). Case of fetishism treated by aversion therapy. *Brit. Med. J.,* **2,** 854-857.
5. WALTON, D. and BLACK, D. A. The application of learning theory and conditioning to the treatment of psychiatric symptoms—hysterical aphonia. To be published.
6. YATES, A. J. (1958). The application of learning theory to the treatment of tics. *J. Abnorm. (Soc.) Psychol.,* **56,** 175-182.
7. DEPT. OF LABOUR (1947). *General Aptitude Test Battery.* United States Employment Service, Washington, D.C.
8. WECHSLER, D. (1944). *The Measurement of Adult Intelligence.* Williams & Wilkins, Baltimore.
9. SCIENCE RESEARCH ASSOCIATES (1951). *Kuder Preference Test Record, Vocational Form C.* Chicago.
10. PSYCHOLOGICAL CORPORATION (1951). *Minnesota Multiphasic Personality Inventory.* New York.
11. EYSENCK, H. J. (1956). The questionnaire measurement of neuroticism and extra-version. *Riv. Psicol.,* **50,** 113-140.
12. CHERRY, E. C. (1953). Some experiments on the recognition of speech, with one or two ears. *J. Acoust. Soc. Amer.,* **25,** 5, 975-979.
13. CHERRY, E. C., SAYERS, B. McA. and MARLAND, P. M. (1955). Some experiments upon the total suppression of stammering. *Nature, Lond.,* **176,** 874.
14. CHERRY, E. C., SAYERS, B. McA. and MARLAND, P. M. (1956). Experiments upon the total inhibition of stammering by external control, and some clinical results. *J. Psychosom. Res.,* **1,** 233-246.
15. MOWRER, O. H. and JONES, H. M. (1943). Extinction and behaviour variability as functions of effortfulness of task. *J. Exp. Psychol.,* **33,** 369-386.
16. SOLOMON, R. L. (1948). Effort and extinction rate: a confirmation. *J. Comp. Physiol. Psychol.,* **41,** 93-101.
17. OSGOOD, C. E. (1953). *Method and Theory in Experimental Psychology.* New York.
18. FRANKS, C. A. (1956). Conditioning and personality, a study of normal and neurotic subjects. *J. Abnorm. (Soc.) Psychol.,* **52,** 143-150.
19. FRANKS, C. A. (1957). Personality factors and the rate of conditioning. *Brit. J. Psychol.,* **48,** 119-126.
20. GUTHRIE, E. R. (1938). *The Psychology of Learning.* Harper, New York.
21. WOLPE, J. (1952). Experimental neuroses as learned behaviour. *Brit. J. Psychol.,* **43,** 243-628.
22. WOLPE, J. (1954). Reciprocal inhibition as the main basis of psychotherapeutic effects. *Arch. Neurol. Psychiat. Chicago,* **72,** 205-226.
23. EYSENCK, H. J. (1956). Modern learning theory. *Proc. Roy. Soc. Med.,* **49,** 12.
24. EYSENCK, H. J. (1957). Drugs and personality. I: Theory and methodology. *J. Ment. Sci.,* **103,** 430.
25. EYSENCK, H. J., CASEY, S. and TROUTON, D. S. (1957). Drugs and personality. II: The effects of stimulant and depressant drugs on continuous work. *J. Ment. Sci.,* **103,** 432.
26. EYSENCK, H. J., HOLLAND, H. and TROUTON, D. S. (1957). Drugs and personality. III: The effects of stimulant and depressant drugs on visual after-effects. *J. Ment. Sci.,* **103,** 432.
27. EYSENCK, H. J., HOLLAND, H. and TROUTON, D. S. (1957). Drugs and personality. IV: The effects of stimulant and depressive drugs on the rate of fluctuation of a reversible perspective figure. *J. Ment. Sci.,* **103,** 432.
28. EYSENCK, H. J. and AIBA, S. (1957). Drugs and personality. V: The effects of stimulant and depressant drugs on the suppression of the primary visual stimulus. *J. Ment. Sci.,* **103,** 432.
29. CRESPI, L. P. (1942). Qualitative variation of incentive and performance in the white rat. *Amer. J. Psychol.,* **55,** 467-517.
30. EYSENCK, H. J. (1955). A dynamic theory of anxiety and hysteria. *J. Ment. Sci.,* **101,** 28-51.

THE TREATMENT OF TWO PHOBIC PATIENTS ON THE BASIS OF LEARNING PRINCIPLES*†

VICTOR MEYER

Institute of Psychiatry, University of London, Maudsley Hospital

THIS paper is presented as an illustration of the possibility of applying experimental method and some of the principles available in psychological theories of learning to the treatment of psychiatric symptoms. As such, it is somewhat similar to an earlier study by Jones.[1] It differs from the latter, however, in that it demonstrates the importance of individual differences in personality structure and the manner in which such differences dictate modifications of therapeutic techniques.

The treatments to be described were based mainly on the principle of primary stimulus generalisation.[2] According to this principle, a conditioned reaction is not only evoked by the original conditioned stimulus but also, to some degree, by a series of stimuli more or less similar to the original one. The more dissimilar the new stimulus, the less intense is the conditioned reaction.

Many phobic patients display anxiety so intense when presented with certain environmental situations that they are not amenable to any therapeutic approach. However, the generalisation principle suggests that the presentation of an environmental situation which resembles the original one but evokes a reduced amount of anxiety can be exploited therapeutically. In such a situation, one can attempt to substitute an adaptive normal reaction for the original unadaptive anxiety response. A graded continuum of similar situations can then be employed, moving towards the original one, so that the original unadaptive responses can be eliminated. This is essentially one of the methods advocated by Jersild and Holmes[3] for the treatment of children's fear, and its theoretical basis has been elaborated by such writers as Guthrie[4] and Wolpe.[5] The latter, among others, has demonstrated the usefulness of these techniques in experiments on animals and has applied them successfully in the treatment of a series of psychiatric patients.[6]

* Thanks are due Dr. D. Hill, Dr. D. A. Pond and Dr. J. D. Dewsbery, consultants to the Bethlem Royal and Maudsley Hospitals, for their permission, encouragement and assistance in carrying out the treatment. A debt is also acknowledged to Dr. M. B. Shapiro, Mr. H. Gwynne Jones and Mr. J. Inglis for offering valuable suggestions.
† Reprinted by permission of the author and the Amer. Psychol. Ass. from (1957) *J. Abnorm. (Soc.) Psychol.*, **55**, 261-266.

SUMMARY OF CASE HISTORIES

For the purposes of this paper, a complete case history of each patient is not essential. A brief summary of the psychiatric notes will suffice.

CASE 1—The patient, a married woman of 48 years, was admitted to the hospital for investigation of suspected temporal lobe epilepsy. Apart from blackouts, she complained of an excessive fear of going out.

No family history of psychiatric disorder or epilepsy was reported. The birth and developmental milestones seemed normal. She left school at the age of 15 and had a successful work history up to the time of her illness. Her marriage was fairly satisfactory, but there were no children. Before her illness, she was described as quick-tempered but a good mixer, cheerful, hardworking and conscientious.

Her blackouts started at the age of 28 during pregnancy. Since then, she had suffered 18 blackouts. They all followed physical exertion or emotional upset and were usually preceded by an aura of dull sensation in the chest. She usually lost consciousness, fell limp, and hurt herself on several occasions. On recovery she vomited and felt " horrible."

At the age of 44 she began having peculiar " feelings." These consisted of epigastric sensations, followed by a " horrible " sensation of being about to fall. These episodes occurred frequently when she was about to go out or when she was outside on her own. Occasionally, when she was unable to control these feelings, she tended to panic and then to suffer one of her blackouts.

As a result of these symptoms, she developed a strong fear of going out on her own, of traveling on public conveyances and of having sexual intercourse for fear of an attack. From the age of 46 she refused to go out unaccompanied. Shortly before the admission to the hospital, she was occasionally unable to go out with friends or even with her husband. She gradually became more and more anxious, depressed (entertaining suicidal thoughts), and fearful. Losing confidence, she resigned from a responsible job and stopped caring for her home. She continued working until admission, but needed to be accompanied all the way to and from work. On admission she was pleasant, sociable, co-operative, rational, and well oriented.

The results of all investigations were negative with respect to temporal lobe epilepsy. Except for some mild abnormalities shown on the air-encephalogram, all the tests contraindicated organic involvement. In view of the possibility that the attacks might be of cardiac origin, she was referred to cardiologist. He could find no abnormalities in the cardiovascular system.

The patient was diagnosed as exhibiting a phobic state with blackouts of unknown nature and was referred to the psychology department for the symptomatic treatment of her phobias.

CASE 2—A man of 42 years was admitted to the hospital for investigation of blackouts. He also suffered from excessive tension and various fears, mainly related to entering enclosed and crowded spaces.

Two instances of psychiatric disorder were reported in the family history: His mother had a " nervous breakdown," and his elder brother experienced difficulty in going out alone. The patient's early development and childhood seemed normal. He left school at the age of 14 and worked successfully as a precision grinder. He had been happily married and had two children. Before his illness he was described as undemonstrative and timid, but affectionate as a father and husband.

At the age of 22 he had several fainting attacks on parades when serving in the armed forces. Following these, he developed episodes of apprehension which usually occurred in crowded places. He felt tense, flustered, and experienced an urge to run away in a panic. Strange or crowded places and feelings of boredom were associated with the onset of these episodes. The presence of a friend and strong interest tended to prevent their development. Up to the age of 38, he could preserve control and avert panic. After that time, control became more tenuous. On 4 occasions, episodes of panic terminated in fainting attacks. As a result, he became worried about himself and sharply curtailed his social activities. Shortly before admission to the hospital, he had a feeling of apprehension in a barber's shop, panicked, mounted his bicycle and shortly afterwards collapsed. After this accident he refused to ride the bicycle and would not go out. He became anxious, tense and depressed.

He was treated by his own physician with phenobarbitone with very little success. On examination for possible temporal lobe epilepsy, the results were negative. When admitted to the hospital, he appeared very tense and anxious, but rational, well oriented, and co-operative. He was reluctant to talk about himself and needed much encouragement.

Like the first case, he was referred to the psychology department for symptomatic treatment of a phobic state.

TREATMENT

CASE 1

The patient was interviewed twice with the aim of getting detailed information about her phobic symptoms. The rationale of the treatment was then explained and discussed with her. During this time the experimenter (E) endeavored to establish good rapport. According to the theory outlined, this is essential since E becomes part of the various environmental situations during treatment and, by establishing an effective relationship, he becomes a reassuring stimulus, tending to reduce anxiety.

No exact record of each treatment session was kept, and therefore, some of the description lacks precision. Since the most likely place for the abnormal behavior to occur was a door leading to the " outside " and the " outside " itself, the hospital roof garden, which has walls but no ceiling, was selected as a starting point for treatment. On the first occasion, the subject (S) entered the garden with E. She only reported mild " thumping in the stomach " throughout this session. Next day she reported feeling perfectly well and volunteered to enter the garden on her own. When she had gone twice on her own without any signs of the symptoms recurring, the place of treatment was changed to the main hospital garden. She went out several times with E on successive days, then was required to go out on her own to meet E, and then to seek and find him. Since S appeared rather dependent on E's presence, other staff members of the ward were asked to participate in the treatment without S's knowledge of prearrangement by E. She went out with various nurses and patients for walks in the garden. Similar expeditions took place during the evening. Not more than 2 sessions (30 min each) were given each day. When asked to go into the garden on her own, she did without any difficulty. From that point, she was encouraged to take frequent walks into the garden during the daytime and the evenings.

The next stage consisted of E's taking walks with the patient outside the hospital grounds. These started in back streets and were gradually extended into the main street; the distance covered increased gradually day by day. She also went out with other people. Eventually, she was able to set out on her own to meet E and others outside. She was taken out at least 3 times when feeling " upset." She took 4 bus rides accompanied by E and frequently volunteered to go shopping with other patients. After 2 weeks (16 sessions) of this treatment, she was able to make short expeditions on her own without difficulty.

She spent the subsequent 16 days going for walks with *E* and other people and on her own. Short trips on buses were included, and at least 3 times she went out on her own in the evening. She spent 3 weekends at home but was instructed to go out on her own only if she felt confident. She managed to take 3 short walks near her house. On the last day of treatment she traveled some 3 miles away from the hospital and back. During the whole treatment, she never reported any symptoms except occasional mild thumping in the stomach. Her behavior on the ward improved. According to the psychiatrist in charge and the nursing staff, she had very few " upsets " and was more cheerful. She felt confident and eager to be discharged.

The treatment took about 5 weeks, and the patient claimed to have enjoyed it. When she was discharged, her relatives and friends were told that she should be encouraged to go out on her own provided she felt confident and not upset. It was planned that she should be seen once every 2 weeks in the outpatient department for follow-up purposes and, if necessary, to modify management.

Follow-up—For nearly 5 months the patient worked regularly and was unaccompanied when visiting the hospital. She took occasional solitary walks and was able to do her shopping. Each working day she was met at the station by a friend who traveled with her to the factory; on the return journey she was met by her husband. She managed to get to the station on her own, and on 2 occasions when the friend failed to meet her, she experienced no difficulties. A month after discharge from the hospital she developed an acute chest pain for which she was treated by her doctor. Also, while on a bus with some friends, she had one of her blackouts without any warning and was unconscious for about 45 min. Despite these difficulties and worries, she continued to work and to go out on her own. At the end of the fourth month, she increased the frequency of her unaccompanied expeditions, and for the first time in 2 years attended adequately to her housework. She also went to work on her own 7 times in succession when her friend was on vacation. She reported occasional feelings of anxiety, but she never panicked and was able to ward off the attacks by thinking about treatment and handling a mascot (a piece of candy) which she kept throughout the treatment. The last time she was seen, she felt cheerful, confident about going out on her own, and practically cured of " unreasonable fears."

Three days after the last interview, the patient died following one of her sudden blackouts when traveling with friends. The cause of her death was attributed to left ventricular failure; postmortem examination demonstrated heart disease.

CASE 2

Two extensive interviews with this patient indicated that his anxiety was not associated with any specific stimulus but was more generalised and might depend on a variety of factors. For this reason, a modified technique was adopted, aimed at enabling S, by a process of conditioning, to cope efficiently with his anxiety no matter where it arose. First, a course of systematic desensitisation was given, based on Wolpe's[6] relaxation techniques. This form of treatment failed, since the patient reported that he could not evoke any increased anxiety by thinking about stressful situations. He remained tense and anxious throughout the sessions, but reported no changes in feeling; GSRs similarly indicated no disturbances.

The conditioning of anxiety-relief responses was then attempted by means of a technique similar to that described by Wolpe.[6] An inductorium with a maximum inflow of 6V was applied to 2 fingers; the strength of the current was controlled by turning a knob. The patient was told to say aloud " calm yourself " when the shock became unbearable. As soon as the patient said this, E switched off the current. Wolpe has reported that many of his patients experienced relief from anxiety in disturbing situations when they used these words associated with the release from shock-induced tension.

Since it appeared that S was most likely to manifest his symptoms in a crowded cinema, it was decided to initiate a procedure similar to that used with the first patient. It was planned to visit the local cinema at a time when it is usually relatively empty and then gradually delay visits, going later and later each day until eventually the visit would be made at a time when the cinema is commonly quite full. The effect of boredom was also taken into account since the patient saw at least part of the same picture each day. During the first week, the patient received 5 or 6 electrical conditioning trials immediately before visiting the cinema with E. After some 30–40 min, both S and E returned to the hospital, where 5 or 6 further conditioning trials were given.

After 7 days of this treatment, there was no change in S's behavior. During most of the visits to the cinema, he reported feelings of tension and an urge to leave. Following a weekend at home, he said that he still felt depressed, anxious, and tense, and although the " calm yourself " technique helped him slightly, he considered that he was generally unimproved by the treatment.

In every respect, the patient's reactions to the treatment differed from those manifested by Case 1. Whereas Case 1 reacted very quickly to the treatment and a good rapport was easily established, Case 2 remained aloof and detached.

At this stage, Case 2 was reconsidered. A plausible hypothesis was derived from Franks's study[7] concerning the conditionability of extraverts and introverts and from Eysenck's theory of anxiety and hysteria.[8] From

these ideas, it seemed to follow that Case 1 would condition better and
extinguish less rapidly than Case 2. Similarly, both cases should be more
neurotic than average and Case 1 should be more introverted than Case 2.
These inferences were supported by the patients' scores on Franks's eyeblink
conditionability measure and on the Maudsley Personality Inventory. On
the theory* that inhibitory drugs decrease conditionability and heighten
satiation effects, Case 2 was given 10 mg of dexedrine (excitant) for 4 days.
As soon as the effects of the drug became apparent, he was submitted each
day to the same treatment procedure as during the previous week.

Throughout this second stage of treatment, the patient felt cheerful
and relaxed and enjoyed going to the cinema. At no time did he display
any symptoms. On the second day, he was left alone in the cinema. On
the last day, he managed to stay alone in a crowded cinema without any
difficulty. During the following weekend he went home but took 10 mg of
dexedrine each day. He traveled alone on buses, rode his bicycle, and went
to a cinema with his wife. He reported no feelings of disturbance. On his
return from the weekend, the dosage of dexedrine was reduced by 2·5 mg a
day with an equivalent amount of placebo substituted without the patient's
knowledge. The conditioning procedure and the visits to the cinema on his
own continued daily after the administration of the drug and the placebo.
On the fourth day, he received 10 mg of placebo only. During this stage
of treatment, he gradually became tense and anxious and reported feeling
slightly depressed. After each treatment session, however, he said that he
felt better temporarily and at no time did he feel tense and anxious in the
cinema.

During the next weekend at home, he was given 1 placebo tablet for the
Saturday and none for the Sunday. He coped with traveling and riding
his bicycle, but felt somewhat tense and anxious. He maintained that the
cause of these symptoms was the fear that the treatment might fail and that
he might have to stay in the hospital. He expressed a strong desire to leave,
saying that he had not felt this desire before the treatment started. He also
claimed that his present anxiety and tension had a " different quality since
he could find a reason for these feelings."

The first day after his return from this weekend, he was given a final test.
He had to travel on a bus some 3 miles away from the hospital, return, and
then visit, unaccompanied, another very crowded cinema. He reported
that before the bus ride he felt tense and worried, but on his return, he had
recovered, regained his confidence, and felt cheerful. He also enjoyed the
cinema and reported that he " never felt better."

---

* There is some evidence to support this theoretical position. Unpublished studies at
Maudsley Hospital on amobarbital sodium and dexamphetamine sulfate by Franks and
Trouton, and on arecoline and methyl atropine by Franks, Lavertey and Trouton have
yielded results consistent with the notions applied therapeutically in the present study.

The rationale of the treatment was explained to him and every step of the treatment (except the substitution of placebo) was discussed with him. After the final test he was discharged.

Follow-up—It was planned to see the patient once every 2 weeks. He kept his first appointment only, reporting considerable improvement in traveling and in visiting crowded places. He had also gained confidence in himself and in relation to strangers and his superiors. He still occasionally got his " queer feelings " of worry, strain, and fear of fainting, but these were very mild and not very disturbing. The only difficulty he experienced was when riding his bicycle, but he continued to cycle to and from work. Two weeks later he sent a letter, saying that he could not keep the appointment since he was in financial difficulties. Apart from these difficulties, he was managing very well and had mastered his fear of cycling completely. He could cope easily with any uncomfortable feelings he experienced.

Three months later he sent another letter, informing E that he was progressing very well. He had taken his children to the coast for a holiday, cycled to and from work without any difficulty, and visited cinemas regularly.

DISCUSSION

This paper attempts to demonstrate the application of some aspects of learning and the personality theory to the symptomatic treatment of psychiatric patients. At present, the experimental findings are not completely consistent, and the theories themselves are in early stages of development. The available findings, however, suggest rational experimental techniques for symptomatic treatment.

It cannot be strongly maintained that a mere stay in the hospital could account for the recovery from the symptoms, since both patients stayed in hospital well over a month prior to treatment, and according to their verbal account and the observation of their behavior in stressful situations, there was no indication of any improvement. In the present state of knowledge, however, it cannot be argued with any degree of assurance that the improvement of these patients' long-standing phobic symptoms was due to the treatment given. Even if there was sufficient evidence to maintain that the treatment was responsible for the improvement, so many relevant factors were uncontrolled that one would not know which aspect of the treatment was relevant and which irrelevant. These relationships can only be established by more extensive and well-controlled research.

Moreover, the usual objections made against symptomatic treatment on *a priori* grounds lack force. It seems plausible to argue, as Jones[1] has, that " Much evidence points to the fact that neuroticism is largely a constitutional defect for which no effective radical therapy is yet available. The individual of neurotic constitution in certain environmental circumstances develops certain symptoms. The rational therapeutic approach is then to treat the symptoms and to modify the environment so as to avoid their recrudescence or the development of fresh symptoms. The more specific the treatment, the more likely may be its success."

Several implications of theoretical and practical interest emerge from this study: (*a*) Since both cases manifested blackouts of an unknown nature, particularly Case 1, the phobic symptoms presented were not certainly known to be functional in origin. The treatment, however, was oriented towards a functional analysis of the disorder. (*b*) It would be desirable to know whether, following a course of treatment like that described, the neurotic reactions are eliminated or merely overshadowed by a stronger normal reaction. Although Wolpe[5] provides some evidence that neurotic reactions in cats can be eliminated, the question must remain open on the present evidence. (*c*) Although on clinical grounds Case 1 was regarded as an hysterical personality and Case 2 as a dysthymic, objective psychological tests indicated the reverse. It seems likely, moreover, that the etiology of the phobic states must have been quite different in the 2 cases. One would like to know how 2 patients showing such a considerable difference in conditionability came to develop more or less similar patterns of abnormal behavior. (*d*) The results obtained during the course of treatment are consistent with Eysenck's theory[8] concerning the dynamics of anxiety and hysteria. They also indicate, in accordance with Eysenck's view, that for the purpose of treatment, adequate regard must be paid to the importance of certain individual differences as related to the disorders presented. (*e*) The use of drugs may facilitate and speed up successful treatment of this type, and this theory of individual differences may give a rational basis for the selection of drugs.

SUMMARY

The treatment of 2 phobic patients has been described. Case 1 manifested an excessive fear of going out on her own; Case 2 displayed disabling symptoms in the form of an excessive fear of going into enclosed and crowded places. Both cases had blackouts of unknown nature.

The treatment program for both cases was mainly based on the principle of primary stimulus generalization. Owing to the more " diffuse " nature of the anxiety displayed by Case 2 an additional simple conditioning technique was employed.

Case 1 responded to the treatment immediately and an improvement in her general behavior was observed. The effects of treatment persisted for nearly 5 months, when the patient died of left ventricular failure.

Case 2 failed initially to respond to treatment. An attempt was made to account for this failure in terms of Eysenck's theory of anxiety and hysteria. From the theory, inferences were made with respect to the patient's behavior on objective psychological tests; the results were consistent with the inferences. The treatment was modified according to the theory and the patient responded as expected. Four months after discharge from hospital, the patient seemed to be managing well and to feel much improved.

REFERENCES

1. JONES, H. G. (1956). The application of conditioning and learning techniques to the treatment of a psychiatric patient. *J. Abnorm. (Soc.) Psychol.*, **52**, 414-419.
2. HULL, C. L. (1943). *Principles of Behavior.* Appleton–Century, New York.
3. JERSILD, A. T. and HOLMES, F. B. (1935). Methods of overcoming children's fears. *J. Psychol*, **1**, 75-104.
4. GUTHRIE, E. R. (1935). *The Psychology of Learning.* Harper, New York.
5. WOLPE, J. (1952). Experimental neurosis as learned behavior. *Brit. J. Psychol.*, **43**, 243-268.
6. WOLPE, J. (1954). Reciprocal inhibition as the main basis of psychotherapeutic effects. *Arch. Neurol. Psychiat.*, **72**, 205-226.
7. FRANKS, C. M. and LAVERLEY, S. G. (1955). Sodium amytal and eyelid conditioning. *J. Ment. Sci.*, **101**, 654-663.
8. EYSENCK, H. J. (1955). A dynamic theory of anxiety and hysteria. *J. Ment. Sci.*, **101**, 28-51.
9. FRANKS, C. M. (1956). Conditioning and personality: A study of normal and neurotic subjects. *J. Abnorm. (Soc.) Psychol.*, **52**, 143-150.

NEW METHODS IN PSYCHOTHERAPY :
A CASE STUDY*

A. A. LAZARUS, M.A.(RAND)

Johannesburg

" *Cure comes through learning healthy personal relationships now, and not by stewing over past emotional frustrations.*"—SALTER[1]

THE GENERAL medical practitioner is frequently quoted as saying that more than half the patients he encounters in his daily rounds are " just plain neurotic." Since the general practitioner cannot spend hours treating his neurotic cases, a large number of them receive no therapy other than tonics and sedation. Others, less fortunate, succumb to the exhortations of swamis, mystics and a host of pseudo-scientific practitioners. This is an alarming situation. The initial responsibility for the psychological welfare of his patients usually rests with the family doctor, but the field of psychotherapy is itself so confusing that many doctors have expressed undisguised scepticism about its value. Most medical men do not have time to venture into the complicated polemics of orthodox Freudian psycho-analysis, or the claims of Jungian analysts, or the counter-claims of any other deviant psycho-analytic school. Similarly, the average doctor is not concerned with the differences between the various eclectic therapists or any other of the numerous controversies which characterize the field. It is therefore confusing, even for the average professional person, to view the many methods of treatment that are employed for emotional illness. But even more confusing is the fact that " roughly $\frac{2}{3}$ of a group of neurotic patients will recover or improve to a marked extent within about 2 years of the onset of their illness, whether they are treated by means of psychotherapy or not."[2]

The last decade, however, has seen the growth of a new behaviourist psychotherapy built on the firm scientific bedrock of neurophysiology. Its concepts stem from carefully controlled laboratory experiments and its therapeutic tools are derived from the laws of learning. This Journal has already printed several articles dealing with the experimental and theoretical background, methodology, therapeutic efficacy and clinical advantages of behaviour therapy.[3-6] The present article is intended to provide the general practitioner with a broad working knowledge of this approach. We firmly believe that more intimate team-work between doctor and psychotherapist

* Reprinted by permission of the author and the editor of the *S. Afr. Med. J.* from (1958) *S. Afr. Med. J.*, **33**, 660-663.

will, in the long run, prove most beneficial. We also hope to disprove the myth that psychotherapy, by its very nature, must always be difficult, time-consuming and inefficient.

Where necessary, the behaviourist or objective psychotherapist employs all the usual psychotherapeutic techniques, such as support, guidance, insight, catharsis, interpretation, environmental manipulation, etc., but in addition to these more " orthodox " procedures, the behaviour therapist applies objective techniques which are designed to inhibit specific neurotic patterns. His orientation is away from the analysis of hypothetical " minds-within-minds," and his focus of attention is placed instead on his patient's behaviour. Patients learn to behave in a maladaptive fashion and if one is to cure the patient these ways of behaving must be eliminated. Wolpe's[7,8] experimental evidence and clinical research have revealed that neuroses are acquired in anxiety-generating situations and that successful therapy of the neuroses therefore depends on the reciprocal inhibition of neurotic anxiety responses. His methods have yielded a 90 per cent level of " apparently cured or much improved " cases.[8] It is probably safe to say that regardless of differences in theory or technique, the " cures " that occur are accompanied by kinds of changes in personality that can be interpreted as involving learning.[9] Recognizing that neuroses are learned within a social milieu, much emphasis is placed on the fact that the patient is not a clinical label but a human member of society and therefore all specific procedures are applied within the very broad context of social adaptation. This broad social and cultural emphasis by no means precludes the application of detailed or specific procedures where indicated. Behaviour science is concerned with the entire range of activity from the most complex aspects of human interaction right down to the firing of a single neurone. Thus the behaviour therapist does not limit himself to a specific technique—his repertoire of therapeutic methods is sufficiently large and flexible to fit the needs of the individual patient. Therefore the objective therapist is able to swing the focus of attention back and forth from the individual and his or her parts, to the individual in his or her social setting. Another difference between the behaviour therapist and most other psychotherapists is the fact that the behaviourist is not bound by any fixed ritual to delve into the remote history of all his patients. As Rachman[6] has shown, many impressive cures have been effected without any attention being given to the causative factors involved. In our view, " the emphasis in psychological rehabilitation must be on a *synthesis* which would embrace a diverse range of effective therapeutic techniques, as well as innumerable adjunctive measures, to form part of a wide and all-embracing re-educative programme."[10]

The presentation of a treatment project should clarify many of these issues and enable the doctor to appreciate more fully the advantages of modern behaviourist psychotherapy. The following case was selected for several reasons: (1) a variety of techniques was employed; (2) many of our general statements are clearly illustrated; and (3) the didactic elements of the case are not obscured by its complexities. We propose to present a fairly detailed account of each session from the initial diagnostic interviews until the termination of therapy.

THE CASE OF L.H.R.

Extract from G.P.'s Letter of Referral

" This is to introduce Mr. L. H. R., aged 36 years. . . . He appears to be suffering from anxiety and tension . . . tranquillizers have not helped and his condition seems to have deteriorated in recent weeks. . . . "

Initial Interview* (time 75 min)

After putting the patient at ease, a detailed life history was taken. Here are the relevant points: Youngest of 5 children; unhappy home life (inadequate father, stern and over-solicitous mother); poor sibling relationships; childhood terrors retained until early puberty (fear of the dark, nightmares and kidnappers); extreme masturbatory guilts during adolescence; volunteered for active service but was rejected owing to high blood pressure and " blackouts " (no " blackouts " for past 12 years); work situation unsatisfactory (employed as a draughtsman although he has an architectural diploma); poor social and interpersonal relationships (" I have a few friends but most people try to ride me "); principal interests " painting, sketching and science fiction," present adjustment towards sex satisfactory (" We hope to get married if I can get a better job "); his 3 brothers were killed on active service; his father died shortly after the war from " heart failure "; his sister is married and lives in Canada; patient shares a 2-roomed flat with his mother.

Asked to express his problems in his own words, Mr. L. H. R. replied: " I've always been jittery and too particular about things. I suppose I expect too much of myself. Anyhow most of the time I just feel . . . miserable. I sometimes get stupid thoughts like doing away with myself . . . I'm already 36 and what have I got to show for it? . . . My worst trouble is that I'm always checking and re-checking everything. You know, even when I know for sure that the door's locked I've always got to go back and make sure again and again. It's like that with everything. At work, for instance, I'll check the scales again and again and even though I know that the detail is correctly mapped, I go over the figure about 10 times before I do the next one. Sometimes it nearly drives me mad but I've just got to go on and on . . ."

General impressions—Well-groomed, pleasant looking, slender build, active, tense and agitated, timid and reserved. He appears to have little (if

* Unless otherwise stated, the patient was seen twice-weekly.

any) insight. At this stage, he could be summed up as an anxious, compulsive and inhibited individual.

Second Interview (time 40 min)

This session was largely an extension and elaboration of the previous interview. Certain areas of the patient's history were discussed and checked. Additional information emerged, such as the fact that he was still being dominated by his mother and that his compulsive acts (which started in early puberty) became more severe after the death of his father. " In the last few months things have really been worse than ever—quite unbearably so. I don't know why this is, but I suppose that it has to do a lot with the way my mother has been carrying on. . . . She's been going at me pretty solid. . . . She says that it's a pity that I wasn't killed up North instead of the others. Of course she doesn't mean anything by it, but it's upsetting. . . . Also my girl friend and her don't get on so well and my mother said that if I marry her, she'll cut me out of her will."

The discussion then turned to the more detailed and intimate aspects of his home background. The Willoughby Neurotic Tendency Inventory[11] was applied and the score (63) indicated a high level of neurotic disturbance. The qualitative conclusions were: " This person shows obvious insecurity mingled with feelings of hypersensitivity and guilt."

Third Interview (time 2 hr)

This session (apart from a brief discussion on relaxation) was devoted solely to diagnostic psychological testing. The patient was shown to have " superior " Mental Alertness as measured by the N.I.P.R. Test A/1/1[12] and his corrected IQ was 120 on the South African Individual Scale. Selected items on the Thematic Apperception Test[13] together with the Holsopple–Miale Sentence Completion Blank[14] revealed significant clinical trends. Apart from obvious compulsive features, these records indicated underlying trends of unexpressed hostility towards parental figures (especially towards the maternal figure), coupled with generalized anxiety. There was also evidence that he avoided personal challenge presented by others and offered little himself. Although aggressive responses were prevalent throughout, more often than not these impulses were intrapunitive (i.e. " self-punishing ").

Readers who are at all familiar with Freudian writings will find this case rife with analytic material. From the behaviouristic viewpoint, however, the important aetiological factors are briefly the faulty habits which were generated in the home situation and then reinforced by subsequent stress situations. It follows, therefore, that the therapy programme was designed to eliminate or reduce the frequency and intensity of these non-adaptive responses.

Fourth Interview (*time 1 hr*)

Approximately 30 min of this session were devoted to further discussion about the patient's early home life. The patient was allowed free rein and dwelt mainly on the " injustices of his upbringing." Certain of his statements suggested paranoid elements but most of his remarks had the ring of helplessness and self-pity. After about 20 min, the interpretation was suggested that the patient's remarks seemed to indicate feelings of hostility towards the individual members of his family. He immediately countered with vehement over-protestations about their " underlying good intentions." The therapist's non-commital " uh-huh " precipitated a severe reaction: The patient immediately covered his face and wept. After a while he looked up and said, " You're right, I hate the . . . lot of them! " This significant admission led to further uncontrolled weeping which gradually subsided when the therapist finally managed to impart his acceptance, approval and sympathy together with the fact that the patient's feelings and reactions were " normal and quite justifiable." The remainder of the session consisted of training in progressive relaxation.[15]

Fifth Interview (*time 1 hr*)

Mr. L. H. R. stated that he was generally feeling much better, but that " my mother is now getting me down more than ever before. . . . Let's face it, I'm financially dependent on my mother . . . and my work has been slower than ever because of that . . . checking and re-checking." The patient then switched the emphasis to his early sexual difficulties and a frank discussion followed which was designed to dissipate residual guilt-feelings by sanctioning his conduct and by imparting non-moralistic insight into all matters pertaining to sex. The patient was then given preliminary training in " assertive responses "[8,16] (i.e. he was provided with specific instructions on handling all interpersonal relationships adequately and spontaneously " standing up for his own rights ").

Sixth Interview (*time 1 hr*)

After a short discussion about Mr. L. H. R.'s girl friend, further training in assertive responses was given. The patient was urged to be assertive in all situations. He complained that the mere thought of being assertive made him feel afraid, but he was told that with practice, these techniques would soon come to him automatically. Training in progressive relaxation completed the remainder of this session.

Seventh Interview (*time 1 hr*)

The patient spoke at length about his father and about his present attitude towards his mother (" If I ever want to live, I've got to break away from her "). His compulsive behaviour was then discussed and the patient summarized the situation as follows: " If I could only stop myself from this business of re-checking everything 10 times then I'd have a chance. I know I'm good at my work but I'll never get senior posts until I manage to work faster. . . . These compulsions are the things that mess up my whole life."

Eighth Interview (*time 40 min*)

Approximately 20 min were devoted to additional training in assertive responses by means of " psycho-drama " (i.e. the therapist assumed the role of various " threatening figures " and the patient was required to oppose them). The rest of the session consisted of relaxation therapy with preliminary hypnotic suggestions. He responded well to the hypnotic procedures and a catalepsy of his right arm was easily induced.

Ninth Interview (*time 40 min*)

The patient seemed unusually excited. " It's working," he announced as soon as he walked in, " yesterday for the first time, I stood up to my mother and she got such a shock that she just said nothing. . . . I even asked my boss for a raise. I didn't get it, but at least I asked. . . . " The therapist expressed his approval and delight at his progress and encouraged him to continue practising this new habit of assertive responses. (One obviously has to use one's discretion in advising assertive behaviour as the aim is definitely not to make people become objectionably aggressive. In this instance, Mr. L. H. R. was so very inhibited that there was never any risk of making him permanently aggressive and at best, by acquiring assertive habits, he would be able to achieve a better balance in his assertiveness–submissiveness ratio and not serve as a perpetual doormat for the rest of his life.) Hypnotic relaxation was then administered for 15 min and a glove anaesthesia was induced without difficulty.

Tenth Interview (*time 30 min*)

The patient was hypnotized and given more or less the following instructions while in a deep hypnotic trance: " You feel calm and relaxed, deeply relaxed and peaceful. Now I want you to imagine yourself at work. You still feel calm and relaxed. Now imagine yourself drawing a plan and checking as you go along. You're quite relaxed. You check it once. Everything is correct. You make sure and go over it again. You are still calm and relaxed. You begin to check it a third time, but now suddenly you feel anxious. You feel uneasy and tense. Rapidly the tension mounts. (The patient was writhing and breathing very heavily at this stage.) You leave the plan. You do not check it again. Now you start a new drawing. Picture the new situation. As soon as you start the new activity you are once again calm and relaxed. You feel calm and peaceful. . . . When I count up to five you will open your eyes." When asked to recall what had transpired while under hypnosis, the patient at first appeared to be completely amnesic, but after a while he was able to recollect the entire session and reported that he had visualized the situation " just as though I was there at the time."

Eleventh–Nineteenth Interviews (*time of each—30 min*)

The hypnotic procedure employed in the previous interview was applied, with slight modifications, until the end of the nineteenth interview, when the patient reported that his compulsions no longer troubled him in the work situation. " I'm turning out 5 times more work than before. . . . Sometimes I still tend to fuss over things more than I ought to, but that doesn't worry me." Specific instructions in assertive behaviour were also given prominence throughout these interviews. On the twelfth interview, the therapist was about 20 min behind time and Mr. L. H. R. politely reprimanded him by saying. " You should have told me that you were running late and I would have slipped down for a haircut meanwhile." This was indeed an impressive improvement from his previously inhibited and almost obsequious behaviour. The therapist apologized for the delay and later expressed his strong approval of Mr. L. H. R.'s assertive behaviour.

Twentieth Interview (*time 30 min*)

The patient was not seen for nearly 5 weeks. He had had an emergency appendectomy and had developed certain complications after the operation. " I've been back at work now for 2 days. . . . I've been doing a lot of thinking this past month and you'll be surprised to hear what I've done. . . . I've asked Betty (his same girl friend) to marry me. . . . I've accepted a job in Cape Town. . . . My aunt recently lost her husband and she is coming to live with my mother. . . . We plan to leave town as man and wife before the 16th (less than 3 weeks). . . . Do you approve of all this ? . . ." The therapist expressed his strong approval of all Mr. L. H. R.'s decisions. The need to continue practising assertive behaviour was again impressed upon him.

Twenty-first Interview (*time 1 hr*)

This interview took place 15 days after the previous one. Mr. L. H. R. was accompanied by his fiancee. She was interviewed privately and seemed a sensible person with considerable understanding and insight. At the end of the interview she said, " Now that L. has learnt to stand on his own two feet, I'm sure we will make out just fine." Mr. L. H. R. was then asked to come in, and the conversation terminated with a general discussion about their future plans.

Periodically he communicated with the therapist by letter. Eight months after therapy, en route to Rhodesia, Mr. L. H. R. telephoned the therapist and reported that he had maintained a satisfactory adjustment. " I have conquered the compulsions for good and everything is better than I ever expected."

DISCUSSION

This case was not presented for its dramatic interest, since it is by no means spectacular and it is certainly not intended as a " model case."

The first 4 interviews employ the usual diagnostic and psychotherapeutic procedures but, after that, the more objective techniques are brought into clearer focus. It is soon apparent that the patient's principal problems are " inhibitions and compulsions," and from the sixth interview onwards, the therapist is obviously of the opinion that if these two factors are eliminated, the rest will automatically fall into place. By the eighth interview, the emphasis is present-and-future orientated and, contrary to analytic preachings, little time is devoted to " digging up the past." The reader will have observed the fact that the compulsive features were adequately reduced without any attention being given to the causative factors involved.

We should like to give a brief theoretical explanation of our hypnotic procedure as applied to the patient's compulsive acts. It is generally agreed that obsessional or compulsive symptoms have the effect of allaying or inhibiting anxiety. We know, for instance, that if a patient is prevented from satisfying his compulsive urges he displays acute anxiety until he finally carries out his ritual. Now if we reverse this process (i.e. the patient becomes anxious when performing his compulsive act and feels complacent when avoiding compulsive behaviour) the compulsive acts should automatically fall away. This, at least, is the theory behind the hypnotic procedure employed. Wolpe,[8] however, reports more sophisticated objective techniques, with wider applicability, for handling compulsive and obsessional neurotics. " Orthodox " practitioners would argue that symptom removal without the elimination of the " underlying cause " does not constitute a " cure." Rachman,[6] however, has shown that " too great a concern with ' underlying causes ' may under certain circumstances even impede therapeutic progress." Eysenck[17] expertly summarizes the situation as follows: " According to Freud, there is a ' disease ' which produces symptoms; cure the disease and the symptoms will vanish. According to the alternative view, there is no ' disease,' there are merely wrong habits which have been learned and must be unlearned."

The bulk of the treatment (i.e. 19 interviews) extended over 10 weeks and the total time spent with the patient amounted to less than 16 hr. He was considered " much improved " in terms of Knight's 5 criteria[18]— symptom improvement, increased productiveness, improved adjustment and pleasure in sex, improved interpersonal relationship, and increased stress-tolerance.

SUMMARY

Some important practical and theoretical advantages of behaviour therapy are outlined. These include objective techniques, controlled experimental backing, effective short-term therapeutic programmes, and a high level of cured and improved cases. A treatment project is presented in some detail in the hopes of providing the general medical practitioner with additional insight into the dynamics of behaviour therapy.

REFERENCES

1. SALTER, A. (1953). *The Case Against Psychoanalysis*. Medical Publications, New York.
2. EYSENCK, H. J. (1952). *The Scientific Study of Personality*. Routledge & Kegan Paul, London.
3. WOLPE, J. (1950). *S. Afr. Med. J.*, **24,** 613.
4. WOLPE, J. (1953). *S. Afr. Med. J.*, **26,** 825.
5. LAZARUS, A. A. and RACHMAN, S. (1957). *S. Afr. Med. J.*, **31,** 934.
6. RACHMAN, S. (1958). *S. Afr. Med. J.*, **32,** 19.
7. WOLPE, J. (1948). *An Approach to the Problem of Neurosis Based on the Conditioned Response*. M.D. Thesis, University of the Witwatersrand, Johannesburg.
8. WOLPE, J. (1954). *Arch. Neurol. Psychiat.*, **72,** 205.
9. BUGELSKI, B. R. (1956). *The Psychology of Learning*. Henry Holt, New York.
10. LAZARUS, A. A. (1956). *S. Afr. Med. J.*, **30,** 707.
11. WILLOUGHBY, R. (1934). *J. Soc. Psychol.*, **5,** 91.
12. NATIONAL INSTITUTE FOR PERSONNEL RESEARCH—Mental alertness A/1/1 (a test for matriculated persons).
13. MURRAY, H. A. (1943). *Thematic Apperception Test Manual*. Harvard University, Boston, Mass.
14. HOLSOPPLE, J. Q. and MIALE, F. R. (1954). *Sentence Completion: A Projective Method for the Study of Personality*. Thomas, Illinois.
15. JACOBSON, E. (1938). *Progressive Relaxation*. University of Chicago Press, Chicago.
16. SALTER, A. (1952). *Conditioned Reflex Therapy*. Allen & Unwin, London.
17. EYSENCK, H. J. (1957). *The Dynamics of Anxiety and Hysteria*. Routledge & Kegan Paul, London.
18. KNIGHT, R. P. (1941). *Amer. J. Psychiat.*, **98,** 434.

THE RELEVANCE OF LEARNING THEORY TO THE TREATMENT OF AN OBSESSIVE-COMPULSIVE STATE*

D. WALTON, B.A., DIP.PSYCH.

Principal Clinical Psychologist, Winwick Hospital, Warrington

DESCRIPTION OF DISORDER

THE PATIENT, a man of 33 years, was admitted to hospital for the investigation and treatment of 4 disabling compulsions.

He was obsessed with the idea of germs and dirt and washed his hands innumerable times per day. He had to conform to an elaborate ritual before each meal to be certain that his hands were washed properly. If there was a delay before a meal, following the completion of this ritual, he was forced to wash again.

He was prevented from walking along corridors, paths, pavements or roads because he was forced to clear, by kicking, every small piece of stone or paper out of his way. He reported that he feared people might fall over the stones. He had even been forced to alight from his bicycle in order to kick small objects from the road. These 2 major compulsions were incapacitating.

A further compulsion was an inability to close any door and remove his hand from the door-handle without first frequently testing the door to see that it was closed.

He was also forced to tap a cigarette very many times before lighting it.

Two months after admittance to hospital he had completed a course of deep insulin therapy with little effect. An independent observation at that time was, " If not under constant supervision and direction his life would be fully occupied in these compulsive acts." Intensive largactil treatment was commenced several days later. Following limited therapeutic improvement, it was suggested that the patient might respond to a course of treatment based on learning theory. The largactil dosage was reduced gradually to 75 mg t.d.s. in order to conform with theoretical requirements based on certain personality-drug action postulates (see below).

* Specially written for this book.

PROPOSED THEORETICAL MODEL (I)

The compulsions were regarded as drive-reducing responses, evoked originally in a traumatic situation. In such a situation intense anxiety would have been generated and the compulsion would have resulted in a reduction or cessation of the anxiety-inducing stimulus. The reaction potential of the compulsion would have developed as the product of the habit strength and the fluctuating drive strength (anxiety).

As a modification of these behavioural abnormalities was the aim, according to the present theoretical formulation, reference to the causes and background situations which precipitated the compulsions was not strictly necessary. It could be hypothesized, however, that following certain petty thefts guilt and anxiety occurred and the resulting strength of the 2 major compulsions became associated with the very strong reinforcement favouring conditions, that is they became anxiety-reducing compulsions. The conditioned stimulus for the 2 subsidiary compulsions may have been an awareness of possible imperfection, an awareness which had something in common with the original conditioned stimulus for the 2 major compulsions (primary stimulus generalization).

THERAPY, TYPE (I)

A method of treatment was evolved based on:
(1) The learning theory constructs of reciprocal, reactive and conditioned inhibition.
(2) The reciprocal inhibitory effects of drug-action when related to anxiety-provoking situations.
(3) The relevance of personality to the optional growth of reciprocal inhibition following drug-administration.

Three quarters of an hour before the patient attended for his appointment he was given 75 mg largactil. This was designed to " reduce " anxiety during the treatment session. The dosage was an arbitrary one. It was based on the psychiatrist's estimation of the optimal dosage required to reduce anxiety yet minimizing any drowsiness (exaggerated reactive inhibition) which might become in turn associated with the treatment situation and so hinder progress in that situation (conditioned inhibition). It was recognized that although the largactil might exert no real chemical therapeutic effect this was unimportant as a reduction in anxiety might well occur as a result of being on treatment (placebo effect) and so conform with the requirements of the theoretical model devised above.

This formulation was prompted following exploratory-therapeutic results with a dysthymic patient who complained excessively of pains behind the eyes and of considerable tension.[1] In order to reduce the frequency of these complaints, it was predicted that under a depressant drug (sodium amytal) reactive inhibition would be generated more quickly and so, if the patient was asked voluntarily to complain, then there should, over a period of trials, be a rapid decline in involuntary complaints because of the rapid build up of conditioned inhibitory potential. It was found, however, that dosages of up to 9 gr merely increased the number of his complaints and resulted in an apparent increase in elation. Dosages in excess of 9 gr administered $\frac{1}{2}$ hr before each session resulted in a very significant drop in frequency due presumably to sedation having been achieved and to the accumulated conditioned inhibitory potential. Figure 1 shows the results. On E.E.G. examination his sedation threshold[2] was found to be high, consistent with his dysthymic symptoms. This exploratory study suggested that the results might be of therapeutic value in the present treatment-programme, in that if a crucial sedation level could be found below which there was a decrease in anxiety, with a minimal growth of inhibitory potential, then there should be a rapid break-up of his instrumental compulsive habits dependent on this anxiety.

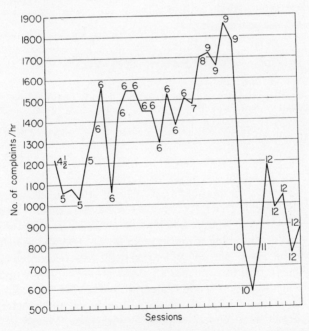

FIG. 1. Figures on graph represent the different dosages of sodium amytal (in grains) administered prior to each session.

The patient was also given 75 mg largactil $\frac{3}{4}$ hr before each main meal so as to " reduce " the anxiety in the period usually occupied in washing his hands.

Apart from the reciprocal inhibitory effects of the largactil, two other methods were adopted to act simultaneously to achieve the same effect, that is to reduce the anxiety. The first of these was designed to deal specifically with the compulsion to pick up stones and paper. A graded series of " walks " were planned. These ranged from very clean floors of a sheltered corridor, recently washed corridors and stairways leading eventually to a roadway under construction with half bricks forming its basis. The patient was first only allowed to walk along the " clean " thoroughfares until he found little or no apprehension developing, then he was allowed to go on to the next stage. He did this always under the influence of largactil. The psychologist walked in front of him on these excursions and showed that there was no chance of falling.

Under largactil he was also taken to the wash-bowls in order to effect a response decrement, though he was not required to wash. This method is similar to Jones'[3] alternative suggestion for the removal of a tremor in a male patient, especially evident when he had to write in front of others and particularly so when in the presence of his superiors at work. Although Jones successfully applied a conditioning treatment and a generalization technique, he suggested that if the tremorous patient had been able to spend a considerable period each day with his employer, though not requested to write, a later request for his signature might produce little evidence of a tremor.

It was hypothesized that any reduction of anxiety associated with the 2 major compulsions would in turn exert a beneficial effect on the 2 remaining compulsive acts, particularly if they arose through a process of stimulus generalization from the same conditioned stimulus.

Outcome of Therapy (I)

The patient attended for eighteen 20-min sessions. From the first session onwards there was a good response until some 6 weeks later he was virtually symptom free. The psychiatrist in charge of the case reported the day before discharge, " A remarkable lessening in tension, and in his compulsions. After 3 weeks he was able to walk along broken brick and stone paths without kicking the stones out of the way. He now washes his hands the normal number of times per day and does not overtly have the feeling of guilt that compelled him to this ritual. Now fit for discharge." The day the patient left hospital he was interviewed. He admitted that he was ready to leave hospital and that he was feeling as well as before his illness. He agreed that none of the 4 compulsions were present.

After leaving hospital he worked for his old firm for 3 months. He was dismissed for slowness and for being too exact. He then joined a local plumbing firm for 2 months but again lost his job, the reason being given that in bad weather the employer could not afford to pay his staff! A short time after this he attended a psychiatric OP clinic, where he was advised to return to hospital. His main symptoms were a general slowness (he had to do things well) and excessive handwashing. His wife reported that in spite of these 2 symptoms he was not now troubled by " stone-kicking " or the picking up of small objects from a road and that he could go out very much more than when he was ill originally.

Some 7 months after discharge he was admitted to hospital. The stone-kicking compulsion no longer bothered him, whilst the compulsion concerning the checking of doors to see that they were shut and the repetitive tapping of a cigarette were no longer problems. Excessive handwashing and over-thoroughness were his main symptoms.

DISCUSSION

The theoretical model constructed to account for the development and treatment of his compulsions was inadequate, though the patient did respond immediately to treatment. Few sessions were required to eliminate his compulsions, in contrast to his failure to respond to other therapeutic methods. This suggested that the model was not necessarily incorrect but incomplete.

The following considerations appeared relevant to the development of a more complete model. First, the present result contrasts with those obtained with patients suffering from chronic symptoms.[4,5,6] The first of these cases was a young girl, who had been aphonic for 7 years. Treatment was successful and neither the aphonia nor alternative symptoms emerged at the end of 2 years. The second case was a young woman who suffered from neuro-dermatitis for nearly 2 years, perpetuated by compulsive scratching. A learning theory formulation prompted a line of treatment which rapidly resulted in the dissipation of the neuro-dermatitis. There have been no other symptoms or a recurrence of the skin-condition over 4 years. Both these patients contrast with the present one in that they were suffering from long-standing symptoms, the latter from symptoms of more recent onset.

It may be, that in the chronic phase, neurotic symptoms exist in their own right divorced from the original cause. The treatment demanded may therefore be specific to the symptom or habit, without recourse to knowledge of the initial cause. In the acute phase, neurotic symptoms may arise more directly from an acknowledged source of anxiety or situation of stress, though the pattern of anxiety reduction may only be an exaggeration of methods which have previously been adopted and found to be successful in the reduction of anxiety. In this sense there is of course no real " acute " breakdown, but only a period in which there is an intensification of previously learned anxiety-reducing responses.

The initial model may have failed therefore in as much as it proposed a line of treatment more suitable for a long-standing symptom. The alternative, with regard to treatment might be, first, to determine the patient's position on the introversion–extraversion dimension and to make inferences, partly on the basis of this information, and partly from direct questioning, on his characteristic methods of anxiety reduction. After this, one might need to assess the extent to which his present symptoms occurred because there were present in the environment stresses which were directly incompatible (e.g. doubt) with his own methods of anxiety reduction (e.g. order)—such than an intensification of previously learned anxiety-reducing responses was demanded. This would be particularly the case if no other adequate method of reducing anxiety had previously competed with his compulsions and if the compulsions had been particularly effective in reducing such anxiety.

Once this information had been acquired, treatment would logically consist of the patient *learning* either alternative methods of anxiety reduction or applying the same methods to a lesser degree. It would then follow that the patient would build up a tolerance of environmental stresses (e.g. uncertainty, doubt) which previously his own learned methods of anxiety reduction found intolerable. In other words his own methods of anxiety reduction produced another set of situations which created excessive anxiety and called for an intensification of his compulsions.

The Maudsley Personality Inventory[7] showed that the patient was markedly introverted. It also emerged that for as long as he could remember he had been slow in completing tasks. He admitted that accuracy and neatness were qualities he always demanded and that he would always remain at a task until it was complete. Such qualities as slowness, accuracy and persistence are consistent with his marked introversion and with some of the differences which have been demonstrated experimentally between introverts and extraverts.[8,9,10]

One might hypothesize, therefore, that all of these qualities were learned patterns of response by which anxiety was reduced or doubts about adequacy of performance, for example, minimized. It would then follow that any situation which produced uncertainty, doubt, or was incomplete, would result in anxiety and in an intensification of previously learned anxiety-reducing habits, particularly if the drive level was very strong. This interpretation is of course consistent with Eysenck's[11] theory that introverts condition particularly well, that socialization is mediated by conditioning, and that under conditions of equal environmental pressure introverts are expected to be over-socialized and to be concerned with such social qualities as persistence, accuracy and approval.

It subsequently emerged that there were many situations, before his breakdown, which contained uncertainty and doubt. First, he stole a quantity of lead from his firm. As the plumbing manager was an accomplice there was always a doubt that he may talk about their joint escapade. The patient became very upset after this incident and decided not to steal any more material. The work-site then changed to one where the patient now lives. He made a concrete yard and path at the back of the house by " collecting " half-bricks and cement from the site. He also " annexed " a clothes post, though he did ask the joiner and foreman for it (a situation which presumably again maximized his anxiety because of the possibility that the foreman might also mention the incident to someone else). A similar incident occurred involving a quantity of paint and one of the painters on the site.

It is now possible to revise the original model and to suggest that his symptoms (compulsions) were exaggerations of previously learned and effective patterns of anxiety reduction (order, certainty, slowness and persistence) and that they arose because there were present in the environment stressor factors which were directly incompatible (uncertainty, doubt, etc.) with his own initial method of anxiety reduction, thereby calling for stronger measures. The fact that his compulsions were so clearly maladaptive, suggests that the very strong drives associated with his misdemeanours were not efficient in motivating an adaptive response, an interpretation in line with the Yerkes–Dodson[12] law.

The indicated method of treatment would be to build up, through a process of learning, the patient's tolerance of the uncertain or the doubtful, to increase his speed without serious detriment to his accuracy and so to minimize the anxiety associated with any such situation in which, for example, threat of failure was important. Since the compulsions arose, it is hypothesized, from this anxiety associated with the need for social approval, their extinction would logically take place. In fact an attempt is made to reduce the patient's over-socialization from which his compulsions presumably arise. It is again in line with the Yerkes–Dodson[12] law for as the drive level is reduced by building up the patient's tolerance of the uncertain, and so removing a set of stimuli which are likely to produce extra anxiety, so is a more optimal drive level achieved and less maladaptive responses called for.

THERAPY, TYPE (II)

It will be remembered that the rigidity of the patient's compulsions was considered to be partly explainable on the grounds that no other adequate methods of anxiety reduction had competed with them and that he was very likely therefore to use the same methods again. Since this method produced a set of environmental stimuli which were inacceptable, and called forth further anxiety-reducing responses, a method which did not possess these harmful side-effects would help the individual to abandon his rigid, though previously useful, method of anxiety reduction in its favour. In other words, the greater the magnitude of the incentive used as an alternative reinforcement to anxiety reduction by such as slowness and accuracy, the greater the alternative reaction potential for any given level of habit strength and so the greater the patient's tolerance of the uncertain. Drive level would then more approach the optimal and call for less extreme and maladaptive compulsions (cf. Yerkes and Dodson law).[12]

Hull's corollary XIV[13] seemed relevant to this formulation: competition of incompatible reaction potentials (paraphrased from Hull by Hilgard),[14] " When reaction potentials to two or more incompatible responses occur in an organism at the same instant, each in a suprathreshold magnitude, only that reaction whose momentary reaction potential is greatest will be evoked." Both the compulsions and the alternative reaction potential would be in a suprathreshold magnitude. To increase the magnitude of the incentive associated with the alternative reaction potential would presumably momentarily increase this reaction potential so that its evocation would gain priority over that of the compulsions.

Before treatment proper began three predictions were made. As they were based on the patient's clinical condition, his first reactions to these situations represented a base-line against which to evaluate the efficacy of the therapy adopted.

(1) That if he was asked to complete the Progressive Matrices[15] under stressed conditions (20 min time limit), SD (drive stimuli) would be maximized and rapid diminution of SD demanded. The reaction potential would then be partly a multiplicative function of previously acquired habit strength and intense anxiety, i.e. a high degree of accuracy would be demanded, slowness would result and there would be a low speed–accuracy ratio. The very strong drive of anxiety and presumably fear of failure will thus have interfered with his performance.

(2) The same response would be observed if the Thematic Apperception Test[16] was administered to him. He would show long initial reaction times, long total reaction times and produce very meagre stories.

(3) There would be a very intropunitive response to the Superiority–Inferiority Test.[17] This might arise because the expression of aggression would maximize those conditions of which he was most afraid, i.e. if aggression was shown he would be *uncertain* or *doubtful* of people's attitudes towards him. This prediction can also be made on the basis of Eysenck's[11] theory, viz. " socialization in our particular culture pattern stresses the inhibition of overt aggressive activities . . . and the introverts should therefore have attitudes strongly supporting those ethical and moral agencies and conceptions which act in such a way as to inhibit overt aggressive and sexual behaviour."

He was first tested on the above three measures and the results recorded. His inefficient methods of anxiety-reduction were fully explained to him and the results from Table 1 which were all consistent with the initial predictions, were presented in illustration. On the Progressive Matrices[15] ('38) he attempted relatively few items though the majority of those attempted

TABLE 1

Changes in test scores as therapy progresses

Progressive matrices ('38)

1st day	20 min stress test: 28 correct out of 31 attempts:
1 week later	42 correct out of 45 attempts:

Superiority—inferiority scale

	Extra-punitive	Intro-punitive
I would be:	8	16
I ought to be:	7	17
Most people would be:	9	15

	Extra-punitive	Intro-punitive
I would be:	20	4
I ought to be:	18	6
Most people would be:	18	16

T.A.T.

Initial reaction times:	80 sec	8 min	2 min 40 sec	2 min 32 sec	3 min 30 sec
Total reaction times:	2 min 55 sec	8 min	3 min 40 sec	3 min 22 sec	5 min 20 sec
No. of words per story:	67	0	33	30	34
Initial reaction times:	52 sec	85 sec	13 sec	45 sec	35 sec
Total reaction times:	3 min 10 sec	4 min 2 sec	2 min 25 sec	2 min 40 sec	3 min 20 sec
No. of words per story:	105	91	98	100	119
Initial reaction times:	25 sec	25 sec	26 sec	30 sec	15 sec
Total reaction times:	2 min 8 sec	1 min 10 sec	1 min 50 sec	2 min 5 sec	1 min 30 sec
No. of words per story:	85	37	77	88	71

1st day · 1 week later · 2 days later · 1 day later

were correct; the T.A.T. initial and total reaction times were ponderously slow and his productivity minimal; whilst the Superiority–Inferiority Scale showed him to be markedly intropunitive.

Discussion took place with the patient until he voluntarily admitted that it would be far more beneficial if he could combine an increase in speed with no serious detrimental effects on his accuracy and that he would welcome such a change as he had been losing his jobs because of such slowness, a side-effect of his own making. He also admitted that the intropunitive picture, although reflecting his likely response, did not represent his true feelings.

Two simultaneous therapeutic approaches were then adopted. The first of these consisted in the development of the incentive used as an alternative reinforcement to anxiety reduction by such as slowness and accuracy. The second consisted of an introductory statement to the patient along Wolpian lines,[18] stressing that, although he may feel resentment and could not express this because of anxiety, the outward expression of this aggression would reciprocally inhibit the anxiety. Examples were given from Wolpe of how this could be achieved. In other words the two approaches were designed to reduce anxiety and to produce more optimal drive-level conditions so that adaptive rather than maladaptive responses could be learned.

In order to increase the reaction potential alternative to slowness and accuracy, the Progressive Matrices[15] was given again under stressed conditions. The rewards associated with retaining the same degree of accuracy though speeding up his performance were stressed before testing. It was considered that if this increase in speed could be demonstrated to him, the incentive would be sufficiently great to overcome the reinforcement to anxiety reduction by such as slowness.

Table 1 shows the very striking increase in " productivity " during the second stress testing session. Although he obtained only 28 correct out of 31 answers in the first session, he increased his score to 42 correct out of 45 answers on the second. He was most impressed and enthusiastic over the fact that he obtained 14 more correct solutions without an increase in the number of errors. In order to avoid an interpretation of deception by the examiner, the latter had marked the test with the patient.

The patient was then asked to complete the same 5 T.A.T. plates as before, bearing in mind the results he had just achieved with the Matrices. Table 1 shows that there was a marked increase in productivity and speed. The repeat T.A.T. stories were then compared with the first set and the patient asked to compare them for quality. He admitted that the repeat stories were far more interesting and, what was more important, he felt that he had done a better job on them in spite of spending far less time in completing them. In order to prevent the patient from considering that such improvement was a function of the familiarity of the material, a set of 5 other T.A.T. plates was provided and the patient asked to create stories just as he had done with the other plates. Table 1 shows the results. He maintained his improvement in speed and productivity.

It had by now become apparent that by demonstrating his ability to overcome his slowness, an incentive had been provided which could be extended therapeutically. He was encouraged to attend classes in occupational therapy and to apply in practice what he had just learned. At the same time as these experiments were being carried out, therapy based on the principle of reciprocal inhibition was in progress. Several weeks after the commencement of this approach, there was a shift towards extrapunitive type responses on Fould's test,[17] a shift which the patient considered to be representative of his response to real-life situations. Following the initial experimental–therapeutic sessions and the Wolpian approach the patient showed rapid progress. His hand-washing compulsions quickly reverted to normal frequency, whilst there was a general increase in his speed. The other major compulsion and the 2 minor compulsions were not in evidence during the patient's second stay in hospital. He was discharged from hospital symptom-free.

SUMMARY AND OUTCOME OF THERAPY

The first type of therapy was based on:

(1)   The learning theory constructs of reciprocal, reactive and conditioned inhibition.

(2)   The reciprocal inhibitory effects of drug-action when related to anxiety-provoking situations.

(3)   The relevance of personality to the optimal growth of reciprocal inhibition following drug-administration.

There was an immediate response to therapy. Eighteen 20-min sessions, covering 6 weeks, were all that were required to remove the 4 compulsions. He was discharged symptom-free.

Seven months later he was admitted to hospital again. The stone-kicking compulsion no longer was present, whilst the compulsions over the checking of doors and the repetitive tapping of a cigarette were no longer problems. Excessive hand-washing and over-thoroughness were his main symptoms.

A revised theoretical model resulted in a further method of therapy. This method consisted of " reducing " the patient's over-socialization from which, it was hypothesized, his compulsions arose.

This was achieved by building up the rewards associated with an alternative reaction potential. Two methods were used, one consisted of demonstrating the inefficiency of his old methods and of showing that they were based on a false assumption; the second consisted of the development of self-assertion by the method of reciprocal inhibition.

The validity of the revised model was tentatively demonstrated by the patient's satisfactory response to therapy. On discharge his hand-washing compulsions were no longer present. He has now been free from this compulsion for 4 months, whilst he is not anything like as slow as he was originally.

The stone-kicking compulsion has not been in evidence since he was in hospital on the first occasion over a year ago. He still hesitates a little when shutting doors, though this has never really bothered him since his first treatment sessions over a year ago. The same applies to the cigarette tapping. This he no longer considers to be a problem.

All in all, one major and two minor compulsions have not bothered him for over a year, whilst the hand-washing compulsion has, following the revised treatment model, been absent for four months.

Four months after the termination of his second set of treatment he and his wife reported that everything was going well. His wife considered that he was far better than when he left hospital the first time.

REFERENCES

1. WALTON, D. (1958). Reciprocal inhibition, sedation threshold, practice and the treatment of compulsions and schizophrenic slowness. *Bull. Brit. Psychol. Soc.*, No. 36.
2. SHAGASS, C. and NAIMAN, J. (1956). The sedation threshold as an objective index of manifest anxiety in the psychoneurosis. *J. Psychosom. Res.*, **1**, 49-57.
3. JONES, G. (1958). Neurosis and experimental psychology. *J. Ment. Sci.*, **104**, 434.
4. WALTON, D. (1958). The application of learning theory to the treatment of hysterical aphonia. *Bull. Brit. Psychol. Soc.*, No. 34.
5. WALTON, D. and BLACK, D. A. The application of modern learning theory to the treatment of chronic hysterical aphonia. *J. Psychosom. Res.* In press.
6. WALTON, D. (1959). The application of learning theory to the treatment of a case of neuro-dermatitis. In *Behaviour Therapy and the Neuroses*, ed. by H. J. EYSENCK.
7. EYSENCK, H. J. (1956). The questionnaire measurement of neuroticism and extraversion. *Riv. Psicol.*, **50**, 113-140.
8. HIMMELWEIT, H. T. (1946). Speed and accuracy of work as related to temperament. *Brit. J. Psychol.*, **36**, 132-144.
9. EYSENCK, H. J. (1947). *Dimensions of Personality*. Routledge & Kegan Paul, London.
10. FOULDS, G. A. (1952). Temperamental differences in maze performance. *Brit. J. Psychol.*, **43**, 33-41.
11. EYSENCK, H. J. (1957). *The Dynamics of Anxiety and Hysteria*. Routledge & Kegan Paul, London.
12. YERKES, R. M. and DODSON, J. D. (1908). The relation of strength of stimulus to rapidity of habit formation. *J. Comp. Neurol Psychol.*, **18**, 459-482.
13. HULL, C. L. (1952). *A Behavior System*. Yale Univ. Press, New Haven.
14. HILGARD, E. R. (1956). *Theories of Learning*. Appleton–Century–Crofts, New York.
15. RAVEN, J. C. (1938). *Progressive Matrices*. Sets A, B, C, D and E. Lewis, London.
16. MURRAY, H. A. (1943). *Thematic Apperception Test Manual*. Harvard Univ. Press, Cambridge.
17. FOULDS, G. A. (1958). Superiority–inferiority index in relation to frustrating situations. *J. Clin. Psychol.*, **14**, 163-166.
18. WOLPE, J. (1958). *Psychotherapy by Reciprocal Inhibition*. Stamford Univ. Press.

LEARNING THEORY APPLIED TO THE TREATMENT OF A PATIENT WITH OBSESSIONAL RUMINATIONS*†

J. R. BEVAN, B.SC.

Senior Clinical Psychologist, Hellingly Hospital, Hailsham, Sussex

THE PATIENT was a housewife, aged 29. She had married at the age of 22. There were 2 children, boys aged 6 and 4 years. Five weeks before the first psychiatric interview a Jehovah's Witness had come to her house and left some pamphlets. The patient read these and became preoccupied with the news of the world crisis and correlated this with the statements in the pamphlets. The patient also complained that " awful thoughts " would poke into her mind as though another brain was present. She would see a man and woman together and would think, although they were strangers, that they were having an affair. These thoughts would come to her when she was in a bus or out walking. A diagnosis of obsessional neurosis was made at the first interview (week 6, from the commencement of the illness). She attended the clinic a week later very distressed. Two ECT were given and she became relatively free from compulsive thoughts for 4 weeks.

Week 11—She had relapsed and had unpleasant compulsive thoughts every day. These were of a sexual nature abhorrent to her.

Weeks 12–21—She was admitted to hospital and given a course of 6 ECT. Four weeks after the completion of the course she had had one relapse into compulsive thoughts at home. In hospital compulsive thoughts had been confined to ½-hr periods. She said that she was happier in hospital than at home.

Weeks 23–52—She was sent on leave and was seen at intervals of from 4 to 6 weeks at the out-patient clinic. Compulsive thoughts about religion, and sex and religion in combination, returned. The relationship between her " bad days " and her menses was charted and acetazolamide was prescribed for the 10 pre-menstrual days.

Week 56—She was reported as feeling almost entirely free from compulsive thoughts for the past 4 weeks. Her medication was drinamyl and acetazolamide.

* The author's thanks are due to Dr. D. Rice, Medical Superintendent, Hellingly Hospital, for permission to summarize and publish the case and to Mr. D. Walton, Principal Clinical Psychologist, Winwick Hospital, Lancashire, who advised on the initial conditioning procedure.

† Specially written for this book.

Week 58—Two weeks later severe obsessional thoughts had returned. She was given a course of 4 ECT and re-admitted.

Week 60—In hospital she was put on chlorpromazine 100 mg and amytal 6 gr 6-hourly. Then chlorpromazine was increased to 200 mg tds for 6 days. Ten days after admission she was reported as largely symptom-free under heavy sedation, apart from 2 recent attacks. Leucotomy was discussed with her and she received the suggestion favourably.

Week 66—She became very distressed during the next 6 weeks. Five ECT were given and it was reported that her obsessional thoughts were largely broken up. Her obsessional thoughts returned whilst she was at home one week-end.

Week 70—A moderately successful 2-day leave was reported, but a lot of diffuse anxiety was present.

Week 72—She was seen by the psychologist. Her case had been discussed at an earlier date and it was agreed to carry out a procedure based on learning theory.

SYMPTOMS AT THE COMMENCEMENT OF THE CONDITIONING PROCEDURE

The current ruminations that she reported to the psychologist were about the possibility of war and the claim of the Jehovah's Witnesses that the end of the world is imminent and foretold by passages in the Bible. She would also worry about being ill and being unable to manage at home. The occurrence of religious and sexual images together had been mentioned as a feature of her obsessional thinking but she did not report this to the psychologist although she recollected imagining men exposing themselves to her whilst she was coming to hospital.

Psychological Tests

Maudsley Personality Inventory	Neuroticism 37 ⎱ = Dysthymia
	Extraversion 14 ⎰
Progressive Matrices ('38)	Grade II
Mill Hill Vocabulary Scale	Grade III+
Epstein test	Over-inclusion score 9
	Under-inclusion score 5
Nufferno level test, GL/3A.35	Score 366
Nufferno stressed speed test A(1)	Accuracy 18
	Speed 191
Minnesota Multiphasic Personality Inventory	L score 3
	F score 2
	K score 13

Hypochondriasis	T score 44	Paranoia	T score 50
Depression	,, 78	Psychasthenia	,, 65
Hysteria	,, 61	Schizophrenia	,, 57
Psychopathic Deviate	,, 48	Hypomania	,, 35
Masculinity–Femininity	,, 45		

Her score on the stressed test was low compared with her accuracy and score on the level test, but there was an absence of supporting evidence for psychosis either clinically or from other test results. The test results did not appear to be in disagreement with her psychiatric diagnosis and confirmed the psychiatrist's opinion that she was of above average intelligence.

Rationale of Treatment

It was decided to use the principle of reciprocal inhibition, using chlor-promazine to block anxiety, in a conditioning situation, the aim being to increase her tolerance for the anxiety-provoking stimuli. It was also regarded as important that reactive and conditioned inhibition should not be allowed to develop and thus increase $_sE_R$.

Procedure carried out by the Psychologist

The patient took 100 mg chlorpromazine $\frac{3}{4}$ hr prior to coming to the psychologist's office. Headlines in her daily paper of violence in various parts of the world and the H-bomb had previously triggered off compulsive thinking about the end of the world and the Jehovah's Witnesses views on this. The reading of this paper had been one of the earliest generalizations of her anxiety and it was decided to make use of this part of her generalization continuum.[1] At the first interview the current copy of the paper was placed on a ledge in the far corner of the room and the patient was asked if she would pick it up and read it. This she did calmly. She was required to read the paper aloud, a fresh issue each day, on 4 occasions. If at any time she became anxious or bored (this being interpreted as reactive inhibition building up) she was told to stop reading. She would be slightly worried during the day after reading passages about the H-bomb and missiles (it was pointed out that she was by no means the only person to feel this), but never for the entire day. She did not report any compulsive thinking about the end of the world. She was encouraged to read the paper by herself in the lounge after these 4 sessions. During this time she was told that it was desirable that she should read some Jehovah's Witnesses pamphlets in the near future. She agreed to do this reluctantly but without marked anxiety.

Week 74—She spent a week-end at home during which she became worried about the housework not being done. When watching the TV in hospital her mind would race on about religion and being in hospital. She also mentioned that passages in Revelation about fire and brimstone and the end of the world had frightened her the most when she had first been compelled to look up passages in the Bible after reading the pamphlets at the commencement of her illness.

Week 75—The psychologist was on leave at this time but her psychiatrist required her to read through Chapter 20 of Revelation. She told the psychologist she was now " fed up with it." She was asked to read it once more in the presence of the psychologist. She did this rapidly and without any report of anxiety. She was not required to read this any more as there seemed to be some likelihood of reactive inhibition building up.

The patient continued with the chlorpromazine dosage as before. The next day she was shown the Jehovah's Witnesses magazine with an article entitled " The Good News of the Kingdom." This she agreed was similar to that which had originally triggered off her compulsive thinking. She read for 20 minutes and reported no anxiety. She continued with the article from where she had left off when it was presented on the next day. She reported some disturbance and was told to stop as soon as this happened.

Week 76—She returned from 5 days at home to report that she had been upset on the first day because she had felt indifferent to her husband. The same procedure was carried out with the magazine article. During the sixth session a discussion was initiated to enable the psychologist to judge better the extent to which the subject was provocative of anxiety. She showed a slight degree of anxiety. The psychologist confined his opinion to stating that the sect professed a dogma by no means acceptable to all and that the end of the world had been foretold many times throughout history. She was seen on 2 more occasions after this for further reading. On the last occasion the patient reported feeling very cheerful.

Week 77—Two days later she went on 10-days leave and arrangements were made for her to be seen by a psychiatrist at the out-patients clinic.

Week 81—She had been seen at the clinic on 2 occasions and some ruminations about religious matters had been reported. The psychologist mentioned that perhaps extension of leave for this patient was premature and that she may not have been fully desensitized to the anxiety-provoking situation.

Week 82—She was then asked to return to hospital and was seen by a consultant psychiatrist who found that she reported recurring thoughts of violence or injury to her husband and bouts of weeping. She reported having had doubts about ever getting better and about religious and sexual matters, but she did not seem unduly perturbed by these at the time and on the whole seemed better than she had been in the past.

Week 83—She reported similar symptoms as the above to the psychologist. She could not say what set off her bouts of depression. It was supposed that her anxiety must be pervasive and liable to be set off by many stimuli so " Anxiety-Relief " response conditioning was initiated as described by Wolpe.[2]

Week 85—This procedure was carried out during the next 10 days during which time it was observed by nursing staff that she had become friendly with a male patient and she admitted that she had become very fond of him. She discussed the problem with her husband. It was agreed by all concerned that staying in hospital would only prolong a situation likely to cause her and others distress. She agreed that she should go home on leave. She had tried out the anxiety-relief response and found that she could stop herself crying but would still feel miserable.

Week 92—She was seen at the out-patients clinic by a psychiatrist and was found to be no longer suffering from obsessional religious and catastrophic ruminations but had said she was in love with another man. She was found to be aware of her responsibilities to her husband and children. It was felt that the mild depression resulting from this situation would be overcome by time, if nothing else. 50 mg largactil tds was prescribed.

Week 122—The patient was seen at monthly intervals at the clinic. All these interviews were given by psychiatrists who had not dealt with her case prior to this last series of attendances at the clinic. Sometimes she has been tearful and preoccupied by idealized thoughts of her boy-friend. She has been tearful about this situation at home. No evidence of endogenous depression has been observed. Her husband is aware of the situation. At the last interview she said that she had felt much better over the last 4 weeks and had not cried for a month. When asked about her attitude to the illness she said that she had no idea what had caused the disturbance. Of her attitude to the other man she said that her husband " Does not realize how deep it went with me." There has been no mention of a return of her original ruminations during this period.

There have been a number of treatments involved in this case. It is not claimed that the approach based on learning theory is solely responsible for the patient no longer suffering from her original very distressing symptoms but it was not until after a desensitization procedure had been carried out in addition to ECT that she was freed from her tendency to ruminate along her original lines. Previous ECT sedation and interviews had always been followed by a return of her obsessions.

REFERENCES

1. JONES, GWYNNE. Neurosis and experimental psychology. *J. Ment. Sci.*, **104**, 57.
2. WOLPE, J. (1958). *Psychotherapy by Reciprocal Inhibition*, pp. 180-181. Oxford Univ. Press, London.
3. EYSENCK, H. J. (1957). *The Dynamics of Anxiety and Hysteria*, p. 58. Routledge & Kegan Paul, London.

STRENGTHENING OF INCOMPATIBLE REACTIONS AND THE TREATMENT OF A PHOBIC STATE IN A SCHIZOPHRENIC PATIENT*

D. WALTON, B.A., DIP.PSYCH.

Principal Clinical Psychologist, Winwick Hospital, Warrington

DESCRIPTION OF DISORDER

THE PATIENT, a young man of 22, was admitted to a mental hospital early in 1952, suffering from catatonic schizophrenia. Frequent relapses and stupor had necessitated forced feeding. He used to lie in bed motionless, staring into space, taking no notice of anything. He did not speak when spoken to, or even look at the speaker. Later in the year he was transferred to a second mental hospital for the purpose of a leucotomy. This move coincided with improvement and he was made a voluntary patient. It was during this period of improvement that it was first discovered that he was very pre-occupied and worried over sex, masturbation, pregnancy and marriage.

Several months later he relapsed once more into an uncommunicative catatonic state. Medical certificates completed in April and May, 1953, said, " He is quite motionless, withdrawn and inaccessible, almost like a statue with arm bent, a fixed stare and a complete absence of any suggestion of interest in the surroundings. He has to be fed and dressed."

Psychological testing was undertaken about this time to provide a base-line against which to assess response to leucotomy. He was so unresponsive, however, that testing had to be undertaken when he was sedated by sodium amytal. Considerable sexual content emerged, confirming to some extent previously acquired information. The strong sexual content, amidst dis-organized thinking, is readily apparent in the following Rorschach responses:

Card II—" Internal organs of a hurting pregnancy doctor. It is what I am, what I am when I want to marry my own girl. Leave the hospital as a voluntary patient. I'd like to take the nursing profession. Perhaps not nursing profession. Too much communistic, wards, communistic impressions, dark digestible foods, brought to table not taken away. This one with one with pregnancy. The colour skin, not red."

* Specially written for this book.

Card VIII—" Helping the medical profession and psychologists in which I am here at the present to help. This is the . . . is in front of a lady, with that being the penis, and that the rectum. May I go in reverse to rectum. Red, white and blue, orange, with a rich. . . . Causes quite a lot of disease in my own mind to children. And if in the part of the orange and pre-digestive properly causes quite a lot of diseases in the child growth, and perhaps in the persons, should the juices mixed even if they are mixed with distilled water or if they are used on their own with them being distilled."

Card IX—" Woman in birth, having twins. The top half with the teats and the waste matter and venereal disease is more prevalent in women than men, with urine the wrong way at the wrong time. You can pass urine without passing waste-matters. Sitting down, using the right hand and the left hand. A circulatory system of the blood starts in the right hand and ends up in the left hand. Nature in reverse, the baby is at the top with which they should be at the lower end of the body, with gravitational force."

A short time later a leucotomy operation was performed. Some 5 months later he was discharged from hospital " relieved." Shortly after a 4-year follow-up had shown that he had made satisfactory progress, he was re-admitted to hospital suffering from residual schizophrenia. He was then reported to be very asocial, detached and vague in manner and to be given to praying at the bedside in the middle of the day. He was again very preoccupied with sex and became confused when discussing such material. He appeared to be very tense and to show autonomic lability in the presence of women.

Psychological testing completed at this time confirmed the clinical findings. The Venables[1] and Minnesota[2] assessments showed that he was very withdrawn and over-suspicious. The Maudsley Personality Inventory[3] showed him to be markedly introverted but not neurotic. Projective testing again demonstrated an abnormal preoccupation with sex, pregnancy and birth.

The patient was then referred to the psychology department for treatment. It was decided to concentrate on his sexual difficulties, as they seemed both disturbing to him and readily accessible to treatment based on learning theory constructs. Apart from his psychosis, his condition was regarded as a phobic state in relation to women, his abnormal preoccupation with sex resulting from this.

TYPE OF THERAPY

The type of therapy employed was the method of reciprocal inhibition of anxiety responses,[4] the " strengthening of incompatible reactions."[5] This method has been described in detail by Jones[5]—" If one response, incompatible with another, is conditioned to the same stimulus as the latter and the new connection progressively strengthened, the probability of evocation of the old response is progressively decreased, and will ultimately reach zero."

Two conditions had thus to be fulfilled. First, a graded re-education programme, based on the generalization gradient, had to be devised. Secondly, there was a need to find an experimental situation in which his anxiety over sex and related matters was sufficiently weak to be superseded. This was one of the major difficulties associated with such treatment for any intrusion of sexual material into the conversation caused a marked avoidance reaction.

Recent experimental work[6,7] has shown, however, that the degree of anxiety in relation to sexually traumatic material can be reduced if the set of the individual is to expect traumatic words. Such knowledge as this, made available to the patient, might help to overcome the early hesitancy and so help to provide a sufficiently weak anxiety response that it could easily be superseded.

In order to maintain the interest of the patient in such treatment it was considered that frequent encouragement might be necessary.

METHOD OF TREATMENT

The male psychologist conducted the experiment up to the end of phase 4. This was to avoid the generation of any unnecessary anxiety on the part of the patient. If a female psychologist had been included before the patient had learned to adjust to the sexual content of the experiment, progress may have been impeded.

Phase 1

In order to be able to assess subsequent improvement he was asked to read as quickly as possible 4 words adjudged by the psychologist, because of their sexual implications, to be disturbing to him. The time taken to read these words was recorded. The words were:

Bed   Bedroom   Wife   Husband

Phase 2

Two of the above 4 words were then combined into a longer list of 11 words. The 2 words were included at natural points in the list. For example, the word *bed* followed the word *rest* which had followed the word *work*. The possible sexual implications of the word *bed* were thus avoided. *Bedroom* followed in a somewhat similar way the words *upstairs* and *sleep*.

Each session, the patient was asked to read as quickly as possible the list of 11 words 50 times. He was told that the list would include some of the 4 original words. Rest intervals of up to $\frac{1}{2}$ min were allowed between the 50 trials. During these rest intervals the patient was encouraged to achieve better results. Phase 2 consisted of 5 sessions. The 11 words were:

House   Room   Garden   Work   Rest   Bed   Upstairs   Sleep
Bedroom   Attic   Roof

Phase 3

The above 11 words were combined into a longer list of 19 words. This list contained the remaining 2 words from the original list of 4. He was asked to read this list as quickly as possible. Times were recorded. The list was:

House   Home   Room   Work   Rest   Bed   Soap   Wash   Toilet
Bathroom   Garden   Wife   Bedroom   Upstairs   Sleep   Husband
Clothes   Attic   Roof

Phase 3 consisted of 20 sessions, whilst each session consisted of 50 repetitions of the 19 words.

Phase 4

The list of 19 words was then combined into sentences. These were typed on cards. One set was "male" in content, the other "female." The sentences were:

MALE: This is the *husband.*[+] He has done a great deal of manual *work* to-day. He is tired and dirty, wants to have a *wash* and *rest*; goes *upstairs* first to the *bathroom,*[+] washes, then to the *bedroom*. Lies on the *bed*[+] and goes to *sleep*. (45 words.)

FEMALE: This is the *wife.*[+] She has worked hard cleaning her *home*. She is tired, goes to the *bathroom,*[+] first to *wash*, then to the *bedroom*. Lies on the *bed*[+] and goes to *sleep*. (33 words.)

Three M.A.P.S. (Schneidman, 1952) background scenes were also chosen (a picture showing entrance to a house; one of a bathroom and toilet, and one of a bedroom). Two figures, one of a male adult, the other of a female adult, were chosen from the M.A.P.S. figures.

The three M.A.P.S. scenes were placed on the table in front of the patient. He took hold of the male figure and, at a signal from the psychologist, placed the figure on the scene showing the entrance to the house and then repeated, as quickly as possible, "This is the husband. He has done a great deal of . . . " He continued to read the printed material and to leave the figure on the first background scene until he had read up to the second cross ([+]) at *bathroom*. He then transferred immediately the male figure to the bathroom scene repeating, as he moved the figure " . . . to the *bathroom*, *washes*, then . . . " As soon as he came to the third cross ([+]) he transferred the figure to the bedroom scene.

The same procedure was adopted for the female figure and relevant printed material.

Phase 4 consisted of 10 sessions. Each session consisted of 20 repetitions of both the male and female material.

Exact times were recorded.

Phase 5

The final phase consisted of material, very similar to the above, spoken in social situations devised to approximate the M.A.P.S. scene of the entrance to a house. Two sets of material were printed, one containing lines for the psychologist to read as the wife, the other for the patient to read as the husband.

The " *husband* " knocked at the door of the psychology department armed with his lines. The door was opened by the male psychologist acting as the wife. The " *wife* " then read the relevant part of *her* lines.

" Hello, what sort of a day have you had at work to-day? "

HUSBAND: " Oh, I am feeling tired and dirty. I have done a lot of work to-day. I think I will go upstairs to the bathroom and have a wash. Perhaps I shall have a doze on the bed afterwards."

WIFE: " Before you do would you go to see John's wife. Her husband is no good at electricity and they say the lights have fused in both the toilet and bedroom. Electricity is just up your street (the patient was a qualified electrician)."

HUSBAND: " Certainly, I will go right away."

WIFE: (On his return.) " How did you get on?"

HUSBAND: " They were right. The toilet and bedroom lights had fused and John's wife was really hindered in her housework. She could not even make the bed or have a good wash." (128 words.)

Ten sessions were completed using this material. Each session consisted of 10 repetitions.

During the early parts of phase 5 a female psychologist merely sat at the far corner of the room and took no active part in the treatment procedure. For the last of the 10 sessions she took over the role of the *wife* in place of the male psychologist.

Two further sentences were added to the existing material. The *wife* had to ask, " Did you fix them for her? " The *husband* replied, " Yes, she was very relieved. She went straight upstairs to make the bed and whilst I was having a cup of tea I heard her having a well-earned wash in the bathroom." (39 words.) There were 5 further sessions, with 10 repetitions in each session.

For the final 10 sessions further material was added. A new member of the act was also engaged, the female EEG recordist. The additional material was:

WIFE: " I think she will come round to thank you for doing such a good job."

HUSBAND: " Yes, she said she would as soon as she had tidied up the bedroom and toilet."

WIFE: (Following a knock on the door). " Oh, I wonder if that is her now? "

HUSBAND: " I should think it is, I will open the door (opens door). Hello, Mary, are the lights working now? "

MARY: " They certainly are. You did an excellent job, that is why I have called round personally to thank you. I do not know what we would have done without your help." (87 words.)

For the final sessions of this phase the male psychologist was merely an observer and time-keeper. The female psychologist acted as the *wife*, the EEG recordist as *Mary*.

The experiment was brought to an end by play-reading sessions and discussions. At first these consisted of the patient and the male and female psychologist. Subsequently the male psychologist was replaced by the EEG recordist. The patient then came for several sessions in which he merely talked to the 2 female members of the staff.

OUTCOME OF THERAPY

Figure 1 shows the results of phases 1 and 2. In phase 2 there were 5 sessions, each consisting of 50 repetitions. Each session was divided into 5 scores, each entered score being therefore the average of 10 repetitions.

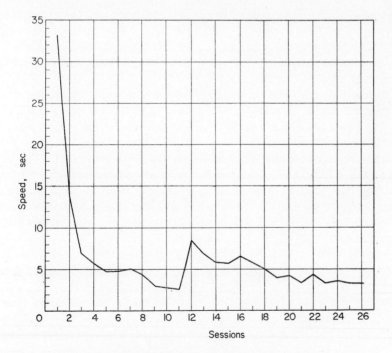

FIG. 1. Speed scores for phase 1 (session 1) and phase 2 (sessions 2–26). Session 1— the patient had to read four traumatic words; sessions 2–26—the patient had to read a list of 11 words, 2 of these were traumatic.

The average speed of reading the 4 " traumatic " words is included to show the increase in speed apparently afforded by placing two of these words in a longer test and so making them appear somewhat innocuous.

At the end of phase 2 the patient was constantly repeating the 11 words in just over 3 sec. This was a very significant increase in speed, for the inclusion of such words into a conversation, a short time previously, would have caused an excessive slowness of response and to have proved obviously distressing to him.

A very satisfactory response also occurred in phase 3. Figure 2 shows the results. Each score represents the average for each session, i.e. for 50 repetitions of the 19 words. There was a consistent improvement over the 20 sessions. At the end of phase 3 he was almost as fast as at the end of phase 2, though the list contained 8 more words.

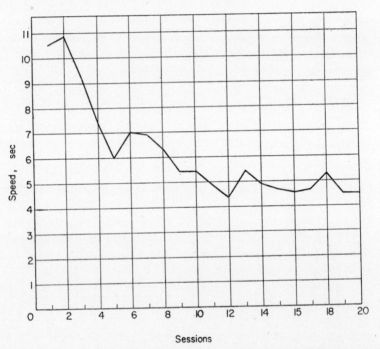

FIG. 2. Speed scores for phase 3. Each score represents the average speed for each session, i.e. the average time taken to repeat 19 words.

This improvement was carried over into the next phase. Over 10 sessions, using both *male* and *female* content, there was a steady improvement in speed. The final sessions were very much faster than anything achieved before. The final 60 repetitions (male material) averaged approximately 9 sec. If one considers that there were 45 spoken words and 3 separate figure placements in phase 4, improvement in speed from phases 1 to 4 was of the order of over 4,000 per cent. The same picture emerged with the *female* material.

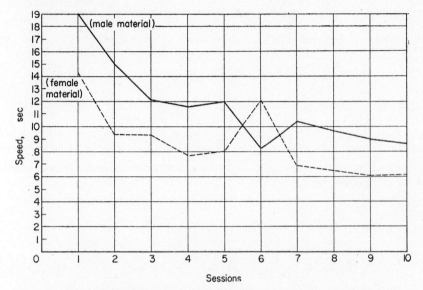

FIG. 3. Speed scores for phase 4. Each score represents the average speed per session, i.e. the average time taken to repeat 45 words (male material) or 33 words (female material) and to make 3 figure placements.

He achieved this same very rapid speed by the end of the tenth session of phase 5. The average speed per spoken word for patient and staff member was $\frac{1}{5}$ sec. The *husband*, it will be remembered, had the larger number of words to repeat. The inclusion of a female psychologist into the act had no detrimental effect upon his performance. He did in fact improve over the 10 sessions.

The addition of 39 words only increased the reaction times slightly. In fact, for the fourteenth session, the average speed of 28·8 sec was almost as fast as the tenth session with 39 words less.

In the final 10 sessions of phase 5, a further 87 words were added, whilst a further female staff member joined the troupe. The final average speed at the twenty-fifth session was some 8 words per sec, that is, considerably faster than at any period of the experiment. At this point the patient had also to cope simultaneously with 2 females! He completed the last phase without hesitancy or blockage and showed little or no apparent discomfort in their presence. If one compares the average speed achieved in phase 1, with the average speed achieved in the final session of phase 5, there was a speeding up of over 5,500 per cent, or a reduction from 8·3 sec per word in phase 1 to 0·15 sec per word at the end of phase 5. In phase 5 the patient had to repeat some 55 per cent of the lines. During the play-reading and discussion sessions which followed he was spontaneous in his speech and seemed to be enjoying himself. A marked reduction in tension was apparent compared with the early stages of the experiment.

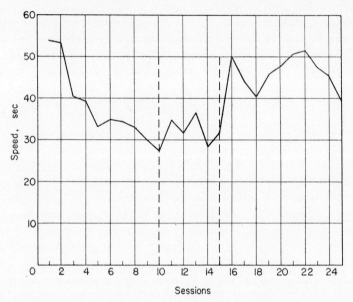

FIG. 4. Speed scores for phase 5. Each score represents the average speed per session—sessions 1–10: 128 words; sessions 11–15: 167 words; sessions 16–25: 254 words.

At the termination of treatment psychological tests, which had been administered before treatment began, were repeated. The Maudsley Personality Inventory showed a reduction in scores on the neuroticism scale (though the score was originally outside neurotic limits), and a significant increase in extraversion. The Venables (assessed by the charge-nurse) also showed that the patient was no longer withdrawn or underactive. The paranoid and schizophrenic peaks on the pre-treatment Minnesota were now within normal limits, though the psychopathic and hypomanic scales reflected abnormally high scores. There is some doubt, however, about the factorial composition of these scales. It seems very probable that at least they reflect the increased sociability of the patient following treatment.

It was agreed amongst medical, nursing and psychological staff that the patient now showed no evidence of his psychosis. On discharge, later in the month, the psychiatric assessment was, " . . . this person made excellent progress under treatment and lost much of his social inadequacy."

The patient was followed up for a year. During this period he returned to his old job. He actually went to bed with a woman several times whilst on holiday and was " going steady " with another girl to the point of becoming engaged. On one occasion he had been into a chemist's shop and had asked a blushing female behind the counter for " rubber goods."

A short time after the year follow-up he was re-admitted to hospital. The main problem appeared to be a lack of self-assertion in social situations. A comprehensive psychological assessment failed to demonstrate a return of his psychosis, whilst he had made obvious strides towards a more adequate sexual adjustment. A short treatment programme was devised in which he was introduced into a graded series of social situations under the influence of sodium amytal.[8] This proved to be effective very quickly and the patient was discharged a short time later.

The present paper is of course concerned with the treatment of the patient's behaviour disorder, rather than his psychosis. Such important changes occurred in his general psychiatric condition, however, that a brief additional comment appears necessary.

The results show that he learned to deal effectively with much previously disturbing material and, although no attempt was made to treat his psychosis, this condition also showed a startling improvement. It is possible that a transfer effect from the treatment of his phobia to the treatment of his psychotic state took place. The work of Broadhurst[9] appears to be very relevant. She found that, " . . . after relatively little practice schizophrenics improve their scores on speed of mental functioning to the level attained by normal subjects without practice . . . improvement in speed scores is not altogether specific to the test given, and shows a transfer effect to a similar but unfamiliar test."

It seems possible that an unintentional experiment on " transfer effect " was carried out. The results may indicate that the speed tasks, associated with the treatment of the patient's phobia, effected a general improvement in the patient's psychiatric condition because of a reduction in intellectual slowness, a slowness which may be basic to psychotic confusion.

REFERENCES

1. VENABLES, P. H. (1957). A short scale for rating " activity-withdrawal " in schizophrenics. *J. Ment. Sci.*, **103**, 197-199.
2. HATHAWAY, S. R. and McKINLEY, J. C. (1951). *Minnesota Multiphasic Personality Inventory.* Manual, Univ. of Minnesota.
3. EYSENCK, H. J. (1956). The questionnaire measurement of neuroticism and extraversion. *Rev. Psicol.*, **54**, 113-140.
4. WOLPE, J. (1952). Objective psychotherapy of the neuroses. *S. Afr. Med. J.*, **26**, 825-829.
5. JONES, H. G. (1958). Neurosis and experimental psychology. *J. Ment. Sci.*, **104**, No. 434.
6. WALTON, D. (1954). An experimental study of a method of using perceptual errors as an aid to diagnosis. *J. Ment. Sci.*, **100**, No. 420.
7. WALTON, D. (1957). A further experimental study of using perceptual errors as an aid to diagnosis. *J. Ment. Sci.*, **103**, No. 432.

8. EYSENCK, H. J. (1957). *The Dynamics of Anxiety and Hysteria*, Chapter 7. Routledge & Kegan Paul, London.
9. BROADHURST, A. (1958). Experimental studies of the mental speed of schizophrenics II. *J. Ment. Sci.*, **104**, No. 437.

THE USE OF SYSTEMATIC DESENSITIZATION IN PSYCHOTHERAPY*

A. A. LAZARUS, M.A.(RAND) and S. RACHMAN, M.A.(RAND)

Johannesburg

As THE result of experiments conducted during the years 1947–48, Wolpe[1] was the first to systematize the principle of reciprocal inhibition in its application to the field of psychotherapy. He provides evidence that neurotic behaviour is " persistent unadaptive learned behaviour in which anxiety is almost always prominent and which is acquired in anxiety-generating situations."[2,3] Successful therapy of the neuroses, therefore, would depend on the reciprocal inhibition of neurotic anxiety responses, i.e. the suppression of the anxiety responses as a consequence of the simultaneous evocation of other responses which are physiologically antagonistic to anxiety. Wolpe[4,5] constructed an elaborate therapeutic system based on the assumption that if a response which is incompatible with anxiety can be made to occur in the presence of anxiety-producing stimuli it will weaken the bond between these stimuli and the anxiety responses. Whereas most psychotherapists report cured or improved cases in the vicinity of 60 per cent, Wolpe claims a 90 per cent level of cures or " marked improvements " with his methods. By applying the x^2 test for significance, he proved that it is highly improbable that the higher proportion of his successes are due to chance factors. Arising from this, the following query has frequently been raised: Would Wolpe's techniques prove as effective in the hands of other therapists?

This paper illustrates that Wolpe's technique of " systematic desensitization based on relaxation " has proved highly effective in the treatment of anxiety states by two independent psychotherapists. The illustrative cases were treated individually by one or other of the co-authors. Although the limited scope of this article covers primarily the use of desensitization, Wolpe has described a wide range of therapeutic methods to cover the entire field of neurotic behaviour disorders.

The rationale and application of systematic desensitization based on relaxation first appeared in this Journal in 1952. It involves a planned attack on neurotic anxieties, designed to reciprocally inhibit these unadaptive reactions by means of relaxation responses. Jacobson[6] has shown that intense muscle relaxation affects the autonomic nervous system so that the

* Reprinted by permission of the author and the editor of the *S. Afr. Med. J.* from (1957) *S. Afr. Med. J.*, **31**, 934-937.

characteristic effects of anxiety are inexorably suppressed. It is therefore to be taken as axiomatic that relaxation inhibits anxiety—their concurrent expression is physiologically impossible.

PROCEDURE

Wolpe's articles[4,5] on reciprocal inhibition therapy contain descriptions of numerous types of techniques. Because the present article is restricted mainly to systematic desensitization, we propose to present a detailed description of this procedure only.

An inquiry is first conducted in order to ascertain which stimulus situations provoke anxiety in the patient. The patient is told that he can add to or modify this list at any time. The stimuli are then categorized by the therapist and the patient is asked to rank the stimuli in order, from the most to the least disturbing. This ranked list of noxious stimulus conditions is referred to as the hierarchy. In case 3 for example, one would refer to the " ambulance hierarchy " and the " hospital hierarchy." Hierarchies can contain from 5 to 25 items. The hospital hierarchy mentioned above consisted of the following stimulus situations: a hospital in the distance, a hospital 10 corners away, walking past the hospital, standing outside the gates, walking in the grounds, standing outside the foyer, in the foyer, walking in the corridors, standing in a small ward of 4 beds, in a larger ward, in a surgical ward with a few bandaged people in bed. The construction of the relevant hierarchies generally takes 1–3 interviews and the patient is concurrently given practice in hypnotic and relaxation procedures. Hypnosis is not an essential requirement and in those cases where the patient refuses to be hypnotized or requires prolonged practice the procedure can be omitted and deep non-hypnotic relaxation employed instead.

When the hierarchies have been worked out, the subject is told which stimuli are to be presented in the individual session and advised to signal with his hand if a stimulus presentation disturbs him unduly. This is an important instruction and should on no account be omitted, for the arousing of anxiety during the session is sometimes extremely damaging. In our experience it has been found that with most patients it is possible by closely observing his facial expressions, bodily tension, respiration and so forth, to perceive such disturbances before the patient actually signals. When such disturbances occur the therapist immediately " withdraws " the stimulus and calms the patient. No session should be concluded when a disturbance occurs, but before rousing the patient the therapist should continue and present a further " easy " stimulus which has already been successfully overcome. The reason for this is to be found in the commonly observed fact that the last item of any learning series is well retained.[7] Anxiety which occurs at the *end* of a session is likely to require a longer period before dissipating.

When the preliminary instructions have been given, the patient is relaxed (hypnotically or otherwise) and then told to visualize the various stimuli; e.g. "Picture a hospital in the distance. . . . Now stop picturing that and go on relaxing." Each stimulus is visualized for 5–10 sec and 2–4 different items are presented each session. Each item is generally presented twice. When the requisite number of stimuli have been presented the patient is slowly roused and then asked for a report on his reactions. If the items were visualized vividly and without undue disturbance, the therapist then proceeds to the next stimuli in the following session. The items lowest in the hierarchy (i.e. the least disturbing ones) are introduced first and the therapist proceeds slowly up the list depending on the progress achieved and the patient's reactions. In this way it is possible for the patient to eventually picture formerly noxious stimuli without any anxiety whatever. This ability to *imagine* the noxious stimulus with tranquillity then transfers to the real-life situation (see below).

ILLUSTRATIVE CASES

CASE 1—A married woman of 34 was referred for treatment of an anxiety neurosis of 5 years' duration. She had received intermittent treatment during this period, including a brief spell of psychoanalysis, without apparent success. Two weeks before her first interview she had been advised to consider the possibility of undergoing a leucotomy.

She complained of attacks of fear with sweating, trembling and severe headaches. A wide variety of situations appeared to provoke these attacks, which tended to occur most severely and frequently in the late afternoon and in dull, overcast weather. The anxiety-producing situations included walking in the street, being outdoors in the afternoon, shopping, telephoning, crowds of people and places of public amenity. She also reported an inability to cope in social situations and disturbing feelings of inadequacy and inferiority. Her sexual activity had been disrupted in recent months as the anxiety had increased, and was unsatisfactory. She had been taking 2–3 " tranquillizing " tablets per day for a short period with slight, variable results.

Application of the thematic apperception test and the Willoughby neurotic tendency inventory[8] revealed neurotic trends such as guilt, hypersensitivity and a marked lack of confidence (the Willoughby score was extremely high—87—indicating severe neurotic disturbance).

The patient was instructed in the use of assertive responses and deep (non-hypnotic) relaxation. The first anxiety hierarchy dealt with was that of dull weather. Starting from " a bright sunny day " it was possible for the subject to visualize " damp overcast weather " without anxiety after 21 desensitization sessions, and 10 days after the completion of this hierarchy, she was able to report that, " The weather is much better, it doesn't even bother me to look at the weather when I wake up in the morning " (previously depressing). In addition to this improvement she was also able to go out for short periods during the afternoon. The following hierarchies were then dealt with: telephoning, shopping, having guests at the house, walking in the street, going to places of public entertainment, sitting in the garden in the afternoon.

Two weeks after the completion of the last hierarchy, the patient was given the Willoughby test again. Her score had dropped 40 points to the slightly inflated score of 47. There was also increased sexual responsiveness, a slight improvement in interpersonal relationships and increased self-confidence. The patient was now taking a refresher course in stenography with the intention of obtaining employment. She had not worked for 7 years. She voluntarily reduced her dose of " tranquillizers " to one a day and dispensed with them completely 1 week later.

At this stage the patient's husband fell seriously ill and she was able to support him emotionally despite the considerable effort involved. As her husband's health improved, she suffered a minor relapse for 2 weeks and then returned to her improved state spontaneously. (A similar post-stress reaction has been reported by Basowitz et al.[9] in their study of paratroop-trainees in the U.S. These observations suggest an interesting and profitable line of investigation.)

During the course of therapy, part of the reason for the development of the anxiety state in this patient was unearthed. When she was 17 years old she had become involved in a love affair with a married man 12 years her senior. This affair had been conducted in an extremely discreet manner for 4 years, during which time she had suffered from recurrent guilt feelings and shame—so much so, that on one occasion she had attempted suicide by throwing herself into a river. It was her custom to meet her lover after work *in the late afternoon*. The dull weather can be accounted for, as this affair took place in London.

After 8 months of treatment, comprising 65 interviews devoted largely to systematic desensitization, this patient was " much improved " in terms of Knight's 5 criteria.*

CASE 2—A 32-year-old medical practitioner stated that he had developed a condition of " psychic impotence." He emphasized that he was already fully aware of the aetiological considerations—he first experienced sexual difficulties 3 months previously when he was harassed and in a state of tension. " Since then, I enter sex with a feeling of uncertainty and am frequently unsuccessful."

This case is atypical in that no " anxiety hierarchy " was constructed, but the patient was conditioned to become completely relaxed before the sex act. This required 8 treatments in all. After 4 interviews he had become proficient at relaxation and systematic desensitization was then begun. This consisted of his visualizing certain pre-coital scenes accompanied by hypnotic relaxation. In a 17-month follow-up there has been no recurrence of the disturbance.

CASE 3—A 14-year-old boy was referred for treatment of a " simple " phobia. He had suffered from a fear of ambulances and hospitals for a period of 4 years. He stated that he was frightened by the sight of ambulances and avoided them wherever and however possible, e.g. by planning his journeys in advance and changing direction when an ambulance was sighted. He reported having fainted on several occasions when an ambulance was near by. He was also scared of hospitals and nursing homes and refused to visit these institutions.

His social and scholastic adjustments were both satisfactory and systematic desensitization was commenced after an initial period of training in relaxation. Separate hierarchies of noxious situations were constructed for the ambulance and hospital phobias. The ambulance-hierarchy ranged from easy (non-disturbing) stimuli such as a parked ambulance in the distance and a derelict ambulance in a scrap-yard, to difficult ones like sitting in an ambulance (*a*) next to the driver or (*b*) in the back. In the hospital-hierarchy the first easy situation was a distant hospital which could be barely seen and the final one, a surgical ward. Three days after the third desensitization session, the subject walked past a parked ambulance with its rear doors open and experienced no anxiety. Two further situations of a similar nature occurred during the course of therapy and neither of these evoked fear. After 10 interviews he was much improved and was able to visit the hospital and approach ambulances without difficulty. After a 3-month period there has been no recurrence of the earlier fears. A prolonged follow-up of this case is being undertaken.

CASE 4—A 34-year-old engineer was treated for a speech disturbance characterized by lengthy and frequent " word blocks," accompanied by considerable tension and facial grimaces. When first interviewed he stuttered on about 12–25 per cent of words, with " blocks " averaging 3–4 sec. His attitude towards speaking situations was poor and he experienced difficulty in handling interpersonal relationships. His Willoughby score was 57, indicating a high basal level of neuroticism. He received 30 hr of therapy over 9 months. Therapy sessions were usually administered once a week. Training in progressive

---

* Symptom improvement, increased productivity, improved adjustment and pleasure in sex, improved interpersonal relationships, increased stress-tolerance.[10]

relaxation was followed by systematic desensitization. Among others, the following hierarchies were treated: time-pressures (especially speaking on the telephone, as he conducted many of his occupational affairs by long-distance calls), telling jokes, public speaking, difficult "audiences," i.e. specific people with whom he had speech difficulties.

Progress was gradual, but by the termination of therapy a substantial gain in speech fluency had been achieved. He is still seen once every 3 months and the gain appears to be permanent, with occasional deteriorations occurring during periods of stress. He is under instruction to continue relaxation and solitary speech practice at his own convenience, and also to increase the frequency and duration of these activities whenever a period of stress is encountered.

Two innovations in this case should be mentioned. The patient was instructed to practise daily speaking (reading) aloud when alone. The rationale for this procedure is based on the "spread of effect" phenomenon, positive transfer of training, and the observation that most stutterers speak more fluently when not in company. Stuttering appears to be essentially a *social phenomenon*. The second modification employed in the present case was that of speech practice in noxious situations (e.g. a public hall) under controlled conditions of relaxation. The patient was required to make a public address and accordingly was made to practise the actual speech in the hall on 6 occasions before the actual event, alternately relaxing and speaking. In this way he was enabled to make the speech with only a few blocks when the event took place. Generally, the symptoms were all greatly reduced and the stuttering pattern characterized by very occasional complicating sounds or facial grimaces. His Willoughby score had decreased. During the period of therapy he had become engaged and seemed to be managing interpersonal relationships more easily. He was recently married and delivered a completely fluent wedding speech.

Case 5—A married woman of 29, who had been a competent theatre sister in England for a number of years. She stated that from as far back as she could remember she had been a tense and anxious person, but as the result of a traumatic incident at the age of 24 she developed overwhelming phobic reactions to dogs. Accordingly, she underwent more than 3 years of psychoanalysis, but towards the end of this period her condition had deteriorated and, as it was interfering with her work, she was forced to resign from the hospital. In the hope that a change of environment might improve her condition, she and her husband came to South Africa. When first interviewed, she said that while she had overcome her fear of dogs, she was in a state of chronic anxiety and felt that suicide was her only release. Her rigid posture with perpetual tremblings and clammy hands indicated a deep-seated anxiety condition. It seems that the psychoanalytic treatment had merely blanketed her specific phobia with general anxiety.

Treatment consisted, in the first place, of 15 training periods in progressive relaxation. After 6 weeks' treatment (28 interviews) she responded well to hypnotic techniques and a further 4 interviews were devoted to deep hypnotic relaxation. At this stage the patient reported that she was generally relaxed and complacent in nearly all situations but that her original phobia for dogs had returned. An anxiety hierarchy was constructed and systematic desensitization applied. At first she reported acute disturbance when visualizing the feeblest scene (a small dog in the distance) but after 25 hypnotic desensitization treatments she was able to report only relatively mild anxiety when visualizing herself near a group of angry and snarling dogs. It took a further 4-5 weeks, however, before the patient was able to enter real-life situations involving dogs without experiencing acute anxiety (Wolpe states that there is sometimes a tendency for the real-life improvement to lag behind somewhat). At this stage, the patient was discharged from therapy, but returned about 3 weeks later and complained that her original phobia for dogs had returned. After only 3 further hypnotic desensitization treatments her phobia disappeared. She was seen 7 months later before returning to England. She reported that she was perfectly well and that she was returning to her previous hospital job; 5 months later she wrote a letter stating that she was still completely over her trouble and had not relapsed in any respect.

DISCUSSION

Two procedural problems which require clarification are (1) the optimal number of stimuli to be presented per session and (2) the optimal duration of stimulus presentations.

On theoretical grounds one would predict that the fewer stimuli presented at any one session, the more effective would be the result. Too many stimuli presented in close succession increase the risk of retroactive inhibition (interference) and there is abundant evidence to prove the superiority of distributed over massed practice.[7] Nevertheless, the therapist should not proceed too slowly as this might affect the patient's confidence in the treatment.* Regarding the duration of stimulus presentations, we have as a general rule used brief presentations (about 8 sec) for the first few items in any hierarchy, increasing the time periods as a function of the patient's adaptation. No negative effects can be traced to this procedure, but we are not in a position to claim that this is the most efficient temporal arrangement. Further evidence on this specific point is required.

An extremely important problem raised by Wolpe is the transfer of "consulting-room desensitization" to real-life situations. He quotes a dramatic example[4] of this transfer in a patient with a human-blood phobia who, very shortly after desensitization, was able to actively assist the victim of a serious road accident. Evidence is also presented by the case of a 20-year-old woman seen by one of us, on 5 occasions only, during a brief holiday in Johannesburg, who complained of long-standing acrophobia (among other things). After the second desensitization session, she was able to stand on a fifth-floor balcony without discomfort. Four months after her return home, she wrote to say that she had successfully undertaken a horse-riding excursion in very rugged mountain terrain. In addition to these two excerpts, the illustrative cases reported in this article also suggest that transfer is both positive and lasting.

The following are some additional impressions of the desensitization technique:

Our experience has been that the greatest benefit is derived when the therapist commences desensitization on the patient's most pressing current problem. An early desensitization success tends to speed up subsequent learning processes.

An observation not mentioned by Wolpe is the spontaneous recurrence of the anxiety symptom in some instances. In these cases, however, the spontaneous recurrence generally dissipates fairly rapidly and the patient returns to his improved condition with little further effort. These spontaneous recoveries of former anxiety symptoms, while of brief and sporadic nature, must nevertheless be handled with extreme care because

* In the present series 2–4 items were presented per session.

of the feelings of acute depression which they usually engender in the patient.

What conditions indicate systematic desensitization therapy? On theoretical and experimental grounds (see Gantt[11] and Jones[12] for example) it may be expected that phobic states, where concrete and definable stimuli produce the neurotic reaction, would be most amenable to this technique. In fact, wherever clinical symptomatology permits the ready construction of appropriate hierarchies, and where specific rather than " free-floating " anxiety is present, systematic desensitization is strongly indicated.

SUMMARY

A detailed description of Wolpe's systematic desensitization psychotherapy is presented.

Five selected cases treated individually by one or other of the co-authors are described. The favourable results obtained indicate the value of these methods in the management of various types of neurotic disturbances.

Some clinical observations and additional suggestions which might assist in the development of the technique are noted.

REFERENCES

1. WOLPE, J. (1948). *An Approach to the Problem of Neurosis Based on the Conditioned Response*. M.D. Thesis. University of the Witwatersrand, Johannesburg.
2. WOLPE, J. (1950). *S. Afr. Med. J.*, **24**, 613.
3. WOLPE, J. (1952). *Brit. J. Psychol.*, **43**, 243.
4. WOLPE, J. (1952). *Brit. J. Psychol.*, **26**, 825.
5. WOLPE, J. (1954). *Arch. Neurol. Psychiat.*, **72**, 205.
6. JACOBSON, E. (1938). *Progressive Relaxation*. University of Chicago Press, Chicago.
7. McGEOCH, J. and IRION, A. (1952). *The Psychology of Human Learning*. Longmans, Green & Co., New York.
8. WILLOUGHBY, R. (1934). *J. Soc. Psychol.*, **5**, 91.
9. BASOWITZ, H., PERSKY, H., KORCHIN, S. and GRINKER, R. (1955). *Anxiety and Stress*. McGraw–Hill, New York.
10. KNIGHT, R. P. (1941). *Amer. J. Psychiat.*, **98**, 434.
11. GANTT, W. H. (1944). *Experimental Basis for Neurotic Behavior*. Hoeber, New York.
12. JONES, M. C. (1924). *J. Exp. Psychol.*, **7**, 328.

THE APPLICATION OF LEARNING THEORY TO THE TREATMENT OF A CASE OF BRONCHIAL ASTHMA

D. WALTON, B.A., DIP.PSYCH.

Principal-Psychologist, Winwick Hospital, Warrington

DESCRIPTION OF DISORDER

THE PATIENT was referred for the treatment of a long-standing asthma. There was a history of status asthmaticus. He was also a chronic bronchitic. The patient's history of asthma dates from his early twenties. It first occurred at a time when he had become emotionally entangled with his sister-in-law's daughter and found it very difficult to extricate himself. The onset of his bronchitis, which ultimately became chronic, was 2 years later.

There were other complicating factors. During the war he did not join the forces because of the family business. His parents were very restrictive and far too possessive. He could do little about this, partly because of his somewhat retiring personality and partly because his reserved occupation kept him at home. When hostilities came to an end he bought himself a sports car and started to enjoy himself. He became more free from family influences. During this period, that is between the ages of 25 and 30, he was free of asthma. The return of his asthma corresponded with the arrival of his first child. He had married when he was 29. The asthma has persisted for the past 7 years. Two years ago a status asthmaticus occurred.

His personality was such that he always found it very difficult to express aggression or resentment verbally, whilst he was more often than not self-effacing. He showed poor social skills, an ineffective communication of ideas and a great deal of vacillation in making decisions. These were all important vocational considerations because his job, as works manager, demanded that he should meet visitors to the factory and try to secure orders for his firm. Whenever he had to meet such people an attack almost always took place and embarrassingly he would have to resort to the " pump." In fact, he showed a marked dependence on the " pump " and would always have it with him. Other situations which were either liable to produce or had produced asthmatic attacks were, for example, when he had to express a personal opinion about his job to strangers; when he had to make a ruling for older people in his factory; when he felt a person ought to be criticized for poor work but he could not tell them; when he felt resentment and could not express the same, or when, for example, he had to sack an objectionable and difficult secretary.

His asthmatic attacks seemed therefore to arise out of his relations with other individuals. Anxiety and/or resentment appeared always to be present. With his parents, for example, he appeared unable to express his resentment over their possessiveness because of anxiety.

TYPE OF THERAPY

As his asthmatic attacks seemed to be related to anxieties evoked in the course of his relations with other people, therapy was based on the principle of reciprocal inhibition. The type of response chosen to inhibit anxiety was the assertive. The method of treatment closely followed the suggestions of Wolpe for the development of assertive responses.

A generalization technique was also adopted to remove the patient's abnormal dependency on the " pump." He was asked to draw up a hierarchy of situations ranging from the most disturbing to the least disturbing. He was instructed to try to leave the " pump " at home in the latter situations. When he was able to do this with little or no resulting anxiety, he was to try to leave the " pump " at home in the situation next on the list, and so on.

OUTCOME OF THERAPY

In all the patient attended for 8 sessions. There was a very rapid response to treatment. Very early on he went out of his way to meet people whom previously he avoided, whilst after 1 month he had coped very adequately with two visiting executives. About this time he had to visit his son in hospital. This involved driving through very dense fog for over 3 hr. He found little difficulty in doing this.

Simultaneously with an improvement in his social relationships there was an abolition of his asthmatic attacks. He has now been virtually free of asthma for 8 months, in spite of having to deal with those situations which previously seemed to bring on an attack. He has more or less abandoned his " pump " except in the most potentially traumatic of situations. He is now enjoying his job and says that many things which previously worried him are no longer problems.

REFERENCE

WOLPE, J. (1958). *Psychotherapy by Reciprocal Inhibition.* Stanford Univ. Press.

PART III

THERAPY BY NEGATIVE PRACTICE AND CONDITIONED INHIBITION

INTRODUCTION

In 1932, there was published a very famous book by Knight Dunlap, entitled *Habits, Their Making and Unmaking*. In this book, Dunlap discussed at great length his revolutionary principle of " negative practice," by which he meant the active, conscious practising of habits which the patients desired to get rid of. The fact that this method appeared to go counter to common sense, as well as to much psychological theorizing, made it something of a rogue elephant, and it was not used as much as its possible importance seemed to justify. When used properly, it appeared to give satisfactory and even impressive results; unfortunately, its use was often perfunctory and conditions inappropriate; results could not be expected to be very favourable under such conditions.

More recently, experimental work stemming from certain predictions deriving from Hull's theory has shown promise that " negative practice " may be deducible in its effects from learning theory, particularly that part of it dealing with " conditioned inhibition," and for the first time certain parameters have been specified which delimit the functioning of Dunlap's principle. The theoretical considerations involved and some of the experimental work referred to, are discussed in the paper by Kendrick; this paper is of necessity somewhat technical and the reader more interested in clinical applications may prefer to turn to the application of these principles to the treatment of tics by Yates and Gwynne Jones, or to the treatment of hysterical aphonia and neuro-dermatitis by Walton.

While " negative practice " and " conditioned inhibition " have been grouped together in this chapter and while it is quite likely that the former is merely an example of the principles accounting for the latter, it is not impossible that this view may be mistaken, and that negative practice may derive its effectiveness from quite different postulates. It is possible that negative practice succeeds in breaking up habits by making conscious and deliberate the steps involved in their execution; as every sportsman knows, conscious attention to the swing of the golf club or the follow-through of the tennis racket, effectively disrupts the adequate performance of habitual acts without involving massed practice of erroneous patterns. Here is an area where much more experimentation is needed before the facts can be regarded as firmly established. It would seem that the type of experimental clinical work here discussed can make a genuine contribution to the solution of these theoretical problems, as well as to actual treatment.

NEGATIVE PRACTICE AS A
PSYCHOTHERAPEUTIC TECHNIQUE*

G. F. J. LEHNER

Department of Psychology, University of California, Los Angeles

INTRODUCTION

NEGATIVE practice as a specific psychotherapeutic technique has received little attention as a clinical device although it seems applicable to a variety of different disorders. This lack of interest and infrequent use of the technique may be due to such factors as (1) the absence of explicit instructions for its application, (2) the absence of case histories illustrating its use, (3) underestimation of the technique as a mere mechanical relearning procedure, (4) contradictory results reported by the few persons who have tried it, and (5) difficulty in fitting the phenomenon into a systematic conceptual framework of either learning or therapy. It is the purpose of the present paper to summarize briefly the available information concerning the use of negative practice, to present more explicit instructions for its application as derived from clinical experience with the technique, and to relate it more explicitly to certain theoretical formulations. Wider acquaintance with negative practice may lead to an extension of its use and a sharpening of the technique as a therapeutic tool.

The first formulation of negative practice was made by Dunlap,[1] with subsequent modifications by him.[2,3,4] The theory of negative practice grew, in part, out of shortcomings in the widely accepted law of frequency, which has been subjected to various criticisms. Peterson,[5] for example, writing in 1922, discussed learning when frequency and recency factors are negative and stated: " . . . it is obvious that one may profit by errors as well as by successes, a fact that is not easy to explain on the recency-frequency view."[6] Gengerelli[7] likewise made an effective attack on the frequency-recency theory of learning.

Theoretically, the possible rôles of repetition *per se* in habit formation are three, designated by Dunlap as the *alpha*, the *beta* and the *gamma* hypotheses. The *alpha* hypothesis, which had served as a keystone to learning theory, is stated by Dunlap as follows: " A response (that is, even a single response) to a given stimulus pattern definitely increases the probability that on the recurrence of the same, or substantially the same, stimulus pattern,

* Reprinted by permission of the author and the editor of the *J. Gen. Psychol.* from (1954) *J. Gen. Psychol.*, **51**, 69–82.

the same or approximately the same, response will occur."[2] When Dunlap found that *practicing* certain previously learned " wrong " responses (e.g. consistently typing *hte* for *the*) led to the dropping out of these responses, he questioned the adequacy of the *alpha* hypothesis and proposed the accessory *beta* and *gamma* hypotheses.* The *beta* hypothesis[8] states that repetition has no effect on the probable recurrence of a response except insofar as certain other factors operate through it. The *gamma* hypothesis states that repetition of a response decreases the probability that that response will occur again with repetition of the stimulating situation. It is the *beta* hypothesis on which the technique of negative practice is based, and not on the *gamma* hypothesis, as believed by some writers.[9]

Thus, in the *beta* hypothesis, motivation may be directed towards the goal of maintaining a response or habit (" positive " factor), or directed towards the elimination of a response or habit (" negative " factor). Similarly, ideational and affective components may be " positive " or " negative," as Dunlap[4] points out. The importance of motivational factors is also indicated in his emphasis on the fact that (1) the patient must " desire to cure the habit " and (2) the therapist must give careful instructions and " reassurance as to the value of the technique." Desire to be cured, and confidence in the therapy (and therapist) are of course important in other psychotherapeutic procedures. If negative factors decrease the probability of recurrence then repetition may be used for the abolition of a habit.

Dunlap[1] has reported successful application of the technique of negative practice to a variety of problems, such as the treatment of typing errors, tics, stammering or stuttering, thumbsucking (in 4- and 5-year-old children), enuresis, masturbation and homosexuality. In a later publication[2] he reports that Dr. Blanche Weill had success with negative practice in the treatment of enuresis in children; that Dr. John Bentley had " remarkable success with a group of confirmed finger-nail biters of college ages." Unfortunately, Dunlap fails to provide detailed description of the applications of the technique to these various problems, to inform us of the course of treatment, the nature of the cures, etc. This absence of detailed information concerning the use of negative practice may well be a contributing factor to its misuse or lack of use to-day.

HISTORICAL SUMMARY

(1) *Positive Results*

The first experiment reporting on the use of negative practice after Dunlap's statement of the *beta* hypothesis was that of Wakeham,[10] who attempted to eliminate certain habitual errors in piano selections from Bach's

---

* Dunlap, in his *Habits* (1942), changed the order of these hypotheses so that the beta became the gamma and vice versa. We shall use the original order, since that is the more common usage in the literature.

Toccata and Fugue in D minor. He practised the selections daily for 2 weeks with the wrong notes deliberately inserted. On the fifteenth day he played the pieces without error, and after several errorless performances called in a pupil for a demonstration of his success—only to find that the errors reappeared. The presence of an audience was a contributing factor in Wakeham's difficulties, and failure to control this factor and to practice the selections in the presence of an audience suggests itself as a possible explanation for his results.

Wakeham[11] later reported the application of negative practice to the correction of typing errors in another individual. This person consistently repeated the beginning letter of a word at the end of the word, e.g. *guyg* for guy and *cityc* for city. After 1 day of practice (exact amount not indicated) errors of this type dropped from 52 per cent to $12\frac{1}{2}$ per cent of the total errors, but such errors as *cit* for city then occurred and accounted for 35 per cent of the total errors.

Holsopple and Vanouse,[12] to test the value of negative practice, used beginning shorthand students ($N = 11$) who had made the same spelling error at least four times in transcribed typing. The incorrectly typed words were divided into two groups for each student—one group of words was subjected to negative, the other to positive practice, for 8 typewritten lines. Dictation was then given of material containing each practiced word at least four times. Examination of the transcribed notes showed that errors for the negative practiced words were reduced to zero, while those words subjected to positive practice showed 30 per cent errors.

Ruhl[13] performed a similar experiment, investigating typing errors in two groups of beginning typing students, one of which practised errors positively ($N = 41$), the other negatively ($N = 44$). Results showed no significant differences between the two groups, although the absolute amount of decrease of errors favored the negative practice group.

With two groups of advanced typing students no difference appeared with practice between the negative practice ($N = 32$) and the positive practice ($N = 33$) groups. Again it is difficult to evaluate these findings because inadequate information is given concerning the application of negative practice.

Kellogg and White,[6] using a simple stylus maze with six blind alleys, checked the speed of learning of three groups of 25 subjects each with the following learning procedures: (1) trial and error, (2) the *beta* hypothesis, in which the subject repeated each blind alley error, and (3) the retracing of an equivalent portion of the true pathway opposite the error just made (this was intended as a check on (2)). Results showed that the negative practice group was superior to the other two in terms of errors made and ratio of trials to errors. Kellogg and White concluded: "To the extent that the techniques employed here are adequate tests of the Dunlap theory, they strongly support the *beta* hypothesis of negative practice."

Fishman[14] used negative practice on 2 cases of speech blockage (inability to speak at all for a period of time after attempting to initiate speech, i.e. tonic spasm) and 3 cases of stammering (repetition of initial letters, syllables and words, i.e. clonic spasm). Of these 5 cases, the 2 speech blockage cases had more blockages after 1 month of treatment. One case increased 43 per cent; the other 33 per cent. The stutterers, however, all had decreases in the occurrence of stuttering, ranging from 58 per cent to 82 per cent.

Case[15] investigated the use of negative practice with 30 stutterers. Ten stutterers completed the course of treatment and were discharged as cured after intervals ranging from 4 to 14 months (average time 9 months). " All of these were discharged as cured and an investigation at the end of the year failed to show any remissions in this group. The criteria of cure consisted in a report by the individual that he no longer stuttered under normal circumstances, observation to this effect by the experimenter and substantiating reports from the patients' parents and friends." The other 20 cases discontinued treatment " either because the defect no longer acted as a social barrier or because of extraneous factors such as change in residence." Three cases of speech blockage were found to become worse under negative practice though Case points out that these cases also had poor social adjustment. Case's major conclusions were as follows: " . . . results obtained in this limited study of the stutterer and speech blocker indicate that Dunlap's technique of negative practice (when used) to bring the involuntary clonic spasm under voluntary control is immediately successful in those cases whose only sustaining cause is the involuntary habit itself. In other cases successful procedure appears to necessitate uncovering the predisposing, precipitating, determining, and sustaining causes before negative practice can be successfully applied. In the majority of these cases a permanent cure demanded that the predisposing and sustaining causes be eliminated concurrently with, or prior to, the application of negative practice."

Rutherford[16] reported success with negative practice in training children having cerebral palsy (athetoid type) with speech disorders. These children grimaced and made unusual body movements during speech. Both the speech and associated movement showed improvement under negative practice training. No statistics are given but the method used is described in considerable detail.

In a recent experiment with speech problems Sheehan[17] employed a procedure closely related to negative practice. Stutterers were asked to read passages and to speak all stuttered words over and over to a criterion of fluency. Less stuttering resulted under this condition than in control readings. Sheehan interpreted the results in terms of approach-avoidance conflict and reinforcement through anxiety-reduction. Stuttering was considered the resultant of an approach-avoidance conflict between speaking and retreating from speaking. The experimental technique reinforced approach (normal speech) responses rather than avoidant (fear-motivated, or stuttering) responses, resulting in improved fluency.

Another technique using a type of negative practice with stutterers is that of " faking " stuttering by means of a voluntary syllable repetition, or " bounce." Meissner[18] studied the effect of such voluntary nonfluency on stuttering, and found that this technique decreased stuttering.

The work reviewed thus far presents evidence which supports the technique of negative practice or at least does not contradict it—with the exception of the speech blockage cases referred to by Case and Fishman, which became worse with the use of negative practice. The following experiments provided results which seem to refute the value of negative practice.

(2)   *Negative Results*

The first of these studies is that of Poindexter,[19] who investigated typing errors made by beginning students. Thirty-six students were divided into three equal groups. Group (1) practiced errors positively five times immediately after making the error, Group (2) practiced the errors negatively, and Group (3) did " nothing " with respect to the errors. In the results obtained, Group (2) tended to have the slowest typists who made the most errors, though none of the differences between the groups were significant. No mention was made of the instructions given to the subjects except that they were asked to repeat the error positively, negatively, or not at all. This implies a misconception in the use of negative practice, namely, that negative practice means repetition *per se* of the error. The *beta* hypothesis expressly states, " repetition has *no* effect on the probable reoccurrence of a response *except insofar as certain other factors operate through it*."

Another experiment apparently casting doubt on negative practice is that of Peak, Brooks and Hobson.[20] In their experiment two groups of 24 subjects each were equated for intelligence and ability to spell. One group practised positively, the other negatively, on words missed twice on a spelling test. On a spelling test subsequent to this practice, the negative practice group showed a slightly higher percentage of errors. Again, apparently, the assumption is made that repetition *per se* is sufficient, but in addition there is some reason to wonder whether the students knew the correct spelling of the words (previously missed twice) which they practised. Thus the original cause of the error was still present. Dunlap, of course, never claimed that a correct response will just appear as a result of practising errors, nor denied the efficacy of positive practice.

A summary of the above review of the applications and the results of negative practice is given in Table 1.

THEORETICAL CONSIDERATIONS

A consideration of the theoretical aspects of negative practice and its place in a systematic formulation has received relatively little consideration.

TABLE 1

Disorder	Source	Claim	Data of statistics
Enuresis	Dunlap	benefit	none
Homosexuality	Dunlap	benefit	none
Masturbation	Dunlap	benefit	none
Tics	Dunlap	benefit	none
Typing errors	Dunlap	benefit	1 case 100 per cent improved
Typing errors	Wakeham	benefit	1 case minor improvement
Piano errors	Wakeham	some benefit	1 case (?) improvement
Spelling errors	Holsopple and Vanouse	benefit	11 cases 100 per cent improvement
Maze errors	Kellogg and White	benefit	25 cases learned w fewer errors and smaller error t ratio than controls
Stuttering	Dunlap[1,2]	benefit	none
Stuttering	Fishman[14]	benefit	3 cases 58–82 per cent improvement
Stuttering	Case	benefit	10 out of 30 cases cured
Stuttering	Meissner	benefit	24 cases; representing less stuttering in exp. than control gr.
Stuttering	Sheehan	benefit	20 cases; significant mean improvement
Speech block*	Dunlap[1]	benefit	none
Speech block*	Fishman[14]	harmed	2 cases became more blocked
Speech block*	Case	harmed	3 cases became more blocked

Theoretical considerations of the technique should probably involve discussions of its relationships to such factors as (1) meaning and operational definition of such terms as voluntary and involuntary and positive and negative aspects of behavior, (2) the relationship between motor activity and self-instructions for self-stimulation, a problem to which Shaffer has made reference.[21] This discussion should also involve consideration of the means whereby past stimuli and their effects are brought into play in the present, thus permitting choice reactions (voluntary behavior) in terms of which a response does or does not appear. Negative practice may be thought of in one sense as a means of replacing old cues with new ones, thereby replacing the past with the present. While most psychotherapeutic techniques rely primarily upon verbalizations of the patient (and the cues and self-stimulation involved in this motor activity) for bringing about this shift in cues of new for old, negative practice engages other motor responses. It is quite probable, of course, that verbalizations, especially the self-signalling type, also play an important rôle in negative practice.

* Speech block: speech block and stuttering are generally considered the same disorder, speech blocks usually referring to severe cases of stuttering.

One of the attempts to relate negative practice to a systematic point of view was made by Guthrie.[22] He related negative practice to his theories of conditioning, believing that the value of negative practice lies in making explicit the cues which initiate an act—cues of which the subject may be unaware, and which, through conditioning, come to lead to behavior which the subject cannot control. Success in negative practice, therefore, lies in reconditioning the first or initiating cues upon which the act depends to the total act, thereby bringing under voluntary control the serially controlled behavior which was involuntary.

Peak,[23] in an article relating negative practice to theories of learning, discussed primarily the adequacy of the *alpha*, *beta* and *gamma* hypotheses in accounting for the results of negative practice. She maintained that the *beta* hypothesis, in terms of which negative practice results are most frequently interpreted, must be rejected, pointing out that (1) the *alpha*, *gamma* and *beta* hypotheses are so ambiguous with respect to the meaning of repetition that their evaluation must await the clarification of this term; (2) if *alpha* is interpreted to mean that repetition of a stimulus-response sequence increases the probability that the stimulus will produce the response regardless of consequences, then *beta* as usually stated does not follow from a disproof of *alpha* and *gamma*; and (3) that negative practice experiments do not provide a situation in which all factors save repetition of a stimulus-response sequence are held constant.

According to Peak, the significant question is not whether repetition is necessary but what must be repeated in order to produce learning and under what conditions it is practised. Regardless of the theoretical structure employed in explaining negative practice results, what is clearly involved in all such situations is interference between antagonistic responses, for the correct response and the incorrect response cannot be performed simultaneously and one must be chosen to the temporary exclusion of the other. The primary theoretical task then is to enumerate the factors which strengthen the correct act and those that may weaken the incorrect one.

Among a few other attempts of theorizing about the technique of negative practice is the recent work of Sheehan[17] who utilized negative practice with speech problems and who presents an interesting analysis of its dynamics in terms of non-reinforcement of the stuttering responses and of the approach-avoidance conflict hypothesis. The stutterer is in a conflict situation because he has a tendency to approach the word, i.e. he needs to say it, but he has a competing tendency to avoid the word because of fear that he may stutter on it. In normal speech it is the approach response which is emphasized because it is reinforced; in stuttering, however, the stuttered responses also receive reinforcement. The effectiveness of negative practice is due to the fact that (1) the non-reinforcement technique made the normal speech attempt, rather than the stuttering response, the instrumental act leading to reinforcement, and that (2) it substituted the approach response of speaking for the avoidance response of holding back at the point of reinforcement.

APPLICATION OF TECHNIQUE

(1) *General Considerations*

Certain factors which we found to be important in the application of negative practice are summarized below:

(1) The patient should desire to eradicate the response, and this desire must be reinforced and sustained by the therapist through reassurance, suggestion, and emphasis on the fact that negative practice has been found to be effective in removing undesired habits. The subject must undertake negative practice within the constantly maintained attitudinal framework of " *this*-is-wrong-and-I-am-not-going-to-do-it-later."

(2) Any motivations, or situations (Dunlap's " positive factors "), which tend to keep the " unwanted " response active as a tension-relieving device must be eliminated so that the response may be termed " habit residual." The elimination of the causes still operating to sustain the habit involves the use of other therapeutic techniques. In many habits, however, the original causes have ceased to operate (as in many cases of stuttering, for example).

(3) The correct response must be available to the patient (e.g. the stutterer must know the correct mode of speech, the poor speller the correct spelling of the words he mis-spells, etc.).

(4) In practice sessions with the therapist the patient must be cautioned and aided (verbally, with the aid of mirrors, by various demonstrations, etc.) to reproduce in the practiced response a response as nearly like the involuntary response as possible. This may take the form of repeating responses which occur spontaneously in the sessions or of reproducing characteristic responses upon command of the therapist. The former method seems preferable whenever possible.

It should perhaps be emphasized that in negative practice the usual (involuntary) response may not be the one that is practiced—the practiced response is only an approximation of the motor pattern which is to be eliminated. As Dunlap states: " What is repeated in negative practice of a motor habit is not the actual response involved in the habit, but a new response, in which only the behavior pattern of the habitual response is repeated, with affective and ideational components quite different from those involved in the habit. This, of course, is quite in accord with the generalization that *the response in practice is not the response learned.* This principle can be reversed to say that *the response repeated in negative practice is not the response unlearned.*"

(2) *Specific Considerations*

Except for minor changes for particular patients, the following outline covers the application of negative practice as we have come to use it:

(1) One or two practice sessions are scheduled with the patient each week. The first 5 sessions are usually limited to 30 min, after which they are increased to 1 hr. This is usually the maximum time that practice can be maintained without the appearance of disorganizing effects—immediate motivation decreases and fatigue appears. Short rest periods of a few minutes every 10 or 15 min of practice are used. It is especially important in the early phase of practice to terminate the session when the subject no longer shows any progress in approximating the involuntary response through his voluntary efforts.

(2) The situation is structured in somewhat the following words: " Usually we consider that practicing an act makes it easier for us to perform that act. That is often the case, but sometimes where we have learned an act, as you seem to have learned your stutter (or whatever behavioral symptom the patient presents), we find that in order to get rid of the act we have to repeat it, i.e. practice it. This may sound paradoxical, but by repetition, by practice, we hope to bring your ' involuntary ' response back under ' voluntary ' control—which means that you regain control over the response. The procedure for doing this involves your close co-operation. When you come for your practice sessions, we shall sit and chat—about anything you like—and during your conversation I shall stop you and ask you to reproduce the act you wish to eliminate. The attempt to reproduce the act will be difficult at first . . . but I'll try to help you in many different ways to do it correctly. Your job is to try to follow the instructions and to remember that you are practicing a response which you wish to eliminate." The value of negative practice in other cases is usually cited as further encouragement for the patient. These instructions are repeated in the first few sessions, with additional comments reinforcing the attitude that the response practiced is the response to be eliminated.

(3) Following these initial instructions, conversation is carried on with the patient in order to create as favorable an environment as possible for observing *au naturel* the symptom to be treated. As the symptom appears the conversation is interrupted (the interrupting of the patient's speech may require considerable tact with stammerers and stutterers, many of whom resent any breaking into their speech) and the patient is asked to repeat the mistake he has just made. This is at first difficult for him, since he is not always aware of his mistakes, and even when he is aware of them he is incapable of readily reproducing them. It is therefore important that the therapist carefully describe, define, or demonstrate the act performed so that the patient may know what is expected of him. Providing the patient

with a mirror with which to observe his own performance is an excellent aid in some cases (though a number of patients prefer to do without a mirror).

(4) The patient's first attempts to reproduce his symptom voluntarily may result in something only coincidentally similar to what is wanted. Usually only gross aspects of the symptom appear in these early efforts, and it is the therapist's job to encourage a progressive refinement until the voluntary act matches the involuntary. We have found it wise, especially in early sessions, not to require the *total* " involuntary " response to be repeated " voluntarily," but only those aspects of it which show signs of being more readily mastered; yet at the same time the therapist must be something of a perfectionist and insist that negative practice approximate the original as closely as possible. The patient must not produce just any stammer, or tic, or gesture—or he may merely add a new habit to the one he already has!

It is the therapist's job, also, to note accessory habits associated with the main symptom, such as general or specific changes in muscular tonus, changes in position of hands, of feet, of head, etc. These concomitant phenomena accompanying the " involuntary " act must be included in the practiced act. For example, head rotation involving the neck muscles often accompanies an eye tic, and these different movements must be practiced together.

(5) In the course of negative practice the patient will frequently give the involuntary response while attempting to produce the voluntary. The therapist must be aware of this possibility and learn to differentiate between these two acts—otherwise there is no negative practice. The patient may even have to be asked at times whether he performed the particular act or whether it just happened.

(6) As practice continues, the patient finds more and more success in his efforts to repeat the act, and remarks like " Oh, I see now what I'm doing," or " That's it now," are obtained. As the patient learns to recognize the cues for correctly executing the " voluntary " act he comes to see, of course, the relationship between what he is doing " voluntarily " and what he did " involuntarily "—with a falling away of the latter as the response is perfected.

(7) This falling away of the involuntary responses becomes progressively more noticeable in the practice sessions, and the patients usually report— enthusiastically—a similar general decrease. A rather sudden improvement is sometimes interpreted by the patient as a sign of recovery with a concomitant desire to stop practicing. Cessation of practice, at this point, we have found, has not led to complete cure, but rather to a reinstatement of the original syndrome. When the patient has gained good mastery of the involuntary in the voluntary response, practice sessions by the patient alone may be permitted, though if the symptom involves a considerable tying together of different responses it is not advisable.

(8) As treatment progresses, the percentage of involuntary responses in the final practice sessions approaches zero while that of the voluntary responses increase. Generally, this disappearance of the symptoms is sufficient to enable the patient to terminate the practice sessions and to make satisfactory adjustments outside the therapeutic situation. In some cases, care must be taken that the patient does not believe continued success is dependent upon a continuing therapeutic relationship. Continuing reliance on the therapist for maintenance of status must be avoided.

(3)   *Value of Technique*

With these factors taken into consideration, we have found the technique of negative practice useful for the following purposes:

(1) For cases in which the disorder could best be characterized as a " habit residual."

(2) For cases in which the patient (initially, at least) wanted symptom alleviation without prolonged therapy, but where the symptoms appeared not to be habit residual in nature. In this instance negative practice serves not only as a direct attack on a specific symptom, but a rapport-building device for obtaining information, directly or indirectly, and for the subsequent (or concomitant) administration of other therapy. Additionally, in many of these response disorders the response still serves to sustain the disorder because the response is socially unacceptable to both the patient and others.

(3) As a training device for introducing students into therapeutic procedures. Negative practice, because it is relatively simple to use, provides the student with a therapeutic procedure that serves as a confidence-building device for his dealings with patients. The cases used for this purpose must, of course, be carefully selected.

Initial contact with the patient is for the purpose of making some diagnosis in terms of which a particular type of therapy may, or may not, be initiated. Information for ascertaining the dynamics of the case and for determining whether or not the behavior can be regarded as a " habit residual " is elicited. The answer to this latter question has been the determining criterion for selecting or rejecting negative practice as a therapeutic technique for a specific case. If it is believed to be " habit residual," negative practice is instituted—with the reservation that later practice sessions may elicit information requiring a change in decision. It is a truism, of course, to anyone engaged in clinical work that in the early stages of contact the patient frequently, deliberately or otherwise, gives incorrect information.

If the case seems not to be habit residual, then we prefer to use other psychotherapeutic techniques, although negative practice may be started (1) as a means of establishing a better working relationship with the patient (as, for example, the kind who comes with a speech difficulty and says, " There is nothing wrong with me except my speech and if that clears up these other things will just disappear ") and (2) as a screen for introducing and utilizing other therapeutic procedures.

It may be of interest here to quote from Dunlap[3] concerning the application of negative practice to different types of cases. He says: " Some cases involve habitual *motor* patterns of various sorts as their conspicuous features. Some cases involve predominantly *affective* and *ideational* habits. Most cases involve *both* factors in varying degrees. Many of the habits dispelled are indeed *symptoms* of deeper disorder, the causes of which must be discovered and removed, or, since in some cases the causes are by nature not removable, the patient must be helped to respond to them in better ways. On the other hand, it is also true that in most cases, the ' symptoms ' must be removed. In more cases than we earlier suspected the removal of a symptom is the key to the resolving of the total difficulty, for *the symptom is often a sustaining cause* which keeps alive the neurotic condition or maladjustment " (italics added).

This view is substantiated by our own experience, which has shown that removal of the symptom sometimes leads to alleviation of a condition believed to be otherwise sustained. For example, a socially maladjusted stutterer may, when the stuttering ceases, make adequate social adjustments. Stuttering may be not only a symptom of social maladjustment, but a cause of the maladjustment.

CONCLUSION

The literature on negative practice briefly reviewed here, and the summary outline of the application of the technique for various kinds of disturbances should serve, it is hoped, to stimulate further use of this procedure and lead to a sharpening of this tool for the alleviation of disturbances. The varying degrees of success with which the technique has thus far been employed may well reflect the lack of specificity in procedures employed. Further use of the technique, with careful consideration of its application in certain cases, should increase its value.

REFERENCES

1. DUNLAP, K. (1928). A revision of the fundamental law of habit formation. *Science*, **67**, 360-362.
2. DUNLAP, K. (1930). Repetition in the breaking of habits. *S. Mo.*, **30**, 66-70.
3. DUNLAP, K. (1932). *Habits, Their Making and Unmaking*. Liveright, New York.
4. DUNLAP, K. (1942). The technique of negative practice. *Amer. J. Psychol.*, **55**, 270-273.
5. PETERSON, J. (1922). Learning when frequency and recency factors are negative. *J. Exp. Psychol.*, **5**, 270-300.
6. KELLOGG, W. N. and WHITE, R. E. (1935). A maze test of Dunlap's theory of learning. *J. Comp. Psychol.*, **19**, 119-148.
7. GENGERELLI, J. A. (1928). Preliminary experiments on the causal factors in animal learning. *J. Comp. Psychol.*, **8**, 435-457.
8. CARROLL, R. (1929). Analysis of the Beta Hypothesis. *Sch. Soc.*, **29**, 543-545.

9. FLETCHER, J. M. (1930). Dunlap's theory of the treatment of stuttering. In *A Symposium on Stuttering*, ed. by R. West. *Amer. Soc. Study Dis. Speech*. Madison, Wisconsin.

10. WAKEHAM, G. (1928). Query on " A revision of the fundamental law of habit formation." *Science*, **68**, 135-136.

11. WAKEHAM, G. (1930). A quantitative experiment on Dr. K. Dunlap's " Revision of the fundamental law of habit formation." *J. Comp. Psychol.*, **10**, 235-236.

12. HOLSOPPLE, J. Q. and VANOUSE, I. (1929). A note on the Beta Hypothesis of learning. *Sch. Soc.*, **29**, 15-16.

13. RUHL, R. A. (1935). Negative practice versus positive practice in the eliminating of typing errors. *J. Gen. Psychol.*, **13**, 203-211.

14. FISHMAN, H. C. (1937). A study of the efficiency of negative practice as a corrective for stammering. *J. Speech Dis.*, **2**, 67-72.

15. CASE, H. M. (1940). Stuttering and speech blocking: A comparative study of maladjustment. Ph.D. dissertation, University of California at Los Angeles, pp. 78.

16. RUTHERFORD, B. R. (1940). The use of negative practice in speech therapy with children handicapped by cerebral palsy, athetoid type. *J. Speech Dis.*, **5**, 259-264.

17. SHEEHAN, J. G. (1951). The modification of stuttering through non-reinforcement. *J. Abnorm. (Soc.) Psychol.*, **46**, 51-63.

18. MEISSNER, J. H. (1946). The relationship between voluntary nonfluency and stuttering. *J. Speech Dis.*, **11**, 13-23.

19. POINDEXTER, A. (1936). The factor of repetition in learning to type. *Kentucky Person. Bull.*, **17**, 3-4.

20. PEAK, H., BROOKS, J. and HOBSON, B. (1941). Positive and negative practice in the correction of spelling errors. *J. Psychol.*, **11**, 103-114.

21. SHAFFER, L. (1947). The problem of psychotherapy. *Amer. Psychol.*, **2**, 459-467.

22. GUTHRIE, E. R. (1935). *The Psychology of Learning*. Harper, New York.

23. PEAK, H. (1941). Negative practice and theories of learning. *Psychol. Rev.*, **48**, 316-336.

24. MOWRER, O. H. (1938). Preparatory set (expectancy)—a determinant in motivation and learning. *Psychol. Rev.*, **45**, 62-91.

THERAPEUTIC METHODS IN STUTTERING AND SPEECH BLOCKING*

H. W. CASE

Professor of Psychology, University of California, Los Angeles

ALTHOUGH one of the most common of human complaints, stuttering has constantly baffled and eluded the efforts of those who have attempted to probe its causes and beginnings. It is this same elusive nature of the disability which, unfortunately, has placed serious obstacles in the way of the development of a satisfactory method of treatment.

In Europe the tendency has been to group all speech defects, consisting of abnormal variations in the vocal production of words, under two general terms: stuttering and stammering, which are often used interchangeably. However, in the United States, Greene[1] uses the term stuttering to include only those cases where the difficulty is not caused by any physical disability of the vocal apparatus nor by lesions in the central nervous system. The speech abnormalities caused by impairment or deformity of the organs of sound production he classifies under the general heading of stammering. Those defects due to the presence of injuries or growths in the brain are grouped under the general heading of aphasia.

If we examine other authorities, we find there is a great deal of confusion in the use of the term stuttering. Obviously, any form of classification is arbitrary and used for convenience in handling case material and case histories. Therefore, in this paper " stuttering " will be used to designate repetition of the clonic form of speech spasm and " speech blocking " will refer to the form marked by very long tonic spasms.

Two approaches to the problem will be considered throughout this paper. The first is the efficacy of certain forms of treatment. The second is an attempt to aid in discovering the causes of the maladjustment. These two approaches are followed by the investigation of case histories and experimentation with a group of subjects.

The University of California, Los Angeles, did not operate a speech clinic during the period in which this investigation was conducted. Therefore, the supply of subjects for observation, treatment, and experimentation was limited to individuals applying directly to the Department of Psychology for aid in overcoming their difficulties.

* Specially written for this book.

Unfortunately, this has resulted in securing a highly selected group of patients who, with few exceptions, had all presented a history of treatment at one or more institutions. They had received little or no benefit from the previous treatment at these corrective institutions or the disorder had recurred. The majority of them sought relief from their handicap but at the same time were skeptical of such a possibility. They had heard of the efficacy of negative practice[2] as a method of treatment and were anxious to see if it would be the key to their particular problem.

The voluntary application of patients for aid provided an opportunity to work with and to study other types of maladjustments not found in speech clinics devoted solely to speech maladjustments. These other maladjustments were usually of a type which might be classified under the loose term of neurotic. This contact with a large group of cases having differing symptoms has modified and influenced the work carried on with speech disorders. It is believed this influence has been of decided value toward understanding and solving the numerous problems of speech defects.

In all instances the individual applied for advice or treatment to help overcome his handicap and not for experimental purposes. Thus, observation and experiment were carried on coincidental with the treatment.

As one portion of the total pattern was uncovered, it led to additional pertinent and related aspects which were deemed necessary of investigation. Therefore, as a result of the constant evolution of problems within problems, the *data* in some of the cases is more comprehensive and detailed. Throughout the study the results were limited by the number of subjects available.

The subjects used in this problem were 30 men and women who came to the Department of Psychology seeking relief from the handicap of either stuttering or stammering. Twenty-six were males and 4 were females. The average age was 24 and ranged from 8 to 39 years. Eighteen of the total group were enrolled in the University as students. The remainder were individuals who came of their own accord or were recommended to the department to obtain relief from their disability. This group comprised 4 patients who had not completed high school, and 8 who had graduated from high school but not from college.

The investigations involved two lines of approach. The first was to test several methods and combinations of methods of treatment. An attempt was made to determine through the use of case records and a study of the progress of each patient: (1) whether the adjustment of environment of the individual advocated by Fletcher[3] would result in an improvement of the individual's malfunctioning speech and elimination of incorrect speech habits; (2) whether the breaking-up of the specific habit through the use of negative practice as formulated by Dunlap[2] would eradicate the specific habit and restore the subject's adjustment (as should be the case if Johnson's hypothesis that the stutterer is maladjusted as a result of his stuttering is tenable)[4]; (3) whether a combined attack on the problem through the use of positive adjustment techniques applied on the basis of information ascertained by the interview and case study method, as well as a specific attack on the habit itself by means of the technique of negative practice, would produce the desired results more readily than either method used singly; and (4) whether both stuttering and speech blocking would yield to the same method of treatment; or whether, as Fishman[5] found evidence, speech blocking would not show improvement when treated with certain techniques.

Second, in conjunction with these four lines of investigation an attempt was made to determine whether negative practice could be made more effective by the imparting of a faradic punishment shock to the patient during a mistake in his voluntary reproduction of his stuttering spasm. It is essential that the emotional content of the situation surrounding the condition of stuttering by the patient be reproduced as accurately as possible during the negative practice situation. This is just as important as accurate reproduction of the specific manner of stuttering by the individual patient. In fact the more accurate the emotional situation induced, the less difficult it is for the patient to accurately reproduce his stuttering. The faradic punishment shock (administered through two metal rings attached to the patient's fingers) was used to build up the emotional intensity of the practice situation. The purpose was to determine whether the shock would have the effect of keeping the individual attending to the task of making his voluntary reproduction a continuously improving duplication of the involuntary stuttering spasm. However, this procedure was used only in a limited number of cases because the intense fear expressed by the majority made it appear an inadvisable technique for these specific cases. Nevertheless, in these cases where this technique was not used it was necessary to reproduce the emotional situation in which stuttering occurred by other structured means suitable to each individual case.

Of the entire 30 cases, 10 completed the course of treatment. These were discharged as completely cured, and an investigation at the end of a year showed that no relapses had occurred. The criteria of a cure consisted of a report by the individual that he no longer stuttered or blocked, observation to this effect by the experimenter, and reports from the patient's parents and friends substantiating that he no longer stuttered or blocked.

All the cures were males. Fifteen cases had ceased treatment either because they had reached a point at which the defect no longer acted as a social barrier or because some factor such as a change in residence had necessitated their discontinuing treatment.

Two of the women presented cases of considerable disability, while the other two were of a minor nature and did not handicap the individual involved. At the completion of treatment neither of the 2 severe cases had attained a satisfactory cure. One showed definite improvement, the other only a slight change. The additional female cases were examined but treatment was limited to consultation and advice to them and their parents. Since the nature of the cases rendered it inadvisable to attempt additional techniques, it was impossible to determine their degree of improvement.

Twenty-five of the 30 cases were stutterers, i.e. suffered from clonic spasms during varying speaking conditions and 5 were speech blockers, i.e. suffered from tonic spasms during certain speaking conditions. For the speech blocking group 3 cures were accomplished; the 2 remaining cases showed about 50 per cent improvement. Of the group of stutterers, 7 showed complete cures, 13 showed definite improvement.

The average time for the stutterers discharged as completely cured was 8 months; the maximum number of months 13 and the minimum number 4. The average length of period of treatment for this group equalled $1\frac{1}{2}$ hr per week. Some of the cases treated only once a week showed as satisfactory progress as those treated two or more times a week.

An important factor in the recovery of those finally discharged as cured is possibly found in their exceptionally regular attendance and in their desire to find a solution to their problem.

For the group reporting improvement but no cures, the time of treatment was short, ranging from 1 to 30 weeks, with the group average around 4 weeks. The attendance of these patients was poor. To cover three periods of treatment a period of 3 months was sometimes required. Many of these individuals appeared to be in the group described by Thorpe[6] as not wishing to recover from their handicap. Such scattering of the hours of treatment effectively prevented the patient from learning to reproduce his stuttering spasms voluntarily when this technique was used as a formulation of Dunlap's[2] negative practice.

Other symptoms accompanying the stuttering spasm appeared to be of two types. In the first group may be classed those which Van Ryser[7] has described as comprising part of the stuttering spasm. These " starters " are various stereotyped movements of the body parts, such as a jerk or similar movement, which are used to start the flow of words, or a movement used to time the moment of speech—such as winking an eye or moving a foot during speech. In addition, muscle spasms appeared comparable to those found in psychoneurotic behavior. These were usually involuntary tics appearing in non-speaking intervals. In the cases treated, such tics were mainly localized in the muscles of the face and eyes. Besides these clonic muscle spasms, several stutterers presented other strongly ingrained involuntary habits such as nail-biting, picking the face and nervously playing with any handy item when not engaged in conversation. From a standpoint of treatment it was found necessary to correct these items concurrently with the stuttering spasm.

For the purpose of comparing and contrasting the different therapeutic techniques used, four case histories in which cures were effected will be considered since the techniques used in the rest of the cases were essentially the same. For convenience they will be divided into two groups: the first comprising those individuals who stuttered and the second those individuals who suffered from speech blocking.

In all the cases an effort was made to make a careful history of the factors preceding, entering into and accompanying the disorder through interviewing the individual suffering from the disorder, his parents, marriage partner, and close friends whom it was thought could throw light upon the history of the case. Dunlap[2] has described the factors entering into the formation of a neurosis in terms of various causes. We have, according to his terminology, the primary, predisposing, determining, precipitating and sustaining causes. In reviewing the results, wherever an analysis of the case history appears to reveal these causes they will be mentioned in connection with the specific adjustment problem. To accomplish this purpose it is necessary to examine each case in terms of its history and see how the treatment had to be adapted to the specific maladjustment.

Two cases of stutterers, of which the history of one is given below, presented very little social maladjustment or social disability and showed no sustaining cause other than that of the actual habit pattern. Both of these cases had presented considerable social maladjustment, excessive worry and introspection concerning the disability, during the early period of their lives. Both cases had stuttered from about the age of 6. They had taken drastic steps during their high school careers to overcome the handicap and to obtain an adequate social and economic adjustment. These 2 cases were treated with negative practice 1 hr per week for 4 months. The disability appeared to be a residual pattern of speech habits, definitely connected with certain speaking situations, which readily broke down under negative practice.

CASE 1—Spoke very rapidly and repeated any word preceding a long or unfamiliar word. He said he did this to avoid stuttering on the strange word. He came of English ancestry. He was 21 years old and in excellent physical condition, although slight in build for his 5 ft 2 in. In a family of six he was the only boy. Two of his 3 older sisters were married and not living at home. No other member in the family stuttered. His mother had always been sickly; his father was a domineering person. He started to stutter at the age of 6 and claimed the difficulty followed an attack of measles.

During his grammar school years he had been subject to many childhood diseases, but after entering high school his health had improved greatly. While in grammar school his sisters had tormented him about his speech but when he entered high school, they paid less attention to his difficulty. In high school he became acquainted with several boys and became a member of the school glee club. During the last 2 years of school he became interested in politics and successfully held school office. He also had made friends with 2 or 3 girls.

When first interviewed he had been out of high school 2 years and was living alone. He supported himself by working as a night clerk in a grocery store and during the day selling silk hose at sorority houses. The work did not appeal to him but it paid well enough to make his plans for marriage feasible. He associated with a crowd of lively young people and led them in various enterprises they undertook. He could not understand why he continued to stutter. The speech difficulty did not interfere with his business ability as he never stuttered when giving sales talks or speaking publicly. He experienced the difficulty only when talking informally or casually.

It was decided that since his case presented no serious maladjustment, his speech difficulty was an involuntary habit pattern appearing only in certain situations. His treatment consisted of negative practice on routine words. After mastering the technique, it was enforced by faradic shock applied only during periods of casual conversation. At the end of 4 months he was discharged as cured. No relapse had occurred 6 months after his discharge.

Case 1 showed intelligent insight into his problem. He had taken steps on his own initiative to correct the source of his difficulty. However, this was not sufficient to break down the involuntary habit pattern of stuttering built up in prior years. Treatment was necessary to eliminate the involuntary habit which itself acted as a sustaining cause.

Five cases gave histories that appeared to be considerably similar in the onset and the progress of the disorder, with one outstanding exception. This exception lay in the fact that the individual attempted to fight it, spent much time introspecting about it, attempted numerous cures and finally had ended up by withdrawing from social activities because the embarrassment of the handicap became too great. Negative practice was tried. After a few preliminary attempts it appeared little progress was being made. It was then decided that certain other techniques should be attempted. These cases were analyzed as to ways and means of eliminating the sustaining causes which appeared to be social and vocational maladjustments. In eliminating the sustaining causes the desired results were obtained through the co-operation of clubs, friends, parents and employment centers. Once the individual discovered that society was not turned against him he usually acquired new confidence. Whether this tended to make him amenable to negative practice or whether the improvement in speech was a natural evolution due to his general improvement is difficult to determine. The only safe generalization is that it seems probable sustaining causes must either be removed prior to the application of negative practice or concurrently with it to assure satisfactory results. Examples of the habit complicated by additional problems is illustrated in Cases 2 and 3.

CASE 2—Stuttered by repeating whole phrases such as: " Boy do I—boy do I—boy do I—boy do I—boy do I get seasick." Sometimes he would vary this to: " Boy—boy—boy—boy—do I get seasick." His stuttering was accompanied by an intense constriction of the diaphragm and exhaustion of air in the lungs. In a bad spasm he would turn very red or slightly purple. When talking, he would become extremely tense and suffer from tremors. He was 32 years of age, in good health, of medium build and about 5 ft 7 in. tall. At the time of treatment he lived at home with his mother and father who were 48 and 54 years old respectively. He was interested in automobiles and had helped build a racing car. He piloted an airplane for the sport and often went sailing on a friend's cruiser although he complained of seasickness.

He claimed to have fallen on his head at the age of 6. Stuttering first appeared at the age of 7 when he entered first grade. Both he and his parents attributed his disability to the fall. They had attempted to correct his speech by reminding him of his difficulty and cautioning him to speak slower. His father had sometimes beaten him for stuttering. During childhood he suffered from numerous childhood diseases which left him rather sickly until manhood. He was always belligerent toward other children and would fight any child who dared tease him about stuttering. His attitude, though nervous, was always aggressive.

His father was neurotic and irritable. His mother—a very large woman—invariably complained of a weak heart or a nervous headache whenever something did not please her. She managed to keep the boy from marrying by convincing him she would die if he left home. She did not get along very well with her husband.

He had several girl friends with whom he had sexual intercourse at irregular intervals. He was intensely asocial and extremely jealous of a girl to whom he claimed he was engaged although he rarely saw her.

After using negative practice on his speech problem for 4 weeks, it was decided that the treatment itself would not break the habit. During the practice hour of treatment he would show good results but his written records fluctuated daily.

A program of adjustment was outlined which encouraged him to stay away from his mother's influence and to spend most of his time in the company of his friends with common interests. He was also persuaded to center his interest on a congenial young girl and cultivate her friendship.

As he proved to be a fairly suggestible person, the clinician—in order to obtain his confidence—assured him that seasickness would no longer trouble him. The suggestion proved very effective and thereafter he was seasick only once while under observation. He was given some insight into his business problems and encouraged to approach them with more confidence. The " pep " talk worked very well in his case and his work improved to a degree that won a minor promotion for him.

These procedures occupied a little more than a year. For 9 months he was treated by the negative practice method at a frequency of twice a week for one hr each period. The treatment was enforced by the use of faradic shock toward the end. During treatment periods he deliberately excited his disability in order to make the practice hour one in which he would most likely stutter.

After he became socially and vocationally adjusted, the negative practice had a much more beneficial effect; the voluntary spasm broke down by being voluntarily controlled. Throughout the treatment three rest periods were inserted, each of 1 month duration.

Twelve months after conclusion of the treatment he was more balanced emotionally and mentally, had little or no trouble with his speech, reported that he used the telephone regularly and was 12 lb heavier.

In Case 2 the home was not actually broken by separation but there was a constant disagreement between the parents. The young man, while not suffering from excessive maternal affection, was just as securely under his mother's domination, held by the constant threat that it he ever left her she would immediately have heart failure and he would thus be her murderer. He held a small position with a large industrial company. His father, a minor executive, constantly declared that he did not ever expect his son to amount to anything. He belittled the boy's friends and refused to allow him to bring girls to the house, insinuating that the only girls he could obtain must be of poor character. Once fear of his superiors was removed, the young man had a clash with his father in which he won equal rights. Then, when a similar clash with his mother proved that she did not die from the shock (although she did produce an apparent nervous prostration), he gained a measure of self-confidence in his home and in his vocational life. This allowed a direct attack upon the stuttering habit by use of negative practice. Lacking reinforcement of the various sustaining causes, the habit broke down and the boy was discharged as cured.

CASE 3—When first interviewed his speech defect consisted of becoming stuck on the second syllable of polysyllabic words. He would repeat the second syllables of such words several times with accompanying facial grimaces. He was constantly moving, crossing and recrossing his legs and arms, fidgeting nervously in his chair and biting his nails. When he first reported for treatment, he was 21 years old, a junior in the university and registered in a fine arts department. Although he was 6 ft tall and unusually thin, a medical examination failed to reveal any defects either in the speech organs or his metabolism. The doctor reported that his being underweight was not important.

He was an only son but had a sister 4 years older than he who had been married for 6 years. His father and mother were retired after mutually successful careers as sales-people. There was no quarreling or discord in the home, but inasmuch as his parents wanted him to become a salesman he had considerable difficulty pleasing them because they severely criticized his speech. He had started to stutter when he first began to talk and had continued the habit. Stuttering varied with his moods. He claimed to suffer from fairly regular periods of depression about twice a month. During such times his speech was worse. On other occasions the habit would not bother him. He had been to speech classes in public schools and to a clinic where he had been taught to speak very slowly. When interviewed, he spoke in this manner but stuttered nevertheless. He could read aloud fluently without stuttering or hesitating.

For companionship he depended solely upon his parents, a circumstance that arose during his childhood when constant traveling had not allowed him to become acquainted with other children. As soon as he would leave the university, he immediately went home for the day to study, read or play the piano or organ. His favorite reading matter was philosophy or Adlerian psychology. He was neither interested in light reading nor in amusements. Once a week he attended a motion picture but only, he said, because he felt a compulsion to go.

He masturbated and professed no interest in girls, saying that he neither liked their company nor the things they talked about. His immediate problem was what to do when he graduated from college. He felt that taking subjects in the university was fruitless and he could see no way to support himself since he had always planned to be a salesman.

For treatment, a system of negative practice was attempted and as it was impossible for him to attend more than once a week, the periods were made 1 hr long. After instructing him in the method to be followed and explaining its theory of habit breaking, it was found extremely difficult to achieve success by any criteria because of periodic fluctuations. Two months later it was decided that this factor prevented definite ascertainment of possible improvement and therefore a new attack was formulated. A program of socialization was planned involving activity in university clubs. He was persuaded to engage in short and informal conversations around the campus and to take more interest in a young lady who had shown some interest in him. At the end of approximately 4 months' treatment he felt sufficiently at ease with people to want to see whether he could make a success of door-to-door salesmanship. He was encouraged to do this because it was felt that a tentative success in this field would negate any compulsion to attempt selling through fear and would encourage development of his music once his desire to sell was no longer important.

Prior to his first selling experience, a conference was held with him wherein he was convinced that he would have very little difficulty. As he was in one of his periods of relatively little stuttering he got along nicely the first few days. When after 2 or 3 weeks he showed some signs of relapsing, a period of negative practice was utilized in conjunction with talks and consultations once a week.

He showed rapid improvement under the treatment and at the end of a total of 11 months' treatment was discharged. At the time of his discharge he was planning to be married. He had made a fair success of selling and was enjoying a rather restricted social life. " My only regret," he said, " is that I have missed out on so many years of my life."

Approximately 1 year later some misunderstanding separated him and his fiancée. A recurrence of his stuttering appeared although in a mild degree. He gave up selling and re-entered the university, finding that he preferred music to selling. A period of adjustment followed while he adapted himself to the changed conditions. He soon found another girl and began to support himself by playing in churches and other places.

This case is interesting since it shows the same general forms of maladjustment as Case 2 summarized earlier. However, the maladjustment seems to have arisen from completely different sources. No strife existed between the parents in this home, yet their very success in managing their lives acted as a cause in influencing their son to become discontented and to feel handicapped. Combined with this was profuse reading in the works of a school of psychology which placed great emphasis on the inability of the son to equal his father's achievements. In addition, the conditions under which he lived during his childhood tended to develop an asocial behavior in him. These factors seemed to be the primary and sustaining causes.

The vocational adjustment carried out in this case consisted in an indirect attack upon the casual patterns. The young man was allowed to attempt selling although the clinician knew that he could not achieve much success. Music seemed to be a better vocational choice because it was his hobby and because he already had offers for his services in that line. After discovering that selling lacked the glamour and glory that his parents had led him to believe, he reverted to the thing he could do most successfully and continued the study of music.

Although his engagement to the girl had not turned out as he hoped, it served as a stimulant during the time he was facing the public as a salesman, lessening his stuttering through a new self-confidence. The negative practice aided and finally succeeded in breaking the actual spasm habits when the tension of the sustaining causes had been relieved. Now, due to his success while selling, he is convinced that he could be a salesman if he wished without suffering any speech handicap.

It seems therefore, that unless social adjustment is undertaken in cases displaying severe social maladjustment, the patient will not entirely succeed in freeing himself of the stuttering handicap. It would appear that if adjustment is undertaken only in the social and vocational sphere, it will not be sufficient to break the involuntary habit. Therefore negative practice or some equally efficient method of unlearning the specific habit pattern—or of bringing the involuntary clonic spasm under voluntary control—must be used in conjunction with the techniques of social and vocational habilitation. This is indicated tentatively by the fact that the only 2 cases yielding to negative practice alone were those in which social adjustment was undertaken by the patients themselves, in an effort to remedy their specific maladies. Both of these patients had eliminated the sustaining causes; the only factor which remained was the involuntary habit.

Considering the group suffering from the tonic form of speech spasm commonly known as speech blocking, it was found that members of this group when submitted to the treatment accorded the clonic or stuttering forms of speech maladjustment (i.e. negative practice, negative practice with electrical reinforcement and social adjustment) immediately became worse instead of showing improvement. This observation seems born out by Fishman[5] who found that cases exhibiting blocking tendencies were harmed rather than benefited by the use of negative practice in attacking the habit.

The procedure found most effective for the treatment of stuttering consisted of negative practice used concurrently with an attempted social adjustment. Since the speech block increased when negative practice was attempted, it was decided to use some other method. An analysis of the first 3 cases revealed that all of them had the disability under so-called formal situations (that is, circumstances in which they were required to express an opinion subject to criticism by a group or where they were the center of group attraction). Their case histories revealed that all 3 cases completely lacked training in adjustment to any form of social activity outside the home. Further investigation revealed a large amount of social maladjustment, not only for group situations, but for less formal ones concerning only 2 persons. The home life of the speech blocker appeared to resemble closely that of the stuttering group.

On this basis it was decided to try to adjust the individual to social groups by a positive (though indirect) method, the technique involving his participating in various activities outlined for him. Since each of the patients had formulated numerous reasons why he did not enjoy the company of other people, it was first necessary to extract his promise to disregard, for the time, his reasons for not participating in social situations and to follow instructions implicitly. A schedule was arranged for each boy requiring him to engage in a certain number of tête-à-tête conversations daily with friends he met around school. Each day he was to increase the number of conversations and the size of the group. When he finally began to show enthusiasm for his acquaintances and no longer proffered elaborate rationalizations for not talking to people, he was introduced to larger groups.

These larger groups were found in one of the informal clubs composed of boys and girls on the campus. As they were chiefly social and service clubs, membership was quite irregular—a fact which worked to the patient's advantage since his (compulsory) regular attendance soon won him the reputation of being one of the most reliable and steady members. After some weeks the patient would take an active part in affairs of the club and become appointed to committees and other offices.

If during attempts to establish social confidence in the individual he was found to be undergoing undue mental stress in forcing himself to do assigned tasks, certain negative measures were then used. The result was that within a short time the individual would of his own volition suggest the procedure originally desired. For example, a boy who was under treatment for speech blocking blocked when talking to people (especially girls) and believed that people stared at him unnaturally when he talked to them or even while he was passing them. An attempt to get him to engage in social activities, especially in simple friendly chats with one or two other boys, failed entirely. He always discovered some reason why he could not spare time to speak to anyone throughout the day. Finally, it was decided to force the issue with him. Without explaining how negative practice would work, he was told to go for the next 3 days without speaking to anyone outside of his family. At the end of 2 days he entered the office declaring that he would simply have to speak to someone or go crazy. It seems hardly necessary to remark that further difficulty along the desired course was eliminated.

It might be mentioned here that the individual's co-operation and one of the most important factors in obtaining it, appeared to lie in the manner in which suggestions were given by the clinician. By repeated trials, it was found that direct suggestion at the beginning of treatment could be modified as the individual improved to increasingly indirect suggestion. By the time of recovery, the individual was usually able to think through his problems and achieve a satisfactory solution with little difficulty. This process involved a gradual weaning of the patient from the clinician's care and supervision. As confidence and improvement grew, the intervals of check-up were spaced increasingly farther apart until finally the individual only dropped in to see if the plans he had thought out for himself met with approval.

To illustrate the points mentioned above concerning speech blockers who achieved remedial successes and adjustments, a summary is presented of a case of this type.

CASE 4—A freshman at the University, age 18, in excellent physical condition, height 5 ft 7 in., weight 140 lb.

His difficulty had started when he was 7. It manifested itself under certain conditions in complete inability to speak. It was particularly apparent when he attempted to recite in class, or speak to a girl or stranger, at which time he would block. Experimentation bore this out. He gave no symptom of stuttering or of repeating syllables.

As a child he had been healthy. His diet had been normal. However, neither during childhood nor during adolescence had he had many friends, preferring to isolate himself with a few boys all of whom had peculiarly rigid views on morals and life.

At home he suffered much criticism for his actions and his inability to speak in a group; as a result he was very conscious of his defect, dreading any situation in which he might be called upon to speak. He was nervous when first interviewed, shifting his position constantly, showing facial tics and playing restlessly with his fingers. He reported having a sister with whom he formerly quarreled. His father was a fairly successful lawyer. His mother was a neurotic who felt the best solution to the boy's difficulty was to nag him about everything he did at home.

He was shy with the opposite sex. If he called on a girl, he always took a friend along for moral support. He had a number of old-fashioned ideas about girls. He would not speak to those who smoked, wore short skirts or used slang, and as a result he spoke to very few. His immediate sex problem was masturbation which he practiced excessively.

In the usual clinical session negative practice could not be used because it appeared to the clinician that it would not be useful here; instead, several steps were taken to build up his social situation and experience so as to give him confidence.

In the first place—because he felt everyone stared at him and thought him a fool when he tried to talk to them—he was told to go 2 days without speaking to anyone. When he came in for the next consultation he was glad to accept instructions to talk to designated people and, later, never to pass anyone he recognized without speaking. Next, he was introduced to a club composed of members of both sexes and instructed to take an active part in all of its meetings. Finally his father was willing to allow him to find a place to live with a group of men at the University.

As he had no idea of how to treat a member of the opposite sex, several consultations were arranged for him with a young lady (a graduate student in psychology) with whom he discussed some of his attitudes toward girls. During these discussions simple points of etiquette were also taken up. Under this program of socialization the boy improved rapidly and at the end of 3 months was discharged as cured. A year later a check-up revealed that he had joined a fraternity and had become a very social individual. He no longer had any difficulty in talking to groups of people or to girls he knew. With him the problem appeared to have been a complete lack of training in speech forms used in social etiquette. When he learned how to speak in these situations, the blocking disappeared.

An outstanding fact regarding the majority of speech blocking cases is that they recover as soon as they no longer feel they are not a part of the group surrounding them.

These results have indicated an effective treatment for stuttering to be the combination form outlined below:

(1) The use of negative practice,[2] not by means of arbitrary words or phrases, but by conversing with the patient under conditions causing him to stutter and requiring that he deliberately reproduce his error immediately after a mistake. This is directed toward the end that when the patient has learned to stutter at will, he will be able to control the involuntary spasms. It has been found that by deliberately repeating the spasm for about 5 times (varying according to the particular components of the case), the patient will no longer be able to reproduce the spasm perfectly, the tendency being toward increasing ease in saying the word and a lessening of the clonic spasm. In each case it seems important to follow the negative form by the correct speech.

(2) A plan of social habilitation should be worked out, based upon the individual's past social history. This plan should be carried out in conjunction with negative practice in those cases which appear to be socially maladjusted.

(3) Although not all cases were so treated, the ones showing greatest success were those changed—after mastering the technique of voluntary stuttering—to negative practice reinforced by faradic shock. The reinforcement of faradic shock apparently enhanced the effectiveness of negative practice.

(4) When the stuttering spasm has been almost obliterated in the tête-à-tête situation, the individual is graduated to the group situation where once again negative practice should be used.

(5) A study of each case reveals that the stutter is greatly increased during moments of embarrassment, such as asking a young lady out. Throughout the treatment, by taking advantage of peaks of the fluctuations marking progress the clinician can aid in breaking down the associations or " conditionings " which surround such situations by having the individual undergo them with a minimum risk of suffering the speech spasm.

(6) Definite periods of rest from the treatment appear advisable. These may vary from 1 to 3 months, depending upon the conditions involved. A rest period inserted about the time the individual reaches a peak in his progress tends to eliminate the ensuing slump which usually follows such periods and to greatly lessen the plateau effect in the unlearning of the habit. Essentially, these rest periods seem to prevent the patient's becoming completely adapted to the treatment, which would render it non-effective, and thus forestalls him from becoming " stale."

(7) Vocational adjustment should be undertaken in those cases in which it seems necessary.

(8) In order to prevent a recurrence of the maladjustment or shift of symptoms, the patient must be gradually " weaned " from dependence upon the clinician to a state of complete dependence upon himself.

(9) It is also important that tics, fingernail biting and other associated neurotic habits be broken at the time the individual is overcoming the speech habit.

The procedure which seems indicated for the correction of speech blocking on the basis of case findings appears as follows:

(1) Discussion of his particular problem with the patient, stressing the inadvisability of attempting to force the situations in which blocking is brought about.

(2) Arrangement of situations by the patient and the clinician in which the patient can talk to other persons under a minimum of strain and a constant increase of very brief informal conversations with people.

(3) As soon as the patient discovers that blocking no longer bothers him (through elimination of formal situations and the substitution of two-person informal situations), he should be advanced into larger informal groups, especially those stressing social activities.

(4) During this period, by advice when sought and indirect suggestion, the clinician should attempt to find further solutions of the patient's problems, e.g. the amount of outside work to be engaged in if he is a student, the selection of his work, etc.

(5) Finally, as in the case of the stutterer, the individual should be " weaned " from dependence upon the clinician until he is able to make and follow his own decisions.

CONCLUSION

In conclusion it may be well to point out that the therapeutic methods tried out in this study are not antagonistic to each other, but rather complimentary in attaining certain ends. The therapeutics have consisted of eliminating sustaining causes wherever possible and where present. After this elimination has taken place (if it has been present), a direct attack upon the habit has been made by means of negative practice in the case of stuttering. In the case of speech blocking the use of already acquired skills has been made available in new situations through a learning process.

REFERENCES

1. GREENE, J. S. (1935). Treatment of stutter type personalities in medical-social clinic. *J. Amer. Med. Assn.*, **104**, 2239-2242.
2. DUNLAP, K. (1932). *Habits, Their Making and Unmaking.* Liveright, New York.
3. FLETCHER, J. M. (1928). *The Problem of Stuttering.* Longmans Green, New York.
4. JOHNSON, W. (1934). Influence of stuttering on the attitudes and adaptations of the stutterer. *J. Social Psych.*, **5**, 415-420.
5. FISHMAN, H. C. (1937). A study of the efficiency of negative practice as a corrective for stammering. *J. Speech Dis.*, **2**, 67-72.
6. THORPE, L. P. (1938). Psychological mechanisms of stammering. *J. Gen. Psychol.*, **19**, 97-109.
7. VAN RYSER, C. (1937). The growth of the stuttering spasm. *Quart. J. Speech*, **23**, 73.

THE THEORY OF "CONDITIONED INHIBITION" AS AN EXPLANATION OF NEGATIVE PRACTICE EFFECTS: AN EXPERIMENTAL ANALYSIS*

D. C. KENDRICK

Department of Psychology, Institute of Psychiatry, Maudsley Hospital

As LEHNER[1] has pointed out, one of the reasons why "negative practice" has received little attention as a practical clinical device is the "difficulty in fitting the phenomenon into a systematic conceptual framework of either learning or therapy." Clearly Dunlap's[2] formulation of the *beta* and *gamma* hypotheses is in no sense a theoretical statement; it is merely a statement of fact, a description of certain observable phenomena, rather than an explanation of why these phenomena occur or even a clear indication of the conditions under which they occur. The dropping out of habits through repetition is not deduced from a firmly established set of laws or principles; it is simply affirmed as a fact on the basis of observation. It is only recently that it has become possible to derive these obscure phenomena from modern learning theory, particularly from that form of it due to Hull.[3]

Hullian learning theory lends itself very readily to experimentally testable predictions. These predictions may sometimes appear to be paradoxical, i.e. they are the opposite from those which would be expected from common-sense reasoning. Such a paradoxical prediction is that made by Gleitman *et al.*[4] formulated for the purpose of criticizing Hull's inhibition theory.[3] "Hull and his co-workers believe that habit strength becomes asymptotic to a maximum value and they usually assume that it does not decay with time. Furthermore, they assert that I_R and sI_R result as a necessary consequence of the *evocation* of the response, regardless of the presence or absence of positive reinforcement. Withholding reinforcement leads to extinction only indirectly; when no further increase in reaction potential occurs, the inhibitory action of I_R and sI_R grow unopposed.

"From these assumptions it follows that the ordinary learning curve should not be monotonically increasing, but instead should rise to a maximum and then eventually return to the base line. For, as the habit is repeatedly reinforced, sE_R approaches its asymptote. Once this asymptote

* Specially written for this book. The writer's experiments reported in this section were carried out with the aid of a Bethlem Royal and Maudsley Hospitals' Research grant.

is approximated, further reinforcements cannot add any further effective increments to the habit strength. Only I_R and $_sI_R$ can then be generated to any extent. (That $_sI_R$ is not yet at its asymptote is obvious; since extinction has not yet occurred, $_sI_R$ must be capable of further growth.) This means that from here on, further reinforcements can only lead to a *decrement* in performance, and will eventually cause the total elimination of the response. A pause between trials may at first lead to some recovery due to I_R dissipation, but this recovery will be short lived. Further trials must add to $_sI_R$ until it is approximately equal to $_sE_R$, at which point no more recovery can take place. The learning curve will have reached the base line, never to come up again. Necessarily, then, there is no learned act which can be performed for any length of time; its very repetition— regardless of reinforcement—must lead to its eventual elimination. This prediction is at odds with everything we know about the course of learning. .... The learning curve must return to *zero*, regardless of the spacing of trials, and must do so in the *same number of trials* required for experimental extinction after $_sE_R$ has reached asymptote."[4]

This notion, that the constant repetition of a habit leads to its extinction despite the fact that the habit is always rewarded when it is performed, is by no means a concept original to Gleitman *et al.* Pavlov, in 1926, stressed the fact that under certain circumstances conditioned reflexes lose their strength even though they are still being reinforced. He considered that the reason for this loss of effectiveness was that the conditioned stimuli after a considerable amount of practice passed into a state of inhibition. The growth of this type of inhibition was facilitated when the conditioned stimuli were applied at short intervals of time, i.e. massed practice. Hovland[5] drew attention to experimental extinction curves which were characterized by a larger response on the second or third extinction trial. He suggested that the reason for this was that a negative adaptation to continuous rein- forcement took place; he termed this process " inhibition of reinforcement." He argued that if this negative adaptation took place, then the transition to non-reinforcement would produce a disinhibiting effect, resulting in an augmentation of the response on the second or third extinction trial. Hovland predicted that the " inhibition of reinforcement " effect would be more marked as the number of massed reinforcements was increased and that when reinforcements were distributed, inhibition of reinforcement would be dissipated between successive reinforcements. He successfully tested these hypotheses.

Gardner and Nissen[6] found that repetition of habits can lead to a worsening of performance, or " fading " as they termed it. They found the effect to be quite common in animal experiments of a prolonged nature. They could find no adequate explanation for this effect in the literature because, as they pointed out, the relapse occurs *after* the correct response has been maintained over numerous trials and there is no known emotional upset to cause anything like an experimental neurosis. They considered that explanations such as fluctuations in attention, distraction, Hull's oscillation principle, and Spence's lawful variations in the algebraic summation of excitatory and inhibitory values accruing to the alternatives from trial to trial, had to be strained to the utmost to account for the relative permanency of the relapse.

The Russian school has long recognized the fact that avoidant shock conditioning has great advantages over nonavoidant shock conditioning in animals.[7,8] Razran,[9] in considering this knowledge, came to the conclusion that " over-reinforcement " operates as a markedly negative factor in conditioning and that partial conditioning proving to be a superior conditioning technique is due largely to non-overreinforcement.

In this brief review of the literature, brief because prior to 1956 little experimentation was carried out in investigating this topic in animal studies, one common element can be found, and that is that *the effect is produced more rapidly when trials and reinforcements follow each other in close temporal contiguity.* Apart from this major agreement in the literature, the reasons for this phenomenon are diverse. Kendrick[10] used the term inhibition with reinforcement to cover the three main hypotheses: stimulus inhibition, inhibition of reinforcement, and extinction brought about by a habit of not responding, i.e. conditioned inhibition.

There are several criticisms that can be made against the logic, and indeed the theoretical use that Gleitman *et al.* make of the Hullian theory, even though they may have had their tongues in their cheeks when they made the prediction. Gleitman *et al.* assume—and this is pure assumption— that once a habit is asymptotic to a maximum value, that habit can no longer be reinforced. This assumption of course fits in very nicely with Hovland and Razran, and would appear to give some stronger theoretical support to their arguments. But in Hullian theory the principle of reinforcement is that in close contiguity with a habit there occurs a state of drive reduction which has resulted from the performance of that habit in question. The question now is: if a habit is asymptotic but is performed under strong deprivation, can we also assume that there is no drive reduction as well as no reinforcement? Obviously this cannot be the case; according to the definition of reinforcement you cannot have one without the other. It is just as easy to assume that once a habit is asymptotic there occurs a behavioural oscillation in the strength of the habit which is at some point less than maximum, which would allow a very small amount of reinforcement again to take place. It is well known that Hull was inconsistent in his treatment of conditioned inhibition. Before Gleitman *et al.* made their prediction, Osgood[11] had pointed out the inconsistency of the multiplicative function of habit strength ($_sH_R$) with positive drive (D) and the additive function of the negative habit strength $(_sI_R)$ with the negative drive state (I_R). Jones[12] summarizes these criticisms against the inhibition theory and proposes a new learning equation which treats the positive and negative habits in the same way, that is they are both subject to the same laws, and similarly the positive and negative drive states. From the new equation:

$$_s\bar{E}_R = f(D - I_R) \times (_sH_R - _sI_R)$$

the same prediction can be made without postulating the inhibition of reinforcement effect.

In the modifications that have been made to Hullian learning theory since it was first published in 1943, one major change has been that *reactive inhibition is no longer considered as a peripheral phenomenon*. It is now considered that there is no positive relationship between effort and the amount of reactive inhibition generated, and so is regarded as a centrally generated phenomenon. Eysenck[13] has redefined the conditions under which $_sI_R$ develops. In a situation where performance is continuous, I_R builds up to a critical level, this level depending upon the strength of the primary drive (D) present at that moment.[14] Once this critical level has been reached, an automatic resting response is produced (an involuntary rest pause, IRP). These IRP's allow the dissipation of I_R below the critical level, which produce an increment of $_sI_R$. After the I_R has dissipated below the critical level, performance is once again resumed. In the normal type of massed practice where there is a slight pause between trials as in animal experiments or the usual 5-sec interval between trials on the pursuit rotor, I_R may not have developed to a critical level. The *voluntary* rest pause, however, acts in a similar way, in that it allows some I_R to dissipate and so a further increment of $_sI_R$ is produced. Eysenck treats $_sI_R$ as a habit with all the properties of a positive habit. When performance is resumed after a rest pause and all I_R has dissipated, $_sI_R$ will undergo extinction until the next voluntary rest pause, because of the failure of reinforcement to occur. But because $_sI_R$ is a habit, there is spontaneous recovery and so when there is a considerable gap between sets of trials, say a day, $_sI_R$ recovers and, because of this, from day to day there is an increase in the strength of $_sI_R$. It can therefore be seen that with this increase in $_sI_R$ from period to period, depending upon how quickly $_sI_R$ is accumulating, there will come a time when $_sI_R$ may equal $_sH_R$, in which case the chances of the performance of the habit are 50:50. Now supposing that the habit in question is at asymptote and therefore there is only a slight oscillation in its strength; if the habitual act is now repeated it can only lead to more $_sI_R$ being accumulated and so reducing the chances of the habit being performed. This process could be carried out to the point where the chances of the performance of the habit are very remote. We must point out here the difference between Gleitman's and this formulation. Gleitman asserts that $_sI_R$ must equal $_sE_R$, not $_sH_R$. His prediction could not possibly work in this case, because, when all I_R had dissipated there would be no drive to sensitize $_sI_R$ and therefore the habit would recover. In the reformulation of the learning equation this difficulty is overcome. When the equation is multiplied out, it allows for both $_sH_R$ and $_sI_R$ to be activated by the same drive (D). From this equation a further prediction can be made—which would be impossible to make using the original equation: once a habit had been extinguished—by the process suggested, then any increase in drive would only serve to increase the potentialities of *both* habits proportionally, so no recovery would take place.

The evidence from animal experiments will now be reviewed concerning the validation of these theories. Calvin et al.,[15] taking the Gleitman prediction at its face value, carried out an experiment which purports to show the paradox in operation. Their experiment was quite simple. They had an elevated straightway 10 ft long with sides 2 in. high, and there were a goal and a starting box separated from the alley-way by guillotine doors. The subjects were 24 three-to-four-months old albino rats. The animals were randomly assigned to one of four groups in which the amount of food reward and the spacing of the practice were varied as follows: Group (1), 10 g spaced; Group (2), 10 g massed; Group (3), 12 g spaced; and Group (4), 12 g massed. The procedure was that at the beginning of each trial the subject was placed in the starting box, the door immediately opened and the subject's time in reaching the goal box recorded. After the animal entered the goal box it was allowed to eat for 10 sec from a food dish containing wet mash. Under massed practice conditions the animal was then returned to the starting box and immediately run again, while under spaced conditions the subject was placed on an adjacent table for 3 min before being run again. Each subject ran 30 trials per day. The high drive subjects were allowed to eat 10 g of wet mash and the low drive subjects 12 g of wet mash in the goal box. If the subject failed to enter the goal box 5 min after the starting box door had been opened, the subject was placed in the goal box with reward present. If this occurred on two successive trials the series was discontinued until the following day. Calvin's criterion of extinction was that the subject must refuse to enter the goal box on two successive 5-min trials on two successive days.

The results of the experiment were that all animals met the criterion of extinction, that massed groups had significantly slower running times and that under high drive conditions the subjects took significantly longer to extinguish than under low drive conditions.

This experiment was heavily criticized by Dinsmoor.[16] He would not accept Calvin's results as showing the operation of the Gleitman prediction. He argued that the subjects may have stopped running because: (1) they were not hungry; (2) they may have scooped up wet mash in their paws and eaten it in the starting box or any convenient stopping place along the runway; (3) they may have become ill; (4) the runway was too long; (5) test room temperatures may not have been controlled; (6) once a rat did dawdle for whatever reason for 5 min on a given trial it was placed in the goal box so that this behaviour was reinforced. It can also be added that the resting response may still further have been reinforced by the fact that any unconsumed food that was left was placed in the home cage immediately after testing with the animal. Although some of Dinsmoor's criticisms may seem a little feeble and Calvin answered many of them himself,[17] he could not explain away the fault of reinforcing the non-running behaviour. This procedure probably vitiates the whole experiment.

Landfried and Wike[18] also report a similar experiment to Calvin's, but with a runway which was only 46 in. long. They had two groups of rats, one group which performed 30 massed trials a day and the other which performed 15 massed trials a day. They found that after 42 and 65 days respectively neither group extinguished, although any non-running behaviour was reinforced exactly as Calvin had done. These results originally suggested to the writer[19] that the effort variable in running 10 ft instead of 46 in. had had a significant effect, in that the total number of stimuli impinging on the central nervous system may have produced a greater amount of inhibition, but as will be shown later this is not the case.

Keehn and Sabbagh[20] also investigated the phenomenon of conditioned inhibition with reinforcement in an avoidance learning situation. They used two groups of albino rats, 5 males to a group. The animals were trained in a Skinner-type box 45 cm high with floor dimensions 30 cm $\times$ 25 cm. Shocks were delivered through grid floor. A turn of a treadmill turned off a light signal for shock and so allowed escape from the shock. Each subject of Group (1) was placed in the apparatus for 55 sec after which a light signal came on for 5 sec to be followed by shock unless the treadmill was turned in the meantime. One hundred trials were given on the same day with intervals of 50–70 sec. Group (2) differed only in that the 100 trials were given in blocks of ten on ten successive days. Keehn and Sabbagh found that the total number of " true " avoidance responses in Group (2) fell away considerably, and liken this result to those of Calvin et al.[15] and Kendrick.[10] Group (1), however, showed no decrement. But as Kendrick[19] pointed out, this experimental technique was the very one which should have avoided gross decrements in performance. It is well known that avoidant conditioning facilitates speed of conditioning and leads to durability of the conditioned response. Kendrick concluded that the difference between the two groups was not due to inhibitory factors but to the subjects' reactions to massed and spaced shocks, a greater conditioned fear response being produced with massed shocks.

Kendrick[10,19,21] in a series of experiments has manipulated the variables under which the phenomenon of inhibition with reinforcement develops.

In his first experiment[10] he attempted to repeat Calvin *et al.*'s experiment in some measure, but at the same time controlling for the criticisms made against Calvin. Kendrick used two identical 10 ft long runways made of wood, with open tops. Instead of using a food reward he used thirst as the primary drive. (This was done so that the reward on every trial could be measured exactly instead of using the clumsy method of allowing the animal a certain time to consume some food, when obviously on the first few trials they would eat faster than on the last trials, so producing unequal reinforcements throughout a set of trials.) A complete account of the methodology of this experiment can be found in Kendrick's article,[10] but it is sufficient to say here that among the variables controlled were; husbandry, light dark cycle, test and colony room temperatures, drive, heredity, testing procedures, age, sex, room illumination, reinforcement and food. Kendrick used two groups of 5 male albino rats selectively bred for emotionality and non-emotionality; though these factors were irrelevant to the main point of the experiment, they were to produce some interesting results. It was found that when these animals were run on 30 massed trials a day for a water reward of $\frac{1}{4}$ ml of water per trial under a deprivation level of 23 hr, *all animals had met very stringent extinction criteria within* 40 *days*. The criteria were that on three consecutive days a subject must refuse to run for water twice consecutively within the first 5 trials. A refusal was defined as the animal's failure to stop a running time-clock within 5 min of the starting box door being opened. All animals met these criteria, seven subjects actually running no trials on the three extinction days. Kendrick plotted the group mean median running times and found that there was no evidence for a gradual swing-back of the learning curve towards the base line, only an abrupt cessation of the curve on the extinction days. He found that on this measure there were no differences between the groups. He did find, however, that when the means of the first 5 trials and the last 5 trials per day were computed, there were significant differences between the two groups, in that the emotional strain group showed large warm-up effects and a tailing off in running times towards the last trials. These effects were not very apparent in the non-emotional animals. He found further that the emotional group completed on significantly fewer days the full 30 trials (testing was discontinued if a subject had two successive refusals after the first 5 trials, but this was not counted as extinction, as it had been in Calvin's experiment). Kendrick accounted for these facts using Eysenck's notion of $_sI_R$ extinction at the beginning of a series of trials after I_R has been allowed to dissipate, so that the first few trials are slow, but then, when the $_sI_R$ is extinguished, the running times are once again nearly maximum, so that median running times remain fairly constant. He argued that the effect was not found in the non-emotional group because their tolerance for inhibition was greater than that of the other group, so great in fact that the strength of $_sI_R$ must almost be equal to that of $_sH_R$ before any effect of the inhibition is shown in the depression of performance. Kendrick then pointed out that since $_sI_R$ is being experimentally extinguished it must spontaneously recover after a rest period, so that the strength of $_sI_R$ is growing continually over a period of time but its growth is not evident until the level of toleration is approached.

After a rest period of 30 days following extinction, Kendrick found no spontaneous recovery whatsoever. From all these results he concluded that the Gleitman hypothesis that this extinction was akin to experimental extinction could not be maintained, and that the inhibition was brought about by the interplay of the massing of trials and the drive level, which in turn controlled the tolerance threshold for inhibition, and individual differences in the animals.

Kendrick then directly attacked the question of tolerance level and drive. He used a completely new apparatus, an enclosed horseshoe-shaped runway, 10 ft long, with internal illumination and a goal box in the form of a Skinner-type apparatus. Not only did the animals have to run 10 ft, but they also had to press down a bar three times with a downward thrust of

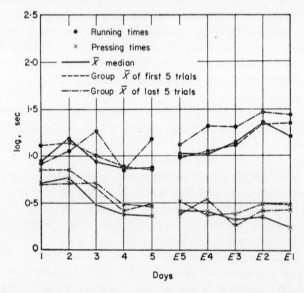

FIG. 1. The learning curves of the low drive group in the second experiment, over Periods 1 and 2. Period 1 consists of the first 5 days' testing per animal plotted as the means for the three subjects. Period 2 consists of the consecutive 5 days' testing prior to extinction per animal plotted as the means for the three subjects.

60 g before a reward of $\frac{1}{4}$ ml of water was forthcoming. He had two groups of 3 brown hooded rats each, all the rats being brothers of a highly in-bred strain. Each animal was allowed 15 ml of water a day only; as they

only ran 25 trials a day instead of 30, they received 6·25 ml in the testing situation, the rest being used to manipulate drive. Thus Group (1) had the residue of water 23 hr before testing, thus constituting high drive, and Group (2) had the residue 1 hr before testing, i.e. low drive. The criteria of extinction were slightly modified, two consecutive refusals of 3 min each in the first 5 trials on two consecutive days now being counted as extinction. The prediction made by Kendrick was that according to the drive/inhibition toleration hypothesis, other things being equal, Group (2) should extinguish significantly sooner than Group (1). This hypothesis was verified, all 3 animals of Group (2) extinguishing before any animal of Group (1) extinguished. (The testing of Group (1) was not completed.)

Several important results emerged from this experiment, as can be seen from Fig. 1. Not only is the warm-up effect shown, but also the median running time curve slopes back towards the base line, an effect that was not observed in the previous experiment. Kendrick considered this to be further evidence of the drive/inhibition tolerance hypothesis. When tested post-extinctively it was found that when the animals were tested under conditions of high drive there was no recovery of the response. This appeared to support the reformulation of the learning equation produced by H. G. Jones,[12] as this result would be quite inconsistent with the original equation. It was found that the running response only had been extinguished, and not the bar pressing response. This result was accounted for very simply; as the reward is more immediate to the bar pressing response one would expect the bar pressing response to be stronger than the running response, therefore less conditioned inhibition would be necessary to equal the running $_sH_R$.

Continuing with this apparatus and keeping the criteria of extinction the same, Kendrick then designed a rather larger experiment in which the drive, effort and reinforcement schedules were varied. The drive variable was manipulated in the same manner as in the previous experiment, and the effort variable was manipulated by defining low effort as the effort needed to run 4 ft as against 10 ft. The reinforcement variable was 66 per cent as against 100 per cent reinforcement. Thus as the subjects all ran 25 trials a day, the subjects received a reward on 15 trials only with 66 per cent reinforcement, the rewarded trials being randomly distributed. Kendrick had four groups of male albino rats, 3 rats per group, all subjects having the same father and the mothers all being sisters and sisters to the father. The groups were as follows: Group (1), 23 hours' water deprivation (high drive), runway length 10 ft (high effort), 100 per cent reinforcement; Group (2), 1 hour's water deprivation (low drive), high effort, 100 per cent reinforcement; Group (3), high drive, high effort, 66 per cent reinforcement; Group (4), low drive, runway length 4 ft (low effort), 100 per cent reinforcement. The following conditions were kept constant: pre-testing experience, colony and test room temperatures (68 to 72°F), litter weaning (21 days), caging and diet. No animals were ill during the experiment, and there was a mean body weight increase of 18 g during the experimental period.

The main aims of this experiment were: (1) to see what effect partial reinforcement would have in this situation; the obvious prediction to make from previous work would be that the intermittent reinforcement would delay the extinction, if Hovland's concept of inhibition of reinforcement was correct; (2) to try and repeat Landfried's work in which he could not obtain extinction with a short runway, and (3) to repeat Kendrick's first experiment on drive level. The results of this experiment were very surprising. Group (2) took significantly fewer trials to extinction than did Group (1), as would be predicted, but the number of days to extinction was not significantly different, this being due to the fact that the variance of Group (2) was rather large. Group (4)'s performance was almost identical with that of Group (2), there being no differences between the two groups, thus discounting the effect of effort on this process. Group (3) extinguished significantly faster than Group (1), which was against all predictions, and which tends to refute the " inhibition of reinforcement " hypothesis. Figures 2, 3, 4 and 5 show the individual groups, learning and extinction curves. It was once again found that when the low drive groups were tested

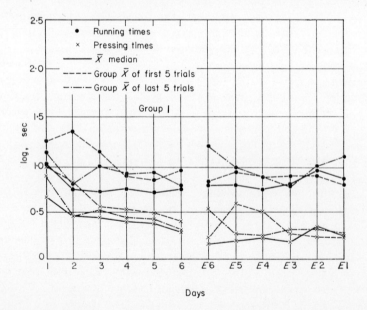

FIG. 2. The learning curves of Group (1) over Periods 1 and 2 in the third experiment. Period 1 consists of the first 6 days of testing per animal plotted as the means for the three subjects. Period 2 consists of the consecutive 6 days' testing prior to extinction per animal plotted as the means for the three subjects.

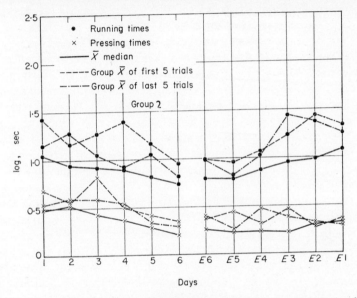

FIG. 3. The learning curves of Group (2) over Periods 1 and 2 in the third experiment.

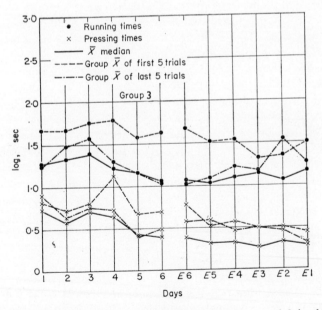

FIG. 4. The learning curves of Group (3) over Periods 1 and 2 in the third experiment.

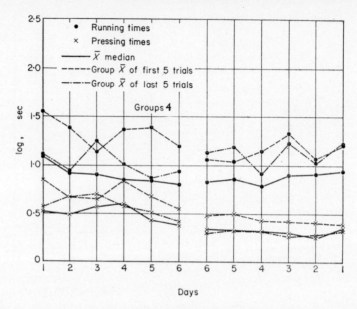

FIG. 5. The learning curves of Group (4) over Periods 1 and 2 in the third experiment.

post-extinctively under high drive conditions, there was no recovery of the response. It was also found that there was no disinhibition when the drive was changed from thirst to hunger. (It had previously been found in the second experiment that external changes in stimuli had no disinhibiting effects either.) Lastly, it was found in this experiment that both habits (i.e. running and bar pressing) were extinguished.

The prediction concerning drive level on extinction has been shown to operate experimentally, in that the extinction is brought about faster under conditions of low drive than high. This speeding-up of the extinction process would seem to be dependent on two factors: (1) a lower $_sE_R$ and (2) a lower tolerance for I_R, both factors being caused by the drive variable. It was originally predicted that effort would significantly affect speed of extinction in the following way. Since many more responses are needed to cover 10 ft than 4 ft, presumably the C.N.S. is stimulated more often, but not in a greater degree, therefore as there is more stimulation there should be more inhibition developed. But this prediction in this case was not supported, no differences being found due to effort level, which tends to contradict the hypothesis that this type of extinction is stimulus-produced. This result suggests that it is the total number of times an action sequence is carried out irrespective of the components of the sequence which is fundamental in the production of I_R.

The results of the partial reinforcement group were certainly the most surprising. When one compares Fig. 4 with Fig. 2, the differences between the two groups are very apparent. Partial reinforcement has had two main effects: it has depressed learning, which is consistent with Postulate 4 of Hull[3] which asserts that $_SH_R$ is dependent upon the number of reinforced trials, and it has speeded up extinction. At no point does the median running time learning curve of Group (3) approach anywhere near the speeds of Group (1). The fact that Group (3) extinguished significantly faster than Group (1) suggests that the " inhibition of reinforcement " hypothesis cannot be supported, especially as there was no evidence of disinhibition following non-reinforced trials. A test of x^2 was carried out to see if the trials following a non-reinforced trial were consistently faster; the results for both running and pressing speeds were negative. It is assumed therefore that the non-reinforcement not only affects learning but also increases the production of I_R (or a type of inhibition which may be called extinctive inhibition which may summate with I_R).

One of the main characteristics of this last experiment was that the median running times of all groups tended to be balanced, that is they rose to a peak and then declined again. It will be remembered that in the first experiment this was not the case. There are many differences between the two experiments, but a main difference is that in the first experiment a selectively bred group of animals was used, whereas in the last one a genetically pure group of animals was used. In the selectively bred animals the tolerance was very marked; the reason for this may have been that the selective breeding has led to characteristics which have hitherto gone unnoticed, and that these animals are different from pure strain animals in many other ways.

CONCLUSIONS

From this series of experiments, the writer has concluded that the continual repetition of a habit in the same stimulus situation will ultimately lead to the extinction of that response. The experiments have shown that the explanation for this extinction can best be looked for in the formation of a negative habit ($_SI_R$) which develops when I_R dissipates during voluntary rest pauses, or in the case of continuous performance, when I_R reaches a critical level and forces a rest pause. The fact that the extinction is permanent suggests: (1) that Gleitman's formulation is incorrect, as is the original learning equation and (2) that the reformulation of the equation accounts for the facts more adequately. The fact that it was shown that there was no recovery of the extinguished response under increased drive also lends support to the reformulation. The lowered toleration for I_R under low drive has been demonstrated.

The habit of not responding is not a simple negative habit; the animals do not just do nothing but *they do something else irrelevant to the primary drive at that time.* The non-responding habit is characteristic to each individual animal, no two animals do exactly the same thing, and the non-responding habit is relatively stable, as it is produced again after 36 days' rest.

In considering the concept of negative practice, the conclusion is drawn that this is a misnomer. In repeating the incorrect response I_R and $_sI_R$ are being accrued to this particular habit. Exactly the same process would occur if we repeated the correct response too many times, in the same situation. Lehner[1] was correct in a sense in saying, " what is clearly involved in all such situations is interference between antagonistic responses." The antagonistic responses are $_sH_R$ and $_sI_R$. But to assert that " negative practice may be thought of in one sense as a means of replacing the past with the present," cannot be sustained experimentally as it has been shown that when extinction has been established both external and internal changes in the stimulus situation do not produce a recovery of the positive response. Similarly the hypothesis of " inhibition of reinforcement " cannot at this point be substantiated by experimental evidence.

REFERENCES

1. LEHNER, G. F. J. (1954). " Negative practice " as a psychotherapeutic technique. *J. Gen. Psychol.*, **51**, 69-82.
2. DUNLAP, K. (1932). *Habits, Their Making and Unmaking.* Liveright, New York.
3. HULL, C. L. (1943). *Principles of Behaviour.* Appleton–Century, New York.
4. GLEITMAN, H., NACHMIAS, J. and NEISSER, U. (1954). The *S–R* reinforcement theory of extinction. *Psychol. Rev.*, **61**, 23-33.
5. HOVLAND, C. I. (1936). " Inhibition of reinforcement " and phenomena of experimental extinction. *Proc. Nat. Acad. Sci.*, **22**, 430-433.
6. GARDNER, L. P. and NISSEN, H. W. (1948). Simple discrimination behaviour of young chimpanzees: comparisons with human aments and domestic animals. *J. Genet. Psychol.*, **72**, 145-164.
7. STARYTZIN, S. E. (1926). The method of forming motor association-reflexes in dogs through stimulation of the pads of their paws. *Sbornik Posviashehonny Bekhterevu.*, pp. 133-145.
8. PETROPAVOLVSKY, V. P. (1934). The methodology of conditioning motor reflexes. *Fiziol. Zh. SSSR*, **17**, 217-225.
9. RAZRAN, G. H. S. (1956). Avoidant vs. unavoidant conditioning and partial reinforcement in Russian laboratories. *Amer. J. Psychol.*, **69**, 127-129.
10. KENDRICK, D. C. (1958). Inhibition with reinforcement (conditioned inhibition). *J. Exp. Psychol.*, **56**, 313-318.
11. OSGOOD, C. E. (1953). *Method and Theory in Experimental Psychology.* Oxford University Press, New York.
12. JONES, H. G. (1958). The status of inhibition in Hull's system: A theoretical revision. *Psychol. Rev.*, **65**, 179-182.
13. EYSENCK, H. J. (1956). " Warm-up " in pursuit rotor learning as a function of the extinction of conditioned inhibition. *Acta Psychol.*, **12**, 349-370.
14. KIMBLE, G. A. (1949). An experimental test of a two-factor theory of inhibition. *J. Exp. Psychol.*, **39**, 15-23.
15. CALVIN, A. D., CLIFFORD, L. T., CLIFFORD, B., BOLDEN, L. and HARVEY, J. (1956). An experimental validation of conditioned inhibition. *Psychol. Rep.*, **2**, 51-56.
16. DINSMOOR, J. A. (1956). Absurdum revisited: A comment. *Psychol. Rep.*, **2**, 255-256.
17. CALVIN, A. D. (1956). Reality revisited. *Psychol. Rep.*, **2**, 257-259.

18. LANDFRIED, D. E. and WIKE, E. L. (1956). A note on " Experimental validation of conditioned inhibition." *Psychol. Rep.*, **2**, 485-488.
19. KENDRICK, D. C. (1958). $_sI_R$ and drive level: A reply to Keehn and Sabbagh. *Psychol. Rep.*, **4**, 646.
20. KEEHN, J. D. and SABBAGH, U. (1958). Conditioned inhibition and avoidance learning. *Psychol. Rep.*, **4**, 547-552.
21. KENDRICK, D. C. (1959). Conditioned inhibition and the drive and effort variables. *Bull. Brit. Psychol. Soc.*, 38, 6A-7A (Abstract).

THE APPLICATION OF LEARNING THEORY
TO THE TREATMENT OF TICS*

A. J. YATES†

University of New England, New South Wales, Australia

SINCE the classic work in 1907 by Meige and Feindel[1] on the treatment of tics as examples of learned habits, little progress in this field has been reported, although their results were encouraging. In 1932, however, Dunlap[2] claimed that undesirable habits (including tics) could be eliminated by making the subject repeat them voluntarily and deliberately. But Dunlap gave few details of his procedure and no experimental demonstration of its validity, merely asserting that the tics disappeared rapidly. While his technique of negative practice has been accepted (at least in so far as the treatment of tics is concerned) in at least one modern textbook of psychology,[3] an adequate rationale and experimental confirmation of its utility are still lacking.

More recently, attempts have been made to derive methods for the treatment of behavioral disorders from the constructs of modern learning theory.‡[4-11] This paper reports a rationale for such treatment in the case of a tiqueur and the results of experiments carried out in order to test the validity of the deductions made from the theory.

THE TIC AS A LEARNED HABIT

The following theoretical model is proposed to show that some tics can be conceptualized as learned responses of a particular kind. The justification for proposing such a model lies in the deductions which are derived from it concerning treatment.

It is hypothesized that some§ tics may be drive-reducing conditioned avoidance responses, originally evoked in a highly traumatic situation. In this situation, intense fear is aroused and a movement of withdrawal or

---

* Reprinted by permission of the author and the Amer. Psychol. Ass. from (1958) *J. Abn. Soc. Psychol.*, **56**, 175-182.

† The author would like to thank J. Inglis and H. G. Jones for helpful discussion on the theoretical part of the paper, and Linford Rees for permission to carry out the investigation.

‡ Earlier experiments have been reviewed by Hilgard and Marquis,[12] Crafts *et al.*[13] and Lehner.[14]

§ It is not suggested that tics can arise only in the way hypothesized. Some tics appear to arise from simple imitation, especially in young children, or as an avoidance response originally arising from some irritating but non-traumatic stimulus such as a tight collar. The proposed treatment, however, should be applicable to any tic which is a learned response.

aggression is made. If the movement produces or coincides with the cessation of the fear-inducing stimulus, it acquires strength through reinforcement. On subsequent occasions, through stimulus-generalization (including internal symbolization), conditioned fear (" anxiety ") may be aroused, which is then reduced by the performance of the movement. In this way, the tic comes to be elicited by a large variety of stimuli and eventually achieves the status of a powerful habit.

Several points should be noticed about this model. First, although no direct experimental evidence is available to show that tics do arise in this way, two lines of investigation suggest that the formulation is a reasonable one. Wolpe,[11] Solomon and Wynne,[15] and others have demonstrated that animals placed in a highly traumatic situation develop conditioned avoidance responses which apparently reduce the anxiety associated with the original situation and which are highly resistant to extinction. Again, clinical investigations of the history of tiqueurs[16] have led some workers to suggest that the tic is an avoidance response arising originally in a highly traumatic situation, especially in childhood. Second, the kind of response evoked may be determined partly at least by the mode of response characteristic of the subject in any stressful situation. Malmo and his colleagues[17,18] have presented evidence suggesting that some neurotics react to stress with cardiovascular responses, whereas others react to the same stress with muscular responses. Experiments by Lacey et al.[19] similarly suggest that the nature of the stressful situation is not a major variable, at least so far as autonomic functions are concerned.

The suggested model follows closely the two-factor theory of learning expounded by Mowrer.[8] In terms of Hullian[20] learning theory, the reaction potential of the tic at a given moment may be conceived as a multiplicative function of the habit strength ($_SH_R$) of the tic (determined mainly by the number of times it has previously been evoked) and the momentary drive strength of anxiety (D), which fluctuates from time to time. Since habit strength increases as a simple negatively accelerated positive growth function and eventually reaches an asymptote, further performance of the tic cannot increase its habit strength beyond a given point.

DERIVATION OF METHOD OF TREATMENT

According to the model, then, the tic may be treated as a simple learned habit which has attained its maximum habit strength. In terms of the theory, it should be possible, therefore, to extinguish the habit by building up a negative or incompatible habit of " not performing the tic." If the subject is given massed practice in the tic, then reactive inhibition (I_R) should build up rapidly.* When I_R reaches a certain critical point, the patient will be

* With massed practice the tic will also, for the most part, cease to be reinforced, because, since anxiety is only intermittent in S, it will be unaccompanied by drive reduction.

forced to " rest " or not perform the tic. This habit $(_sI_R)$ of not performing the tic will be associated with drive-reduction due to the dissipation of I_R and hence will be reinforced. With repeated massed practice, therefore, a negative habit (" not doing the tic ") will be built up, incompatible with the positive habit of doing the tic. Furthermore, the repeated voluntary evocation of the tic should *not* serve to increase the habit strength of the tic, since it is already asymptotic and consequently not subject to strengthening by massed practice.

At any given moment, therefore, the effective reaction potential of the tic (i.e. the *ability* of the patient to perform the tic) will be a resultant of the forces in the equation

$$_s\bar{E}_R = (_sH_R X D) - (I_R + _sI_R)$$

As $_sI_R$ increases, $_s\bar{E}_R$ should diminish to a point at which the excitatory and inhibitory parts of the equation are equal. The response tendency of the tic will then be below threshold level, and behaviorally, extinction should be complete. During this process, of course, $_s\bar{E}_R$ would be expected to show fluctuations, since it is affected by a number of factors (notably drive level) which are uncontrolled $(_sO_R)$. Any increase in drive may, of course, temporarily mask the effects of an increase in $_sI_R$. It is interesting to note that Calvin et al.[21] recently produced evidence to show that the continued evocation of a habit under conditions of massed practice in rats eventually leads to its extinction, although the process may be a slow one.

The optimum conditions of massed practice under which conditioned inhibition $(_sI_R)$ may be expected to grow most rapidly and effectively are unknown with respect to the extinction of tics. The present experiments represent, therefore, an attempt to discover these conditions.

THE PATIENT

The S was a female psychiatric patient, 25 years old, who was highly co-operative and apparently had a strong desire to get well. She was of high average intelligence, and was markedly neurotic and slightly more extroverted than the average normal as measured by the *Guilford–Martin Personality Inventory of Factors, S, T, D, C, R.* Four clear-cut tics were chosen for the experiment: a complex stomach-contraction breathing tic, a nasal " explosion " (expiration), a coughing tic, and an eyeblink tic. These tics appeared to have started originally following two very traumatic experiences about 10 years previously when S felt that she was being suffocated while undergoing anaesthesia; she said she was terrified that she was going to die and struggled madly. She could not bear the thought of an anaesthetic mask and could not tolerate any object being placed over her face.

---

* Eysenck[22] has shown that these scales are reasonably good measures of neuroticism (C and D scales) and introversion–extraversion (R scale).

Superficially, at least, these tics seemed to be conditioned avoidance responses originally established in a traumatic situation.* She also said she felt a need to do the tics and experienced relief when they occurred (i.e. they were drive-reducing). They varied markedly from time to time in frequency of occurrence. It was decided to treat the four tics concurrently but independently.

Experiment 1

Sessions 1–100

The purpose of this experiment was to test the general hypothesis that massed practice leads to a significant decrement in the ability of S to respond voluntarily.

Two sessions per day were carried out, each consisting of five 1-min trials for each tic under conditions of massed practice, with 1-min rest between each set of five trials.† S was instructed to reproduce each tic as

TABLE 1

Changes in mean frequency of four tics under conditions of voluntary evocation

Stomach			Eyeblink		
Sessions	M	σ	Sessions	M	σ
1–50	52·83	4·06	1–50	36·96	4·74
51–100	40·54	3·90	51–100	31·96	2·48
112–150	41·69	2·58	101–150	31·30	1·63
151–175	19·40	2·15	151–200	26·87	2·00
176–200	15·26	1·57			
201–220	11·95	1·09	201–220	26·04	1·60
221–285	9·67	1·04	221–285	20·34	1·74
286–315	8·11	0·75	286–315	21·14	1·48

Nose			Throat		
Sessions	M	σ	Sessions	M	σ
1–50	45·56	5·41	1–50	42·00	4·17
51–100	35·11	3·02	51–100	32·18	3·55
112–150	32·06	3·13	101–150	31·52	3·53
151–180	23·71	2·73	151–200	23·91	2·25
201–220	18·97	4·25	201–220	20·37	3·33
221–248	13·23	2·12	221–285	15·51	2·10
286–315	8·05	1·90	286–315	12·88	1·73

* Presumably, escape in such a situation from the noxious stimulation was effected by the patient becoming unconscious.
† Designated henceforward the standard procedure.

accurately as possible and to repeat it without pause during the practice periods. No stress was laid on speed. A complete session lasted exactly 45 min. One such session was carried out at the hospital each day under supervision; S carried out the other on her own. The order of practising the tics was varied at random. The score recorded was the number of tics per min as counted by E in the case of the nasal and throat tics and by S in the case of the stomach and eyeblink tics. This procedure was followed for 100 sessions (50 days).

The frequency of occurrence of each tic per minute (under test conditions) almost invariably showed a steady decline from trials one to five within a single session. It was considered that the average of the five trials per session would give a reliable estimate of the strength of the tic under conditions of voluntary evocation in any particular session. The mean score for the first 50 sessions was compared with the mean score for the second 50 sessions for each tic separately.

The results (Table 1) are remarkably consistent for the four tics. The mean score for the second set of 50 sessions is significantly lower than the mean for the first set of 50 for each tic (values of t were as follows: stomach, 15·42; eyeblink, 6·60; nose, 11·93; throat, 12·68; p was $< 0·001$ in each case). The results, therefore, are in accordance with prediction and offer support for the general theory.

Experiment 2

Sessions 101–150

Three hypotheses were tested over Sessions 101–150.

Hypothesis 1—It seemed reasonable to contend that further massed practice under standard conditions would produce a further decline in the tic frequency. To test this hypothesis, the eyeblink and throat tics were practised under standard conditions.

Hypothesis 2—The difference between means of the first and second sets of 50 sessions in Experiment 1 might be due to I_R not completely dissipating between sessions. To test this hypothesis, practice on the stomach tic was discontinued for 11 sessions; during the ensuing Sessions 112–150, standard conditions were resumed. If the decline in Experiment 1 were due to I_R alone, the mean for Sessions 112–150 should not be lower than that for Sessions 1–50, i.e. recovery of function should take place.

Hypothesis 3—To test the notion that the growth of $_SI_R$ would be facilitated by increasing the duration of massed practice, the nasal tic was practised for 15 min daily without a break under instructions to keep the amplitude as strong and as constant as possible. This procedure apparently had the desired effect of increasing the number of involuntary rest pauses, a crucial factor in the growth of $_SI_R$, since in the last few minutes of the period, the rate of responding typically dropped to 3–4 per minute. Five sessions (one per day) were carried out in this way, the prolonged period always following practice on the other tics to avoid interference with them. No standard practice on the nasal tic was carried out at this time. During Sessions 112–150, standard conditions were imposed. It was predicted that the mean for Sessions 112–150 would be significantly below that for Sessions 51–100.

The results of this experiment are reported in Table 1. Hypothesis 1 was not confirmed. For both eyeblink and throat tics, the mean frequency per session was not significantly below that for Sessions 51–100 (for the eyeblink, $t = 1.570$, $p = > 0.05$; for the throat, $t = 0.927$, $p = > 0.05$). However, no recovery of function took place, since in both cases the mean for Sessions 101–150 was significantly lower than that for Sessions 1–50 (for the eyeblink, $t = 7.982$, $p = < 0.001$; for the throat, $t = 13.563$, $p = < 0.001$).

Hypothesis 2 was not confirmed. The mean for Sessions 112–150 was significantly lower than the mean for Sessions 1–50 ($t = 14.928, p = < 0.001$). However, the mean for Sessions 112–150 was not significantly different from the mean for Sessions 51–100 ($t = 1.589, p = > 0.05$).

Hypothesis 3 was confirmed. The mean for Sessions 112–150 was significantly lower than the mean for Sessions 51–100 ($t = 4.655, p = < 0.001$). Although the decline was not very large, it should be remembered that only five sessions of increased massed practice were given.

During this experiment, therefore, S seemed to be on a plateau with respect to three of the tics, but recovery of function did not take place, even when practice was entirely discontinued for a week. Further, it was apparent that the growth of $_sI_R$ could be facilitated in some degree by increasing the amount of massed practice.

Experiment 3

Sessions 151–200

Three hypotheses were again tested over Sessions 151–200.

Hypothesis 1—Practice of the eyeblink and throat tics was continued under standard conditions on the assumption that during Sessions 50–150 S had been on a plateau with respect to these tics; it was predicted that further practice would eventually induce a decline.

Hypothesis 2—It seemed probable that within the standard practice conditions, the intensification of the response would increase the rate of decline. Dunlap[2] stressed the importance of instructing S to pay careful attention to the tic. S was, therefore, asked to reproduce the stomach tic as precisely and as intensively as possible. The conditions of practice were otherwise standard.

Hypothesis 3—The prolongation of the period of practice for the nasal tic was continued. However, the method was varied. Each day, at the *end* of the hospital session only, S did 15 min massed practice of the nasal tic as in Experiment 2. In the second session of that day, the nasal tic was not practised (since the I_R associated with the 15-min practice period might not have wholly dissipated and could affect performance). However, at the *beginning* of the hospital session each day, the nasal tic was practised under standard conditions. This served as a measure of the influence of the previous day's intensive practice. The standard nasal practice was followed by the throat and eyeblink tics, which always preceded the stomach tic to avoid the effects of fatigue induced by that tic under intensive conditions. In this way, at least 12 hr elapsed between the intensive and the standard nasal practises. During this experiment, there were 20 intensive and 30 standard practice periods for the nasal tic.*

The results, as shown in Table 1, supported Hypothesis 1. The mean for Sessions 151–200 was significantly lower than the mean for Sessions 101–150 for both eyeblink and throat tics (for the eyeblink, $t = 12\cdot137$, $p = < 0\cdot001$; for the throat, $t = 9\cdot931$, $p = < 0\cdot001$).

With regard to Hypothesis 2, the results obtained with the stomach tic were not directly comparable with those obtained in Sessions 1–150 because of the altered instructions within the standard conditions. When, however, Sessions 151–175 were compared with Sessions 176–200, a significant decline was apparent in the latter set ($t = 7\cdot793, p = < 0\cdot001$). The hypothesis may, therefore, be regarded as supported.

Hypothesis 3 was also supported. Extensive massed practice led to a striking decline in frequency, the mean for Sessions 151–180 being significantly below that for Sessions 112–150 ($t = 11\cdot608, p = < 0\cdot001$).

The results of Experiment 3 suggested, therefore, that the standard procedure led to a continuing decline in frequency, that extensive massed practice had a very striking effect on frequency of response, and that increasing the intensity of response within the standard situation also led to a decline in frequency.

Experiment 4

Sessions 201–220

The purpose of Experiment 4 was to test more rigorously the hypothesis that the decline in frequency of the four tics was a function of the growth of sI_R rather than of the accumulation of I_R. When practice on the stomach tic was discontinued in Experiment 2, S later reported that she had been unable to inhibit it during the 15-min practice of the nasal tic. Hence, the earlier experiment seemed inconclusive. S was, therefore, given a 2-week holiday during which no practice of any kind was carried out. It was predicted that no recovery of function would take place. Following

---

* The numbers are unequal because S was later allowed to do the 15-min practice on her own at week-ends.

this interlude, the four tics were practised under standard conditions only, for 20 sessions.

The results, as shown in Table 1, indicated that the eyeblink tic showed no change following complete rest ($t = 1.00$, $p = > 0.05$). The other three tics all showed a significant further decline during Sessions 201–220 compared with the level reached in Experiment 3 (for the stomach, $t = 8.37$, $p = < 0.001$; for the nose, $t = 3.98$, $p = < 0.001$; for the throat, $t = 4.49$, $p = < 0.001$). The decline was particularly striking in the case of the nasal tic. The hypothesis that no recovery of function would occur seemed, therefore, to be supported, but the significant decline following rest in the case of three tics remained to be explained.

Experiment 5

Sessions 221–275

Three hypotheses were tested in this experiment.

Hypothesis 1—Massed practice under standard conditions was continued for the eyeblink and throat tics, the prediction being that a further significant decline would result.

Hypothesis 2—Massed practice under standard conditions but with intensification of the response was continued for the stomach tic, the prediction being that a further significant decline would result.

Hypothesis 3—It was decided to test whether the rate of growth of $_sI_R$ could be significantly increased by an increase in the *rate* and *intensity* of repetition of the nasal tic. To test this hypothesis, the 15-min period of massed practice was used. This period was divided into periods of 5 sec of massed practice followed by 10 sec of rest. During the 5 sec S performed the nasal tic as rapidly and as intensively as possible. It was expected that I_R would accumulate more rapidly and would dissipate less between individual

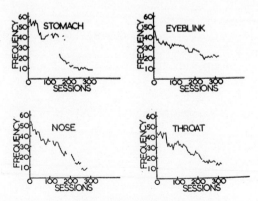

FIG. 1. Changes in frequency of four tics voluntarily evoked under various conditions of massed practice.

tics. Because 10 sec of rest would thus be expected to have a high reward value, $_sI_R$ should be more strongly reinforced. Apart from the change in procedure for the 15 min of practice, the method adopted was identical with that described in Experiment 3.

The results, as shown in Table 1, indicated that all three hypotheses were confirmed* (for the eyeblink, $t = 13·67$; for the stomach, $t = 8·26$; for the nose, $t = 5·21$; for the throat, $t = 6·16$; p was $< 0·001$ in each case).

Experiment 6

Sessions 276–315

The purpose of this experiment was to test the hypothesis that a very prolonged period of massed practice followed by a prolonged rest would lead to a significant decrement in response. It had been found that in Sessions 201–220 a highly significant decline took place on three of the four tics following 2-weeks' rest, the decline being most striking in the case of the nasal tic. The possibility arose, therefore, that the crucial set of conditions for increasing $_sI_R$ rapidly lay in a combination of very intensive practice followed by a long rest. In general, it was hypothesized that optimum increments of $_sI_R$ would be obtained if sufficient massed practice were given to allow the accumulation of a maximum amount of I_R, followed by a rest period sufficient to allow the complete dissipation of I_R. To test this hypothesis, four 1-hr sessions were given, during which uninterrupted massed practice of the nasal tic was carried out. The other tics were not practised during these sessions, each of which was separated from the next by a 3-day interval. There were no standard practices of the nasal tic during this period. The other tics were practised under the usual conditions during the second daily session only (i.e. once per day, constituting Trials 276–285). At the end of this period, the patient was given a 3-week holiday during which no practice of any kind was carried out. Following this rest, 30 standard sessions (286–315) were given for all four tics.

The results, as shown in Table 1, indicate that the nasal tic showed a very significant decline in the mean for Sessions 286–315 compared with Sessions 221-248 immediately preceding the four 1-hr practices ($t = 7·99, p = < ·001$). Throat and stomach tics showed a significant but much smaller decline (for the throat, $t = 6·43$, $p = < 0·001$; for the stomach, $t = 8·32$, $p = < 0·001$). The eyeblink tic showed a small but significant recovery ($t = 2·32$, $p = 0·02$). Thus, the hypothesis was generally supported.

At the conclusion of this experiment, the mean score for the last 30 sessions (286–315) was compared with the mean score for the first 30 sessions (1–30).† The percentage decrement in the frequency of voluntary responding

---

* Table 1 shows the means for Sessions 221–285 for eyeblink, throat and stomach tics. Sessions 276–285 were, however, actually performed for these tics during Experiment 4 while the nasal tic was being given four one-hour practices.

† For the stomach tic, the comparison was between Sessions 151–180 and 286–315.

for each tic was as follows: nasal, 84·14; throat, 68·83; stomach, 63·42; eyeblink, 51·47. The course of decline is shown in Fig. 1, in which each point represents the average of five sessions (i.e. 25 1-min trials). Gaps in the curves indicate rests or changes in treatment.

CHANGES IN INVOLUNTARY TICS

It is notoriously difficult to obtain a reliable estimate of the rate of involuntary responding in tics, which fluctuates markedly from day to day, even from hour to hour. While a *change* in the rate of response would be very difficult to assess reliably, a complete cessation of involuntary responding outside the test situation would be apparent to *S*, to her acquaintances, and to *E*. *S* had not reached this clinical criterion at the end of Experiment 6. At the end of the series, however, she was asked to write a frank account of her experience over the period of treatment, both in relation to the tics and to her general adjustment.

Her report indicated that the nasal tic " has almost vanished. It returns occasionally . . . every now and then . . . but most definitely it does not plague me every few minutes as before. It is absent for days on end." The eyeblink and throat tics were reported as sharply reduced in frequency. The stomach tic, however, had changed very little. She also reported that she had " improved in all departments generally," was " able to relax in a bus or train, able to read or execute a crossword puzzle." There was continual reference to the fact that not doing the movement did not leave her frustrated. She concluded that she was, " not tired of the treatment, if anything now that I have a taste of success the desire is greater." She also pointed out that " one of the striking features is that my closest friends notice the change." The specific and general changes were confirmed by her physician.*

DISCUSSION

The results obtained in these experiments support the theory proposed to explain the genesis of certain tics and the deductions made from it regarding a rational method of treatment. Within the test situation there was objective evidence of a striking decline in the rate of voluntary responding for all tics. The rate of decline was most striking in that tic (nasal) which received the largest amount of massed practice. There was no evidence of any recovery of function following prolonged rest. The data further suggest that the optimum conditions for the production of conditioned inhibition may be a period of very prolonged massed practice, leading to the accumulation of large amounts of reactive inhibition, followed by a very prolonged rest to allow for the total dissipation of reactive inhibition. There was subjective

* During these experiments, *S* received no other treatment but saw her physician for a few minutes about once a month.

evidence suggesting that conditioned inhibition generalized beyond the test situation itself and that most generalization occurred with respect to the tic which had received most massed practice. It is not suggested, however, that the results outlined above can be unequivocally interpreted. Under clinical conditions of testing and with limited time available, perfect experimental control and balance of design proved impossible to obtain. Thus, it is possible that the decline in Sessions 286–315 in the nasal tic was a function entirely of the amount of massed practice given and not of the combination of practice and rest. Although no standard practices were carried out on the nasal tic between the four 1-hr periods, S reported that she became much worse outside the test situation during this time. However, during the 3-weeks' rest period which followed, she reported that she rapidly lost the tendency to perform the tic involuntarily, which suggests that the rest was an essential part of the treatment. These results imply that the cumulative reinforcement associated with the dissipation of reactive inhibition may continue for longer periods of time than is commonly supposed. This interpretation is consistent with the findings of Jahnke and Duncan.[23]

A number of considerations which arose during the experiments merit brief mention. It would have been useful to have left one tic untreated and to have taken control readings under standard conditions at regular intervals. Under these conditions, little or no conditioned inhibition would be expected and the prediction would be that the untreated tic would not decline during the course of the experiment. Second, an objective measure of the frequency of each tic outside the test situation at the beginning and end of the experiments is highly desirable. It should not be too difficult to measure the frequency of tics reliably in a natural situation. Third, attention should be paid to the amplitude as well as the frequency of the tics; a measure of both variables would be useful. Fourth, S should be instructed from the start to reproduce the tic as accurately as possible in order to facilitate the growth of I_R.

Nevertheless, certain features of the obtained results are highly suggestive. The shape of the curves suggests, in some respects at least, the obverse of a learning curve. There is no evidence of an initial rise in frequency, indicating that the habit strength of the tic was probably at its asymptote before massed practice was begun. Again, the decline in frequency appears to proceed according to the usual learning process. There are periods of stability (plateaux) followed by sudden falls, suggesting that a negative habit was actually being learned. This finding agrees with the results of Edmonson and Amsel,[24] who found that in the extinction of conditioned avoidance responses, long periods during which no change took place, alternated with sudden sharp declines. The curves also show the sessional fluctuations common in learning curves, where all the relevant factors (notably, in this n stance, drive level) cannot be controlled.

An important problem concerns the relationship between the anxiety and the tic. S reported at the end of treatment that she was much less anxious than formerly (reflected in many particular examples of behavior she gave). This reduction in anxiety follows directly from the theory. If the ability to respond is significantly reduced, then the anxiety leading to the tics will persist. However, since no traumatic event happens in fact as a result of the anxiety, the latter, being itself a conditioned response, gradually extinguishes. This formulation suggests an alternative method of treatment. If the tics are prevented from occurring, then reduction of the anxiety should follow. When this happens, the tics will also decline, since they are a response to anxiety. Meige and Feindel[1] reported cases in which paralysis of facial tics for several days led to their disappearance for a period of several months. This hypothesis also receives support from the findings of Solomon and his colleagues[25] that conditioned avoidance responses can be extinguished in dogs by presenting the CS a large number of times but preventing the avoidance response by restraint. The usual extinction procedures, which formerly had been unsuccessful, could then be applied. These arguments are the principal justification for symptomatic treatment. It is interesting to note that they follow directly from Mowrer's two-factor theory. Mowrer himself has strongly opposed symptomatic treatment[8] although making use of it in the treatment of enuresis. In terms of the theory, it would also be predicted that this method of treatment would be most successful with children because $_sH_R$ would presumably be at less than asymptotic strength. Thus, as soon as negative practice began, most of the repetitions of the tic would be contributing towards the growth of $_sI_R$ rather than $_sH_R$, and the growth of the negative habit (not-doing-the-tic) would proceed more rapidly than the growth of the positive habit.

SUMMARY

A theoretical model was proposed to show that some tics may be conceptualized as drive-reducing conditioned avoidance responses, originally evoked in a traumatic situation.

From this model, a method of treatment was derived. It was predicted that if the tics were evoked voluntarily under conditions of massed practice, a negative habit of " not-doing-the-tic " should be built up, resulting ultimately in the extinction of the tics and that this extinction should generalize beyond the test situation.

The results of a number of experiments support the validity of the theory. There was a significant decline in the ability to respond voluntarily under various conditions of massed practice and rest.

The optimum condition for the growth of the negative habit appeared to be the combination of very prolonged massed practice followed by prolonged rest.

Subjective reports of the patient indicated considerable clinical improvement outside the immediate test situation.

REFERENCES

1. MEIGE, H. and FEINDEL, E. (1907). *Tics and their Treatment*. S. Appleton, London.
2. DUNLAP, K. (1932). *Habits, Their Making and Unmaking*. Liveright, New York.
3. BORING, E. G., LANGFELD, H. S. and WELD, H. P. (1948). *Foundations of Psychology*. Wiley, New York.
4. CHERRY, C. and SAYERS, B. McA. (1956). Experiments upon the total inhibition of stammering by external control and some clinical results. *J. Psychosom. Res.*, **1**, 233-246.
5. JONES, E. L. (1955). Exploration of experimental extinction and spontaneous recovery in stuttering. In *Stuttering in Children and Adults*, ed. by W. JOHNSON. Univ. of Minnesota Press, Minneapolis, pp. 226-231.
6. JONES, H. G. (1956). The application of conditioning and learning techniques to the treatment of a psychiatric patient. *J. Abnorm. Soc. Psychol.*, **52**, 414-419.
7. LIVERSEDGE, L. A. and SYLVESTER, J. D. (1955). Conditioning techniques in the treatment of writer's cramp. This volume, pp. 327-333.
8. MOWRER, O. H. (1950). *Learning Theory and Personality Dynamics*. Ronald Press, New York.
9. RAYMOND, M. J. (1956). Case of fetishism treated by aversion therapy. *Brit. Med. J.*, **2**, 854-857.
10. WISCHNER, G. J. (1950). Stuttering behavior and learning: A preliminary theoretical formulation. *J. Speech Dis.*, **15**, 324-335.
11. WOLPE, J. (1952). Experimental neuroses as learned behavior. *Brit. J. Psychol.*, **43**, 243-268.
12. HILGARD, E. R. and MARQUIS, D. G. (1940). *Conditioning and Learning*. Appleton–Century, New York.
13. CRAFTS, L. W., SCHNEIRLA, T. C., ROBINSON, ELSA A. and GILBERT, R. W. (Eds.) (1950). *Recent Experiments in Psychology*. McGraw-Hill, New York.
14. LEHNER, G. F. J. (1954). Negative practice as a psychotherapeutic technique. *J. Gen. Psychol.*, **51**, 69-82.
15. SOLOMON, R. L. and WYNNE, L. C. (1954). Traumatic avoidance learning: the principles of anxiety conservation and partial irreversibility. *Psychol. Rev.*, **61**, 353-385.
16. GERARD, MARGARET (1946). The psychogenic tic in ego development. In Anna Freud, *et al.* (Eds.). *Psychoanalytic Study of the Child*. Vol. 2. Inter. Univ. Press, New York. Pp. 133-162.
17. MALMO, R. B. and SHAGASS, C. (1949). Physiologic study of symptom mechanisms in psychiatric patients under stress. *Psychosom. Med.*, **11**, 25-29.
18. MALMO, R. B., SHAGASS, C. and DAVIES, F. H. (1950). Symptom specificity and bodily reactions during psychiatric interview. *Psychosom. Med.*, **12**, 362-367.
19. LACEY, J. I., BATEMAN, D. E. and VAN LEHN, R. (1953). Autonomic response specificity. *Psychosom. Med.*, **15**, 8-21.
20. HULL, C. L. (1943). *Principles of Behavior*. Appleton–Century, New York.
21. CALVIN, A. D., CLIFFORD, L. T., CLIFFORD, B., BOLDEN, L. and HARVEY, J. (1956). Experimental validation of conditioned inhibition. *Psychol. Rep.*, **2**, 51-56.
22. EYSENCK, H. J. (1957). The questionnaire measurement of neuroticism and extraversion. *Riv. Psicol.*, **50**, 113-140.
23. JAHNKE, J. C. and DUNCAN, C. P. (1956). Reminiscence and forgetting in motor learning after extended rest intervals. *J. Exp. Psychol.*, **52**, 273-282.
24. EDMONSON, B. W. and AMSEL, A. (1954). The effects of massing and distribution of extinction trials on the persistence of a fear-motivated instrumental response. *J. Comp. Physiol. Psychol.*, **47**, 117-123.

25. SOLOMON, R. L., SIDD, J. J., WATSON, P. D. and BLACK, A. H. (1955). The use of d-tubocurarine in the extinction of fear in dogs. *Amer. Psychologist*, **10**, 395. (Abstract).
26. MILLER, N. E. (1951). Learnable drives and rewards. In *Handbook of Experimental Psychology*, ed. by S. S. STEVENS. John Wiley, New York, pp. 435-472.

CONTINUATION OF YATES' TREATMENT OF A TIQUEUR*

H. Gwynne Jones

Department of Psychology, Institute of Psychiatry, Maudsley Hospital

When Yates carried out his investigations into the effects of negative practice on the tics displayed by a psychiatric patient,[1] his aims were experimental rather than therapeutic. The series of experiments he describes were devised to determine the optimum conditions of massed practice for the extinction of the tics. Though the patient improved considerably in the course of these experiments, Yates intended to apply his findings in a second, treatment-oriented, phase of the study. Owing to unforeseen circumstances he was unable to undertake this task and had to pass it to the writer.

Though further experiments might have been performed to clarify unsolved problems, it was decided to proceed with treatment in the light of the main implications of Yates' study. These were considered to be:

(1) That uninterrupted massed practice over a period as long as 1 hr is most favourable to the development of $_sI_R$. This is equivalent to experimental extinction.

(2) That prolonged rests from practice are favourable to the extinction process.

(3) That the particular patient being treated could be relied upon to carry out and record exercises in her own home. This was extremely important as it enabled intensive treatment over a period of 34 weeks to be completed with the patient never visiting the hospital more than twice in one week (33 visits in all).

During the first few weeks of treatment attention was focused on the nasal responses† and the 1-hr " experimental extinction " sessions, initiated by Yates, were continued. It soon became evident, however, that, though the other tics had improved considerably during the experimental phase, the patient's stomach tic was troubling her greatly. It had always been the most distressing of her tics, both physically and psychologically, and the writer formed the impression that it constituted the initiating and central manifestation of a variable and complex tic sequence. The main attack was therefore turned upon this symptom through most of the period.

* Specially written for this book.
† For the sake of clarity the involuntary movements are referred to throughout as " tics ": the voluntary reproductions of these movements are described as " responses."

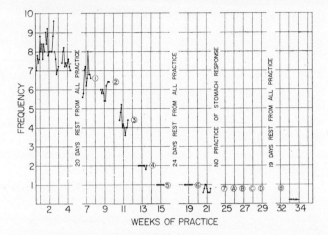

FIG. 1. Changes in frequency of the stomach responses during the course of training:
1 to 8 = 1-hr experimental extinctions;
A to D = Massed practice of stomach " flutters."

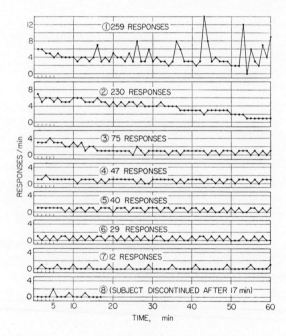

FIG. 2. Successive experimental extinctions by massed practice of the stomach
responses.

The entire sequence of stomach training is presented in Fig. 1.

Experimental extinctions, one-week rest periods and weeks of Yates' standard procedure* were presented in sequence. Long rests from all practice were inserted to coincide with holiday periods.

The average frequencies of response during the 5 min of each session of the standard procedure are plotted in the figure: the curves so formed are continuations of those presented by Yates. As is evident from these data, the experimental extinctions produced marked declines in these frequencies. Statistical tests cannot be applied to the later differences owing to the lack of variance within the standard periods. The differences between the three standard periods preceding the first three extinctions are highly significant ($p = < 0.001$). At the end of this training the patient could only produce one stomach response in each session of the standard procedure (i.e. one in 5 min). During the experimental phase this same response was evoked as often as 20 times in 1 min. It is evident, then, that complete long-term extinction of a voluntary response can be achieved as readily in humans as in animals.[2]

The course of events during the successive extinctions is presented in Fig. 2. The usual phenomena of successive experimental extinctions are all evident, including the successively diminishing spontaneous recovery

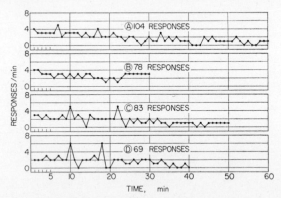

FIG. 3. Successive periods of massed practice of stomach " flutter ". Each response represents a series of 10 rapid shallow stomach movements.

indicative of the growth of $_sI_R$. On the final occasion the patient was unable to continue after 17 min. No responses were observed by the writer but she claimed that 4 abortive ones had been made.

As, towards the end of training, the stomach tic had also lost much of its intensity and had tended to develop into a " flutter ", an attempt was made to apply negative learning to a similar response. The patient was

* Standard procedure involves the maximal voluntary evocation of responses during five 1-min trials separated by 1-min rest periods.

asked to make 10 shallow stomach movements in rapid succession and to repeat this sequence as frequently as possible throughout prolonged massed practice periods. This procedure proved to be unsatisfactory as the patient found it extremely difficult to make these responses and kept changing their character. The frequencies observed are plotted in Fig. 3.

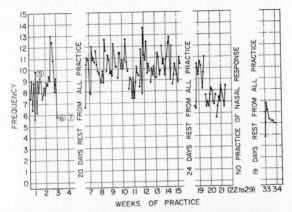

FIG. 4.   Changes in the frequency of the nasal responses during the course of training: 5 to 7 = 1-hr experimental extinctions.

Figures 4 and 5, analagous to Figs. 1 and 2, refer to the nasal responses. For completeness, the experimental extinctions carried out by Yates (Y_1 to Y_4) are included. Extinction 5 was the first to be observed by the writer and he rapidly became impressed with the potency of reactive inhibition. Towards the end of the period the patient gave every manifestation of physical exertion when attempting to produce a response. When one was achieved she slumped in her chair for many seconds. This behaviour somewhat alarmed the writer but, when the patient's pulse rate was counted immediately after the completion of the session, it was found to be only 72 beats per min. Immediately the massed practice ended, the patient appeared to be entirely relaxed and comfortable. In further exploration of the nature of the inhibition, the patient was told, at the end of the fifty-ninth minute of period 6, that only 1 min remained and was asked to respond as rapidly as possible. Despite every effort to comply she was only able to produce one response as in the previous minute. During period 7, though the starting level was a little raised, the total number of responses increased considerably. For the reasons given earlier, further massed practice of this response was not attempted.

As can be seen from Fig. 4, the massed practice described had no inhibitory effect on the standard rate of responding. There is a significant decline overall, resulting mainly from the difference between the periods before and after the extended final rest period ($p = < 0.001$).

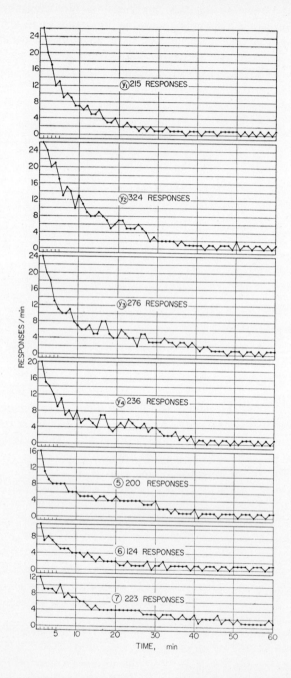

Fig. 5. Successive experimental extinctions by massed practice of the nasal responses.

Figures 6 and 7 present the data concerning the throat responses. Only the standard procedure was applied until the late stages of training. There is a significant, shallow, uniform decline in frequency throughout this period. Three experimental extinctions and a long rest period were then followed by a significantly lower frequency ($p = < 0.001$) in the last standard period. The third of these experimental extinctions, like the last in the nasal series, produced an increased number of responses. Response production was

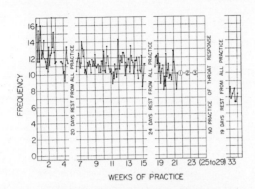

Fig. 6. Changes in frequency of the throat responses during the course of training: 1 to 3 = 1-hr experimental extinctions.

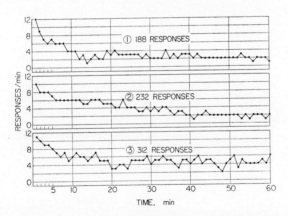

Fig. 7. Successive experimental extinctions by massed practice of the throat responses.

also strikingly more irregular. This coincided with an exacerbation of the throat tic, which improved during the subsequent rest period. Yates[1] observed a similar sequence of events but, in the present instance, the patient also suffered from a throat infection.

The eyeblink response was only given standard practice throughout. The data are presented in Fig. 8. Here again there is a shallow decline in frequency throughout training, and this is steeper after the final rest period.

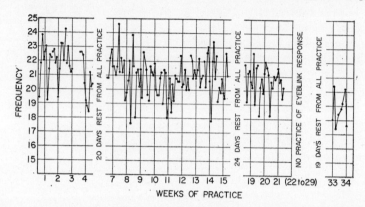

FIG. 8. Changes in frequency of the eyeblink response during the course of training.

In general, the expectations derived from Yates' data[1] have been confirmed by these further applications of massed practice. Of major interest is the demonstration, in the case of the stomach response, of the possibility, by persisting with successive experimental extinctions, of generating such a high level of conditioned inhibition as to almost completely inhibit a voluntary response in a human subject.

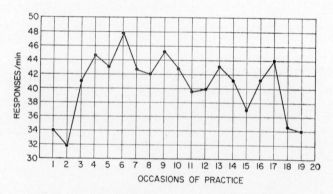

FIG. 9. Standard practice of an inspiratory response.[3]

CHANGES IN THE TICS

As in Yates' study,[1] no objective measures were taken of the frequency of the tics and reliance was placed on the psychologist's informal observations, the patient's own reports, and psychiatric assessment. There is little doubt that there was considerable amelioration of these symptoms throughout treatment and a general improvement in the patient's emotional state. Seventeen months after discharge, a follow-up psychiatric assessment was made and the patient was rated as " much improved." The existence of any direct causal relationship between this improvement and the procedures described cannot, however, be claimed. No single case study can provide satisfactory evidence concerning the efficacy of a therapy. The writer's interest in this investigation derives from the application of psychological principles to psychiatric problems and the testing of the soundness of generalizations, derived from the laboratory, in real-life situations.

Despite the improvement described, the patient is still a tiqueur. Her tics are far less noticeable, are more easily brought under control and cause far less social embarrassment, but can be temporarily exacerbated by illness and by social and vocational frustrations.

No evidence of " symptom substitution " was observed during the treatment but, as has been described, there was a tendency for the stomach tic to become modified in form. These changes were, however, consistent with a lessening of the vigour of the movements.

DISCUSSION

It is not surprising that conditioned inhibition does not completely generalize from an imperfect voluntary imitation of a complex involuntary response to the involuntary response. What does seem surprising, however, is that the results of the present investigation give no reason to believe that this generalization is increased when the voluntary response is completely extinguished. The eyeblink response received less massed practice than any other and yet the eyeblink tic was probably the most responsive to the treatment. Various hypotheses can be advanced to explain this discrepancy but doubt must remain concerning the adequacy of the explanation of the effects of negative practice in terms of conditioned inhibition.

An excellent example of effective negative practice with little massed practice is provided by Ernest.[3] She treated a girl of 13 with a severe inspiratory tic by applying Yates' standard procedure which, with only one tic, required only 5-min practice spread over 10 min. Nineteen sessions of practice were spread over some 7 months and the girl occasionally practised at home. Towards the end of this period the tic completely disappeared and has not returned during several months follow-up. The average frequencies of response during each practice session are presented in Fig. 9.

Dunlap[4] claims good therapeutic results from the application of negative practice but stresses the manipulation of conscious attitudes rather than the development of inhibition. As most athletes are well aware, the paying of conscious attention to the performance of an habitual movement can radically alter the performance of that movement. Similarly, the conscious

imitation of a tic may radically alter the neuro-muscular mechanisms underlying the tic. Such factors may well interact with factors related to conditioned inhibition. Clearly, negative practice merits further investigation.

REFERENCES

1. YATES, A. J. (1958). The application of learning theory to the treatment of tics. This
    volume, pp. 236-249.
2. KENDRICK, D. C. (1959). The theory of conditioned inhibition as an explanation of
    negative practice effects: an experimental analysis. This volume, pp. 221-235.
3. ERNEST, E. (1959). Personal communication.
4. DUNLAP, K. (1946). *Personal Adjustment*. McGraw-Hill, New York.

THE APPLICATION OF MODERN LEARNING THEORY TO THE TREATMENT OF CHRONIC HYSTERICAL APHONIA*

D. WALTON, B.A., DIP.PSYCH.(LOND) and D. A. BLACK, M.A.

Winnick Hospital, near Warrington, Lancashire; Rainhill Hospital, near Liverpool

INTRODUCTION

LEARNING theory has already been applied by the present authors to the problem of stammering. A specific case was reported[1] in which the genesis of a stammer was explained by means of a theoretical model. The outcome of treatment deduced from this model suggested that the method was valid and further work on the same lines was encouraged.

The present paper therefore reports a further application of learning theory, this time to a case of chronic hysterical aphonia. A theoretical model is proposed to explain both genesis and chronicity; a method of treatment is deduced; and the results are reported, together with a follow-up of almost a year.

The literature on this type of case is both sparse and conflicting and would suggest, in the authors' view, that the time is now ripe for the validation of a method of treatment based on an experimentally tested model. Thus was the present formulation prompted. In particular, two assumptions were questioned, first that most published work treated acute and chronic aphonia alike, and secondly that the removal of a chronic aphonia, as with any other symptom, has often hitherto been expected to result in the development of an alternative symptom.[2]

The nearest approach to an experimentally verifiable hypothesis concerning differences between acute and chronic aphonia, with any implication for treatment, was proposed by Kretschmer[3]: " an hysterical habit . . . is one which began as a voluntary process and has become gradually automatic from repetition . . . hysterical habits include disorders of . . . speech (aphonia)."

Despite Kretschmer's earlier recognition of the therapeutic implications behind such differences, Henderson and Gillespie[4] appear not to have followed

* The authors are grateful to Dr. B. Finkleman, Medical Superintendent, Rainhill Hospital, for permission to publish the present study. We would also like to thank Dr. G. C. Heller and Dr. H. Astley-Cooper whose co-operation greatly assisted this study.

Reprinted by permission of the authors and the editor of *J. Psychosoma. Res.* from (Aug., 1958) *J. Psychosomat. Res.*

up these implications. Their own suggestions for treatment are partly empirical and partly notional, based on various *ad hoc* theoretical frameworks. The absence of any experimentally founded postulates in their approach precludes any prediction of the likely effects of such treatment. Often, also, it is difficult to decide whether they regard all hysterical aphonics as being homogeneous or whether they recognize differences to exist.

Amongst the methods they advocate are the use of free association, hypnosis and the use of special methods in the case of patients resistive to psychotherapy. Some confusion arises here because presumably the latter category is more likely to include the chronic case who has not responded to treatment and whose continued aphonia resembles Kretschmer's " hysterical habit." If this is the case the habit presumably exists in its own right divorced from the original traumatic events which incurred it. It is therefore difficult for the authors to understand Henderson's and Gillespie's statements, " . . . a patient with a rigid (hysterical) paralysis must be made to move the limb . . . immediate complete success is necessary . . . piecemeal improvement is tedious and often temporary . . . complete function must be restored at one sitting . . . in a proportion of cases the symptom is an hysterical habit which has outlived its usefulness, and which the patient would gladly be rid of if he knew how. *These patients are easily amenable to treatment.*"

Mayer-Gross *et al.*,[5] in a later textbook, similarly do not suggest any method of treatment based on experimentally founded postulates. They make certain empirical suggestions for treatment which are open to the same criticisms as those applied to Henderson and Gillespie. Several methods are raised for consideration. They suggest, for example, that hypnosis or suggestion under narcosis, together with an understanding of the environmental factors in the causation of the illness, might be of remedial value.

The fact that the present patient failed to improve following several years of intensive treatments similar to those suggested by Henderson and Gillespie and Mayer-Gross tends both to support the previous remarks against the use of empirical methods in the treatment of such chronic cases, and to indicate the predictive difficulties inherent in using any such *ad hoc* theoretical frameworks.

The present study arose following the suggestion that the patient might respond to a course of treatment based on learning theory.

SUMMARY OF CASE-HISTORY

The patient's family background was thought to be relevant to the development of her aphonia, though nothing of significance is reported to have occurred before the age of 11.

The patient's father left home when she was 11 and was divorced 5 years later. He is reported to have left his wife because she was always stealing. Until the patient (henceforth to be referred to as *M*) reached the age of 11 her father was said to have been distant with her and she felt that she was not wanted by him. On occasions her mother is reported to have made it equally obvious that *M* was in the way. After *M*'s eleventh birthday, the mother went out to work though she continued to steal. She is reported to have tried to force *M* into stealing.

A significant incident is said to have occurred when *M* was visiting her father who was ill. *M* alleges that on this occasion incest was attempted by her father. The mother meantime continued to steal. About this time *M*, who was 14, was ill in bed with septic tonsillitis. Two detectives visited her and in her room found a quantity of postal orders stolen by her mother from a local Pools firm.

At the age of 15 *M* left school and went to work in a wholesale chemists. About this time her mother was working in a Chinese café. Her mother is said to have tried to arrange a marriage between her daughter and the Chinese proprietor for a sum of money. *M*'s grandfather prevented this. On another occasion when *M* and her mother went to help with the Christmas decorations in the café, her mother conveniently left *M* in the basement with the proprietor.

Her mother remarried when *M* was 17. *M* went to live with her mother and stepfather. About this time she is said to have had a minor throat operation. When she regained consciousness she found she had lost her voice. A short time after this she was admitted to a neurosis unit for the first time. From early 1951 to 1957 her voice was at best nothing more than a whisper.

Up to the time that *M* was referred to the Psychology Department for the symptomatic treatment of the aphonia she had been a voluntary patient in the neurosis unit on 4 separate occasions. By the time of her fourth admittance she had been aphonic for some 7 years and completely mute for 2 of these years. No significant change had occurred in her condition in spite of intensive psychotherapy, hypnosis and several physical methods of treatment which included modified insulin, ether and methedrine abreactions, narco-analysis and LSD. Before treatment began *M* was examined by the ENT surgeon who expressed the opinion that she would not speak again, although he could find nothing physically wrong with her vocal chords.

SYMPTOMATIC TREATMENT OF THE APHONIA

Proposed Theoretical Model

The assumption underlying most published work on hysterical aphonia that the removal of the symptom must necessarily result in the development of some alternative symptom was questioned. It was proposed instead that there are certain cases of chronic hysterical aphonia in which the symptom originally developed as a conditioned avoidance response; that because it satisfied a temporary need it become reinforced; that thereafter it existed in its own right as a habit, and that this habit was divorced from the original circumstances which first incurred the aphonia. If such a model is correct then many of the symptoms of which she complained may not have resulted, as did the aphonia, from the original traumatic incident(s) but have resulted secondarily from being aphonic (i.e. from having a symptom or disability which she could not understand or control). The removal of the aphonia would logically result in the dissipation of the other symptoms. Alternative symptoms would then be unlikely to occur.

Derivation of Method of Treatment

A method of treatment was evolved based on: (a) The learning theory constructs of reactive inhibition (I_R) and conditioned inhibition ($_sI_R$). (b) Eysenck's postulates that those people predisposed to extroverted patterns of behaviour (and thus to hysteric-psychopathic disorders in cases of neurotic breakdown), develop reactive inhibition quickly; and that this inhibition dissipates slowly.

Method of Treatment (Phase 1)

M was required to read from a book into the microphone of a tape recorder. The book chosen was judged by the two psychologists concerned to be basically uninteresting to M. The explanation given was that: " her voice needed systematic exercise and that this could be achieved by her reading, or trying to read, aloud from the chosen book for periods of 15 min at a time. The volume of her voice would then be measured from the tape recording. If she failed either to maintain the volume of her speech throughout the 15 min or to improve the volume on successive 15 min sessions then it would be evident that she was in need of more extensive exercise. An extra 2 min would be added on to each session, in these circumstances, until improvement was made, when the session would be judged to have attained an optimum length for the most beneficial effects of the exercise to be felt. If, on the other hand, improvements were made within a 15 min session, or from one session to the next, then the exercise must be having effect. In order to avoid excessive fatigue, sessions would then be reduced by 2 min so long as improvement was maintained."

The above method was adopted on the assumption that, Eysenck being correct, hysterics should develop reactive and conditioned inhibition very quickly. They would thus become rapidly motivated towards achieving a shorter session.

The reaction potential of the aphonia (i.e. the ability of the patient to be aphonic) would then be determined by the following equation:

$$_sE_R = (_sH_R \times D) - (I_R + _sI_R)$$

... where $_sH_R$ is the habit strength, D the drive, and $(I_R + _sI_R)$ the sum of the reactive and conditioned inhibition. Thus any attempt to use her voice would rapidly result in a considerable amount of fatigue (I_R). At the same time those stimuli which increasingly became associated with the growth of this fatigue would produce conditioned inhibition $(_sI_R)$. These are the factors which summate to produce the total inhibitory potential (I_R). As this inhibitory potential is increased by M's continual attempts to read, so should the effects of the excitatory potential become counterbalanced (providing the drive level remains constant) until behavioural extinction of the non-adaptive habit (aphonia) occurs. In terms of the equation as $(I_R + _sI_R)$ approaches $(_sH_R \times D)$ in value, so $_sE_R$, the resulting performance, approaches zero.

According to this formulation the aphonia can be regarded as a simple learned habit which, in the case under consideration, had reached maximum habit strength. To eliminate the aphonia would therefore require the building up of a negative habit. Hull[6] has shown, however, that repetition alone does not lead to the establishment of a habit, either positive or negative, but merely provides the opportunity for learning if a suitable reinforcement is present. In the present case both rest and the reduction of the length of the session were reinforcing agents.

The sessions were carried out at the rate of one per day every Monday, Wednesday and Friday. One psychologist $(P.1)$ only was present for this phase.

Both the writers assessed the change of volume throughout a session by separately listening to the tape recording when played back, and making counts at intervals of the number of sentences, phrases or words which each could succeed in hearing well enough to understand. The tape recorder's volume control was kept at a fixed setting both for " record " and " play " for each session. This volume was somewhat louder than natural voice. Other measures taken to ensure constancy of recording conditions were the placing of the microphone, M, and the book in certain marked positions for the first session and adhering to these positions throughout the experiment.

Results (Phase 1)

The validity of this method of treatment was tentatively established for, within a limited number of trials, M showed rapid improvement. She gave the first evidence of a " voiced " cough during the fourth session, whilst the first certain evidence of the use of her voice was noted in Session 6. Towards the end of each of the longer sessions, however, she was hoarse and complained that she felt tired to the extent of being unable to maintain, outside the experimental situation, a comparable level of performance.

Method of Treatment (Phase 2)

There were two sessions each day. M was required to read from the same book and her voice was again recorded. Each session lasted for $\frac{1}{2}$ hr. The second psychologist (*P*.2) was introduced at this stage. During the course of each $\frac{1}{2}$ hr session *M* was interrupted after 5, 10, 15, 20, 25 min and given encouragement by the experimenter. These interruptions were designed specifically to minimize the fatigue presumed to be associated with the rapid development of the I_R and $_sI_R$ in this type of patient.

Now that she had regained the use of her vocal cords it was decided to change the method of the experiment. The necessity for the systematic and controlled exercise of her voice, both to strengthen it and to remove the hoarseness and fatigue when speaking for any length of time, was stressed to *M*.

P.1 supervised the trials on Monday, Wednesday and Friday, whilst *P*.2 was responsible for those trials on Tuesday and Thursday. *P*.2 was included so as to introduce *M* to the idea of speaking normally in a socially expanding group. *P*.2 was only introduced, however, after the patient had had an opportunity of meeting him several times in an informal way. In this way anxiety would be less likely to occur in the experimental situation when *P*.2 was present and *M* would be enabled to cope satisfactorily with this new experience. This is based on Wolpe's principle of reciprocal inhibition[7,8]: " If a response incompatible with anxiety can be made to occur in the presence of anxiety-evoking stimuli it will weaken the bond between these stimuli and the anxiety response."

Results (Phase 2)

By and large the improvement shown in Phase 1 was continued, despite the greater length of the sessions. However, although several new " highs " were achieved in the use of her voice, this improvement fluctuated. In spite of the breaks for encouragement every 5 min she appeared very tired at the end of each session, particularly the afternoon sessions. By now her voice was sufficiently audible for the subject matter of her reading to be understood from beginning to end of each session. The ease with which this could be done varied, but contrasted markedly with the earlier sessions of Phase 1 when it was difficult to distinguish even occasional words at the end of 15 min. But perhaps one of the most important results in this phase was that improvement, when it was made, was made irrespective of whether the well-known *P*.1 or the recently met *P*.2 was conducting the session at the time.

Method of Treatment (Phase 3)

It was now decided that the principle of reciprocal inhibition should be extended so as, firstly, to involve *M* in speaking within a larger group and, secondly, to endeavour to maintain speech in a more socially realistic situation. Having been at pains to maintain good *rapport* hitherto, it was essential that the new group member should not constitute a source of anxiety to *M*. *M* herself was therefore asked to choose a friend from among the other patients. This she did, choosing a young woman whom she had come to know well. With both psychologists present together, the group was now four strong. Instead of the patient reading from a book however, play reading was now adopted. Thus it was hoped to approximate more closely to the conversation of every-day life. A comedy was chosen and *M* was given the part of the character with most lines to speak in whichever scene was being read at the time. Sessions were again of ½ hr duration and were again recorded.

Results (*Phase 3*)

Although there was now no question that her voice was anything other than completely audible and could be maintained satisfactorily during the play readings session, the final sessions of this phase were relatively poorer than those recorded some 10 days previously. The friend also remarked that although *M*'s level of performance with other patients was better than it had been, it was never as good on play reading as it had been on prose reading. Rather than risk possible discouragement, therefore, following the encouragement of the earlier and more satisfactory sessions, Phase 3 was abandoned. The cumulative effect of the reactive inhibition generated over the previous sessions was felt to be a possible explanation of this plateau, or failure at this stage to improve further.

Method of Treatment (*Phase 4*)

This phase of the treatment was based on Eysenck's postulates.[9,10]

(*a*) Stimulant drugs decrease cortical inhibition, increase cortical excitation and thereby produce introverted behaviour patterns. . . .

(*b*) " Stimulant drugs produce dysthymic symptoms and behaviour patterns and reduce hysterical symptoms and behaviour patterns. . . . "

(*c*) " . . . individuals in whom reactive inhibition has developed slowly, in whom weak reactive inhibition is generated and in whom reactive inhibition is dissipated quickly are thereby predisposed to develop introverted patterns of behaviour and to develop dysthymic disorders in cases of neurotic breakdown."

On the theory therefore that a stimulant drug should produce an introverted behaviour pattern and reduce the amount of reactive inhibition generated, *M* was given, to begin with, 10 mg of dexedrine ½ hr before, and later, 15 mg ¾ hr before, each session. Sessions were again of ½ hr duration with the same people present. Play reading continued but often only for part of the session, the remainder of the time being spent on reading by *M* from the original book to give an up-to-the-minute means of comparison with the speech volume of earlier sessions.

Results (*Phase 4*)

Slight but definite improvement of voice was noticed during the first session of this phase but more marked still was *M*'s changed attitude.

Whereas she had often been lukewarm in her attitude towards the treatment, and sometimes even resentful of the rather punishing situation, under the influence of the dexedrine she became persistent and enthusiastic. She herself said she felt compelled to do better and felt disappointed when she did not do as well as she would have liked. Improvement continued over the next two sessions and was maintained, also, outside the experimental situation, but she still expressed dissatisfaction with her rate of progress. At the fourth session of this phase the dexedrine dosage was increased to 15 mg, given $\frac{3}{4}$ hr before the session began. M became even more persistent in her efforts to effect greater improvement whilst her friend, the other patient, reported that during this time there was very little loss of voice during the rest of the day.

At the end of this phase M was given an explanation of the development of her aphonic symptoms. She was of high average intelligence and thought to be capable of appreciating this. It was explained to her how it might be possible for a longstanding intractable habit to develop which might easily, through worry and ignorance of its cause, give rise to other additional symptoms. It was pointed out that the symptom would probably have developed originally as a means of satisfying a need and in doing so it would gradually have become reinforced, particularly if the stress situation was long lasting.

Subsequently to this discussion M was depressed and tearful. The exact cause of this was unknown though it was presumed to have been due to her realization that she might shortly have to return home and find a job. It was suggested to her that it might help her to live away from home. The Psychology Department would carry out a vocational investigation in order to suggest a suitable job. Following this she showed a remarkable change of attitude and a greatly improved and relaxed manner of speaking. She became noticeably very happy and excitedly delighted with her newly-found voice. She talked to patients and staff alike without fatigue and without any limits to the amount she spoke.

Attempts were subsequently made, following a vocational assessment, to place her in work in a chemist's shop. Such work was not readily available at the time, so at her own wish she was discharged and left to find work for herself. She obtained employment as a salesgirl in a large Liverpool store in the city centre. She also found herself accommodation.

FOLLOW-UP

M's progress was followed up at 1, 3, 7, 8, 10, 11 and 20 months after discharge.

For the 6 months immediately following discharge she worked successfully at the multiple store mentioned above. The store is an extremely busy one and her work at a men's haberdashery counter taxed her voice considerably. One of the writers on visiting the store during the sales, was able to hear *M* shouting along the counter in order to make herself heard. This was significant as she had been unable to shout at the time of her discharge from hospital. However, apart from tiredness of voice at the end of the day for the first month or so, *M* showed no other ill-effects and maintained her ability to speak throughout this 6 month's period.

After 6 months *M* managed to obtain the job in the chemist's shop which she had originally wanted and worked there happily for 3 months.

Since discharge *M* has had to meet two severely stressful situations neither of which has precipitated a recurrence of the aphonia. Nor has any other symptom arisen in its place. The first stressful situation involved her accommodation. Apparently her landlady's husband would frequently return home drunk at night, Often he would bring his friends and expect his wife and *M* to entertain them. This did not appeal to *M*, but she could not avoid the situation by going to bed as the husband would come and wake her and bring his friends to her bedroom. The climax was reached when the husband returned home drunk and threatened both his wife and *M* with a meat chopper. *M* went straight to her parents' home, where she stayed till she obtained, with the help of the hospital, fresh accommodation. The second stressful situation occurred when walking home one night about a week before the 7-month follow-up. A man attempted to assault her. She ran to the nearest police station, but the man gave up the chase when a bus passed by. Although very distressed she again dealt with the situation without losing her voice.

When *M* visited the hospital for the 7-month follow-up she was asked to complete the Minnesota Multiphasic Personality Inventory (MMPI). It was considered necessary to have this assessment of her level of adjustment following treatment and the removal of the aphonia, for apart, perhaps, from Wolpe's[7] work little in the way of objective evaluation has been reported in such circumstances. It was also necessary to verify the commonly held view that the removal of a symptom necessarily results in the development of an alternative. Table 1 shows the results of the four MMPI records completed by *M* over a period of 4 years. Significantly high scores are in *italics*.

TABLE 1

Changes in MMPI scores before, during and after treatments

Date	HS	D	Hy	Pd	Mf	Pa	Pt	Sc	Hyp	?	L	F	K
14/8/53	65	*89*	73	74	45	*73*	*81*	*98*	60	50	57	69	40
16/4/57	65	68	75	*87*	41	59	*79*	*79*	*73*	49	64	66	45
25/4/57	46	57	50	63	41	50	59	60	*73*	48	56	55	44
6/11/57	55	62	66	64	43	64	61	68	60	49	56	61	42

In addition *M* had been asked to complete the Maudsley Personality Inventory (MPI) immediately prior to discharge in May, 1957. This was consistent with the MMPI at the time showing a tendency towards extraversion but neuroticism within normal limits.

At the eighth month a further follow-up was afforded by her admission to a general hospital suffering from bronchitis. Her voice was normal during this period. On discharge her previous accommodation was no longer available so she returned to live with her mother. She gave up her job at the chemist's partly to look after her sister and sister's baby and partly because due to poor physical condition her bronchitis had responded only slowly to treatment. The physicians in charge of her case all regarded the bronchitis as genuine.

The consultant whose out-patient clinic she had occasionally been attending for follow-up reports that her voice was still normal after 11 months. The 11-month follow-up has shown:

(1) There has been no recurrence of the hysterical aphonia.

(2) No alternative symptom has developed in spite of the occurrence of two traumatic situations.

(3) Following the removal of the aphonia test results have both returned to and remained within normal limits.

Follow-up on M, January, 1959, 20 months after discharge from hospital*—She has been working now for some considerable time with the Scotch Wool and Hosiery shops. As an assistant in one of the Liverpool central branches, she apparently impressed the management for she is now in charge of one of the suburban branches which had been faring badly. Her purpose has been to put the branch on its feet again and make of it a going concern. By her own account she closes the shop at 5.30 p.m., works in the shop checking and clearing up for an hour or more, sometimes not getting home until 10 p.m., and then frequently stays up till the early hours working on the books. This account is probably true to the extent that she is a conscientious young woman; the shop is in a poor financial position; and being of only a high average intellectual ability she would not find managing a shop's finances any too easy. At the same time one might well allow for some exaggeration of the situation on her part.

M is living at her mother's home at present. This is not satisfactory from *M*'s point of view but she had to leave her last " digs " because the landlord and his family were to move house. As she expects to be married before long she has not considered it worthwhile finding alternative accommodation. She has been engaged for about a year now and her relationship with her fiance seems to be a stable one.

Some months ago *M*'s grandmother died. She had always apparently been a rather forbidding figure in *M*'s life and *M* had not got on well with her. At any rate, for some weeks following her grandmother's death *M* was troubled by alleged hallucinatory appearances of her grandmother watching or following her and lurking in doorways. It seems doubtful whether these were true hallucinations, however, in view of her known hysteroid personality, given to dramatizations. The grandmother's " appearances " have now ceased in any case. *M* continues to visit a psychiatric out-patient clinic from time to time. The consultant psychiatrist in charge of this clinic, who also had charge of *M*'s case when she was an in-patient at this hospital, considered that these visits were more for the purpose of periodic reassurance than for any specific psychiatric treatment. Possibly they also had some prestige value for her.

* Specially written for this book by D. Walton.

M has at no time since discharge lost the use of her voice, despite stress at work, aggravating family circumstances and poor bodily health. The same consultant psychiatrist had feared at one visit that she might be relapsing as she was rather hoarse. She did not lose her voice, however, and in a personal letter to the writer just before Christmas she said, " You will be pleased to know my voice is standing up to all the strain I have had recently—it's wonderful being able to speak like everyone else."

DISCUSSION

In this case a theoretical model is proposed to explain the development of a chronic aphonia; a method of treatment is derived from such a model; an extensive follow-up has been carried out over a considerable period of time, during which the patient has had to meet situations which previously would have aggravated her symptom; and progress has been objectively verified by means of psychological tests. The authors venture to think that this approach marks a development in the application of current psychological procedure to the investigation, treatment and subsequent assessment of the individual psychiatric case.

The significance of the present results is twofold. Firstly its possible relevance to the treatment of other non-adaptive psychiatric symptoms. Secondly its apparent contradiction of some aspects of psychoanalytic theory (following removal of the aphonia there has been no evidence of any alternative symptoms, despite the patient encountering two stressful situations. This might have followed according to psychoanalytic theory).

Support is found for the idea that the aphonia developed originally as a conditioned avoidance response which, because it satisfied a need, became reinforced. The fact that the habit arose at all and the illness became chronic would suggest that the stress was originally long lasting. Because it was long lasting the aphonia would both have become a strong habit and would eventually have existed in its own right independently of the stress situation. Over a period of years, and when the habit had outlasted the original trauma, the habit itself would become the cause for concern. It would have appeared to the patient to be a physical defect, and because of its persistence she would have shown an increase in " neurotic " symptoms. Such symptoms can be regarded in the chronic case as secondary, in that they are the product of the habit and not the other way about as has been thought hitherto in such cases. It is the habit that is primary, and only in the acute stage might one expect to find neurotic symptoms reactive to the stress.

Thus, if the chronic habit can be removed, secondary " neurotic " symptoms will disappear. This in fact happened in the present instance. The absence of any demonstrable neurotic condition following extinction of the habit would then account for the failure of any alternative habit or symptom to develop in place of the aphonia. Such a result also argues against the development of so-called neurotic symptoms as a direct result of any neurotic predisposition. Rather might it argue for the development of symptoms being governed by the interaction of the degree and duration of stress; individual differences in tolerance of this stress, and basic treatment. The introverted neurotic might, for example, tolerate more stress, because the postulated reactive inhibition associated with this stress would tend to build up slowly. The extraverted neurotic would tolerate less stress because the postulated reactive inhibition would build up more quickly. Thus an explanation could be put forward for the introverted neurotic's symptoms (anxiety, depression). Long lasting sources of stress might be tolerated, but, because a solution to the problem is not achieved, anxiety (e.g.) or depression arises. With hysterics less stress might be tolerated, with the result that need-reducing symptoms would tend to develop rapidly. Anxiety and depression would then be less likely to occur.

The demonstration, here, of the independence of an aphonic habit appears of importance in helping to distinguish between the acute and chronic cases, and suggests the particular relevance of learning theory to the treatment of certain chronic symptoms which might be classified as habits.

SUMMARY

A theory is put forward to account for the development of a chronic hysterical aphonia. This leads to the deduction of a method of treatment, of which the application in a specific case is described. The recovery of the patient, whose condition was of 7 years' standing, is tentatively taken as vindication of the proposed theory. The success of this method of treatment, based on learning theory, in the face of the repeated failure of other methods, leads to the discussion of the aetiology of neurotic symptoms. Conclusions emerge which tend to conflict with much hitherto accepted psychoanalytic theory, chiefly that of the non-replacement of the symptom by an alternative, even after 11 months and in the face of considerable stressful provocation.

REFERENCES

1. WALTON, D. and BLACK, D. A. (1958). The application of learning theory to the treatment of stammering. This volume, pp. 123-134.
2. WALTON, D. (1958). The application of learning theory to the treatment of hysterical aphonia. Bull. Brit. Psychol. Soc., No. 34.
3. KRETSCHMER, E. (1943). Text-Book of Medical Psychology. (Translated by E. B. STRAUSS.) Oxford University Press, New York.
4. HENDERSON, D. K. and GILLESPIE, R. D. (1946). A Text-Book of Psychiatry. Oxford University Press.
5. MAYER-GROSS, W., SLATER, E. and ROTH, M. (1955). Clinical Psychiatry. Cassell, London.
6. HULL, C. L. (1943). Principles of Behavior. Appleton–Century, New York.
7. WOLPE, J. (1952). Objective psychotherapy of the neuroses. S. Afr. Med. J., 26, 825.
8. WOLPE, J. (1954). Reciprocal inhibition as the main basis of psychotherapeutic effects. Arch. Neurol. Psychiat. Chicago, 72, 205.

9. EYSENCK, H. J. (1955). A dynamic theory of anxiety and hysteria. *J. Ment. Sci.*, **101,** 422-428.

10. EYSENCK, H. J. (1957). *The Dynamics of Anxiety and Hysteria.* Routledge and Kegan Paul, London.

11. WOLPE, J. (1955). Experimental neuroses as learned behaviour. *Brit. J. Psychol.*, **43,** 243.

THE APPLICATION OF LEARNING THEORY TO THE TREATMENT OF A CASE OF NEURO-DERMATITIS*

D. WALTON, B.A., DIP.PSYCH.

Senior Clinical Psychologist, Winnick Hospital, Warrington

DESCRIPTION OF THE DISORDER

A YOUNG woman of 20 was referred for the treatment of a long-standing neuro-dermatitis situated on the nape of the neck and apparently associated with a compulsive scratching. She used to scratch the irritation consistently and often brought blood.

She was examined and treated initially by two general practitioners and later by a consultant physician, who was a skin specialist. Various treatments were prescribed including ointments, pills, lotions and x-ray therapy. In spite of these, the neuro-dermatitis had persisted for nearly 2 years.

Examination of her family background suggested that there may have been a relationship between the continuance of her illness and the attention she had been receiving because of it.

The family consisted of the father, the mother, the patient and an elder brother. The family had never been in a good financial position. The father was, however, ambitious for his children, particularly the son. Prior to the son going to the University the father had shown him preferential treatment, though the son's entry into the University had exaggerated this trend. Much of the family income had to be set aside for his fees, clothes and books. The patient, still at Grammar School, suffered in as much as there was little money left for her clothes and other needs. Apart from the financial aspects of this unsatisfactory father–child relationship, the father showed much more interest in the son's progress. The father and son used always to go out together every Sunday and return late in the afternoon. Often the Sunday midday meal would be spoiled, despite the wife's protestations. Both the mother and daughter appeared to have been relegated to an inferior position in the family.

Following the development of the dermatitis more concern was shown by the family for the patient's health. In fact, she received far more attention than she had ever received before. At this time the patient was keeping company and had become engaged. Her fiancé was very concerned over

* Specially written for this book.

272

the dermatitis and frequently, on arrival at the patient's home, would rub on the ointment for her.

It was considered that the skin condition may well have originated because of physical considerations, though its *continuance* might have been perpetuated by psychological factors, the understanding and treatment of which could be formulated in terms of learning theory. It was considered, for example, that the rewards initially associated with the continuance of the neuro-dermatitis had reinforced the scratching until it had become a powerful compulsive habit and it was this which had therefore directly perpetuated the skin condition. Until this compulsion came to an end the dermatitis would show little improvement.

TYPE OF THERAPY

The type of therapy adopted was based on Hull's[1] postulate No. 9 (Parts A, C and D). The three parts of this postulate are included below. They have been paraphrased by Hilgard.[2]

(A) The occurrence of a response produces reactive inhibition (I_R) which both inhibits reaction potential and acts as a negative drive.

(C) As a given response is repeated, increments of reactive inhibition summate. The resulting I_R also summates with conditioned inhibition $(_sI_R)$ to produce the aggregate inhibitory potential $(\dot{I}_R.)$

(D) When non-reinforced responses follow each other at short intervals, the aggregate inhibitory potential (I_R) increases as a positive growth function of the number of non-reinforced trials, thus yielding the phenomena of experimental extinction.

To approximate the conditions required to effect this extinction, it was necessary that the patient should achieve no rewards or benefits from her neuro-dermatitis. The members of her family were told not to discuss her skin condition with her, in fact to observe, as far as possible, a complete silence on the subject. The application of ointment by the fiancé was also to stop.

It was also considered that the build-up of this conditioned inhibitory potential could be used further in a therapeutic capacity. This opinion was based on Hull's Corollary 15: " If two or more behavioural sequences, each involving a different amount of energy consumption or work, have been equally well reinforced on equal number of times, the organism will gradually learn to choose the less laborious behaviour sequence leading to the attainment of the reinforcing state of affairs."

In other words, the patient may have achieved attention over the two-year period covered by her neuro-dermatitis from two major sources—first that associated with the continuance of her neuro-dermatitis and secondly attention from her fiancé, independently of that received because of the neuro-dermatitis. One might logically expect that both these behaviourial sequences will have been reinforced many times. With the rapid build-up of inhibitory potential associated with the compulsive-scratching, one would expect the patient to chose the other less laborious method of achieving attention; in this instance the more normal and adaptive one associated with her fiancé.

OUTCOME OF THERAPY

Treatment was entirely successful. Over a period of 2 months the frequency of the scratching decreased until it stopped altogether. This reduction corresponded with a gradual improvement in the neuro-dermatitis. After 2 months this " skin-condition " was negligible, whilst at the end of 3 months it had disappeared. This immediate response to therapy contrasted with her failure to respond to several physical methods of treatment over the previous 2 years.

A follow-up of 4 years has been completed. There has been no evidence of the neuro-dermatitis over this period or of any other skin-condition. The patient reports that no alternative psychiatric symptoms have developed.

The patient has now been married for 3 years and is very happy. She is also successfully employed as a solicitor.

Psychological testing completed after 4 years showed that all her results were within normal limits.

REFERENCES

1. HULL, C. L. (1952). *A Behavior System.* Yale Univ. Press, New Haven.
2. HILGARD, E. R. (1956). *Theories of Learning.* Appleton–Century–Crofts.

Part IV

AVERSION THERAPY

INTRODUCTION

Aversion therapy, from one point of view, is simply the application to the treatment of neurotic symptoms of the kind of notion which appeals to the man in the street when confronted by these mysterious and odd behaviour patterns. Punishment for what is classified as an illness may appear more reminiscent of Erewhon than of the Welfare State, but learning theory does in part indicate that such punishment may be effective provided certain conditions are fulfilled. These conditions are quite strict, and relate to such technical matters as stimulus-response asynchronism; when they are disregarded—as unfortunately they usually have been in the past by practitioners ignorant of the principles of conditioning and learning theory—results may easily lead to a worsening, rather than to an improvement, of the condition requiring treatment. (This may happen when the punishment increases anxiety, without decreasing the strength of the habit involved; anxiety, acting as a drive, multiplies with the neurotic habit and produces an even stronger $_sE_R$ than was present previously.)

Another point which requires stressing is related to the previous one. Aversion therapy should be preceded by careful diagnostic assessment of the *degree of neuroticism* of the patient; as Beech has shown in his paper, a high degree of neuroticism easily leads to the condition mentioned above, in which strong punishment leads to such a marked increase in anxiety that symptoms may be worsened, rather than abolished. That this is not always so is shown by the work of Liversedge and Sylvester, Raymond, Freund and others; they would appear to have established a strong case for aversion therapy to be retained as one of many possible techniques for certain types of symptoms. Clearly here also much further experimental work requires to be done; as Franks has shown so well in his review of the treatment of alcoholism (a field where more than in any other aversion therapy has been tried), most reports published in the ordinary way flout well-established principles of learning theory so flagrantly that results cannot be regarded as being relevant to those principles.

It is likely that aversion therapy by itself will be found useful in only a limited and carefully selected number of cases; it is probable that it will be found useful in many more cases if it can be combined with treatment by reciprocal inhibition. In this way, both the motor habit which is the primary symptom, and the autonomic habit which is the sustaining symptom can be treated simultaneously, and the evil consequences of exacerbation of anxiety drives avoided.

277

ALCOHOL, ALCOHOLISM AND CONDITIONING : A REVIEW OF THE LITERATURE AND SOME THEORETICAL CONSIDERATIONS*

C. M. FRANKS, PH.D.

University of London, Institute of Psychiatry, Maudsley Hospital†

INTRODUCTION

ALCOHOLISM is a grave social, economic and psychiatric problem which has attracted the attention of countless research workers and theorists. From a survey of the recent literature two conclusions emerge. Firstly, that there is at present no general agreement as to the aetiology, dynamics and treatment of alcoholism.[1] Secondly, that the inadequacies of the majority of the experiments reported are such that the findings are often difficult to interpret and highly limited in their value.[2,3] In many cases the conclusions do not follow from the data; in others they are impossible to evaluate because insufficient procedural details are given; other studies attempt to answer a large number of questions and answer none adequately; some findings are based upon extremely small or atypical samples while others are based upon experiments open to such obvious criticisms that serious consideration is unwarranted. Many of these studies are apparently the by-product of the busy clinician's experiences and consequently lacking in rigour of any description. Remarkably few are predictive in their techniques or based upon any clearly formulated and testable theory. It is hardly surprising that so many fail to satisfy the usual criteria of acceptable scientific research.[4]

In the present article emphasis will be largely on those studies and techniques relating to conditioning and learning. It is proposed to review the existing literature and to indicate where, in the author's opinion, more research is needed. Whenever appropriate an attempt will be made to provide a rationale within a specific framework of conditioning and personality theory. The relationship between conditioning and personality has been the subject of much recent controversy and it is essential that this issue be clarified before proceeding any further.

It is usual to differentiate between Pavlovian or classical conditioning (in which the only essential criterion is that the conditioned stimulus and the

* Reprinted by permission of the author and the editor of the *J. Ment. Sci.* from (1958) *J. Ment. Sci.*, **104**, 14-33.
† Now at the New Jersey Neuro-psychiatric Institute, Princetown, U.S.A.

unconditioned, or reinforcing, stimulus are associated by contiguity in some way) and instrumental conditioning (in which the subject receives the reward or avoids the punishment only if he makes the correct, i.e. the conditioned response). Furthermore, classical conditioning may itself be regarded in two ways; if association by contiguity is considered as sufficient then any two stimuli may theoretically become associated with each other so that the occurrence of one evokes the response to the other; if, however, a reinforcement theory of classical conditioning is adopted then the performance of the conditioned response must reduce some learned or acquired drive. It is by no means universally agreed that these categories can be subsumed under the heading of conditioning. Thus eminent workers such as Konorski[5] and Thorpe[6] hold diametrically opposed views.

The many parameters involved in all kinds of conditioning are discussed briefly by Guthrie[7] and in detail by Hilgard and Marquis.[8] There is ample evidence to suggest that the apparent ease in formation of classical conditioned responses, the nature of these conditioned responses once formed, and their resistance to extinction depend in part upon variables such as the reflex under investigation, the modality, duration and intensity of the conditioned and unconditioned stimuli, the nature of the temporal overlap between these two stimuli, the intertrial interval, the conditioned procedure used (e.g. partial or 100 per cent reinforcement) and the method of measuring the conditioning (e.g. amplitude, frequency, latency or resistance to extinction). However, it is not these secondary or external variables that are of primary concern here, for they only partially decide the nature of the conditioned response. According to Pavlov[9,10,11] all forms of conditioning are the direct consequences of two cortical processes, *excitation* and *inhibition*, and the nature of the conditioned response is a manifestation of the laws of cortical functioning as well as being dependent upon the external parameters listed above. It is not relevant to speculate about the physiological property of these hypothetical processes; it is sufficient to consider both as positive molar constructs by means of which it is possible to make predictions about personality and conditioning.

If all forms of conditioning are largely dependent upon certain properties of the central nervous system, then the general concept of " conditionability " becomes a meaningful one. It is then possible to speak of a person as being relatively good or bad at forming and retaining conditioned responses irrespective of the reflex used and the technique used to produce and measure the response. If, however, the nature of the conditioned response is largely dependent upon such variables as mood, attention, volition, motivation, conditioning technique and reflex studied, etc., then the concept of general conditionability becomes of little practical value and all predictions must be made in terms of a specific reflex and a specific conditioning situation. This problem has never been adequately investigated;

it is unknown whether a general factor of conditionability exists and, if so, how much it contributes to the variance of any particular conditioning data.

There are other problems which limit the applicability of conditioning techniques and which require clarification at some stage. For example, the relationships between the various forms of classical conditioning and instrumental conditioning are unknown and the same problem of a general factor arises. It is also necessary to know more about the relationships between age, sex, intelligence and conditioning, the existing evidence being conflicting.[7,8,12,13] Much of the confusion is a result of the multiplicity of techniques used to obtain the data and the diversity of species studied. Bearing in mind the difficulties associated with the concept of condition-ability, it is possible from the experiments of the writer to draw several tentative conclusions about conditioning in man. These experiments were carried out under rigorously controlled conditions in a sound-proof con-ditioning laboratory specially constructed for this purpose.[14] The major reflex studied was the conditioned eyeblink to a tone, although in some cases a psychogalvanic skin response was also recorded. The evidence suggests that:

(1) Introverted normals condition better than extraverted normals[15];

(2) Introverted neurotics (anxiety states, obsessives, reactive depressives) condition better than extraverted neurotics (hysterics and psychopaths)[12,16];

(3) In both normal and neurotic subjects there is no apparent relationship between conditionability and amount of neuroticism[12,15,16];

(4) Contrary to predictions based on a Hullian–Spence learning theory, irrelevant drives, such as hunger in an eyelid conditioning situation, appar-ently have no influence on conditionability[17];

(5) Both amylo-barbitone (sodium amytal) and methyl-pentynol (oblivon) (central depressants) make it more difficult to establish conditioned responses and more easy to extinguish them once formed; dexamphetamine (a central stimulant) has the opposite effects[18,19,20];

(6) In accordance with the Pavlovian concept of excessive excitation setting up a protective inhibition, it has been found that the first effects of a large dose of dexamphetamine tend to be opposite to later effects.[19]

In the above studies the personality framework used is that developed by Eysenck,[21] in which introversion-extraversion and neuroticism are conceived of as orthogonal dimensions, these dimensions being measured by means of personality questionnaires. It should be noted that in general these results apply equally to both sexes and, within the ranges studied, are dependent neither upon age nor intelligence.

Pavlov originally associated neurasthenia in humans with excessive cortical excitation and hysteria with cortical inhibition, but gave little attention to normal personality types.[9] However, since it has also been shown that introverts condition well and extraverts condition poorly, it is possible to discuss the personality patterns and psychopathology of both normals and neurotics in terms of Pavlov's variables. For example, the sufferer from an anxiety state, the obsessive, and (to a lesser extent) the introverted normal, tend to be agitated, hyperactive, tense, reflective, highly sensitive to their environment, over-cautious, hesitant, etc. All these characteristics are consistent with a presumed state of excessive cortical excitation and a readiness to form conditioned responses. Similarly, the hysteric, certain psychopaths and the extraverted normal (to a lesser extent) tend to develop fugues, amnesias, gross conversion symptoms and to be unreliable, impulsive and less responsive and sensitive to their environment. All these characteristics are consistent with a presumed state of excessive cortical inhibition and a relative difficulty in forming conditioned responses.[16,22] In the inhibitory group may also be included certain post-leucotomized and certain brain-damaged individuals. There is evidence to show that brain-damaged patients condition poorly[23,24] and some tentative evidence to suggest that leucotomy may have a similar effect on conditioning. It has been pointed out several times that hysteric and psychopathic reactions are not uncommon following pre-frontal leucotomy and certain other forms of brain damage[22,25] and Kennedy has also stressed the resemblance between these categories, postulating a constitutional similarity between these abnormalities.[26] The reported finding that depressant drugs decrease conditionability whereas stimulant drugs increase conditionability may now be viewed in terms of changes in the processes of excitation and inhibition. With this background in mind it is possible to consider the specific problems of alcohol and alcoholism in terms of conditioning and personality.

EXPERIMENTAL STUDIES OF ALCOHOL IN RELATION TO LEARNING AND CONDITIONING

As far as the present writer is aware* remarkably few experiments have been carried out on the effects of alcohol on any form of conditioning in humans. Gantt[27] found that does of 0·5 to 1·5 ml of alcohol per kg body weight increased the latency of salivary and motor-conditioned responses in 5 dogs and that larger doses decreased the intensity of the conditioned responses. Mead[28] studied simple finger-withdrawal conditioning to light and shock in 6 men under the influence of 30 ml of alcohol in a 20 per cent solution, but his results are inconsistent. Although the present writer has shown that a small amount of a higher alcohol depresses conditioning in man,[20] there is clearly a need for well-designed experiments on the influence of various doses of ethyl alcohol on both the learning of new reflexes in humans and the performance (or extinction) of existing reflexes which have been learned prior to the introduction of the alcohol. Control groups would

* Because of language and other difficulties it is probable that a considerable number of communications from Eastern Europe have been overlooked.

have to be used and the alcohol administered disguised in some way, such as being given in capsule form or by injection through a stomach tube. It is quite possible, since we have preconceived notions of what alcohol should do to us, that suggestion would modify its effects.[29] It would also be of interest, both from the point of view of suggestion and direct conditioning, to compare beer and spirits, in varying concentrations. In general it seems that the function of the central nervous system is less affected by beer than by spirits; however, under certain circumstances, the disturbance caused by beer may tend to persist longer.[3] In view of the Newmans' recent finding that dexamphetamine and caffeine in ordinary therapeutic doses were ineffective in combating the depressant effects of alcohol,[30] it would be of interest and importance to determine just how much of these stimulants are required to restore conditioned reflexes reduced or abolished by alcohol and under what circumstances.

Settlage failed to produce a conditioned response in cats while they were under the influence of sodium amytal.[31] When the effects of the drug wore off, the conditioned response was easily evoked with no further training. It is possible that sodium amytal depresses the peripheral performance of conditioned responses as well as or perhaps instead of the central learnings of these responses. A similar possibility exists with respect to alcohol and remains to be tested. Pavlov was forced to infer the existence of properties of his hypothetical central processes of excitation and inhibition by observation of the behaviour of peripheral organs such as the salivary glands and skeletal musculature. Settlage's findings indicate the hazards of such an inference. The invention of the EEG now makes it possible to observe central changes more directly during the conditioning of any reflex. The Popovs[32,32] established a conditioned EEG "after image" to sound in humans, then gave their subjects alcohol. They found that the conditioned "after images" consistently appeared much later and much less frequently, from which they concluded that alcohol has a true central action. This is consistent with the finding that alcohol depresses learning in both animals[24,35] and man.[36] However, although the main effect of alcohol is apparently cortical,[37] there is ample evidence to show that, unlike the barbiturates, which appear to have a selective action on specific structures, alcohol is a general depressant acting both peripherally and centrally.[38] For example, alcohol impairs maze running efficiency in rats[39-44] although it may be, since the animals were in most cases given intensive doses of alcohol over an extended period, that the impairment in learning is not a temporary effect of the alcohol directly but—as with brain-damaged individuals—a result of some permanent damage originated by the alcohol. This is one reason why studies of conditioning in *alcoholics* may be of limited value; it is only by studying the effects of controlled doses of alcohol on normal humans that the properties of alcohol may be discovered. It has been suggested that chronic alcoholism is rarely responsible for felonies or major delinquencies whereas acute alcoholic intoxication precipitates many crimes.[45,46] It may be that alcohol reduces those conditioned responses we term socialization by means of which we have learned to obey the rules of the society in which we live. In addition, alcohol may help by reducing or abolishing those conditioned fear or anxiety responses which prevent many of us from carrying out crimes.

In human instrumental learning alcohol has been shown to have a deleterious effect, e.g. driving skill[47-50] and Link Trainer performance.[51] It depresses sexual responses in dogs[52-54] and reaction times in dogs and man.[35-53] The early German experiments[55] which purported to demonstrate a decrease in reaction time under certain conditions have since been refuted and the original findings shown to be a consequence of faulty treatment of small sample data.[2] The only reputable worker to report that alcohol has a stimulant effect is Masserman.[56,57] He found that alcohol depresses specific tasks in cats, but in small doses may act as a mild stimulant of both cortex and hypothalamus, as shown by the increased responses obtained from direct faradic stimulation of these regions. The work of Santessen[58] also tends to support the possibility that under certain conditions alcohol may not always act as a cerebral depressant. This, if correct, suggests that research on the size of dose in relation to its effects on conditioning and extinction in humans needs to be investigated. The atypical findings of these two workers may be explicable in terms of some concept of positive and negative induction or in terms of Pavlov's complex paradoxical phases.[9-11,59] However, in the absence of more evidence, any further speculations are premature.

In view of the already discussed relationships between personality and conditioning, any experiments on conditioning under the effects of alcohol should take into account individual differences in personality, particularly in relation to introversion-extraversion. If Shagass' finding is confirmed,[60,61] namely that the sedation threshold of hysterics under sodium amytal is much lower than that of anxiety states, then clear predictions relating this threshold to the effects of alcohol on conditioning may be made. The well-known individual differences in alcohol tolerance of normal subjects[62] may be related to all the above effects, particularly to their degree of extraversion and conditionability. This, however, fails to solve the problem of which personality type is more likely to become alcoholic for, as has been often pointed out,[63,64] there is no good evidence in favour of the existence of an alcoholic personality prior to alcoholism. A related problem is that of temporary personality changes while under the influence of alcohol; there are very many studies of the personality of chronic alcoholics, but remarkably few studies of changes produced by experimental intoxication, despite the fact that the latter has all the advantages of controlled laboratory conditions. Another partially resolved problem is that of the permanence of these changes.

It was once believed that acquired degeneracy in rats due to alcohol could be inherited.[39,65,66,41,40] However, much of these data are unreliable and of dubious statistical significance and better designed studies have failed to confirm this belief.[67-69] There would seem to be no evidence of genetic transmission of acquired degeneracy, although it may be that the changes incurred are permanent as far as the individual organism is concerned.

CONDITIONED RESPONSE THERAPY

Much of the treatment of alcoholics lacks a clearly formulated rationale[68,70,71] and, with a few notable exceptions, such as the work of Voegtlin and his associates,[71-80] this comment is applicable to conditioned aversion therapy even when the therapy purports to be in accord with Pavlovian principles.[81-83] Numerous workers have pointed out the need for rigorous procedures[84,74,72,85] but few have taken this advice. One clinician[86] carefully stresses adherence to the laws governing the acquisition of conditioned responses and then asserts that alcohol should be given *after* the patient feels nauseated. Of the many possible procedures there is no doubt that this form of conditioning (backward conditioning) is the least easy to develop and the most readily extinguished. In addition to such theoretical errors there is a lack of uniformity of procedure and a dearth of technical details in the published reports. It is consequently difficult to evaluate the potentialities of conditioned response therapy and it hardly surprising that reviewers such as Lévy-Valensi[87] conclude that the value of conditioned response therapy so far is fairly limited. The reports range from long lasting and widespread success[88-90] through qualified approval[91] to complete rejection.[92] Feldman[93] concludes that conditioned response therapies offer no better results than treatment by the more dynamic forms of psychotherapy. Numerous clinicians, usually with no supporting evidence, stress the inadequacies of conditioned response therapy unaccompanied by psychotherapy.[94-97,84,98,99] It is often asserted [100-104] that training the patient to become abstinent is no cure and Edlin[105] prefers to regard aversion treatment merely as a method of rendering the addict abstinent while psychotherapy and other means of support are being instituted. A frequent conclusion is that conditioning therapy is merely " symptomatic treatment " which fails to eliminate the underlying cause.[106,107] However, such critics merely present acceptable evidence in support of their assertions and ignore the possibility that a symptom may itself be as harmful as the disease.[108] Conditioning therapy may help the alcoholic to break his habit of drinking and thus enable him to find more socially acceptable ways of solving his problems. In any case there would seem to be no reason why treatment of both symptoms and the underlying disorder should not proceed along conditioning and learning theory lines. It would also seem reasonable to control the motivational factors by such techniques. If the desire to stop drinking is essential to the success of any kind of therapy then this desire may itself be learned. There is much evidence to suggest that attitudinal factors towards alcohol and alcoholism, including the patient's willingness to seek help, are themselves learned and vary from one culture to another.[109],[110]

Apomorphine, and more recently, emetine, are the usual drugs used as the unconditioned stimuli in conditioned aversion therapy. It is sometimes erroneously assumed that the conditioned response established is absolutely specific so that the subject may be in the happy state of having an aversion to spirits, but be able to enjoy the pleasures of drinking wine.[111] A related erroneous assumption is that the subject has to be separately conditioned against all alcoholic beverages.[112]

Apomorphine conditioning is undoubtedly more time consuming for the experimenter than is antabuse therapy. It has the added disadvantage of requiring rigorous procedural techniques. However, it seems that antabuse presents certain hazards as a therapeutic agent. It may cause acneiform eruptions, allergic dermatitis and urticaria. In some patients it may cause fatigue, tremor, headaches, dizziness, gastro-intestinal disturbances, reduced sexual potency and even death.[37],[113-116] For these reasons it may be preferable to use apomorphine, which is agreed by most workers to produce an aversion directly in accord with the conditioning paradigm. (Should the patient become addicted to apomorphine it is always possible to change to another noxious unconditioned stimulus such as emetine.) There is one notable exception to this general agreement. Dent considers that apomorphine is effective in the treatment of alcoholism because of its action on the medulla cells of the brain in suppressing the need for alcohol. Unfortunately, he has never explained this mechanism in print, except to propound a tentative theory in terms of stimulation of the lower centres of the brain.[117] Elsewhere he argues that apomorphine is merely a sedative which reduces the anxiety which is at the root of the addiction.[118] Vencovsky believes in using emetine (or apomorphine) to establish a direct conditioned reaction, followed by the continued administration of antabuse to ensure the reappearance of the reaction symptoms whenever drinking is resumed.[119] This is perfectly consistent, since in the widest sense antabuse therapy must also be regarded as a form of conditioning in which, after the effect of the drug has worn off, the thought, sight, smell or taste of alcohol presumably sets up a conditioned aversion response.

Although the most usual way of producing a conditioned aversion is by the application of some nausea inducing drug, this is by no means essential. Bachet[120] was able to produce conditioned nausea to the sight or taste of alcohol without using any drugs, and as far back as the last century it had been suggested that alcoholism should be treated by associating a painful stimulus with the taking of the alcohol.[121] More recently there has been an accumulation of evidence to show that all kinds of conditioned aversions may be readily produced in both animals and man by the application of electric shock as the unconditioned stimulus.[122,123] Using this technique, Kantorovich[124] was remarkably successful in producing a conditioned aversion not only to the taste of alcohol but also to its smell and sight and even to a photograph of the bottles. There is clearly a need for research into methods other than drugs of producing a conditioned aversion to alcohol.

If drugs are used as unconditioned stimuli, then other problems, totally uninvestigated as far as the present writer is aware, present themselves. For example, apomorphine is supposed to stimulate the so-called "vomiting centre" in the brain. Now, although the precise location of the centre is in dispute[125,126] and hence the specific stimulant action of apomorphine not clear, there is good evidence to suggest that the drug has a cerebral depressant action, especially if large doses are taken. According to Goodman and Gilman[37] even small non-emetic doses of apomorphine may at times be hypnotic. It may be that apomorphine, like sodium amytal[18,19] and oblivon,[20] decreases the ease with which conditioned responses of any description are formed. If this is correct, then, although apomorphine is successful in producing the unconditioned response of nausea, it will render the formation of the conditioned aversion responses to alcohol considerably more difficult. Such an experiment, using varying sub-emetic doses, needs to be carried out for various conditioned responses under laboratory conditions. If it should be found that apomorphine does hinder the formation of conditioned responses then two possibilities arise. Either a suitable drug should be found which produces the required unconditioned response and at the same time has a facilitating effect on the formation of conditioned responses or, prior to each session, the patient could be given a stimulant drug such as caffeine or benzedrine which is known to enhance conditioning. The concept of combining apomorphine with some other drug for various reasons is no new one. For example, Lemere and O'Hollaren[127] suggest that sodium thiopentone (pentothal) should immediately precede any conditioning treatment in order to reduce tension. If sodium pentothal acts as a typical depressant and makes it more difficult for conditioning to take place then this combination of drugs is an unwise one.

The above considerations apply to all forms of conditioned aversion therapy in which drugs are used to produce the unconditioned response. Thus Raymond[128] successfully used this technique to treat a fetishist. Furthermore, if it be conceded that all kinds of psychotherapy may be profitably conceptualized as processes in learning or conditioning[129-140] then the use of stimulant and depressant drugs during therapy may also be considered in terms of this rationale. It might be advisable to combine psychotherapy with a depressant drug when it is desired to extinguish a certain learned pattern of behaviour and to combine psychotherapy with a stimulant drug when new learning is being initiated. A preliminary attempt to make use of similar principles has been reported by Agoston.[141]

PREDICTING SUCCESS IN CONDITIONED
AVERSION THERAPY

It follows from the discussion presented in the first part of this paper that a prediction of success may possibly be made by giving the alcoholic various laboratory tests of conditioning and questionnaire measures of introversion-extraversion. There is some empirical evidence to support this suggestion. Thus it has often been observed that psychopathy (here regarded as a form of neuroticism appearing only in extraverted individuals and related to poor conditioning) contraindicates success.[96,84] However these techniques require experimental validation. Should a direct relationship be demonstrated between laboratory conditioning and responses to conditioned aversion therapy using (say) apomorphine it would seriously weaken the arguments of those who assume[118,142] that the effectiveness of these aversion techniques is in no way based upon conditioning. It may be observed that a similar exposition might be developed for the prediction of success in any form of psychotherapy.

Before discussing what personality type is more likely to respond successfully to conditioning therapy it may be helpful to formulate two related and often confused problems. These are (1) is there such a thing as an alcoholic personality, once the person has become an alcoholic? and (2) what sort of person is most likely to become an alcoholic, i.e. is there such a thing as a predisposing alcoholic personality?

It has often been concluded that alcoholics tend to be introverted[143,144]; it has also often been concluded that alcoholic groups tend to have a high psychopathic (presumably extraverted) element.[145,167,147] Others have reported such phenomena as "compulsive" drinkers, presumably introverted.[148] Numerous workers have attempted to rate alcoholics in terms of introversion-extraversion, but their findings are of little value since the personality criteria used were based largely on subjective impressions and unvalidated concepts.[149-152] It is hardly surprising that their findings vary widely as to the ratio of introverts to extraverts. There have been many attempts to classify alcoholics[101,153] but they have all met with little success and there is considerable disagreement as to the personality structure of the alcoholic. In most cases it is impossible to decide whether the obtained personality picture is related to the chronic effects of the alcohol or whether it is an accurate description of the pre-morbid personality of alcoholics.[154-156] It is consequently difficult to evaluate many of these studies.[145,157,158,147] Hansen and Teilmann[159] examined a group of convicted criminal alcoholics. They split them up into those who were abnormal psychologically and were long-term detainees and those who were under short-term detention and soon released on parole. They found that the former group tended to come from a materially and emotionally undesirable childhood environment, to have a poorer physique and to have a substantial number of subjects with head injuries among its numbers. Despite therapy, only 13 per cent of this group improved, whereas 35 per cent of the other group improved even though untreated. It would be interesting to repeat this investigation predicting success and long-term prognosis for both groups by means of conditioning and personality tests and then to give them both similar forms of treatment. Davies et al.[160] used the Strauss and Bacon Stability Scale[161] and other criteria to establish a prognostic profile but their measures are multi-dimensional and consequently difficult to interpret.

Other studies have found no differences between alcoholic groups and normal controls. Thus Vogel[162] found no differences in suggestibility as measured by the body sway test and Sutherland et al.[64] found no evidence that their alcoholics had abnormal electrocephalograms. Wittman compared 100 alcoholics with 100 matched normals and failed to find any significant differences with respect to personality or background development.[163-166] The general conclusion seems to be that as yet alcoholic and normal groups have not been shown to differ significantly in personality as indicated by a variety of tests and other measures.[167,168,64,84,169,170] This conclusion is limited since, with remarkably few exceptions,[3,171] the measures of personality used have been subjective or complex in their factorial composition. Although, there is as yet no methodologically sound dimensional system of personality which is widely accepted, it is still possible to use personality tests which have high factor loadings on only one factor in some generally recognized dimensional system. There is a need for research into the effects of alcohol on factorially pure measures of personality. Such research could easily be extended to the effects of the widespread addictions, such as morphine, barbiturates, marihuana and even to the much rarer addictions such as paraldehyde, ether, cocaine and chloroform on measures of personality. The problem of what sort of person is most likely to become an alcoholic is considered in the concluding section of this paper.

ALCOHOL AS A THERAPEUTIC AGENT

In the social sense alcohol is widely used as a therapeutic agent to relieve anxiety and tension. Unlike the barbiturates, alcohol is rarely prescribed for this purpose clinically, even on an empirical basis. Unlike the barbiturates almost nothing has been established concerning the effects of various alcoholic beverages on the formation and retention of conditioned responses, although it would seem highly probable that the general effect is to depress them. There is, however, some evidence concerning the effects of alcohol on unconditioned responses, especially the sexual ones. It has been established that alcohol raises the threshold of the erectile and ejaculatory reflexes in animals, so that more than normal stimulation is required to arouse these reactions. In large doses the sexual response is completely inhibited.[53,54,172] Gantt also found that alcohol depresses unconditioned sexual responses far more than any other responses such as the desire for food.[52] The widespread popular belief that alcohol is a sexual stimulant seems to be incorrect. The reason for this belief may be that alcohol inhibits already formed conditioned responses, hence reducing or abolishing those learned patterns of socially accepted behaviour which restrict the normal expression or following through of sexual desires. Thus these desires are possibly unaltered but the conditioned restrictions which prevent their implementation are reduced. If, at the same time, unconditioned sexual responses are depressed and a state of near impotence is produced it seems hardly surprising that a conflict situation may be established. There is some experimental support; thus Andreyev[173] found that alcohol given to dogs daily for two weeks resulted in the breaking down of a stable well-established conditioned response pattern and at the same time produced an experimental neurosis. On the other hand, under certain conditions alcohol considerably reduces the behavioural symptoms of an already established experimental neurosis.[174] According to Gantt[27] alcohol produces these effects by disturbing the central excitation-inhibition balance. It seems that the result depends both on the conditions of administration of the alcohol and on the personality of the recipients.

The above provides a possible explanation for certain problems resulting from alcoholization in normal individuals and attempts to place on a rational basis such generalizations as that of Seliger and Crawford[175] who conclude that alcohol acts as a depressant on the central nervous system and so enables the underlying forces in the personality to find a more direct expression. It also provides a possible—if at present speculative—rational basis for the alcoholic treatment of certain sexual disorders.* Thus the anxious introverted patient who suffers from *ejaculatio praecox* may have excessive socially conditioned responses greatly reduced by alcohol and at the same time the latency period of ejaculation would be considerably increased. Barbiturates are sometimes prescribed on an empirical basis for the treatment of disorders of a similar nature, but alcohol, given under controlled conditions, may have certain advantages and may be less likely to produce drug dependence or withdrawal symptoms. Certainly the vast majority of people who imbibe alcohol are not alcoholics.

* The consideration of sexual abnormalities in terms of conditioning is not new. Over 20 years ago Meignant discussed sexual impotence in this manner[176] and Max[177] successfully treated a case of homosexual fixation by these means. More recently Salter[178] attempted to explain how masochism may arise as a conditioned response and be treated accordingly, and Raymond successfully applied this method to the treatment of a fetishist.[128]

Many problems require investigation, such as the correct dosage and method of administration in relation to the subject's personality. Furthermore, the sexual behaviour pattern and desires of the chronic alcoholic cannot be inferred from a study of the effects of alcohol upon the sexual pattern of normal subjects. Thus Levine[179] found a diminished interest in heterosexual relationships in alcoholics. The possibility of permanent physiological changes in the chronic alcoholic provides yet another variable to be taken into account.

ALCOHOLISM AS A LEARNED RESPONSE

If alcoholism can be successfully treated by a conditioning process then it may be that alcoholism itself is a learned symptom. It is possible to discuss alcoholism as a conditioned response either in terms of a reinforcement theory or otherwise. Many psychologists have emphasized that need reduction is not essential for learning[e.g.180,182] and it is reasonable to build up a classical conditioning paradigm based strictly upon association by contiguity. However, the majority of learning theorists adopt some form of reinforcement theory in which the basic assumption is that the learning of an association between a stimulus and a response requires the presence of some sort of reward or reinforcement, even if this be only in the form of a drive reduction. Even if alcoholism is regarded as a serious symptom in a psychiatric disorder it seems advisable to apply a learning theory rationale and to enquire what drive or need the taking of alcohol reduces.

Welch[183] analyses the concept of " needs " at some length and splits them up into two general groups—pain reduction and enjoyment augmentation. Within these groups needs may be physiological or acquired, they may be known to the subject or he may be unaware of them, the reduction may be accompanied immediately by pleasure or followed eventually by pleasure. Wilkins[184] probably has a similar system in mind when he says that theories of alcohol motivation may be divided into psychological and pathophysiological kinds. It is possible to hypothesize numerous needs or drives of various categories which alcohol drinking may conceivably reduce. Thus Royer[185] has shown a relationship between thirst and alcohol drinking, but it would hardly seem widely applicable to postulate thirst as the primary drive which alcohol reduces. For Peabody[186] and Strecker[144] alcohol satisfies the need to avoid reality by screening unsatisfactory external and internal existences. McFarland and Borach[187] believe that there is a relationship between a physiological need for more oxygen and alcoholic intoxication. They found that satisfaction of this need by the inhalation of a suitable oxygen mixture produced a permanent improvement in the alcoholic, presumably because he no longer had to satisfy his need for oxygen by absorbing large quantities of alcohol. Westerfield and Lawrow[188] found that the restriction of food intake in rats results in a marked increase of alcohol consumption, so that it may conceivably be the need for food that alcohol satisfies. However, as with thirst, it would not seem reasonable to postulate a hunger drive as the primary need which motivates people to drink alcohol (especially as Conger[189] found that alcohol does not affect hunger motivating approach responses). According to Lolli[190] alcoholism might be an attempt to satisfy the need for love and tenderness. It could be argued that alcohol reduces the strong oral and narcissistic drives which alcoholics are supposed to possess.[191]

The most tenable and frequently proposed drive that alcohol is considered to reduce is anxiety. It has been noted that alcohol is taken especially in times of stress[108,192] and theories of alcohol drinking as a tension reducing activity have often been proposed.[e.g.193,194] Horton, in a cross cultural study of certain primitive communities, has shown that there is more drinking in " anxious " societies.[195] Certainly it seems true that anxiety in some form, like alcoholism, is universal. Dynamic psychiatrists, e.g. Freud,[196] Horney[197] and Sullivan[198] agree that anxiety is encountered to some extent in all communities and in all societies. When Strecker, Peabody and others say that alcohol provides an escape from reality, this may presumably be because reality sets up undesirable tensions or stresses which alcohol reduces.

There are many ways of reducing tension or anxiety such as smoking, masturbating, sexual intercourse, gum chewing, sucking sweets. Specific food addiction[199] or general excessive eating may be learned responses which are reinforced by their anxiety-reducing actions. Thus Ullman[200,201] found that compulsive and vigorous eating was positively related to tension-provoking situations. It is also known that certain individuals and certain ethnic groups react to stress by eating.[202] Ferenczi[203] points out that work itself can be effective in reducing anxiety, and Bird[204] describes the case of an " addictive " worker who reacted to stress by continuous work. Why the alcoholic turns to alcohol in preference to these other tension-reducing activities must remain an open question.

Miller[205] was the first person to show that the decrease in the acquired drive of fear or anxiety can serve as the reinforcing agent in the learning of a habit. More specifically, Conger[189,206] has provided data which support the hypothesis that the habit of drinking alcohol when rats are placed in a conflict situation is reinforced by the fear-reducing effects of the alcohol. He found that alcohol decreases learned fear-motivating avoidance responses in rats, but does not affect primary hunger-motivating approach responses. Although it seems acceptable that alcohol reduces the learned drive of anxiety, Conger is forced to consider several possibilities. It could be that alcohol tends to reduce the strength of all learned drives but does not affect primary ones; it could also be that the effects of alcohol are specific to certain drives, whether learned or primary. For example, Gantt has provided good evidence that alcohol reduces the primary physiological responses to stimulation of genital areas. It does, however, seem reasonably established that alcohol reduces fear or anxiety. The work of Masserman and his associates with animals confirms this.[56,57,207,208] It has also been shown that, in rats, alcohol reduces general activity, which may be a measure of general tension.[209,210] The cross cultural studies of Horton[195] suggest that this conclusion is applicable to man also.*

Conger[212] suggests that conflict itself is tension producing and the work of Liddell and his associates[213] supports this view. According to Dworkin[214] alcohol, as well as other hypnotics, such as amytal, nembutal and hyoscine, considerably reduces the behavioural symptoms of tension resulting during the establishment of an experimental neurosis based on a conflict situation. Thus, whether anxiety is regarded as a learned response and discussed in terms of excessive and widely generalized conditioned responses or as a product of conflict situations, it seems that alcohol reduces this anxiety and so provides the reinforcement which a drive-reducing theory of learning postulates.† Thus the act of drinking to reduce tension becomes a learned habit. By a process of stimulus generalization (in much the same way as anxiety itself is a learned generalized response) drinking alcohol in specific tension-provoking situations becomes generalized to drinking alcohol in most situations, whether tension provoking or not. The habit is maintained by those few situations which provide tension and so the learned pattern becomes reinforced.

The question now arises as to why some people become addicts almost immediately and others not at all, even though they also drink to relieve tension. A possible, if speculative, answer is that addiction is related to the conditionability and personality of the individual concerned. If it is true that introverted subjects condition more readily than extraverts then the introvert will develop more conditioned anxiety. Therefore there will be more situations where the need to reduce this drive exists; furthermore, fewer reinforcements will be required for the habit to be learned successfully and the generalization to numerous situations and alcoholic beverages would be greater. No experiments have investigated both the conditionability and the personality of alcoholics. Many practical and theoretical difficulties arise, such as the elimination of subjects with brain damage or other physiological changes resulting from the excessive drinking of alcohol. Furthermore, it is logically unwise to assume that the conditionability and personality

---

* There is experimental evidence to show that other depressants have a similar effect. Thus Bailey and Miller[211] found that the barbiturates abolished conditioned fear responses in cats and Bartholomew, Franks and Marly[20] found that oblivon reduces manifest anxiety in humans.

† If anxiety itself is regarded as a learned response then it is to be expected that alcohol would have the effect of reducing already formed conditioned responses as well as the formation of new ones. As has already been stated, this has never been adequately demonstrated. Since it has been demonstrated that oblivon, amytal and other depressants behave in this manner, it would seem not unlikely that alcohol behaves likewise.

of the well-established alcoholic is the same as in his pre-morbid state. The existing evidence is inadequate and relates largely to the present personality of the alcoholic. Apart from the finding that Korsakov psychotics condition poorly[24,215] nothing is known about the conditionability of alcoholics in relation to personality or otherwise. The relationship between alcoholism and conditionability may well be a complex one. Thus in the early stages alcoholism may be positively related to conditionability but, in view of the findings that many chronic alcoholics are brain damaged[216,217] and that certain brain-damaged patients condition poorly, the chronic alcoholic may condition very poorly. The inability to control their drinking that is characteristic of alcoholics may thus be attributable in the early stages to excessive drive and conditioning and in the later stages to an inability to condition.

If the aetiology and treatment of alcoholism is considered in terms of conditioning, several interesting possibilities arise. Is it possible, for example, to produce relief of tension and other pleasurable feelings associated with alcohol by conditioning techniques, so that an originally neutral and innocuous stimulus is just as effective? This might be of benefit in counteracting the physiological withdrawal symptoms of alcoholism during the earlier stages of treatment. Thus Rubenstein[218] successfully treated morphine addiction along these lines. If Wilczkowski's conclusions are correct (he used no control group or adequate statistical precautions) then it is even possible to condition the physiological effect of alcohol.[219] There is much evidence that the sedative effects of sodium amytal can be conditioned[220] and Metalnikov and Chorine[221] succeeded in producing conditioned serological reactions in animals to a social stimulus. Razran[222] criticized their findings on methodological grounds, but a better controlled experiment by Smith and Dalinger[223] produced similar results. Kleitman and Crisler[224] conditioned the retching behaviour originally evoked by morphine to a sound stimulus. Eagle[225] reports that Bykov was able to condition urinary secretions and even leukocytosis.* On the other hand, Gantt, Katzenelbogen and Loucks[226] failed to condition the rise in blood sugar after an adrenalin injection was paired with either a buzzer or the " preparations for the injection." However, these authors note that hyperglycaemia can be produced under hypnosis merely by the suggestion " you have drunk a glass of sugared water." Furthermore the behavioural effects of alcohol have been produced by suggestion under hypnotism in the theatre on many occasions. After *animal* experiments in the conditioning of various drug effects, numerous authors have independently come to the conclusion that conditioning can only be achieved if the drug concerned produces experiences " meaningful " to the animal.[207,227-229] Thus it would have to be the whole configuration of

* Which, as many studies have since confirmed, refutes Pavlov's claim that the cortex is essential to conditioning.

feelings associated with drinking alcoholic beverages which would have to be conditioned. There would seem to be two not incompatible lines of approach. (1) To provide the general pleasurable effects of alcohol, including well-being and the reduction of tension by an innocuous conditioned stimulus. (2) To condition or teach the subject to use other stimuli to reduce his anxiety, stimuli which are less harmful than alcohol, e.g. sweets or gum. A novel possibility in this respect may be that suggested by Richter.[230] He found that thyroid extract greatly increased the experimental rats' appetite for sugar, so he attempted to induce a craving for alcohol in this way. To his surprise, just the opposite result was produced, the rats either greatly reduced or completely stopped their intake of alcoholic beverages. Since hyperthyroid patients are very rarely alcoholics Richter thinks that a small daily dose of thyroid extract might stop the craving for alcohol, although he presents no rationale for this belief. It might well be, however, that the thyroid functions as a substitute for alcohol in reducing the patient's needs. This hardly commends itself as an effective substitute, but does suggest the need for an investigation of thyroid function in alcoholics.

REFERENCES

1. VOGEL, S. (1953). An interpretation of medical and psychiatric approaches in the treatment of alcoholism. *Quart. J. Stud. Alc.*, **14**, 620-631.
2. JELLINEK, E. M. and McFARLAND, R. A. (1940). Analysis of psychological experiments on the effect of alcohol. *Quart. J. Stud. Alc.*, **1**, 272-371.
3. TAKALA, M., PIHKANEN, T. A. and MARKKANEN, T. (1957). *The Effects of Distilled and Brewed Beverages*, 4 : The Finnish Foundation for Alcoholic Studies, Helsinki.
4. FRANKS, C. M. (1957). Personality theory in Britain, in *Perspectives in Personality Theory* (eds. David, H. P. and von Bracken, H.). Basic Books, New York.
5. KANORSKI, J. (1948). *Conditioned Reflexes and Neuron Organization*. Camb. Univ. Press, Cambridge.
6. THORPE, W. H. (1956). *Learning and Instinct in Animals*. Methuen, London.
7. GUTHRIE, E. R. (1952). *The Psychology of Learning*, 2nd edition. Harper, New York.
8. HILGARD, E. R. and MARQUIS, D. G. (1940). *Conditioning and Learning*. Appleton–Century–Crofts, New York.
9. PAVLOV, I. P. (1927). *Conditioned Reflexes*. Oxford Univ. Press, London.
10. PAVLOV, I. P. (1928). *Lectures on Conditioned Reflexes*, 1. Lawrence & Wishart, London.
11. PAVLOV, I. P. (1941). Conditioned reflexes and psychiatry, in *Lectures on Conditioned Reflexes*, 2. International Publications, New York.
12. FRANKS, C. M. (1954). An experimental study of conditioning as related to mental abnormality. Ph.D. Dissertation, London.
13. RAZRAN, G. H. S. (1933). Conditioned responses in children. *Arch. Psychol., N.Y.*, **23**, No. 148.
14. FRANKS, C. M. (1955). The establishment of a conditioning laboratory for the investigation of personality and cortical functioning. *Nature*, **175**, 984-985.
15. FRANKS, C. M. (1957). Personality factors and the rate of conditioning. *Brit. J. Psychol.*, **48**, 119-126.
16. FRANKS, C. M. (1956). Conditioning and personality: a study of normal and neurotic subjects. *J. Abnorm. Soc. Psychol.*, **52**, 143-150.
17. FRANKS, C. M. (1957). Effect of food, drink and tobacco deprivation on the conditioning of the eyeblink response. *J. Exp. Psychol.*, **53**, 117-120.

18. FRANKS, C. M. and LAVERTY, S. G. (1955). Sodium amytal and eyelid conditioning. *J. Ment. Sci.*, **101**, 654-663.

19. FRANKS, C. M. and TROUTON, D. S. Effects of amobarbital sodium and dexamphetamine sulfate on the conditioning of the eyeblink response. *J. Comp. Physiol. Psychol.* (to appear).

20. BARTHOLOMEW, A. A., FRANKS, C. M. and MARLEY, E. (1958). Susceptibility to response. 3. Eyelid conditioning and PGR response.

21. EYSENCK, H. J. (1953). *The Structure of Human Personality*. Methuen, London.

22. FRANKS, C. M. (1956). Recidivism, psychopathy and delinquency. *Brit. J. Delinq.*, **6**, 192-201.

23. GANTT, W. H. (1950). The conditioned reflex function as an aid in the study of the psychiatric patient. *Relation of Psychological Tests to Psychiatry* (ed. by Hoch, P.H. and Zubin, J.). Grune and Stratton, New York.

24. REESE, W. G., DOSS, R. and GANTT, W. H. (1953). Autonomic responses in differential diagnoses of organic and psychogenic psychoses. *A.M.A. Arch. Neurol. Psychiat.*, **70**, 778-793.

25. MAYER GROSS, W., SLATER, E. and ROTH, M. (1954). *Clinical Psychiatry*. Cassell, London.

26. KENNEDY, A. (1954). Psychopathic personality and social responsibility. *J. Ment. Sci.*, **100**, 873-881.

27. GANTT, W. H. (1935). Effect of alcohol on cortical and subcortical activity measured by the conditioned reflex method. *Bull. Johns Hopkins Hosp.*, **56**, 61-83.

28. MEAD, L. C. (1939). The effects of alcohol on two performances of different intellectual capacity. *J. Gen. Psychol.*, **21**, 3-23.

29. RIVERS, W. H. R. and WEBBER, H. N. (1908). The influence of small doses of alcohol on the capacity for muscular work. *Brit. J. Psychol.*, **2**, 261-280.

30. NEWMAN, H. W. and NEWMAN, E. J. (1956). Failure of dexedrine and caffeine as practical antagonists of the depressant effect of ethyl alcohol in man. *Quart. J. Stud. Alc.*, **17**, 406-410.

31. SETTLAGE, P. H. (1936). The effect of sodium amytal on the formation and elicitation of conditioned reflexes. *J. Comp. Psychol.*, **22**, 339-343.

32. POPOV, N. A. and POVOP, C. (1953). Contribution à l'étude des fonctions corticales chez l'homme, par la méthode des réflexes conditionnés électrocorticaux. I. Action de l'alcool sur les images consécutives et leur conditionnement, 1° note, *C. R. Acad. Sci., Paris*, **237**, 930-932.

33. POPOV, N. A. and POPOV, C. (1953). Contribution à l'étude des fonctions corticales chez l'homme, par la méthode des réflexes conditionnés électrocorticaux. II. De la modification par l'alcool des couleurs des images consécutives et des images consécutives conditionées. *C. R. Acad. Sci., Paris*, **237**, 1439-1441.

34. FROMHERG, K. (1927). Sedative Wirkungen im Tierversuch. *Arch. Exp. Path. Pharmak.*, **121**, 273-298.

35. VARÉ, P. (1932). Influence de l'alcool sur les réactions psychomotrices. *C. R. Soc. Biol.*, **3**, 70-72.

36. ERLACHER, C. (1931). Vergleichende Untersuchungen über die Alkoholwirkung bei Schulkindern, *Z. Pädag. Psychol.*, **32**, 185-196.

37. GOODMAN, L. and GILMAN, A. (1941). *The Pharmacological Basis of Therapeutics*. Macmillan, New York.

38. HORSEY, W. J. (1953). The influence of ethyl alcohol on the spontaneous electrical activity of the cerebral cortex and subcortical structures of the cat. *Quart. J. Stud. Alc.*, **14**, 363-377.

39. ARLITT, A. H. (1919). Effect of alcohol on intelligent behaviour of the white rat and its progeny. *Psychol. Rev. Mongr.*, **26**, 1-50.

40. McDOWELL, E. C. and VICARI, E. M. (1921). Alcoholism and white rats. Influence on maze behavior. *J. Exp. Zoo.*, **33**, 209-291.

41. McDOWELL, E. C. and VICARI, E. M. (1923). Alcoholism and behavior of white rats. II. Maze behavior of treated rats and their offspring. *J. Exp. Zoo.*, **37**, 417-456.

42. MACHT, D. I. and LEACH, H. (1929). Effect of methyl and alcohol mixtures on behavior of rats in a maze. *Proc. Soc. Exp. Biol. Med., N.Y.*, **26**, No. 4.
43. VARNER, W. B. (1933). The effects of alcohol on two maze habits of albino rats. *Psychol. Bull.*, **30**, 616.
44. MILLER, N. E. and MILES, W. R. (1936). Alcohol and removal of reward: an analytical study of rodent maze behavior. *J. Comp. Psychol.*, **21**, 179-204.
45. SELIGER, R. V. (1953). Alcohol and crime. *J. Crim. Law Criminol.*, **44**, 438-441.
46. WINKLER, E. G., WEISSMAN, M. and McDERMAID, G. (1954). Alcoholism and anti-social behaviour. *Psychiat. Quart. Suppl.*, **28**, 242-254.
47. MAYERHOFFER, G. (1933). Recherches psychotechniques concernant l'effet de l'alcool sur le comportment des conducteurs d'automobiles. *Travail hum.*, **1**, 257-177.
48. VERNON, H. M. (1936). The relation of alcohol to road accidents: a preliminary study. *Hum. Factor, Lond.*, **10**, 255-266.
49. DE SILVA, H. R. (1937). *Bibliography on Driving Safety*. Health Bureau for Street Traffic Research, Cambridge (Mass.).
50. NEWMAN, H. W. (1955). Research on alcohol. *Stanf. Med. Bull.*, **13**, 98-105.
51. AKSNES, E. G. (1954). Effect of small dosages of alcohol upon performance in a Link Trainer. *J. Aviat. Med.*, **25**, 680-688.
52. GANTT, W. H. (1940). Effect of alcohol on sexual reflexes in dogs. *Am. J. Physiol.*, **129**, 360.
53. GANTT, W. H. (1944). *Experimental Basis for Neurotic Behavior*. Hoeber, New York.
54. GANTT, W. H. (1952). Effect of alcohol on the sexual reflexes of normal and neurotic male dogs. *Psychosomat. Med.*, **14**, 174-182.
55. KRAEPELIN, E. (1892). Uber die Beeinflussung einfacher psychischer Vorgänge durch einige Arzneimittel. Fischer, Jena.
56. MASSERMAN, J. H. (1940). Effects of analeptic drugs on the hypothalamus of the cat. *Res. Publ. Ass. Nerv. Ment. Dis.*, **20**, 624-631.
57. MASSERMAN, J. H. and YUM, K. S. (1946). An analysis of the influence of alcohol on experimental neuroses in cats. *Psychosom. Med.*, **8**, 36-52.
58. SANTESSEN, C. G. (1934). Ueber die Wirkung von Alkohol und einigen anderen giften auf die Herzhemmung beim Frosch. *Skand. Arch. Physiol.*, **69**, 255-292.
59. ISCHLONDSKY, N. E. (1949). *Brain and Behaviour: Induction as a Fundamental Mechanism of Neuro-Psychic Activity*. Kimpton, London.
60. SHAGASS, C. and NAIMAN, J. (1956). An objective test which differentiates between neurotic and psychotic depression. *A.M.A. Arch. Neurol. Psychiat.*, **75**, 461-471.
61. SHAGASS, C. and NAIMAN, J. (1957). Clinical psychiatric studies using the sedation threshold. *J. Psychosom. Res.*, **2**, 45-55.
62. VICTOR, M. and ADAMS, R. D. (1953). The effects of alcohol on the nervous system. *Res. Publ. Ass. Nerv. Ment. Dis.*, **32**, 526-573.
63. WEXBERG, L. E. (1949). Psychodynamics of patients with chronic alcoholism. *J. Clin. Psychopath.*, **10**, 147-157.
64. SUTHERLAND, E. H., SCHROEDER, H. G. and TODELLA, C. L. (1950). Personality traits and the alcoholic: a critique of existing studies. *Quart. J. Stud. Alc.*, **11**, 547-561.
65. McDOWELL, E. C. (1919). The influence of parental alcoholism upon habit formation in albino rats. *Proc. Soc. Exp. Biol. Med.*, **16**, 125-126.
66. McDOWELL, E. C. (1922). Experiments with albino and white rats. *Am. Nat.*, **56**, 289-311.
67. HANSON, F. B. and COOPER, L. (1930). The effects of ten generations of alcoholic ancestry upon learning ability in the albino rat. *J. Exp. Zoo.*, **56**, 369-392.
68. MARSHALL, J. (1941). Alcohol—a critical review of the literature 1929–1940. *Psychol. Bull.*, **38**, 193-217.
69. MUNN, N. L. (1950). *Handbook of Psychological Research on the Rat*. Houghton Mifflin, Boston.
70. MOORE, M. (1941). Alcoholism: some contemporary opinions. *New Engl. J. Med.*, **224**, 848-857.

71. VOEGTLIN, W. L. and LEMERE, F. (1942). The treatment of alcohol addiction: A review of the literature. *Quart. J, Stud. Alc.*, **2**, 717-803.
72. VOEGTLIN, W. L. and LEMERE, F. (1940). The treatment of alcoholism by establishing a conditioned reflex. *Amer. J. Ment. Sci.*, **199**, 802-809.
73. LEMERE, F. and VOEGTLIN, W. L. (1940). Conditioned reflex therapy of alcoholic addiction; specificity of conditioning against chronic alcoholism. *Calif. West. Med.*, **53**, 269-279.
74. VOEGTLIN, W. L., LEMERE, F. and BROZ, W. R. (1940). Conditioned reflex therapy of alcoholic addiction. III. An evaluation of present results in the light of previous experiences with this method. *Quart. J. Stud. Alc.*, **1**, 501-506.
75. VOEGTLIN, W. L., LEMERE, F., BROZ, W. R. and O'HALLAREN, P. (1941). Conditioned reflex therapy of chronic alcoholism. IV. A preliminary report on the value of reinforcement. *Quart. J. Stud. Alc.*, **2**, 505-511.
76. LEMERE, F., VOEGTLIN, W. L., BROZ, W. R. and O'HALLAREN, P. (1942). Conditioned reflex treatment of chronic alcoholism. V. Type of patient suitable for this treatment. *Northw. Med., Seattle*, **4**, 88-89.
77. VOEGTLIN, W. L., LEMERE, F., BROZ, W. R. and O'HALLAREN, P. (1942). Conditioned reflex treatment of alcoholic addiction. VI. Follow-up report of 1,042 cases. *Amer. J. Med. Sci.*, **203**, 525-528.
78. LEMERE, F., VOEGTLIN, W. L., BROZ, W. R., O'HALLAREN, P. and TUPPER, W. E. (1942). Conditioned reflex treatment of chronic alcoholism. VII. *Dis. Nerv. Syst.*, **3**, 243-247.
79. LEMERE, F., VOEGTLIN, W. L., BROZ, W. R., O'HALLAREN, P. and TUPPER, W. E. (1942). The conditioned reflex treatment of chronic alcoholism. VIII. A review of six years' experience with this treatment of 1,526 patients. *J. Amer. Med. Ass.*, **120**, 269-270.
80. LEMERE, F., VOEGTLIN, W. L., BROZ, W. R., O'HALLAREN, P. and TUPPER, W. E. (1943). Heredity as an etiologic factor in chronic alcoholism. *Northw. Med., Seattle*, **42**, 110-111.
81. MARKOVIKOV, A. (1934). Therapy by combination of persuasion with development of conditioned reflex of vomiting after swallowing alcoholic drink. *Sovetsk. Vrach. Gaz.*, 807-811.
82. ICHOK, G. (1934). Les réflexes conditionnels et le traitement de l'alcoolique. *Prog. Méd., Paris*, **45**, 1742-1745.
83. GALANT, J. S. (1936). Uber die Apomorphinbehandlung der Alkoholiker. *Psychiat.-Neurol., Wschr.*, **38**, 85-89.
84. DIETHELM, O. (1955). Ed., *Etiology of Chronic Alcoholism.* Thomas, Springfield, Ill.
85. VOEGTLIN, W. L. (1947). The conditioned reflex therapy of chronic alcoholism; ten years' experience with the method. *Rocky Mtn. Med. J.*, **44**, 807-812.
86. SPENCER PATTERSON, A. (1950). Modern techniques for the treatment of acute and prolonged alcoholism. *Brit. J. Addict.*, **47**, 3-15.
87. LÉVY-VALENSI. (1939). Le traitement de l'alcoolisme. *Paris Méd.*, **29**, 401-409.
88. FELLION, G. (1952). Traitement de l'alcoolisme. *Concourse Méd.*, **74**, 1877-1878.
89. VOEGTLIN, W. L. and BROZ, W. R. (1949). The conditioned reflex treatment of chronic alcoholism. X. An analysis of 3,125 admissions over a period of ten and a half years. *Ann. Intern. Med.*, **30**, 580-597.
90. ASH, W. E. and MAHONEY, J. D. (1951). The use of conditioned reflex and Antabuse in the therapy of alcoholism. *J. Iowa St. Med. Soc.*, **41**, 456-458.
91. BOITELLE, G., BOITELLE-LENTALO, C., SINGER, L. and DAVY, G. (1952). Resultats de deux ans de traitement anti-alcoolique au service libre de l'hôpital psychiatrique de Lorquin. *Ann. Méd-Psychol.*, **110**, 348-352.
92. WYSS, R. (1949). Nouvelles méthodes de traitement medical de l'alcoolisme. *Gaz. Med. France*, **56**, 583-592.
93. FELDMAN, D. J. (1956). The treatment of chronic alcoholism: a survey of current methods. *Ann. Intern. Med.*, **44**, 78-87.
94. WALLACE, J. A. (1949). The treatment of alcoholism by the conditioned reflex method. *J. Tenn. St. Med. Ass.*, **42**, 125-128.

95. THIMANN, J. (1949). Conditioned reflex treatment of alcoholism. I. Its rationale and technique. *New Engl. J. Med.*, **241**, 368-370.
96. THIMANN, J. (1949). Conditioned reflex treatment of alcoholism. II. The risks of its application, its indications, contraindications and therapeutic aspects. *New Engl. J. Med.*, **241**, 406-410.
97. SHERFEY, M. J. and DIETHELM, O. (1951). Evaluation of drugs in the treatment of alcoholism. *Res. Publ. Ass. Nerv. Ment. Dis.*, **31**, 287-294.
98. LINN, L. (1955). *A Handbook of Hospital Psychiatry: A Practical Guide to Therapy.* International University Press, New York.
99. BOWMAN, K. M. (1956). Alcoholism: theory, problem and challenge. IV. The treatment of alcoholism. *Quart. J. Stud. Alc.*, **17**, 318-324.
100. TABORI, J. (1933). Zur Kasuistik des induzierten Morphinismus. *Zentbl. F. Psychotherap.*, **6**, 88-96.
101. KNIGHT, R. P. (1938). The psychiatric treatment in a sanatorium of chronic addiction to alcohol. *J. Amer. Med. Ass.*, **111**, 1143-1446.
102. FLEMING, R. and TILLOTSON, K. J. (1939). Further studies on personality and sociological factors in prognosis and treatment of chronic alcoholism. *New Engl. J. Med.*, **221**, 741-746.
103. HENDERSON, D. K. and GILLESPIE, R. D. (1950). *A Text Book of Psychiatry.* Oxford University Press, London.
104. CARVER, A. E. (1949). *Brit. Med. J.*, ii, 707-708 (correspondence).
105. EDLIN, J. V., JOHNSON, R. H., HLETKO, P. and HEILBRUNN, G. (1945). Conditioned aversion treatment in chronic alcoholism. *Amer. J. Psychiat.*, **101**, 801-809.
106. KANT, F. (1944). The conditioned reflex treatment in the light of our knowledge of alcohol addiction. *Quart. J. Stud. Alc.*, **5**, 371-377.
107. CARLSON, A. J. (1944). The conditioned reflex of alcohol addiction. *Quart. J. Stud. Alc.*, **5**, 212-215.
108. TIEBOUT, H. M. (1951). The role of psychiatry in the field of alcoholism. With comment on the concept of alcoholism as symptom and as disease. *Quart. J. Stud. Alc.*, **12**, 52-57.
109. KOLLER, A. (1946). Die Behandlung des chronischen Alkoholismus. *Gesundh. u. Wohlf.*, **26**, 611-619.
110. RUSTERHOLS. (1946). Alcoholics anonymous. *Gesundh. u. Wohlf.*, **26**, 626-630.
111. OLLIVIER, H. and KLOTZ, B. (1949). " Aversion-to-alcoholic-drinks " treatment in the fight against alcoholism. *Ann. Méd. Leg.*, **29**, 53-57.
112. DELAY, J., PICHOT, P. and THUILLIER, J. (1949). Les nouvelles chimiothérapies de l'alcoolisme. *Ann. Méd. Psychol.*, **107**, 427-429.
113. JONES, R. O. (1949). Death following ingestion of alcohol in Antabuse treated patients. *Canad. Med. Ass. J.*, **60**, 609-612.
114. MARTENSEN-LARSEN, O. (1951). Psychotic phenomena provoked by tetraethylthiuram disulfide. *Quart. J. Stud. Alc.*, **12**, 207-216.
115. MANN, N. M., CONWAY, E. J., GOTTESFIELD, B. H. and LASSER, L. N. (1952). Co-ordinated approach to Antabuse therapy. *J. Amer. Med. Ass.*, **149**, 40-46.
116. STRECKER, E. A. and LATHBURY, V. T. (1952). Tetraethylthiuram disulfide (Antabuse) therapy; report of two cases. *J. Amer. Med. Ass.*, **149**, 40-46.
117. DENT, J. Y. (1949). Apomorphine treatment of addiction, some recent developments. *Brit. J. Addict.*, **46**, 15-28.
118. DENT, J. Y. (1947). *Anxiety and its Treatment, with Special Reference to Alcoholism*, 2nd edition. Mullan, Belfast.
119. VENCOVSKY, V. (1950). Treatment of alcoholism with tetraethylthiuram disulfide. *Cas. Lek. ces.*, **89**, 258-262.
120. BACHET, M. (1952). Problèmes soulevés par le traitement de l'alcoolisme en créant un réflexe conditionné après inhibition, sans chimiothérapie. *Ann. Méd.-Psychol.*, **110**, 223-227.
121. RUSH, B. (1814). *An Inquiry into the Effects of Ardent Spirits upon the Body and Mind, with an Account of the Means of Preventing and of the Remedies for Curing them*, 8th edition. Meriam, Brookfield.

122. SOLOMON, R. L. and BRUSH, E. S. (1956). Experimentally derived conceptions of anxiety and aversion. In *Nebraska Symposium on Motivation*, ed. by Jones, M. R., 4. University of Nebraska Press, Lincoln, Nebraska.

123. HILGARD, E. R. (1956). *Theories of Learning*, 2nd edition. Appleton–Century–Crofts, New York.

124. KANTOROVICH, N. V. (1929). An attempt at associative reflex therapy in alcoholism. *Nov. Refl. Fiziol. Nerv. Sist.*, 3, 436-447 (Psychol. Abstr. No. 4282, 1930).

125. WANG, S. C. and BORISON, H. C. (1950). The vomiting center: A critical experimental analysis. *Arch. Neurol. Psychiat.*, 63, 928-941.

126. HATCHER, R. A. and WEISS, S. (1923). Studies on vomiting. *J. Pharmacol. Exp. Therap.*, 22, 139-193.

127. LEMERE, F. and O'HALLAREN, P. (1949). Pentothal sodium treatment of alcoholism. *Arch. Neurol. Psychiat.*, 48, 482-484.

128. RAYMOND, M. J. (1956). Case of fetishism treated by aversion therapy. *Brit. Med. J.*, 13 October, 854-857, No. 4997.

129. FRENCH, T. M. (1933). Interrelations between psychoanalysis and the experimental work of Pavlov. *Amer. J. Psychiat.*, 12, 1165-1203.

130. KUBIE, L. S. (1934). Relation of the conditioned reflex to psychoanalytic technique. *A.M.A. Arch. Neurol. Psychiat.*, 32, 1137-1142.

131. DARLEY, J. (1943). Review of counselling and psychotherapy. *J. Abnorm. Soc. Psychol.*, 38, 199-201.

132. SHAW, F. J. (1946). A stimulus-response analysis of repression and insight in psychotherapy. *Psychol. Rev.*, 53, 36-42.

133. SHAFFER, L. F. (1947). The problem of psychotherapy. *Amer. Psychol.*, 2, 459-467.

134. SHOBEN, E. J. (1948). A learning theory interpretation of psychotherapy. *Harv. Educ. Rev.*, 18, 129-145.

135. FREEDMAN, B. (1948). Conditioned reflex and psychodynamic equivalents in alcohol addiction. *Quart. J. Stud. Alc.*, 9, 53-71.

136. SHOBEN, E. J. (1949). Psychotherapy as a problem in learning theory. *Psychol. Bull.*, 46, 366-392.

137. MAGARET, A. (1950). Generalization in successful psychotherapy. *J. Consult. Psychol.*, 14, 64-70.

138. DOLLARD, J. and MILLER, N. E. (1950). *Personality and Psychotherapy.* McGraw Hill, New York.

139. SHOBEN, E. J. (1953). Some observations on psychotherapy and the learning process, Ch. 5, pp. 120-140. In *Psychotherapy: Theory and Research* (ed. by Mowrer, O. H.). Ronald, New York.

140. MOWRER, O. H. (1953). *Psychotherapy: Theory and Research.* Ronald, New York.

141. AGOSTON, T. (1944). Experimental administration of benzedrine sulfate and other central stimulants in psychoanalysis and psychotherapies. *Psychoanal. Rev.*, 31, 438-452.

142. PULLAR-STRECKER, H. A. (1951). Review on the 1949–1950 literature of addiction. *Brit. J. Addict.*, 48, 3-119.

143. STRECKER, E. A. and CHAMBERS, F. T. (1939). *Alcohol, One Man's Meat.* Macmillan, New York.

144. STRECKER, E. A. and CHAMBERS, F. T. (1941). Chronic alcoholism, a psychologic survey. *Quart. J. Stud. Alc.*, 2, 12-17.

145. MANSON, M. P. (1948). A psychometric differentiation of alcoholics from non-alcoholics. *Quart. J. Stud. Alc.*, 9, 175-206.

146. HEWITT, C. C. (1943). A personality study of alcoholic addiction. *Quart. J. Stud. Alc.*, 4, 368-386.

147. BUTTON, A. D. (1956). A study of alcoholics with the Minnesota Multiphasic Personality Inventory. *Quart. J. Stud. Alc.*, 17, 263-281.

148. BACON, S. D. (1949). The administration of alcoholism rehabilitation programs. *Quart. J. Stud. Alc.*, 10, 1-47.

149. DAVIDOFF, E. and WHITAKER, C. A. (1940). Prepsychotic personality in alcoholic psychoses. *Psychiat. Quart.*, 14, 103-120.

150. HOCH, P. H. (1940). Personality factors in alcoholic psychoses. *Psychiat. Quart.*, **14**, 338-346.
151. NORBURY, F. G. (1942). Some mental mechanisms in alcoholism. *J. Amer. Med. Ass.*, **118**, 25-28.
152. WENGER, P. (1944). History of a drinking habit in 400 inmates of a penal institution. *N.Y. St. J. Med.*, **44**, 1898-1904.
153. FLEESON, W. and GILDEA, E. F. (1942). A study of the personalities of 289 abnormal drinkers. *Quart. J. Stud. Alc.*, **3**, 409-432.
154. HAMPTON, P. J. (1951). Representative studies of alcoholism and personality. I. Naturalistic studies. *J. Soc. Psychol.*, **34**, 203-210.
155. HAMPTON, P. J. (1951). Representative studies of alcoholism and personality. II. Clinical studies. *J. Soc. Psychol.*, **34**, 211-222.
156. HAMPTON, P. J. (1951). Representative studies of alcoholism and personality. III. Psychometric studies. *J. Soc. Psychol.*, **34**, 223-234.
157. QUARANTA, J. V. (1947). Alcoholism: a study of emotional maturity and homo-sexuality as related factors to compulsive drinking. M.A. Thesis, Fordham Univ., New York.
158. SCHAEFER, E. S. (1954). Personality structure of alcoholics in outpatient psychotherapy. *Quart. J. Stud. Alc.*, **15**, 304-319.
159. HANSEN, H. A. and TEILMANN, K. (1954). A treatment of criminal alcoholics in Denmark. *Quart. J. Stud. Alc.*, **15**, 246-287.
160. DAVIES, D. L., SHEPHERD, M. and MYERS, E. (1956). The two-years' prognosis of 50 alcohol addicts after treatment in hospital. *Quart. J. Stud. Alc.*, **17**, 485-502.
161. STRAUS, R. and BACON, S. D. (1951). Alcoholism and social stability. A study of occupational integration in 2,023 male clinic patients. *Quart. J. Stud. Alc.*, **12**, 231-260.
162. VOGEL, V. H. (1938). Suggestibility in chronic alcoholics. *Suppl.* 144, *U.S. Publ. Hlth. Rep., Washington, D.C.*
163. WITTMAN, P. (1939). A controlled study of the development and personality characteristics of chronic alcoholics. *Elgin Papers*, **3**, 77-84.
164. WITTMAN, P. (1939). A differential analysis of " adjustment " scores for chronic alcoholics and control. *Elgin Papers*, **3**, 85-93.
165. WITTMAN, P. (1939). Diagrams and analysis of temperament for groups of alcoholics compared with controls. *Elgin Papers*, **3**, 94-99.
166. WITTMAN, P. (1939). Developmental characteristics and personalities of chronic alcoholics. *J. Abnorm. Soc. Psychol.*, **34**, 361-377.
167. LANDIS, C. (1945). Theories of the alcoholic personality. In *Alcohol, Science and Society*, New Haven: *Quart. J. Stud. Alc.*
168. JELLINEK, E. M. (ed.) (1942). *Alcohol, Addiction and Chronic Alcoholism.* Yale University Press, New Haven.
169. SHERFEY, M. J. (1955). Psychopathology and character structure in chronic alcoholism. In *Etiology of Chronic Alcoholism*, ed. by Diethelm, O. Thomas, Springfield, Ill.
170. BLEULER, M. (1955). Familial and personal background of chronic alcoholics. In *Etiology of Chronic Alcoholism*, ed. by Diethelm, O. Thomas, Springfield, Ill.
171. PAYNE, R. B. (1953). The effects of drugs upon psychological efficiency. *J. Aviat. Med.*, **24**, 523-529.
172. FORD, C. S. and BEACH, F. A. (1951). *Pattern of Sexual Behavior.* Harper, New York.
173. ANDREYEV, L. A. (1934). The effect of single and repeated doses of alcohol on conditioned reflexes in the dog. *Arch. Int. Pharmacodyn.*, **48**, 117-128.
174. MASSERMAN, J. H. (1944). Neurosis and alcohol. *Amer. J. Psychiat.*, **101**, 389-395.
175. SELIGER, R. V. and CRANFORD, V. (1949). Alcoholic criminal. In *Encyclopedia of Criminology*, ed. Branham, V. C. and Kutash, S. B. Philosophical Library, New York.
176. MEIGNANT, P. (1935). Réflexes conditionnels et psycho-pathologie: quelque remarques concernant les perversions et les anomalies sexuelles. *Gaz. Méd. Fr.*, **28**, 327-332.

177. MAX, L. W. (1935). Breaking up a homosexual fixation by the conditioned reaction technique: A case study. *Psych. Bull.*, **32**, 734.
178. SALTER, A. (1949). *Conditioned Reflex Therapy.* Creative Age Press, New York.
179. LEVINE, J. (1955). The sexual adjustment of alcoholics. A clinical study of a selected sample. *Quart. J. Stud. Alc.*, **16**, 675-680.
180. BITTERMAN, M. E., REED, P. and KRAUSKOPF, J. (1952). The effect of the duration of the unconditioned stimulus upon conditioning and extinction. *Amer. J. Psychol.*, **65**, 256-262.
181. BUTLER, R. A. (1953). Discrimination learning by rhesus monkeys to visual exploration motivation. *J. Comp. Physiol. Psychol.*, **46**, 95-98.
182. CARPER, J. W. (1953). A comparison of the reinforcing value of a nutritive and a non-nutritive substance under conditions of specific and general hunger. *Amer. J. Psychol.*, **66**, 270-277.
183. WELCH, L. (1952). What is need reduction? *J. Psychol.*, **33**, 153-157.
184. WILKINS, W. L. (1956). Alcoholism: theory, problem and challenge. I. The idea of proneness in relation to alcoholism. *Quart. J. Stud. Alc.*, **17**, 291-295.
185. ROYER, P. H. (1953). Psycho-physiologie de la soif. *Encéphale*, **42** (Suppl. 1), 1-4.
186. PEABODY, R. A. (1930). Psychotherapeutic procedure in treatment of chronic alcoholism. *Ment. Hyg., N.Y.*, **14**, 109-128.
187. McFARLAND, R. A. and BORACH, A. L. (1936). The relationship between alcoholic intoxication and oxygen want. *Amer. J. Med. Sci.*, **192**, 186-198.
188. WESTERFIELD, W. W. and LAWROW, J. (1953). The effect of calorie restriction and thiamin deficiency on the voluntary consumption of alcohol in rats. *Quart. J. Stud. Alc.*, **14**, 378-384.
189. CONGER, J. J. (1951). The effects of alcohol in conflict behavior in the albino rat. *Quart. J. Stud. Alc.*, **12**, 1-29.
190. LOLLI, G. (1956). Alcoholism as a disorder of the love disposition. *Quart. J. Stud. Alc.*, **17**, 96-107.
191. FENICHEL, O. (1945). *The Psychoanalytic Theory of Neurosis.* Norton, New York.
192. WILLIAMS, E. Y. (1950). The anxiety-syndrome in alcoholism. *Psychiat. Quart.*, **24**, 782-787.
193. BACON, S. D. (1945). Alcohol and complex society. In *Alcohol, Science and Society* (Ch. 14). *Quart. J. Stud. Alc.*, New Haven.
194. ULLMAN, A. D. (1952). The psychological mechanism of alcohol addiction. *Quart. J. Stud. Alc.*, **13**, 602-608.
195. HORTON, D. (1943). The functions of alcohol in primitive societies: A cross-cultural study. *Quart. J. Stud. Alc.*, **4**, 199-220.
196. FREUD, S. (1936). *The Problem of Anxiety.* Norton, New York.
197. HORNEY, K. (1937). *The Neurotic Personality of our Time.* Norton, New York.
198. SULLIVAN, H. S. (1947). *Conceptions of Modern Psychiatry.* William Alanson White Psychiatric Foundation, Washington, D.C.
199. RANDOLPH, T. G. (1956). The descriptive features of food addiction. Addictive eating and drinking. *Quart. J. Stud. Alc.*, **17**, 198-224.
200. ULLMAN, A. D. (1951). The experimental production and analysis of a " compulsive eating syndrome " in rats. *J. Comp. Physiol. Psychol.*, **44**, 575-581.
201. ULLMAN, A. D. (1952). Three factors involved in producing " compulsive eating " in rats. *J. Comp. Physiol. Psychol.*, **45**, 490-496.
202. SNYDER, C. R. and LANDMAN, R. H. (1951). Studies of drinking in Jewish culture. II. Prospectives for sociological research in Jewish drinking patterns. *Quart. J. Stud. Alc.*, **12**, 451-474.
203. FERENCZI, S. (1927). *Further Contributions to the Theory and Technique of Psychoanalysis* (Trans. by Suttie, J.). Boni and Liveright, New York.
204. BIRD, B. (1949). One aspect of causation in alcoholism. *Quart. J. Stud. Alc.*, **9**, 533-545.
205. MILLER, N. E. (1948). Studies of fear as an acquired drive. I. Fear as motivation and fear-reduction as reinforcement in the learning of new responses. *J. Exp. Psychol.*, **38**, 89-101.

206. CONGER, J. J. (1949). An analysis of the effect of alcohol on conflict behavior in the albino rat. Ph.D. Dissertation, Yale.
207. MASSERMAN, J. H. (1943). *Behavior and Neurosis*. University of Chicago Press, Chicago.
208. MASSERMAN, J. H. (1946). *Principles of Dynamic Psychiatry*. Saunders, Philadelphia.
209. STEWART, C. C. (1898). Variations in daily activity produced by alcohol and by changes in barometric pressure and diet with a description of recording methods. *Amer. J. Physiol.*, **1**, 40-56.
210. RICHTER, C. P. (1926). A study of the effect of moderate doses of alcohol on the growth and behavior of the rat. *J. Exp. Zoo.*, **44**, 397-418.
211. BAILEY, C. and MILLER, N. E. (1952). Effect of sodium amytal on behavior of cats in an approach-avoidance conflict. *J. Comp. Physiol. Psychol.*, **45**, 205-208.
212. CONGER, J. J. (1956). Reinforcement theory and the dynamics of alcoholism. *Quart. J. Stud. Alc.*, **17**, 296-305.
213. LIDDELL, H. S. (1956). *Emotional Hazards in Animals and Man*. Thomas, Springfield, Ill.
214. DWORKIN, S., BOURNE, W. and RAGINSKY, B. B. (1937). Changes in conditioned responses brought about by anaesthetics and sedatives. *Can. Med. Assoc. J.*, **37**, 136-139.
215. GANTT, W. G. and MUNCIE, W. (1942). Analysis of the mental defect in chronic Korsakov's psychosis by means of the conditioned reflex. *Bull. Johns Hopkins Hosp.*, **20**, 467-487.
216. LEMERE, F. (1956). The nature and significance of brain damage from alcoholism. *Amer. J. Psychiat.*, **113**, 361-362.
217. COURVILLE, C. B. (1955). *Effects of Alcohol on the Nervous System of Man*. San Lucas Press, Los Angeles.
218. RUBENSTEIN, C. (1951). The treatment of morphine addiction in tuberculosis by Pavlov's conditioning method. *Amer. Rev. Tuberc.*, **24**, 682-685.
219. WILCZKOWSKI, E. (1954). Stwierdzenie istnienia naturalnego odrucha warunkowego alkoholowego we krwi u alkoholikow (The presence of natural conditioned response in the blood of alcoholics). *Neurol. Neuroch. Psychiat. Polska.*, **4**, 321-324.
220. LONDON, I. D. (1953). Therapy in Soviet psychiatric hospitals. *Amer. Psychologist*, **8**, 79-82.
221. METALNIKOV, S. and CHORINE, V. (1928). Roles des reflexes conditionnels dans la formation des anticorps. *C. R. Soc. Biol.*, **99**, 142-145.
222. RAZRAN, G. H. S. (1933). Conditioned responses in animals other than dogs. *Psychol. Bull.*, **30**, 261-324.
223. SMITH, S. H. and DALINGER, R. (1933). Hypersensitiveness and the conditioned reflex. *Yale J. Biol. and Med.*, **5**, 387-391.
224. KLEITMAN, N. and CRISLER, G. (1927). A quantitative study of a salivary conditioned reflex. *Amer. J. Physiol.*, **79**, 571-614.
225. EAGLE, E. (1933). Conditioned inhibition of water diuresis. *Amer. J. Physiol.*, **103**, 362-366.
226. GANTT, W. H., KATZENELBOGEN, S. and LOUCKS, R. B. (1937). An attempt to condition adrenalin hyperglycemia. *Bull. Johns Hop. Hosp.*, **60**, 400-411.
227. LOUCKS, R. M. (1937). Humoral conditioning in mammals. *J. Psychol.*, **4**, 295-307.
228. FINCH, G. (1938). Pilocarpine conditioning. *Amer. J. Physiol.*, **124**, 679-682.
229. KATZENELBOGEN, S., LOUCKS, R. B. and GANNT, W. H. (1939). An attempt to condition gastric secretion to histamime. *Amer. J. Physiol.*, **128**, 10-12.
230. RICHTER, C. P. (1956). *Science Newsletter*, **6**, 69-70.

CASE OF FETISHISM TREATED BY AVERSION THERAPY*

M. J. RAYMOND, M.R.C.P.ED., D.P.M.

First Assistant, Department of Psychiatry, St. George's Hospital, London

FETISHISM, or more accurately " erotic fetishism," is the tendency to be sexually attracted by some special part or peculiarity of the body or by some inanimate object. Of all the sexual aberrations, fetishism is one of the most intriguing, perplexing and varied. The literature is rich in detailed case reports and in speculation about theories of causation. I have been able to find, however, only 3 apparently successful results in established cases: one attributed to a co-operative wife,[1] one to psycho-analysis,[2] and the third to temporal lobectomy.[3] I have been unable to find any previous record of a fetishist who responded favourably to aversion therapy. The following case is also of interest in that the fears implicit in psychoanalytical theory, and stressed by East and Hubert,[4] of releasing homosexual or sadistic drives, have not so far been confirmed.

CASE REPORT

The patient, a married man aged 33, was referred in November, 1954, from the out-patient department of a mental hospital for consideration of a prefrontal leucotomy after he had attacked a perambulator. This was the twelfth such attack known to the police, and because of the previous incidents they were taking a serious view of his recent actions in following a woman with a perambulator and smearing it with oil. Since his first involvement with the police his career had been as follows:

First charge (six incidents)—In September, 1948, whilst in the R.A.F., he slashed two empty prams on a railway station before setting them on fire and completely destroying them. He also admitted 5 other incidents involving cutting or scratching prams, which had been the subject of police investigations over a period of months. He was convicted of causing malicious damage and put on probation to accept medical treatment. He then left the R.A.F.

* I am indebted to Dr. Desmond Curran for the opportunity to treat this patient, and for permission to publish this report. I also thank him and Sir Paul Mallinson for much helpful criticism and advice in the preparation of this paper. It is a pleasure to acknowledge the help and co-operation of the nursing staff at Atkinson Morley's Hospital.

Reprinted by permission of the author and editor of the *Brit. Med. J.* from (1956) *Brit. Med. J.*, **2**, 854-856.

and was in a mental hospital from March to April, 1949, before being transferred to a neurosis unit, where he stayed for a further month. The view was there expressed that he was unsuitable for psychotherapy, was potentially dangerous, and should remain in a mental hospital.

Seventh and eighth incidents—He did not remain in a mental hospital, and early in 1950 he smeared some mucus from his handkerchief on to a handbag and also damaged a pram by scratching and cutting it. He was not charged, but was admitted to a mental hospital and stayed there from February, 1950, until June, 1951.

Second charge (ninth incident)—In April, 1952, he deliberately rode his motor-cycle combination into a perambulator with a baby in it. He swerved at the last moment but hit the perambulator and damaged it. He was convicted of careless driving and was fined.

Third charge (tenth incident)—In August, 1952, he damaged a pram and a woman's skirt and stockings by squirting oil on them. He was convicted of causing malicious damage and was fined.

Fourth charge (eleventh incident)—In 1953 he rode his motor-cycle through a muddy puddle, splashing a pram and its coverings and the woman who pushed it. He was charged with driving without due care and attention, but the court gave him the benefit of the doubt.

Fifth charge (twelfth incident)—In September, 1954, came the first incident mentioned. He was charged and convicted of causing wilful damage, and was put on probation to accept medical treatment.

During the court proceedings arising from his latest escapade, the prosecuting counsel, while stressing that the accused deserved sympathy, had said nevertheless that he was still a menace to any woman with a pram. He went on to speak of " a real fear that he may cause serious injury to a baby or mother unless he is put under some form of restraint."

The patient said that he had had impulses to damage perambulators and handbags since about the age of 10, and that, although the police knew of only 12 perambulator attacks, the number of times he had so indulged was legion. He had sometimes made several attacks in one day, but he estimated the average at about 2 or 3 a week, fairly consistently. With the handbags he was usually satisfied if he could scratch them with his thumbnail, and as this could be done unobtrusively, a handbag had only once led him into trouble with the police.

He had received many hours of analytical treatment and had been enabled to trace his abnormality back to two incidents in his childhood. The first was when he had been taken to a park to sail his boat and had been impressed by the feminine consternation manifest when he struck the keel of his yacht against a passing perambulator. The second was when he became sexually aroused in the presence of his sister's handbag. He had been led to see the significance of these events and to understand that perambulators and handbags were for him " symbolic sexual containers," but the attacks continued.

His mother was a paraphrenic who was certified at the age of 54 (when he was 12) and died aged 66. His father died aged 66 (when the patient was 15). His work took him away from home for long periods. There was one sister, 12 years his senior, who had played the maternal role, and to whom he was much devoted.

PERSONAL HISTORY

His physical health as a child had been good, and his schooling had been normal. He left at the age of 14, having reached the top standard.

Occupational—After leaving his elementary school he attended a technical school for 3 years before joining the R.A.F. as an engine fitter. He served for 10 years and was then discharged because of his fetishism. Since then he had worked well at a job requiring a degree of mechanical skill and ingenuity, and also a facility for making personal contacts. He was industrious and successful, and his employers thought well of him.

Sexual and marital—From the age of about 10 he had masturbated, with fantasies of prams and handbags, and particularly of damage being caused to them by their owners. He first had sexual intercourse after his marriage at the age of 27; but intercourse, he said, was only possible with the aid of fantasies of handbags and prams. There were two children, and his wife said that he was a good husband and father. The domestic perambulator and his wife's handbags, however, were not immune from attack, and a handbag filled to capacity and bulging often provided piquancy to his masturbation. While it was true that handbags and perambulators aroused him sexually, his attacks upon them were never accompanied by emission, though he was usually conscious of release of tension.

He described himself as a good mixer, but said he was never perturbed by solitude, and had always been a day-dreamer. He read a good deal, especially adventure and crime novels, and he was keen on gardening and woodwork. His knowledge of perambulators and handbags was considerable, and there was no doubt that a good deal of his leisure time was devoted to them.

TREATMENT

On examination he was found to be a man of good intelligence, who showed no psychotic abnormality. He said he was depressed because he doubted whether anyone could help him and though he said, self-reproachfully, that his trouble was lack of will-power it was noticeable that he gave his history in a facile way and, it seemed, with a certain amount of relish.

In reflecting upon this man's plight, the despair of his family, and his poor response to treatment previously given, the idea was conceived that he might benefit from aversion therapy similar to that used in the treatment of alcoholism.

It was explained to the patient that the aim of treatment was to alter his attitude to handbags and perambulators by teaching him to associate them with an unpleasant sensation instead of with a pleasurable erotic sensation. Though he was frankly sceptical about the treatment, he said he was willing to try anything, for his despair had been deepened by recent sexual arousals when handbags appeared in the ward on visiting-day, and by illustrated advertisements in newspapers.

A collection of handbags, perambulators and coloured illustrations was obtained and these were shown to the patient after he had received an injection of apomorphine and just before nausea was produced. The treatment was given two-hourly, day and night, no food was allowed, and at night amphetamine was used to keep him awake. At the end of the first week, treatment was temporarily suspended and the patient was allowed home to attend to his affairs.

He returned after 8 days to continue the treatment, and he reported jubilantly that he had for the first time been able to have intercourse with his wife without use of the old fantasies. His wife said that she had noticed a change in his attitude to her, but was unable to define it. Treatment was recommenced and continued as before, save that emetine hydrochloride was used whenever the emetic effect of apomorphine became less pronounced than its sedative effect.

He was asked to write an account of the attractive qualities of perambulators and handbags, and this he did between treatments, writing at considerable length and with a wealth of technical detail. He also wrote an account of the ways in which they are commonly and carelessly misused. At this stage his difficulties were discussed and attention was chiefly directed towards the pride with which he had always cherished his eccentricity, the exhibitionistic element in his attacks on perambulators, and ways in which they had become a threat to his liberty. After 5 days he said that the mere sight of the objects made him sick. He was now confined to bed and the prams and handbags were continually with him, the treatments being given at irregular intervals. On the evening of the ninth day he rang his bell and was found to be sobbing uncontrollably. He kept repeating, " Take them away," and appeared to be impervious to anything which was said to him. The sobbing continued unabated until the objects were removed with ceremony, and he was given a glass of milk and a sedative. The following day he handed over a number of photographic negatives of perambulators, saying that he had carried them about for years but would need them no longer. He left hospital but continued to attend as an out-patient.

After a further 6 months it was decided empirically to re-admit him for a boosting course of treatment. He agreed to this, although he did not consider it at all necessary. A coloured cinematograph film was made of women carrying handbags and pushing prams in the careless, provoking ways which he had described previously. The film was started each time just before the onset of nausea produced by an emetic and was continued throughout the period of nausea. He was also given handbags to handle.

When asked to write an account of any change which he thought had taken place, he said that he no longer regarded himself as an expert on perambulators and often made mistakes about them in the street. He wrote: " The will-power had been there all the time, but before treatment prams and handbags had a fascination for me which my will-power was too weak to overcome." The fascination, he said, had become much less because his will-power had " matured."

PROGRESS

Nineteen months after he first had aversion therapy he still appeared to be doing well.

Patient's report—He says that he no longer requires the old fantasies to enable him to have sexual intercourse, nor does he masturbate with these fantasies.

Wife's report—She says that she is no longer constantly worrying about him, and about the possible imminence of police action against him. Their sexual relations have " greatly improved."

Probation officer's report—He says that the patient has made " very noticeable progress " and that " his general attitude to life, his conversation, and his appearance have all shown a marked improvement."

Work record—He has been promoted to a more responsible job.

Police—He has not been in any trouble with the police.

LITERATURE

Among the earliest speculations on this subject are those of the French philosopher Descartes, who was himself a squint fetishist. In 1649[5] he wrote: " From whence came those extraordinary passions which are peculiar to certain men? There is so close a union between mind and body that once we have combined a certain action with a certain thought, the one never subsequently presents without the other." Referring to strange aversions (anti-fetishisms) that some people have, he concluded that they may well have formed in early infancy to " remain imprisoned in the brain until the end of life."

Binet,[6] however, first gave the term " fetishism " its sexual connotation, defining it as the erotic idolatry of something which cannot directly satisfy the ends of reproduction. He stressed that everyone was to some extent a sexual fetishist and that the difficulty was in knowing where the normal became abnormal. Fetishism, he said, arose from an " accident acting on a predisposed subject," and the predisposition was in the form of a general nervous hyperaesthesia. According to Binet the form taken by any sexual perversion was determined purely fortuitously by an external event, and he stated that " the man who can love only men could easily have been a night-cap fetishist or a shoe-nail fetishist." He distinguished a minor and major fetishism. In minor fetishism some effective detail or object was the centre of attraction, but did not overshadow the person to whom the love was gradually transferred. In major fetishism there was no such transference. Minor fetishisms, he said, were not at all obvious or easy to recognize, but in them lay the secret of many strange loves and astonishing marriages.

Krafft-Ebing[7] accepted Binet's conclusion that in connexion with the first awakening of the fetishist's sexual life some event determined the association of lustful feeling with a single impression. The fetishist's abnormality, according to Krafft-Ebing, lies not in what stimulates him, but in what does *not* stimulate him—that is, in his limited sex interest. He classifies fetishes according to the type of fetish object: (1) part of female body, (2) part of female clothing, (3) special materials, (4) animals. Group (1) may be physiological or pathological, but the other three are always pathological.

He stresses its *forensic importance*, because it may present as strange acts aimed at defiling the object or at its theft, and its importance as a *cause of impotence*.

Havelock Ellis[8] states that fetishism tends to occur in sensitive, nervous timid, and precocious individuals, and can usually be traced to a definite starting-point in some sexually emotional episode in early life. The degree to which this influences an individual's subsequent life depends on his " morbid emotional receptivity."

Hirschfeld[1] elaborates Binet's theory and says that the predisposition is not a generalized nervous hyperaesthesia but a specific psychological make-up and that it is only a certain type of " accident " which is capable of arousing fetishism. In summary, he says that " fetishism is based on a conscious or unconscious associative absorption of sensual perception that is in accord with the individual's psycho-sexual constitution."

Freud's[9] views may be briefly, and no doubt inadequately, summarized as follows. A fetish object is a substitute for the woman's (mother's) phallus in which the boy once believed. It remains as a triumph over the castration threat, and saves the fetishist from becoming homosexual by endowing women with the attribute which makes them sexually acceptable. The object may, however, symbolize the boy's last impression before the traumatic discovery which it screens from his conscious memory.

Stekel[10] states that fetishism can be totally explained as flight from the woman, and in his experience homosexuality was the end of every case.

It is, he says, a complicated compulsive neurosis giving rise to impulsive, often sadistic, acts carried out in a twilight state and expressed in symbolism which can be interpreted only by psycho-analysis. Stekel stresses the fetishist's pride in being unusual, his psycho-sexual immaturity, his harem cult, and his impulses to exhibitionism.

Karpman[11] states that sadism is the root of fetishism, though sado-masochistic fantasies may not be present. Common to sadism and fetishism are predominance of fantasy life, depreciation of the sexual partner, and incestuous attachment.

Rarity in females—All authorities agree that fetishism is predominantly a male disorder. Krafft-Ebing[7] considered that pathological fetishism had been observed only in men, and Havelock Ellis[8] noted the " great rarity of fully developed fetishism in women " but thought that slight degrees might occur. Stekel[10] stated that it was " generally a male disease," and Fenichel[12] that it was " very rare " in women. Kinsey *et al.*[13] state that it is " an almost exclusively male phenomenon." Of 7,789 females, they reported only two or three who were regularly aroused by objects not directly connected with sexual activity.

Fetishism in homosexuality—East[14] states that fetishism is not confined to heterosexuals, for in rare cases it is associated with homosexuality. Thoinot and Weysse[15] recorded the case of a male homosexual fetishist who was erotically excited by contemplating the patent-leather shoes of other men.

Frequency as a primary medical problem—In a series of 4,000 patients seen in private practice, Curran[16] found only five cases in which fetishism was the *primary* problem. None of these was on a charge.

Frequency as a legal problem—Fetishism, according to East,[14] is seen infrequently in the criminal courts. It is also quite rare in divorce proceedings (R. Ormerod, 1956, personal communication).

Treatment—Despite the wealth of descriptive case reports, very little has been said about the treatment of fetishism. A search of the literature has revealed only three cases in which successful treatment was claimed.

(1) A case seen by Krafft-Ebing is referred to by Hirschfeld[1] as " one of those rare cases in the literature of sexual pathology in which a therapeutic success has been achieved." The patient was a limp fetishist who, after he married an understanding woman, was " educated " by his wife and eventually cured of his fetishism.

(2) Romm,[2] in a notable case report, states that after 662 hours of analysis over six years, the patient (a hair fetishist) achieved a genital relationship with his wife. In the social and business spheres he became much more effective. On rare occasions, when under environmental stress, he had fetishistic fantasies but with no impulses to action. He retained a more than usual interest in his wife's hairdress.

21

(3) Mitchell, Falconer and Hill[3] reported a case of temporal lobe epilepsy in which the viewing of a fetish object precipitated seizures. Relief of both the epilepsy and the fetishism followed temporal lobectomy.

DISCUSSION

To use aversion therapy in treating this patient seemed a logical approach if one believed that the results obtained in alcoholism are not dependent upon the specific biochemical changes produced by any drug but upon the establishment of a conditioned response. The fetishist's predisposition propounded by Binet as a general nervous hyperaesthesia may well be expressed as an unusual capacity for forming conditioned responses, and this capacity might prove as great an asset in treatment as it was a liability when the fetish was formed. To use nausea and vomiting as a means of producing the aversion was clearly less appropriate than in alcoholism, but familiarity with the procedure, the ease of administration, and reluctance to use other available stimuli favoured its use. Also the modification of attitudes and psychological conversions are more easily obtained in states of exhaustion and hunger, and from that point of view the technique was suitable.

It was thought that should aversion be successfully established there might be some risk that impotence would ensue. According to Freud's[9] view, overt homosexuality might emerge if the protective fetish objects were removed; while Stekel's[10] experience suggested that this would happen anyway. East and Hubert[4] stress the danger of changing a sexual fetish into strong homosexual or sadistic drives by treatment. So far none of these eventualities has arisen.

Romm's case is interesting because apparently the impulses to aggressive action disappeared or were controlled, although unusual interest in what had been the fetish object still remained, and was even occasionally used in fantasies.

Much of what our patient says—for example, that he makes mistakes about perambulators—also indicates that the habits of observation persist to some extent. He insists, however, that observation is more casual and that sexual stimulation never occurs as a result.

SUMMARY

A report is given of a case of fetishism believed to be unique in that the patient responded favourably to aversion therapy. A brief review of the literature is given and discussed in relation to the treatment of this case. It is suggested that the predisposition to fetishism, first discussed by Binet, may lie in an unusual capacity to form conditioned responses, and that this capacity may be used as an asset in treatment.

REFERENCES

1. HIRSCHFELD, M. (1939). *Sexual Anomalies and Perversions.* London.
2. ROMM, M. E. (1949). *Psychoanal. Quart.*, **18**, 137.
3. MITCHELL, W., FALCONER, M. A. and HILL, D. (1954). *Lancet*, **2**, 626.
4. EAST, W. NORWOOD and HUBERT, W. H. de B. (1939). *The Psychological Treatment of Crime.* H.M.S.O., London.
5. DESCARTES, R. (1649). *Les Passions de l'Ame* (CXXXVI).
6. BINET, A. (1888). *Etudes de Psychologie Expérimentale.* Paris.
7. KRAFFT-EBING, R. VON (1939). *Psychopathia Sexualis: A Medico-Forensic Study.* London.
8. ELLIS, H. (1906). *Studies in the Psychology of Sex*, vol. 5. Philadelphia.
9. FREUD, S. (1928). *Int. J. Psycho-anal.*, **9**, 161.
10. STEKEL, W. (1930). *Sexual Aberrations: The Phenomenon of Fetishism in Relation to Sex*, vols. 1 and 2. London.
11. KARPMAN, B. (1934). *Arch. Neurol. Psychiat.* (*Chicago*), **32**, 577.
12. FENICHEL, O. (1945). *The Psychoanalytical Theory of Neurosis.* New York.
13. KINSEY, A. C., POMEROY, W. B., MARTIN, C. E. and GEBHARD, P. H. (1953). *Sexual Behaviour in the Female.* Philadelphia and London.
14. EAST, W. NORWOOD (1949). *Society and the Criminal.* H.M.S.O., London.
15. THOINOT, L. H. and WEYSSE, A. W. (1920). *Medico-Legal Aspects of Moral Offences.* Philadelphia.
16. CURRAN, D. (1954). *Practitioner*, **172**, 440.

SOME PROBLEMS IN THE TREATMENT OF HOMOSEXUALITY

K. FREUND

Psychiatric Clinic, Karls University, Prague*

INTRODUCTION

ALL ATTEMPTS to determine whether any of the methods of treatment applied to cases of homosexuality† do have a therapeutic effect, suffer from the fact that the diagnosis of pathological erotic adjustment relies almost exclusively on verbal exploration. This fact is particularly disturbing in the therapeutic situation where the patients are inclined to deny certain facts in order to appear as cured and therefore to avoid any further treatment, which is often regarded as undesirable by them. On the whole, there does not appear to be any method of treatment the efficacy of which could be said to be very apparent and the proportion of cases of homosexuality where—with or without treatment—heterosexual adaptation is reached appears to be very small.

In order to make a systematic comparison of the number of " cures " following upon a particular method of treatment, and that arising in an untreated group of homosexuals, we would of necessity have to use a rather unreliable and purely clinical criterion; it would follow that the number of persons in the various groups would have to be rather large. Such a comparison would not appear very useful at the present time. It may, however, be useful even at the present early stage to look at a few important problems in this connection. In the first place there is the question of the success of psychotherapeutic treatment and the kind of heterosexual adaptation which may be achieved. In the second place the question arises as to whether, supposing a certain degree of success were to be discovered in psychotherapeutic procedures, this would be reducible to a particular common cause. In the third place an attempt may be made to discover prognostic signs which may throw some light on the probability of achieving

---

* This paper appeared under the title: Sobre el problema del tratamiento de la homosexualidad in the (1958) *Acta Neuropsiquiátrica Argentina*, **4**, No. 3, pp. 233-247. It has been abridged and translated by the editor. As the original publication itself was a translation which showed signs of misunderstandings and downright errors, Dr. Freund's help in clarifying certain points was sought, and the editor is much indebted to him for his kind co-operation.

† As usual, we shall denote as homosexual only those persons whose sexual desires are related exclusively or almost exclusively to persons of the same sex.

heterosexual adaptation. We shall begin with a short review of those methods of treatment which have been recommended in cases of homosexuality. These may be divided into three groups: the use of hormones, the use of various psychiatric methods and the use of psychotherapy.

THERAPY BY MEANS OF HORMONE TREATMENT

Work of this type was begun by Steinach and Lichtenstern.[1] Their claims for successful treatment were contradicted by several other authors who reported failure,[2] although Pfeiffer[3] has also reported an isolated success. In all these cases treatment consisted of the replacement of diseased glands by healthy ones.

Later types of treatment involving the injection of male hormones failed to show favourable results; indeed they often produced a deterioration of the patient's situation because these hormones as administered to homosexual men influenced the *strength* of the drive but not its *direction*. Only Lurie[4] and Myerson and Neustadt[5] believe in the efficacy of hormone therapy.

PSYCHIATRIC METHODS OF TREATMENT

An attempt to use electroshock has been reported by Thompson,[6] but no success was recorded with any of his 6 patients. Owensby[7] claims to have treated 6 homosexuals successfully by means of shock treatment, and Meduna[8] claims to have achieved very good results with some homosexuals through the use of his method of carbon dioxide inhalation.

PSYCHOTHERAPY*

Among older authors, such as Schrenck-Notzing, Forel, Krafft-Ebing (1924), Fuchs, Frey,[9] and many others, hypnosis and suggestion are considered the most appropriate treatments for homosexuality. Fuchs,[10] Frey, and others have published a series of cases which they consider cured. On the other hand, Diethelm[11],p.458 claims never to have seen a single case of homosexuality which was cured by hypnosis, and Allen[12] who prefers psychoanalytic methods, claims that neither hypnosis nor suggestion are of any use in well defined cases of psychosexual aberration.

Moll[13,14,15] reports on a series of therapeutic successes in a large number of quite different sexual aberrations by means of "Assoziations-therapie." This "consists in the appropriate directing of the patient's imagination, and in the methodical advancement of the *normal*, and the methodical suppression of *perverted* associations". For this purpose he advocates persuasion, the use of erotic literature, and similar types of pictorial material.

* This term is used here as covering every therapeutic treatment which does not depend on chemical or physical methods, regardless of whether verbal or non-verbal methods are being used.

Kronfeld[2] reports failure of these methods in contradiction to Moll. Bechterev[16] recommends " distraction therapy,"* in which he uses hypnosis and suggestion as well as persuasion.

A number of psychoanalytic writers claim to have treated cases of homosexuality with good success, although Freud (1920) himself did not make any great claims for his methods. Among authors who have claimed successes are Sadger,[17] Stekel,[18,19] Serog,[20] Ellis,[21,22] and Allen.[12,23] Hadden[24] reports success with a patient who took part in a group therapeutic type of treatment. Kronfeld[2] comments on the other hand: " I know over a dozen homosexuals who have been treated for years by well-known experts in the field of psychoanalysis and who have shown no change whatsoever "; he claims never to have seen any successes with this type of treatment.

The descriptions given by psychotherapists of their successes are not usually very precise. In the majority of cases they simply consist of the statement that the patient has overcome his homosexual desires, is capable of heterosexual intercourse, has married, and other statements of a similar kind. In other cases the behaviour of the patient before treatment is described in so little detail that it is not always clear whether he was in fact homosexual or not. Reports covering months, or even years of careful interview material are only given in the most exceptional cases.

Considering the optimistic reports of psychotherapists working with a great number of quite different methods, it is noteworthy that many authors, and among them the greatest experts in the field, manifest the greatest doubts as to the curability of homosexuality altogether. Hirschfeld[25] claims that he has not seen any cure in any one of the 15,000 cases seen by him. Later[26] he corrects this remark to read that " only in the most exceptional cases " was a change-over to heterosexual behaviour noted. According to Havelock Ellis[27] it is possible for a homosexual man to have heterosexual intercourse but not to fall in love with a woman. Curran[28,29] compared 25 homosexuals who received psychotherapeutic treatment with a similar number of homosexuals who received no treatment; he found that the treatment cases showed neither a better control nor a lessened intensity of their homosexual tendencies than did the cases receiving no treatment. It is noteworthy that the follow-up period in this case averaged between 4 and 5 years. Harris (1948) is of the opinion that only in cases of bisexuality is therapy of any use.

A careful reading of the literature quoted gives one the impression that the cause of these apparent contradictions lies not so much in the *facts* as rather in the *evaluation* of these facts. This is most apparent when we consider the criteria of therapeutic success as used by psychotherapists.

---

* Quite obviously it is essential to make efforts to weaken the disordered drive. In doing so one of the most useful means appears to be weakening of the concentration or else a distraction of the attention of the disordered person from the object of his perverted drive.

The major criterion of success appears to be a change in the sexual behaviour of the patient; a homosexual is regarded as cured when he gives up homosexual practices and succeeds in initiating heterosexual conduct. Complete heterosexuality is regarded by many of the psychoanalytic authors (Stekel, Ellis) as an artefact inherent in our type of civilization; as such they do not even consider it desirable to lead homosexual patients to an exclusively heterosexual type of adjustment. Thus the optimal effects claimed and described by psychotherapists are inevitably rather modest. In those cases in which better results are reported there are always circumstances which throw doubts on the diagnosis either before or after treatment.

BEHAVIOURAL ELEMENTS IN THE
PSYCHOTHERAPY OF HOMOSEXUALS

In comparing the reports of adherents of the various psychotherapeutic schools and their claims of successful treatment of cases of homosexuality, one notices considerable differences between naïvely optimistic publications of authors offering just one publication, the propaganda-type articles of authors returning again and again to the fray and the monographs of the more objective type of therapists. There is, however, no evidence in these writings that there are qualitative or quantitative differences in the heterosexual adaptation of patients submitted to the various psychotherapeutic procedures. There are two possible explanations for this. It is possible that psychotherapy in general is quite ineffective; this is the first alternative. The second is that all psychotherapists make use of the same casual agents in the treatment of homosexuality; from this view the differences between their procedures would then have no relevance to the actual treatment. While the first of these two hypotheses is quite plausible, we will have a look at the plausibility of the second hypothesis. At first sight this might appear superfluous, but it might be useful if we could find certain general features underlying all the different types of psychotherapy. In this way it might be possible to make use of whatever fundamental causal factors might be at work, disregarding accidental features.

Therapists who use hypnosis and suggestion try in every possible way to reinforce the patient's desire to keep away as far as possible from homosexual activity and to enter into heterosexual contacts. At the same time, they try directely to heighten the desirability of heteroerotic objects for the patient and to diminish that of homoerotic objects. In the type of therapy used by Moll, persuasion is used to cause the patient to abstain from homosexual images and behaviour patterns, and at the same time heterosexual images and behaviour patterns are encouraged. As Moll[15] himself says, " this method has many similarities with pedagogy."

While the suggestion is quite plausible that hypnosis and " Assoziationstherapie " obviously share many common features, and therefore presumably make use of similar mechanisms, this does not at first sight appear to be true of the explorative psychotherapeutic types of treatment—at least as long as certain easily overlooked features are not taken into account which occur in the course of these treatments. Most psychoanalysts, including those mentioned above, demand of the patient that during his treatment he should use restraint in his homosexual behaviour and that he should seek the company of members of the other sex. In addition, even psycho-analysts of the classical school seldom succeed in remaining so neutral that the patient fails to get the impression that the therapist is very much concerned to change his behaviour in a heterosexual direction, and in consequence of the transference which the patient develops for the therapist, we may here be dealing with causal that mechanism which we discovered in the types of therapy not making use of explorative treatment. Already in 1911 Moll[13] suggested some such hypothesis when he referred to " suggestion " as the underlying causal element in psychoanalytic treatment of homosexuality.

In view of these considerations, it is not impossible that psychotherapy, in so far as it has any therapeutic effect in cases of homosexuality, owes its success to this particular causal feature which we have isolated in spite of the different modifications encountered in the different types of treatment. To repeat, this causal element is to be found in the *encouragement of behaviour patterns which emphasize restraint or complete abstinence from homosexual behaviour, and which involve heterosexual behaviour.* In addition, it is likely that there is some efficacy in the attempts to devaluate homoerotic desires and associations and to encourage and reward heteroerotic desires and associations.

THERAPEUTIC EXPERIMENTS

If we are correct in assuming that the effect of psychotherapy is not related to systematic verbal exploration, dynamic exploration, abreaction, etc. then we may be justified on a neuristic basis in introducing a behavioural type of therapy which, as far as one can tell, contains the above mentioned causal curative element.[30] We shall compare the effects of this treatment with those reported by other psychotherapists. If conduct shows that no very marked qualitative or quantitative differences between these treatments exist, this may be interpreted either as evidence for the uselessness of psychotherapy altogether, or for the efficacy of the causal element mentioned.

The experimental procedure relies in the main on those methods which have been used particularly in the aversion treatment of alcoholics. It has been used entirely with male patients because very few homosexual women were sent for treatment, none of whom expressed any desire for a cure. Of those male patients sent to us, none were refused treatment.

Treatment consisted in the administration to the patient of an emetic mixture* by subcutaneous injection. When the emetic mixture became effective and as long as the effects lasted, slides of dressed and undressed men were shown to the patient. This constitutes the first or aversion part of the treatment. During the second phase of the treatment the patient was shown films of nude or semi-nude women; these were shown approximately 7 hr after the patient had been administered 10 mg of *testosteronum propionicum*. Our choice of this method of conditioned reflex therapy rests on the assumption that it could be shown that in this way a greater diminution of the valency of the socially unacceptable object and the heightening of the valency of the socially acceptable object could be produced than by any other psychotherapeutic measure.

This procedure was only used on patients whose erotic desires were exclusively or almost exclusively directed towards homosexual experiences and who either were completely incapable of heterosexual behaviour or in whom in any case the frequency of heterosexual behaviour was less than that of homosexual behaviour. Heterosexual adaptation was diagnosed where in such a patient erotic behaviour had changed to such an extent that heterosexual intercourse was far more frequent than homosexual intercourse (information was derived from the patient's own report in so far as this was not contradicted by other information). In consideration of the lack of reliability of the diagnosis of erotic tendencies, we only included those patients in the experiment who had undergone cure in the years 1950–1953, so that a follow-up of at least 3 years would be available for all patients. This follow-up was undertaken in June, 1956; another follow-up was undertaken up to a further two years in May and June of 1958.†

Of the 67 patients treated altogether, a sub-group of 20 had dealings with the police, the magistrates or other official agencies because of their homosexual behaviour. In some of these cases complaints had been withdrawn or punishment delayed in order to make it possible for the patient to undergo medical treatment. In other cases the patient asked to be treated because he hoped in this way to avoid punishment. Only 3 people in this group achieved any kind of heterosexual adaptation and in no case did this continue for more than a few weeks. The same is true of 9 patients who underwent treatment because of unrequited homosexual love. (Three of these reported suicidal tendencies.) Seven homosexual patients were sent or brought by their relatives. One of these is possibly the best adapted patient in the whole group (A); at the time when he first came to our attention he was only 14 years old. In spite of this it is improbable that it is a question

---

* During the first 5 applications a mixture of emetine and apomorphine was administered; after that caffein with apomorphine. Treatment was administered every day but the number of treatments never exceeded 24.

† Subjects who underwent less than 5 treatments were excluded from the follow-up.

of one of those not infrequent homosexual episodes which occur at this age. Another patient who also belongs to this group was 17 years old at the time of treatment. He could not be followed up properly so that although he claims to be perfectly heterosexual, his true state cannot be evaluated.

A fourth group is formed by those patients who claimed to desire treatment in order to escape from the undesirable social position of homosexuals and to be able to marry and start a family. Five of these reached heterosexual adaptation of short duration, ranging from several weeks to several months. The final state of three further patients is not sufficiently known to be evaluated; they claim to be well adapted heterosexually. Nine further persons in this group (A, B, D, E, G—M) who reached good adaptation immediately following treatment had not returned at the time of the last follow-up to homosexual practices. The state of one further patient (C) who achieved heterosexual intercourse for the first time at the end of the second course of treatment, and who reached complete heterosexual adaptation 6 months later, could not be ascertained after June, 1956. Patient (F) remained well adapted for 18 months, but deteriorated from then on until by the end of 1956 his behaviour was almost completely homosexual. Table 1 shows for the four groups of patients, the proportion of successful heterosexual adaptation as ascertained in our follow-up procedures.

TABLE 1

	Sent by police, magistrates etc.*	Unrequited homo-sexual love	Sent by relatives	No obvious external pressure	Total	Pro-portion
No improvement	17	7	5	12	24	51·1%
Short-term heterosexual adaptation	3	2	0	5	7	14·9%
Adaptation lasting for several years	0	0	1	11	12	25·5%
Outcome not sufficiently documented	0	0	1	3	4	8·5%
Total:	20	9	7	31	47	100%

* Not included in calculations in last column.

Table 2 contains a brief summary of the erotic desires and behaviour pattern of those 12 persons who reached relatively long continued heterosexual adaptation. The first row gives the identification of the patient by letter. In the second row is given the age of the patient at the beginning of treatment, and in the third row, month and year of treatment. In the other rows, Nos. 4–8 relate to the state of the patient before treatment, and Rows 9–15 to his behaviour afterwards. Row 4 shows whether the patient ever felt any excitement following bodily contact with a woman (+) or not (−), or whether such contact was never achieved (0). Row 5 shows whether before treatment any heterosexual desires had ever occurred (+) or not (−). Row 6 shows how frequently the patient tried to have intercourse with a woman with (+) or without success (−). When more than 20 attempts at intercourse were made (++) is noted; (0) designates no attempt at all. In the seventh row a (+) shows that the patient was married; (−) that he was single. Row 8 shows whether he reported regular homosexual affairs (++), frequent homosexual intercourse without personal feeling (+), sporadic homosexual intercourse (no.), or whether such intercourse had hitherto not taken place at all (0). Row 9 shows whether patients unmarried before treatment, married afterwards (+) or not (−); the issue of children from such marriages is recorded in Row 10 (pregnancy of the wife is also indicated by a (+) sign). The happiness of the marriage is rated by the patient in Row 11 as happy (+), unhappy (−), or impossible to decide (+−). Row 12 gives details of frequency of heterosexual intercourse; (++) indicates twice weekly, (+) denotes at least once a fortnight, and (+−) denotes at least once in two months. Row 13 shows whether since treatment other women have also called forth sexual desires (+); whether these have been directed entirely to the wife (+−) or whether desire for intercourse has not been clearly homosexual, although never becoming quite heterosexual (−). Row 14 shows whether homoerotic desires have appeared frequently (+), occasionally (+−) or never (0). Row 15 shows how often after treatment homosexual intercourse has taken place.

The following summary could be made of the heterosexual adaptation of these 12 patients in June, 1956. In 3 patients (a, b and l) there is an occasional desire for heterosexual intercourse with women other than the wife. Only one of these (l) claims to have no more homoerotic desires. Four other patients report that their wives have some degree of erotic attraction for them, even outside the intercourse situation, but that other women do not have any sexual attraction for them at all. Five patients have no further heterosexual desires. In all of these heterosexually adapted homosexuals the intensity of homoerotic desires admittedly overbalances that of heteroerotic desires, although some patients claim that homoerotic desires only occur infrequently.

At the time of the second follow-up there was a complete recidivism for 1 patient (f) and another one could not be traced (c). Of the remaining patients, years of follow-up since treatment were as follows: one (m) 4 years, two (j and k) 5 years, four (a, d, e and h) 6 years, three (b, g and l) 7 years.

TABLE 2

	a	b	c	d	e	f	g	h	j	k	l	m
2	14	24	22	33	21	28	28	27	29	31	24	22
3	I–III, 52	VIII–X, 51	VIII–XI, 51 I–V 53	V–VII, XII, 52	VI–VII– IX–X, 52	II–IV, 52	XI, 50 II, 51	II–VII, XII, 52	V–VII, 53	IV–VI, 52	IX, 50 II, 51 V–VII, 51 I–II, 54	VIII–X, 51 III–V 54
4	+	+	−	+	+	+	+	+	−	+	+	−
5	−	−	−	+/−	−	−	+/−	−	−	−	+/−	−
6	0	+1x	0	+1x	++	++	++	0	−5x	++	−1x	−5x
7	−	−	−	−	−	+	−	−	+	+	−	−
8	+	++	++	+	++	++	++	++	1x	++	0	1x
9	+	+	+	+	+	/	+	+	/	−	+	+
10	+/−	+	+/−	+	+	−	−	+	+	−	+	+/−
11	+	++	++	++	++	+	+/−	+	+	−	+	+
12	++	++	++	++	++	−	+/−	++	+	+/−	++	+
13	+	+	+/−	+/−	−	+	+/−	−	−	+/−	+	−
14	+/−	+	+	+	+/−	+	+/−	+	+	+/−	−	+
15	0	0	very frequently until 1953	once a week	0	once every 10 days	3x	1x	0	3x	0	0

Patient *l* who, except for one homosexual episode in 1954 had claimed throughout to be entirely heterosexually adjusted, demanded at the beginning of 1958 to receive further treatment because of renewed homosexual tendencies. He was admitted to hospital and treated for 3 months by means of hypnosis; at the end of this period he claimed to have no further homoerotic desires. He never had any actual homosexual intercourse at any time. His testimony, as well as that of his wife, confirms that they have intercourse at least once a fortnight, and usually once a week. Both consider their marriage as happy in spite of impossible living conditions. They have 2 children.

Patient *j* had a relapse about the same time because he fell in love with a colleague and became impotent with his wife to whom he had been married for 6 years. After treatment by hypnosis he claimed not to be tied to his colleague any more, with whom he had indulged in mutual masturbation, and to be capable of heterosexual intercourse again. According to both him and his wife, it appears that they have intercourse at least once a fortnight and that both are content in their marriage. The wife is ignorant of the maladjustment of her husband.

Patient *a* has had promiscuous relations with women since he left treatment, but claims to have homosexual as well as heterosexual desires. In 1954 he took up a lasting sexual relationship with a girl of the same age whom he married 18 months later because she was pregnant. Both claimed to be happily married and well adjusted. In 1958 this patient had to undergo his military service and appeared as a soldier for investigation in the same year. He now claims, in contradiction to his previous statements, always to have been orientated in a purely homosexual way and never to have enjoyed heterosexual intercourse. He also states that his wife complained that he did not care for her, that he did not make love to her, etc. The wife herself, although she had told her husband that she would not be available for questioning, did turn up in spite of difficulties, and was interrogated on these points. Since the birth of her child she suffers from an endocrine disorder, has added 5 stones to her weight, has ceased to menstruate and has lost her sexual desire to the extent that she does not enjoy intercourse any more. She claims that her husband gets very annoyed at her refusal to have intercourse very frequently and that he demands such intercourse particularly urgently now that he is on furlough. She further claims that they are very happily married and that they hardly ever quarrel. She does not take her husband's statements regarding his homosexual desires very seriously, although he has told her about them occasionally. The patient himself claims never to have had any homosexual intercourse since the termination of therapy.

Patient *b* divorced his wife, to whom he had been married for 3 years, because his wife, who had previously been a prostitute, relapsed in this respect. Very shortly after this he married again. Both he and his wife agree that they have intercourse about once a week, although occasionally as long as 3 weeks may elapse from one occasion to another. During the last year, the patient has fallen in love with a perfectly normal man; he has succeeded three times in getting this man drunk and in embracing and kissing him in this state. From this time onwards there has been a good deal of quarrelling between husband and wife, although until then the marriage was satisfactory. The patient does not leave his wife mainly because of the children. She is still in love with him although she is fully aware of the state of things.

Patient *d* claims to have been happily married over a period of 6 years, but insists that his wife should not come into contact with us (while he was being treated and before she married him she had paid him regular visits at the hospital). His reasons are that she always got very excited when he spoke of his homosexual tendencies and conflicts so that he ceased to discuss them with her; he thought that she would interpret the discussion with a physician at the clinic as a sign that his problem had become more serious. Intercourse takes place about twice weekly and they have 2 children. The patient has homosexual intercourse about once every 10 days.

Patient *e* was under treatment until 1957 and was happily married, with 2 children, according to his own statements. Neither his wife nor his family were aware of his sexual problems and he was constantly worried that our investigations would let the cat out of the bag; consequently we were never able to discuss this case with his wife.

Patient *g*, who has been married for 7 years, has intercourse with his wife every fortnight or three weeks; they have one child. Although they quarrel quite frequently, they nevertheless are very close to each other. Since 1956 there has been homosexual intercourse on three occasions. It was impossible to interview the wife of the patient because of the great distances involved.

Patient *h* has been married for 5 years and the marriage is a very happy one, according to both partners. They have 2 children, and intercourse occurs two or three times weekly. This patient has only had homosexual intercourse once. He tells his wife everything about his inner conflicts and his abnormal sexual desires and she helps him to overcome these.

Patient *k* has been married for 9 years. He claims to be quite happy in his marriage, although he and his wife have small quarrels quite frequently. They have intercourse about once a fortnight. His homosexual activity has increased since 1956 and he has homosexual intercourse at about the same frequency. The wife is emotionally very much tied to her husband; she claims that the marriage is a very happy one and praises his good qualities. According to her, intercourse does not take place more frequently than once a month.

Patient *m* has been married for 3 years and the marriage was very happy for the first two years. Even now, there is no quarrelling between husband and wife although the patient has been in love with another male for the last ten months, and has lost interest in his wife. Homosexual intercourse occurs once every 10 days, and intercourse with his wife about once or twice a week. The wife knows about her husband's troubles but it was impossible to interview her personally because of the great distances involved. There is one child of this marriage.

Of the 10 patients followed up, 8 are at present so well adapted heterosexually that they have heterosexual intercourse exclusively or preponderantly; up to a point they are satisfied with this. Except for patient *l*, however, they all claim that their motivation is still almost exclusively homosexual. Six of them had no homosexual intercourse until 1956, the others had such intercourse only sporadically. In 1958, only three claimed not to have had any homosexual intercourse since treatment. In nearly all patients there is a slow increase of homosexual activity. Only one patient (*a*) claimed to have been really in love with his wife, and he took back this statement in 1958. Only he and patient *l* claimed predominantly heterosexual motivation, but this statement was disclaimed later by *a*, and in the case of *l* there has since been a relapse on 2 occasions.

The heterosexual adaptation of the whole group appears to consist mainly in the fact that the patients have learnt to have intercourse without previous stimulation by the (for them) specific erotic object; this may be the reason why for some of them homosexual intercourse has become more infrequent. One should not overlook, however, the fact that even before treatment 2 patients had become adapted to heterosexual intercourse, one of them the now entirely relapsed patient *l*. (These 2 patients had undergone treatment because of relapses lasting for at least 6 months.)

A comparison of the cases of heterosexual adaptation described here with those described in connection with other types of psychotherapy, is very difficult. Attention has already been drawn to the weaknesses of the existing diagnostic techniques and the consequent inaccuracies in the description of behaviour before as well as after therapy. Another cause of difficulty is the lack of control in the choice of patient. It is probable that most of the patients would not have come for treatment if their efforts at heterosexual adjustment had been successful. Particularly difficult is a comparison of the degrees of disagreeability of treatment consequent upon the different therapeutic procedures, a comparison which is particularly important for the judgment of the motivation of patients. In most of the cases described in the literature, these disadvantages are perhaps mainly of a financial kind. This would not apply to the treatment discussed here because patients were accepted without paying in the hospital, but on the other hand this type of treatment is probably much more disagreeable than any kind of psychotherapy.

We can be fairly certain, however, that those therapists whose descriptions of the success of treatment are encountered in the literature have not dealt with homosexuals sent by the police or other official bodies, and consequently it seemed appropriate to leave out of account in any comparison this group of 20 people. (Accordingly this group has not been included in computing the outcome of treatment recorded in Table 1.) In addition, it should be remembered that because of the unreliability of diagnosis, the length of observation of the patient after the end of treatment is of considerable importance for the accuracy of the determination of his state and the motivation which has led him to treatment; such follow-up observations are much more difficult in the case of patients of this type.

Taking into account all the possible sources of error mentioned, we find on a rough actuarial comparison between cases described here and those described by orthodox psychotherapists in connection with typical psychotherapeutic treatment, that *there are no obvious differences either in the quality or the degree of therapeutic success* of these treatments in so far as such success can be ascertained through the rough and ready clinical methods used. This finding supports the hypothesis that in so far as psychotherapy is effective in cases of homosexuality, this effectiveness depends on the common causal agent already discussed previously.

SUMMARY AND CONCLUSIONS

Hitherto, there has been no proof of the efficacy of any form of treatment as applied to homosexuals. Nevertheless, there appears to be an important distinction between the traditional biochemical and physical methods on the one hand, and the various psychotherapeutic procedures on the other. Successes claimed by writers using biochemical and physical types of treatments have never been verified by later authors, so that the uselessness of these methods appears fairly obvious. Claims of improvements and cures obtained by psychotherapeutic procedures, however, have been verified in a number of cases. The question of the correctness of these claims must therefore still be regarded as open. A comparison of the efficacy of the different psychotherapeutic procedures would be a very ambitious undertaking, and before planning such an experiment an effort was made to estimate the optimal success of such procedures, excepting, of course, occasional special cases. It became apparent that this optimum effect in its poverty was identical or nearly identical with those post-treatment states which had led some of the best known experts in this field to claim that psychotherapy in the case of homosexuality was useless. It follows from this that a control of the efficacy of the various relevant methods of treatment was very much less important than a revision of the therapeutic orientation.

It appeared probable that *all the therapeutic measures considered to be efficacious in the case of homosexuality depended on a common principle.* This principle consists of the *discouragement of homosexual activities* and the *encouragement of heterosexual activities*. (It is also possible that we should add to this the method of devaluating homoerotic desires and to encourage heterosexual desires, in so far as desires can be separated from actual behaviour.) This assumption was strengthened by the fact that there appeared neither very strong qualitative nor quantitative differences between the outcomes of treatments relying on non-verbal, non-explorative psychotherapeutic procedures, and those of a psychoanalytic type. This served as justification to carry out a treatment of homosexuality and to attempt to discover its efficacy, which in simplified form represented the main principle of therapeutic effectiveness previously isolated. It has been shown that the efficacy of this simplified treatment does not appear to be very different from that of other types of treatment of a psychotherapeutic nature.

REFERENCES

1. STEINACH, E. and LICHTENSTERN, R. (1915). Umstimmung der Homosexualität durch Austausch der Pubertätsdrüsen. *Wiener Med. Wchnschr.*, **65,** 145-148.
2. KRONFELD, A. (1923). *Sexualpathologie*. Deuticke.
3. PFEIFFER, E. (1922). Ein geheilter Fall von Homosexualität durch Hodentransplantation. *Deutsche Med. Wchnschr.*, **48,** 660-662, zitiert nach: *Deutsch Ztschr. ges. gerichtl. Med.*
4. LURIE, E. (1944). The endocrine factors in homosexuality. *Amer. J. Sci.*, **208,** 176, zitiert nach: *J. Clin. Endocrin.* (1945).
5. MYERSON, A. and NEUSTADT, R. (1946). Essential male homosexuality and results of treatment. *Arch. Neurol. Psychiat.*, **55,** 291-293.
6. THOMPSON, G. N. (1949). Electroshock and other therapeutic considerations in sexual psychopathy. *J. Nerv. Ment. Dis.*, **109.**
7. OWENSBY, N. M. (1940). Homosexuality and Lesbianism treated with metrazol. *J. Nerv. Dis.*, **92,** 64-65.
8. MEDUNA, L. J. (1950). Clinical and biochemical indications of the convulsive and of the carbon dioxide treatments. Im Sammelband: *Congres International de Psychitrie*. Paris.
9. FREY, E. (1931). Beitrag zur Frage der Behandlung und Heilbar keit der Homosexualität. *Arch. Neurol. Psychiat.*, **28,** 100-125.
10. FUCHS, A. (1926). *Die konträre Sexualempfindung*. Wien.
11. DIETHELM, O. (1950). *Treatment in Psychiatry*. New York.
12. ALLEN, C. (1940). *The Sexual Perversions and Abnormalities*. London.
13. MOLL, A. (1911). Die Behandlung sexueller Perversionen, mit besonderer Berucksichtigung der Assoziations therapie. *Ztschr. für Psychotherapie und Med. Psychologie*, **3,** 3-29.
14. MOLL, A. (1912). *Handbuch der Sexualwissenschaften*. Leipzig.
15. KRAFFT-EBING, R. and MOLL, A. (1924). *Psychopathia Sexualis*. Stuttgart.
16. BECHTEREV, V. (1925). Ueber die Behandlung der krankhaften Triebe und Zwangszuständemit Neuerziehung und Ablenkungstherapie. *Z. ges. Neurol. Psychiat.*, **94,** 237-247.
17. SADGER, J. (1921). *Die Lehre von den Geschlechtsverirrungen*, Wien.
18. STEKEL, W. (1923). *Onanie und Homosexualität*. Wien.
19. STEKEL, W. (1929). Ist Homosexualität heilbar? *Nervenarzt*, 2. Jhrg., 337-343.
20. SEROG, M. (1931). Analyse eines Homosexuellen. *Zentralbl. f. Psychotherap.*, **4,** 750-771.
21. ELLIS, A. (1952). On the cure of homosexuality. *Internat. J. Sex.*, **5,** 136-138.

22. ELLIS, A. (1956). The effectiveness of psychotherapy with individuals who have severe homosexual problems. *J, Con. Psychol.*, **20**, 191-195.
23. ALLEN, C. (1952). On the cure of homosexuality. *Internat. J. Sex.*, **5**, 139-142.
24. HADDEN, S. B. (1958). Treatment of homosexuality in individual and group psychotherapy. *Amer. J. Psychiat.*, **114**, 810-815.
25. HIRSCHFELD, M. (1918). Ist die Homosexualität korperlich oder seelisch medingt? *München Med. Wchschr.*, **65**, 289-300.
26. HIRSCHFELD, M. (1929). Ist die Homosexualität heilbar? *Nervenarzt*, 2. Jhrg., 713-714.
27. ELLIS, H. (1950). *Studies in the Psychology of Sex.* London (orig. 1950).
28. CURRAN, D. (1947). Sexual perversions and their treatment. *Practitioner*, **158**, 343-348.
29. CURRAN, D. and PARR, D. (1957). Homosexuality: An analysis of 100 male cases seen in private practice. *Brit. Med. J.*, **1**, 797-801.
30. FREUND, K. and SRNEC, J. (1953). K otázce mužské homosexuality, analyse změn sexuální apetence během léčby podminováním. Sborník lékarsky., **55**, 125-184.
31. EAST, N. (1950). Delinquency and crime. In: *Recent Progress in Psychiatry* (Ed. by Fleming, G. W. T. H.). Churchill, London.
32. FERENCZI, P. S. (1927). Bausteine zur Psychoanalyse. Zur Nosologie der Homosexualität. **I**, I.P.V. (orig. 1911).
33. FREUD, S. (1920). *Ueber die Psychogenese eines Falles von weiblicher Homosexualität.*
34. FREUND, K. (1957). Otázka pohlavní úchylnosti s hlediska sociálního. Problémy Psychiatrie V Praxi a Ve Vyzkumu. Prague.
35. GIESE, H. (1955-56). Therapie der Homosexualität. *Therapiewoche*, **6**, 85-88.
36. GOLLA, F. L. and HODGE, R. S. (1949). Hormone treatment of sexual offenders. *Lancet*, **256**, 1006-1007.
37. HADFIELD, J. A. (1958). The cure of homosexuality. *Brit. Med. J.*, **1**, 1323-1326.
38. HARRIS, N. (1948). The importance of constitutional factors. In: *Modern Trends in Psychological Medicine.* London.
39. HYNIE, J. (1950). Několik poznámek k podstatě a therapii homosexuality. *Neurol. a Psychiat.* CSL, **13**, 322-328.
40. NEDOMA, K. (1950). Homosexualita v sexuologické praksi. *Neurologie a Psychiat. CSL*, **13**, 328-334.
41. NEDOMA, K. (1951). Homosexuality in sexological practice. *Internat. S. Sex.*, **4**, 219-224.
42. DUNLAP, K. (1932). *Habits, Their Making and Unmaking.* Liveright, New York.

CONDITIONING TECHNIQUES IN THE TREATMENT OF WRITER'S CRAMP*

L. A. LIVERSEDGE, B.A., B.SC., M.B.(MAN.), M.D.(DUKE), M.R.C.P.

Lecturer in Neurology, University of Manchester

and

J. D. SYLVESTER, M.A.(CAMB.)

Research Assistant, Department of Psychology, University of Manchester

THE TREATMENT of writer's cramp is recognized as most discouraging to patient and therapeutist alike. Though included nosologically with the motor neuroses, writer's cramp has hitherto defied any satisfactory aetiological interpretation in terms acceptable to neurologists, psychiatrists and psychologists.

Culpin[1] and Pai[2] thought that writer's cramp occurred merely as one form of disablement in patients of psychoneurotic constitution, and Glover[3] considered it to be a typical example of conversion hysteria; but Critchley,[4] affirming that writer's cramp constitutes a specific impairment of motor skill, was at pains to point out that " to look upon the craft palsies as problems in psychopathology has not proved satisfying even to psychiatrists."

In a recent neurological and psychological re-examination of 20 cases of writer's cramp, one typist's cramp, and one violinist's cramp (to be reported) we concluded that although some of the patients could be regarded as having psychoneurotic tendencies, many showed no evidence of psychological disorder. Indeed, the pattern of mental and emotional make-up of these patients exhibited the widest possible variations. These observations led us to the tentative conclusion that, whatever the origin of writer's cramp, its persistence might be explained by the establishment of a conditioned reflex. The resemblance between the writing in this condition and that observed in certain types of extrapyramidal disease invites the suggestion that this conditioning takes place at subcortical levels, and the partial benefit conferred by the administration of benzhexol hydrochloride (" Artane ") affords some support for this suggestion. It seemed from the clinical evidence that, although the loss of acquired motor skill represents a reaction to a total situation involving the act of writing, the sensorimotor circuit could be regarded in

* The patients were under the care of Dr. Fergus R. Ferguson, to whom we are further indebted for helpful criticism.

Reprinted by permission of the authors and editor the *Lancet*, from (1955, June) *Lancet*, 1147-1149.

terms of afferent stimulus and motor effect. Close observation of the development of the cramp during the act of writing revealed that it tended to arise when the pen or else the writer's hand touched the writing-surface, and was then intensified by the movements of the fingers and thumb as writing proceeded. The trigger stimulus for the conditioned reflex should then be one or both of the following: (1) tactual stimulus of the pen; and (2) tactual stimulus of the hand touching the writing-surface. The motor effect varies from case to case but tends to have two principal components: (1) a tremor of variable rate and amplitude; and (2) a spasm of the muscles of the hand, forearm, and even the upper arm, variable in its extent and intensity but invariably accompanied by excessive pressure of the thumb upon the pen.

Proceeding on the assumption that a conditioning mechanism is at work we reasoned that it might be possible to disturb the reflex by the administration of a sensory counter-stimulus whenever the motor effect took place. After some tentative efforts with feed-back from needle electrodes placed in the muscles of the fore arm, simpler techniques were evolved to deal with the tremor and the pressure of the thumb on the pen. It was felt that by attacking these primary manifestations of the motor dysfunction we might break down the whole sensorimotor chain.

To date we have completed treatment of 6 patients with writer's cramp* and one with typist's cramp. Two other patients with writer's cramp are still under treatment. It seems appropriate to give in some detail the histories and course of 2 of the patients with writer's cramp and of the one case of typist's cramp. The 2 writer's-cramp cases were selected because one had a definite history of psychiatric abnormality and the other was a man whose history and personality were devoid of recognizable psychological disturbance, and in both cases the disturbance of writing comprised both tremor and spasm. The case of typist's cramp is interesting in illustrating a modification of the technique to suit a particular motor problem where the principal disorder was a flexor spasm of certain fingers.

WRITER'S CRAMP

CASE 1—A female typist, aged 49, an intelligent but anxious woman who in the first interviews concealed many facts of her history, passing herself off as single when in fact she had been married and divorced, and had numerous social and personal disturbances in her life. The evolution of her cramp was at once interesting and complex. She took to book-keeping at the age of 18, and for the next 26 years experienced no trouble with her writing although occupied for 6 hr each day in ledger work. At 41 she took a different post as a typist, but it was only after 3 years of this that she developed severe pain in the right thumb. Tenovaginitis was diagnosed. At this time she had already begun to experience stiffness of the whole hand whenever she tried to do her shorthand; and, after an operation had been done to relieve the tenovaginitis, her shorthand became impossible.

* A further patient has since been treated, a man, aged 53, with writer's cramp of 2 years' duration. Six training sessions produced complete cure, which has been maintained for 1 month to date.

She then became a copy typist. Thereafter any attempt at writing produced the pain, cramp, and tremor. In 1953, when she was 49, even copy typing produced cramp and pain in the muscles of the right hand, arm, and forearm. Soon after, the cramp began to show itself in other similar movements, and when first seen in March, 1954, she had an almost constant spasm of the muscles of the right arm and hand. An attempt to write produced a slow and painful exhibition characteristic of writer's cramp. She had been treated with benzhexol hydrochloride without success, had received extensive courses of various sedatives, and had been advised to give up her work. She had become exceedingly depressed and anxious about her condition but was struggling to perform her duties. She subsequently left her work in June, 1954, and review in August indicated a general increase in her depression and despondency, and the cramp and spasm in the right arm had become continuous.

CASE 2—A male clerk, aged 31, noticed in June, 1952, after 2 years in his present post, which involved writing for 4–6 hours each day, that after writing for 5 min he developed a tired feeling in the hand and forearm with tremor. On his continuing to write his arm rapidly became stiff, his thumb tensed, his hand tended to turn over, and his writing became illegible. Two weeks' holiday did not produce any change, and treatment with phenobarbitone and benzhexol hydrochloride proved unsuccessful. In May, 1953, he improved a little spontaneously in that the cramp tended to develop after a longer interval and his writing was fairly legible. There had been no discernible change in his personal, domestic, or economic circumstances to explain this change. Re-examination in August, 1954, showed that he wrote slowly, stiffly, and with a tremor, but his writing was rather more legible than when he was first seen. There were no abnormal neurological signs, and no other movement was affected.

Methods and Results of Treatment of Writer's Cramp

As already stated, tremor and spasm are the two components of the motor disorder. These were assailed in the following way. For the tremor a metal plate was drilled with 9 holes ranging from $\frac{1}{2}$ to $\frac{1}{8}$ in. in diameter. The patient was required to insert a metal stylo, held as a pen is held, into these holes, working from larger to smaller as each size was successfully negotiated. Electrical circuits were arranged so that, whenever the stylo touched the side of the holes, the patient received a shock passing from palm to dorsum of the *left* hand.

A second piece of training apparatus consisted of strips of insulating tape arranged in straight, curved, and zig-zag patterns upon a metal plate and so disposed as to call for all the fundamental finger and hand movements required in writing. Again circuits were so devised as to produce an electric shock for the patient should he deviate in any way in tracing the lined patterns with a metal stylo.

The third retraining mechanism was an ordinary pen adapted in such a manner that excessive pressure of the writer's thumb would again produce a shock. This device was thus triggered by the spasm component of the disorder, in which severe adduction and flexion of the thumb are so prominent.

CASE 1—Treatment was given on 15 successive days, apart from two omissions for Sundays, each session lasting about 30 min. The first five sessions were occupied with training on the holes and the tapes. Progress was fitful, but at the seventh session all the holes and the tapes were negotiated successfully, the tremor having disappeared. The next three sessions were spent in writing to dictation with the electrified pen. On the thirteenth and fourteenth days writing was almost normal, with no evidence of tremor or spasm. On the fifteenth day she wrote for 15 min without effort and considered herself normal. When last seen 3 months after completion of the course she had maintained the improvement. She has now returned to work after an absence of 3 months. Figure 1 illustrates her writing before and after treatment.

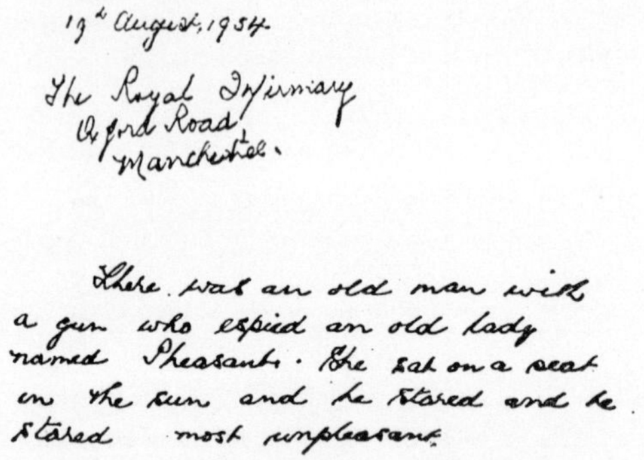

FIG. 1

CASE 2—Tremor was less prominent than spasm in this case. After only two sessions the holes and tapes were overcome, and attention was turned to spasm. In 6 sessions the spasm was abolished and the patient considered himself completely relieved.

Figure 2 illustrates the progress made; it shows in graphic form the frequency per $\frac{1}{2}$ min of the sounds made by the shocking coil during writing in the first, third and fifth of these sessions. It will be noted that on the first occasion the thumb went into continuous spasm after 5 min writing, and that two rest periods did not bring relief. Four months after the end of the treatment this patient is still well and writing normally.

Figure 3 illustrates his writing before and after treatment.

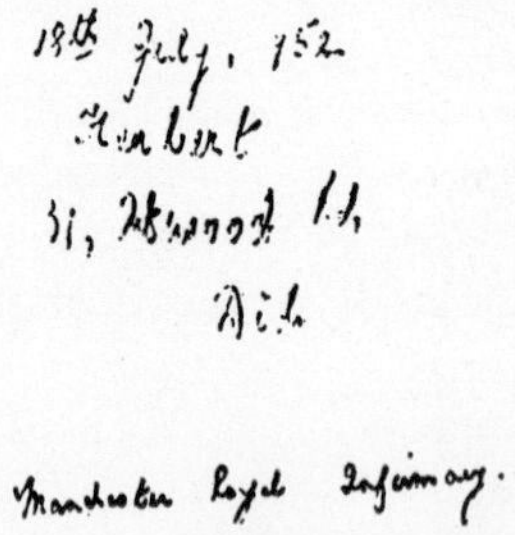

FIG. 3

Cases 3, 4, 5 and 6 were all male, and had had writer's cramp for 3–10 years. After 3–5 weeks' treatment they have shown degrees of improvement which we have estimated as 50–85 per cent of their previous normal. The patient whose performance is estimated at only 50 per cent considered himself cured and asked to discontinue treatment since his writing was now to him quite adequate. In the remaining cases the impairment of function comprises either a slight tremor or a lack of fluidity in the writing, and although one of these patients writes for 7 hr each day in his work as a stockbroker's clerk he does experience some aching in his hand after 3 or 4 hr, and so he has been assessed as an 80 per cent improvement.

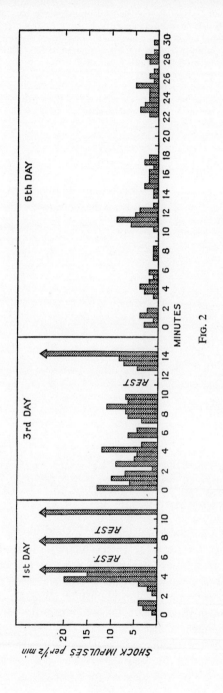

FIG. 2

TYPIST'S CRAMP

CASE 7—A female shorthand-typist, aged 32. In 1949, during a period of domestic stress, and after 13 years as a shorthand-typist in an accountant's office, she began to experience mild cramp in the left hand, accompanied by extension of the left forefinger and adduction of the thumb. After 12 months the other fingers began to flex into the palm. In November, 1951, she was seen at the Royal Infirmary, and psychiatric interviews brought no benefit to her condition. In 1952 she changed her employment, and there was some improvement in her domestic background, though there was still cause for anxiety. Her new work was more responsible and more arduous than her former employment, and in August, 1954, a similar but more painful affection of the right hand developed. After 10 min typing the index finger extended, the thumb adducted, and the remaining fingers flexed into the palm with such force as to produce bleeding if she continued. It was in this state that she returned for further advice.

Treatment and Results

For this case the apparatus was modified so that a small rubber pad was covered with an interweaving pattern of wire connected to the secondary winding of the induction coil.

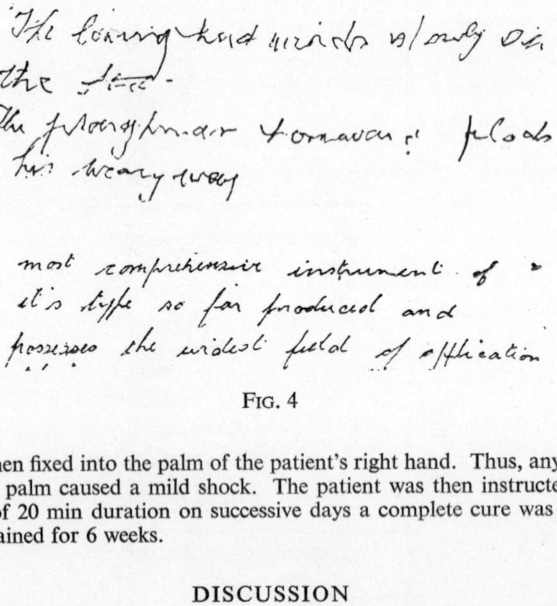

FIG. 4

This pad was then fixed into the palm of the patient's right hand. Thus, any flexion of the fingers into the palm caused a mild shock. The patient was then instructed to type. In three sessions of 20 min duration on successive days a complete cure was achieved, and has been maintained for 6 weeks.

DISCUSSION

Although it is too early to be certain about the long-term effects of treatment, certain preliminary conclusions seem permissible in the light of these experiences. It is encouraging from the clinical point of view to have evolved a means of alleviating a condition which so often has proved intractable. One feels that, in the event of relapse, retraining may be of value, but this remains to be seen. Apart from this, the physiological and pathological implications of the results of this form of treatment are of interest. We suggested above that the acquired motor skill of writing was susceptible to disorganization by a process of conditioning, and that, irrespective of the initial cause of the disturbance, the conditioned reflex would continue to operate, making normal writing impossible. This heuristic approach to the problem led to the evolution of the method of treatment which really amounts to the extinction of the conditioned reflex which is disorganizing the normal pattern of skilled volitional activity. The outcome of this technique of " deconditioning," as it may be called, in patients who differed so much in mental and emotional constitution appears to afford support for our view of the physiological mechanism underlying writer's cramp. Further observation and experiments with the remaining patients are proceeding, after which it may be possible to advance more definitive conclusions.

As regards the technique of treatment it may be suggested that the apparatus merely represents a symbol or a focus for psychotherapy. This suggestion is difficult to refute categorically, but several of the patients had previously had psychotherapy without benefit, and the courses of treatment were arranged so that each patient received treatment sessions from both of us. We feel that this type of therapy can be conducted by anyone with sufficient understanding of the mechanical nature of the disorder to be able to apply the various retraining exercises, and that the psychological element in the treatment is relatively unimportant.

REFERENCES

1. CULPIN, M. (1931). Recent advances in the study of psychoneuroses.
2. PAI, M. N. (1947). *J. ment. Sci.*, **93**, 68.
3. GLOVER, E. (1949). Psycho-Analysis. London.
4. CRITCHLEY, M. (1954). *Proc. R. Soc. Med.*, **47**, 593.

CONDITIONING AND THE OCCUPATIONAL CRAMPS

J. D. SYLVESTER

Institute of Psychiatry, London University

and

L. A. LIVERSEDGE

The Royal Infirmary, Manchester

SINCE publication of the brief report of the attempted treatment of seven cases of writer's cramp by a deconditioning technique, many more patients have been seen and a much fuller account, together with follow-up details,* can now be given.

Writer's cramp is an enduring occupational palsy which has resisted all efforts to cure it or explain it for over a century. Sufferers are unable to write, at any rate for long, either (1) because they find that their hand simply will not move, or else (2) the hand grasps the pen and stabs the paper with great force, due mainly to strong spasm of the muscles of the thumb, fingers and arm (see Fig. 2), or else (3) they are seized with a tremor in the writing hand (Fig. 1).

These three types of motor symptom were described by Poore (1897), who had seen some 32 cases, and his findings are confirmed here following a study of 56 cases. We have observed, however, with our larger sample, that the inhibitionary type (type 1) is comparatively rare (4 examples), while types 2 and 3 (spasm and tremor) often exist together. The spasm may be confined to the small muscles of the thumb and fingers or can include the long flexors of the hand, the writing arm and even the shoulder. The entire body, in fact, may be ultimately involved, when the case is severe and long-standing.

There are over 25 associated types of " craft neurosis," as it has been called. Among those examined at Manchester Royal Infirmary have been violinists, pianists, flautists, typists, and a certain type of cotton-mill worker called a " twister." The overwhelming majority of cases, however, are of writer's cramp, and since the other types do not bring in any new or different conceptions, it will be convenient in this account to refer mainly to the writer's cramp only. There is some resemblance between the symptoms of these cramps and the tremor and rigidity of Parkinsonism, but no physical

* L. A. Liversedge did most of the follow-up work.

condition has ever been found which could account for the cramp. There is no change discernible in the electroencephalogram with onset or during attempts to write. Previous literature on the disease, while extensive, is disappointing, but it may be useful to give a brief summary.

HISTORY OF MEDICAL OPINION OF WRITER'S CRAMP

There seems to be no mention of writer's cramp before a paper by Bruck,[1] which is interesting in as much as it was about this time that the steel pen was ousting the quill in Europe and America. Shortly afterwards there came quite a spate of publications dealing with it. The Index catalogue of the Surgeon-General's Office of the U.S. Army, printed in 1882, lists 53 authors and a 100 articles in French, Spanish, Italian, Mexican, Polish, German and English. One author, Beard,[2] writes of 125 cases in New York. Some of these early writers attributed the disorder to disease of the spinal cord but Zuber,[3] in a lengthy and comprehensive survey of the " spasmes fonctionelles," showed there was nothing known of its pathology and pointed out that in spite of the many wonderful and diverse treatments prescribed, the prognosis was bad. Poore[4] made a careful study of 75 cases of " impaired writing power " and classified 32 of them as suffering from " true writer's cramp." In these he found:

" Dysfunction of the interossi	18 times
" " extensors of the thumb	10 "
" " flexor brevis pollicis	7 "
" " abductor pollicis	7 "
" " flexor longus pollicis	4 "
" " adductor pollicis	3 "
" " opponens pollicis	2 " "

This investigator approached a psychological explanation when he talked of muscles becoming " repugnant to the will," though it was not until after the First World War that this type of account became widely believed. The May Smith and Farmer[5] study of telegraphist's cramp reinforced the view that such cramps are non-organic. By 1931, Culpin[6] was writing: " Enough patients have subjected themselves to analytic treatment to confirm that unconscious mental processes lie behind the symptoms," but he gives no data. Glover[7] describes the disorder as " a typical case of conversion hysteria " and describes a *hypothetical* case, but again no data are given. The data presented in this paper rather supports Critchley,[8] quoted in previous paper. We know of no evidence that any case of craft palsy has ever been relieved by psychoanalysis, but we have seen 5 cases where prolonged courses of psychoanalysis has failed to effect any improvement. In 1953 at Manchester it had become the practice to inform writer's-cramp patients that little could be done for them and that their best course was to try to learn to write with the other hand. After a while some patients returned, now with the cramp in *both* hands. In 1954 it was decided to embark upon a careful study of all aspects of this disorder, looking for psychological causes but having no preconceptions in mind.

RESULTS OF EXAMINATION OF
FIFTY-SIX CASES

All the cases seen exhibit some signs of anxiety but with the great majority of them this anxiety appears to relate to the disability itself and its likely effects on earning capacity; that is, the anxiety mostly seems a result rather than a cause of the cramp, and this is confirmed by the disappearance of anxiety when the cramp is cured. Only 20 of the patients showed any signs of abnormal psychological traits or of a psychoneurotically fertile history. Table 1 gives a breakdown of the clinical and psychological picture of our first 20 cases and Table 2 an analysis of all patients examined. Intelligence was tested (column 5, Table 1) by the Raven Matrices Test. The " Sway Test " (column 11, Table 1) is a test of suggestibility described by Eysenck[9] which correlates with neuroticism: results are classified on a 5-point scale, *A* being " very suggestible " and *E* showing no movement at all.

It will be seen that these patients form a group of such diverse background and character that it could well have been picked at random from the general population; they seem to have nothing in common except, of course, the cramp. A number of them had tried various forms of therapy, including hypnotism and psychoanalysis, without improvement, and at this stage we felt we had made no progress whatever. Accordingly, we directed our attention to the actual physical details of the disability.

PHYSICAL MANIFESTATIONS

There is a good deal of variance in the manifestations of the cramps, but in the " typical " case the patient can use his hand and fingers quite normally in all situations other than the writing one (or typing, violin-playing, etc., whichever cramp it is). People with writer's cramp can type or play the piano quite freely. Writing movements in free air are normal, as is writing on a blackboard (except in one case—a school headmistress whose writer's cramp eventually spread to inability to write on a blackboard also. During treatment, ability to write on a blackboard returned first.) In some cases, where the complaint was of long duration, patients could not lift teacups or similar things without thumb-spasm causing a turning-over of the hand and consequent spilling and dropping; three patients had considerable difficulty in shaving. On the whole, however, the cramp seemed to occur only in the highly specific writing environment: even if *one* sensory channel was removed, the cramp either did not occur or was considerably alleviated. For example, if patients wrote without their hands

TABLE 1

1. Case	2. Sex	3. Age	4. Occupation	5. + or − Mean intell.	6. Marital status	7. Possible recent source of anxiety*	8. Possible historical source of anxiety	9. Sign of psychol. disturb.	10. Att. to job	11. Sway test†	12. No. of siblings	13. Parental econ. status
1	M	58	Despatch clerk	Below	M	Unemployed	Parents continually quarrelling	Yes (Paranoid)	Paranoic	C	6	Poor
2	F	49	Typist	=	Div.	Having to support child herself	1. Broken marriage 2. Mother died when 5–6 yrs. Father remarried woman with 5 children	Yes (Anxiety)	Apathetic	D	0	Good
3	M	33	Clerk Gas Board	Above	M	None elicited	Father, a wife-beater, left home. Bad war exp.	No	Apathetic	A	2	Good
4	M	44	Grocery manager	Above	M	None elicited	None elicited	No	Favour-able	A	1	Poor
5	M	47	Clerk	Above	M	None elicited	Father died when patient 7 yrs.	No	Favour-able	C	2	Fair
6	M	46	Electronic engineer	Average	M	Masturbation guilt	Masturbation guilt	Yes	Anxious	D	2	Poor
7	M	39	Post Office sorter	Above	M	None elicited	None elicited	No	Favour-able	B	0	Poor
8	F	34	Typist	Above	M	Domestic difficulties	None elicited	No	Favour-able	C	1	Fair

* Other than about the writer's cramp itself. † On 5-point scale.

TABLE 1—continued

1. Case	2. Sex	3. Age	4. Occupation	5. + or − Mean intell.	6. Marital status	7. Possible recent source of anxiety*	8. Possible historical source of anxiety	9. Sign of psychol. disturb.	10. Att. to job	11. Sway test†	12. No. of siblings	13. Parental econ. status
9	M	26	Student	Above	Single	In foreign country (Subject of)	None elicited	No	Keen	B	0	Good
12	M	42	Civil servant	=	Single	None elicited	Leg amputated age 23 (road accident)	No	Apathetic	D	0	Poor
13	M	57	Executive N.A.B.	Above	M	Promotion—duties changed from dispensing charity to recovery in fraud cases	Dizziness 17–18 yrs. Gassed 1917	No	Favourable	D	1	Good
14	M	47	Railway clerk	Below	M	None elicited	Mother chronic invalid 28 yrs. Father died when patient 19 yrs.	No	Favourable	C	0	Poor
15	M	27	Toolmaker	=	M	None elicited	None elicited	No	Apathetic	B	0	Fair
16	M	45	Secretary to cashier building firm	Above	M	None elicited	Unhappy war service	No	Favourable	B	4	Good

* Other than about the writer's cramp itself.　　† On 5-point scale.

TABLE 1—*continued*

1. Case	2. Sex	3. Age	4. Occupation	5. + or − Mean intell.	6. Marital status	7. Possible recent source of anxiety*	8. Possible historical source of anxiety	9. Sign of psychol. disturb.	10. Att. to job	11. Sway test†	12. No. of siblings	13. Parental econ. status
17	M	53	Cost clerk	=	M	None elicited	At 18 yrs, mother died, father's 2nd marriage failed	Anxiety	Favourable	E	5	Fair
18	M	61	Rating clerk	Below	M	None elicited	Parental relations poor	No	Apathetic	E	2	Poor
19	M	67	Engineering draughtsman	Above	M	Wife undergoing psycho-analysis	Parental relations poor. German political refugee	No	Very keen	D	0	Good
20	M	54	School Inspector	Above	M	None elicited	None elicited	No	Very keen	C	1	Poor

* Other than about the writer's cramp itself.   † On 5-point scale.

DEPT. OF EXTRA-MURAL STUDIES
UNIVERSITY OF NOTTINGHAM

TABLE 2

All cases

Number of Cases								
Total seen	Neurotic	Writing as occupation	Writing no part in life	Prior trauma of hand	Speech defect early life	Speech defect present	In need of therapy other than for cramp	Average age at onset of cramp	Age range at onset of the cramp
56	10	46	1	6	0	1	3	39 yrs.	12–56 yrs.

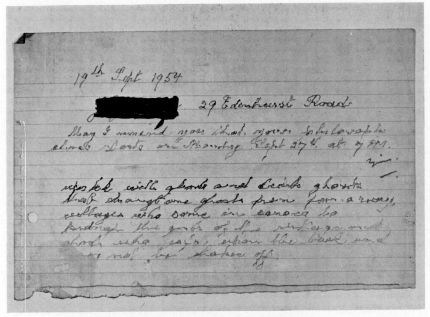

FIG. 1. Writing of a patient with tremor.

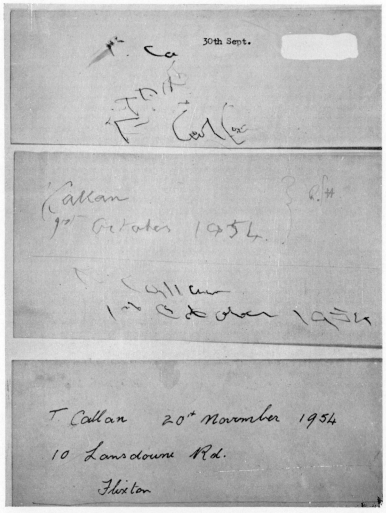

FIG. 2. The writing of a patient with spasm; before, during and after treatment.

touching the paper the cramp tended not to occur. Some patients could start writing perfectly well but would find the cramp coming on after a line or two, while others could sit in a normal writing position and make writing movements, *not* holding a pen, without trouble, but as soon as a pen or similar object touched the forefinger and thumb the spasms and/or tremor began. It all looked very much like a complicated conditioning situation, in fact, and the following theory was evolved.

Hypothesis

Mr. *X*. sits at his office desk one Monday morning prepared to write. As he starts, however, and the musculature is triggered to, in general, move the pen from left to right, he feels, consciously or otherwise, that he is fed up—he does not *want* to write—and this tends to produce innervation of the antagonist muscles. That is, *in the writing situation*, with tactile stimuli from the thumb and forefingers which grip the pen and from the bottom of the hand which rests on the paper, plus the kinaesthetic, visual and somesthetic cues specific to the desk-chair-pen environment, innervation of protagonist is immediately followed by innervation of antagonist. A sufficient number of repetitions of this and the antagonist innervation (efferent) would become a conditioned reflex to the stimulus of proprioceptive feed-back from innervation of the protagonist along with the stimulus-pattern of the writing situation. (Questions of reinforcement, reward, drive-level and so on of classical conditioning studies will be discussed later; for the purposes of this account it is a *postulate* that if R follows S enough times, then R may become conditioned to S (Sylvester, 1955).)

Now, the situation of antagonist innervation becoming a reflex to agonist firing is opposed to and disruptive of, the reciprocal opposed-muscle inhibitionary mechanism (spinal); disruption of this system could produce tremor and spasm (types 2 and 3). In the type 1 case, it is supposed that what becomes conditioned is inhibition of the protagonist innervation pulses (presumably cortical). Put more simply, it was postulated that the elaborate servo-mechanism involved in writing (or playing the violin, etc.) had become out of order due to interfering conditioned responses. If, it was thought, these " wild " responses could be deconditioned, then the disability would be relieved.

Method

Using a patient with both tremor and spasm, we started by inserting needle electrodes into the groups of muscles involved in writing, connecting them to a piece of apparatus which administered an electric shock to the other hand whenever both agonists fired simultaneously. This procedure, however, proved difficult to operate and painful for the patient and was soon abandoned in favour of simpler methods. We decided to attack first the tremor.

1. A metal plate was drilled with holes of diminishing diameter from 1 in. to $\frac{1}{8}$ in. The subject was required to hold a metal stylo in these holes, starting with the largest. Plate and stylo were connected up so that whenever the stylo touched the sides of a hole the subject received a painful electric shock in the other hand. This was immediately successful: after two or three sessions patients who had started with a tremor violent enough to give continuous shocks when in the largest hole could keep the stylo for minutes quite still in the smallest one. The next step was to attack tremor with the hand *moving*.

2. Strips of PVC tape were stuck on to a metal plate and the patient had to trace over these with a stylo; if the stylo came off the tape on to the metal, he got a shock. The tape was cut so as to require the basic movements involved in writing. Again, about $\frac{1}{2}$ hr a day was spent on this. We found that usually patients could accomplish all movements, including writing letters on the tapes, by the end of 6–8 days.

3. A fountain-pen was fitted with a spring contact such that whenever the patient had a thumb-spasm (gripped the pen too hard), he received an electric shock in the other hand. This method was combined with method 2 after the first dozen patients—i.e. the stylo used on the plate was fitted with a sprung contact. Writing with a fitted pen upon paper was usually commenced before the end of the second week of treatment.

In the majority of cases, the patients themselves were able to adjust the apparatus and carry out the programme after the first 5 or 6 sessions, the experimenter merely interviewing them from time to time to guide them according to progress made.

4. The 3 methods so far described are designed for those cases of writer's cramp with spasm and tremor who formed the majority of our subjects. Other cases require different techniques. Case No. 8, Table 1 (case 7 of the earlier paper), for example, had typist's cramp. This case was attacked by taking a small piece of sorbo-rubber, threading and re-threading it with fuse-wire, and strapping it to the palm of the woman's hand so that whenever the fingers spasmed into the palm she received a shock. After three 20-min sessions of typing with this pad, she returned to work wearing a dummy, non-electrified pad in her palm and wore it while typing for a few days.

5. On one type (1) case of writer's cramp the method used was as follows. The patient has pen and paper on a board down the left-hand edge of which is a raised piece of metal, and he is instructed to place his hand so that it is touching this metal and in a normal writing position, holding a pen. Each time the experimenter says " go! " the metal is electrified (the other contact being strapped to the patient's left hand). The patient

is started off by being required to draw a straight line across the paper on each command of " go"; and if he does not start very promptly he receives a shock. After a few pages of straight lines he is put on to wavy lines, then a series of " o's," then figures and finally, to writing words. By this time he has become conditioned to the buzz made by the shocking-coil and whenever his writing pauses it is only necessary to " buzz " the coil to start him off again. After four 1-hr sessions he was able to write freely and continuously in the presence of the experimenter but complained that he could not write without difficulty at work if anyone was watching him. This patient was very neurotic—a lifetime of lack of aggression (which 3 years of psychoanalysis had failed to remedy)—and he was then put into a course of · psychotherapy of the Wolpe–Malleson type (see discussion).

Results

The woman with typist's cramp referred to in method 4 wrote, 15 days after commencement of treatment, " I feel deliriously happy, the last two days I've been typing without the pad . . . no sign of the cramp " (3 Dec., 1954). Four years later she is still quite free of any motor disability.

Treatment has been applied to 39 cases, the follow-up period ranging from 1 month to $4\frac{1}{2}$ years. In 10 cases results are completely disappointing; they all felt themselves improved to some extent and all of them had in fact improved in associated actions such as stirring tea, holding newspapers and so on, but none of them could be said to be cured of writer's cramp.

The remaining 29 cases have all benefited following 3–6 weeks' treatment, the degree of improvement ranging from, to use purely arbitrary figures, 50–100 per cent. Five of these cases have badly relapsed; the remainder are in normal employment—many in improved employment—and most are engaged in writing (etc.) for from 4–6 hr a day.

An analysis of the results is given in Table 3.

Figure 2 shows the writing attempts of patient No. 7, Table 1, before treatment, and his writing during and after treatment. Film records have been kept of many of the patients and are available.

TABLE 3

Number of cases				
Examined	Treated	Cured	Relapsed	Cured and not relapsed (up to $4\frac{1}{2}$ years)
56	39	29	5	24

The Causes of Failure

Three of the failures exhibited no signs of abnormality while two very neurotic patients were cured (and it may be noted that neither of the latter two have developed other symptoms since being relieved of the cramp). Most of the failures and relapses, however, seemed more psychologically abnormal—certainly they had greater anxiety—than those who benefited from the treatment without relapse. Also, the failures and relapses had had the cramp for from 6 to 21 years before having treatment from us. Now, a man who has lost a leg or an arm may easily become embittered and anxious; a man who has lost the control of a hand he still has is in as distressing a situation. He is likely to feel anxious in many situations and, over a period of time, anxiety may become a conditioned response to perhaps the majority of situations a person is likely to meet. He would then appear to be a person with a *general* anxiety. And by now, the failure in writing having produced anxiety so often, a backward trace is formed so that anxiety does now produce the cramp. It seems possible, in fact, that most anxiety cases start with a " focused " anxiety and later become generalized and able to act as stimulus as well as response (dermatitis may be an example). That is, with long-term occupational cramp cases, attacking the cramp-symptoms alone with avoidance-reaction conditioning methods would not be effective; one would have to attack all, or a large number of, or the dominant pattern of, the anxiety-arousing-cramp-arousing stimulus patterns (see the remarks about method 6 in the Discussion). The most favourable time for treatment of writer's cramp seems to be within 3 years of its onset.

What is possibly another factor with regard to failures is whether the actual deconditioning technique used is the right one. With the " typical " case of writer's cramp (tremor and spasm), the methods given in 1–3 seem reasonably suitable, though no doubt they could be improved. Different cases, however, require different treatment techniques. It would obviously be fruitless to apply such methods to a type 1 (movement inhibited) case. Also we early observed that when shock is administered by an experimenter rather than automatically, the benefit is not nearly so great, this being, presumably, a matter of the experimenter's reaction-time (and incidentally lending weight to Pavlov's side of the Pavlov–Guthrie controversy of the thirties). We have not, however, so far been able to develop any completely automatic method for dealing with type 1 cases. It may be of interest to note that as our experience of designing apparatus increased, so did the current patient's rate of improvement. It is also clear that a therapist with a strong analytic prejudice is not likely, *per se*, to be at any advantage in treating this condition; more useful is a knowledge of skeletal anatomy, elementary mechanics and Pavlov.[10]

So far as the 5 relapses go, perhaps one is entitled to ask " what is a relapse? " People have been known to be cured of influenza only to catch it again the following year. Various fortuitous reasons have prevented attempts to re-treat any of the 5 complete relapses, but 2 patients who had regressed to some extent—down to about 70 per cent efficiency—have been re-treated quite successfully and this tends to indicate that relapses could indeed be dealt with.

DISCUSSION

In the light of the data and experience gained in studying these 56 cases of occupational palsy, it is now felt that the hypothesis which led to the methods of treatment, while having turned out fruitful, is really far too simple. The notion that the form of treatment outlined here acts as psychotherapy, with the electrical apparatus serving merely as a symbol, seems unplausible inasmuch as (1) most of our subjects were psychologically normal, (2) treatment was carried out by several different people on the same patient, (3) much of the treatment was performed by the patients upon themselves, and (4) a number of the cases had previously received extensive courses of analytic-type therapy without benefit. Neither is it convincing to suppose that the treatment acts merely as an anxiety-reducer in the way that a *placebo* does (although this might be supported by the fact that over the years many different types of treatment have been claimed as having some success), since several patients had had various forms of physical treatment without benefit. It would, therefore, seem reasonable to conclude that the origin of an occupational cramp is some form of learning or conditioning and the cure, where it occurs, is also some form of conditioning. The question is—*what* form of conditioning? There seems to be a number of possibilities and at least an equal number of objections.

1. If the cramp is conditioned, what is the reinforcement which ensures its continuance? One may advance the suggestion that since these people are bored with writing, the not-writing resulting from the cramp is the reinforcement and that this reward acts more powerfully than the punishment of the anxiety also set up by the inability to write. Avoidance-reaction treatment, in that case, would be adding to the anti-reinforcement anxiety.

2. One may also ask why must it be reinforced? A distinction may be drawn between a conditioned reflex and a conditioned response, a point made by Guthrie[11]; a reflex is what Hilgard and Marquis[12] appear to mean by " substitution." There appears to be evidence that where a specific muscle-contraction is the " conditioned response," motivation, reward and punishment are unimportant; what matters is contiguity.[13-15] It is only with conditioned *responses*—i.e. purposive-type behaviour with variable muscle-contraction patterns—that drive and reward become essential. But " substitution " phenomena are perhaps better not called " conditioned "

at all, the concepts of "association," "neural-connection" and so on being more appropriate. What may be happening in writer's cramp is illustrated in Fig. 3. Following repeated contiguity of efferent pulses to protagonist and antagonist, a connection is formed between the two efferent pathways which is sufficient to disrupt the reciprocal inhibitionary mechanism. When, during treatment, an afferent pain-signal reaches the cortex, the resultant inhibitionary signal to the former protagonist, which accompanies the withdrawal signal to the former antagonist, is strong enough to set the reciprocal inhibitionary mechanism working. This repeated sufficiently, the "wrong" neural connection atrophies; or, alternatively, the strong inhibitionary pulse having become conditioned to the writing situation, it will continue to act to overcome the neural interconnection, without rein-forcement, for fairly long periods of time. Persistence of conditioned responses for the sort of time-periods dealt with here have been reported (motor reflexes in sheep, 2 years by Liddell et al.[16]; flexion reflex in dogs, 2½ years by Wendt[17]).

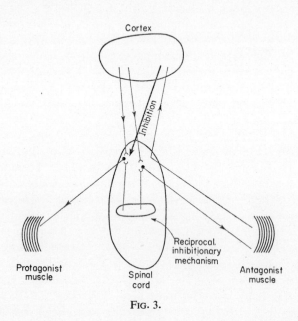

Fig. 3.

3. Another possibility is suggested by the Mowrer–Miller hypothesis. According to this, each writing-movement will tend to inhibit closely follow-ing ones and a drive to cease writing will develop (reactive inhibition). Cessation of writing will then become conditioned to the stimuli present in the writing situation. With the normal person this process is overcome by the positive reinforcement of finding the pen moving as desired—positive

learning effects nullifying the development of conditioned inhibition even with over-learning. With writer's-cramp people, however, the reward is insufficient to produce enough reinforcement. The treatment is now seen as a matter of the conditioned avoidance response nullifying the conditioned inhibition. This hypothesis seems to fit the appearance and variability of writer's cramp better than the others. Of course, it may well be that no one system will account for all cases of the disability.

It may also be a mistake to classify these cases together as functional inability to write (type, etc.). Perhaps it would be more readily dealt with if some method could be found which would enable the patients to be classified according to type of conditioning, neural-connection, or inhibition, or whatever it may be.

A final point may be made with regard to the long-term cases who have perhaps become anxiety-conditioned. The patient mentioned in method 5 was given a sheaf of papers which had formed the original manuscript of an article written by one of the experimenters and he was instructed to read it through and then write " rubbish " all across each page. He was given a continuous electric shock in the left hand which ceased whenever he was actually writing. During this experiment the patient became extremely agitated—sweating, protruding his tongue and breathing heavily, and it was obvious that the distress was not due merely to the electric shock. It looked like panic and was immediately reminiscent of a recent paper by Malleson[18] describing a method of treatment of phobia wherein the patient is induced to " live through " his fears to the point of becoming bored with them. (The method of " role-reversal," described by Sylvester[19] as a method of reducing cognitive rigidity seems to be an example of the same sort of thing at the cognitive level.) This patient can now write fairly well at work or anywhere and it seems possible that even neurotic or long-standing, anxiety-conditioned patients may be helped by sufficiently ingenious techniques derived from learning-theory. It may well be that such techniques will find application in fields right outside psychiatry.

REFERENCES

1. BRUCK, J. (1831). Casper's krit. *Repetorium XXX, vol. II.*
2. BEARD, G. M. (1879). Conclusions from a study of 125 cases of writer's cramp. *Trans. Med. Soc.*, New York, Syracuse.
3. ZUBER, C. (1881). Spasms Fonctionelles. *Dictionaire Encyclopedique des Sciences Medicales.* 3. Serie 10.
4. POORE, G. V. (1878). An analysis of 75 cases of writer's cramp and impaired writing power. *Med. Chir. Trans.* (R.M.C.S.), London, vol. 43.
5. SMITH, MAY and FARMER, E. (1927). A preliminary report of a study of telegraphist's cramp. *Indust. Fatigue Board Report*, No. 43. London. H.M. Stationery Office.
6. CULPIN, M. (1931). *Recent Advances in the Study of Psychoneurosis.* Routledge, London.
7. GLOVER, E. (1949). *Psychoanalysis.* Staples Press, London.
8. CRITCHLEY, MACDONALD (1954). Craft palsy. *Proc. R.S.M.*, **47,** 593.

9. EYSENCK, H. J. (1947). *Dimensions of Personality*. Routledge, London.
10. PAVLOV, I. P. (1927). *Conditioned Reflexes*. Oxford Univ. Press, London.
11. GUTHRIE, E. R. (1935). *The Psychology of Human Learning*. Harper, New York.
12. HILGARD, E. R. and MARQUIS, D. G. (1940). *Conditioning and Learning*. Appleton, New York.
13. HOLT, E. B. (1931). *Animal Drive and the Learning Process*. Holt, New York.
14. GUTHRIE, E. R. (1934). Pavlov's theory of conditioning. *Psychol. Rev.*, **41**, 191-206.
15. MEYER, M. F. (1934). Frequency, duration and recency v. double stimulation. *Psychol. Rev.*, **41**, 177-183.
16. LIDDELL, H. S. (1934). The conditioned reflex. In: *Comparative Psychology* (ed. by Moss, F. A.). Prentice-Hall, New York.
17. WENDT, G. R. (1937). Two and one half year retention of a conditioned response. *J. Gen. Psychol.*, **17**, 178-180.
18. MALLESON, N. (1959). Panic and phobia. *Lancet*, 225-227.
19. SYLVESTER, J. (1956). Cognitive rigidity and role reversal. *Jnl. Soc. Research*. III. Pretoria.
20. WOLPE, J. (1958). *Psychotherapy by Reciprocal Inhibition*. Stanford University Press.

THE SYMPTOMATIC TREATMENT OF WRITER'S CRAMP*

H. R. BEECH

Department of Psychology, Institute of Psychiatry, London

GENERAL

THE PROBLEM of writer's cramp has received a good deal of attention in the past mainly from neurologists, and, more recently, from psychiatrists. Even a brief search through the literature will reveal some variation in the accounts given of symptomatology, aetiology and treatment of this disorder. Perhaps the greatest divergencies are found when it comes to matters of aetiology and treatment.

One clear description of the disorder is given by Jelliffe[1] who states that the disturbance represents an abnormal nervous modification of certain co-ordinated muscular activities, commonly manifested in tonic contractions, perhaps accompanied by pain, and occasional clonic shocks or tremors. He points out that typically the cramps occur only when the muscle groups involved are used in co-ordinated activity, while independent activity of these affected muscles does not produce any disturbance. In other words the abnormality is seldom manifested outside the act of writing. Jelliffe concludes that " the implication of mental impulses is highly probable."

Most investigators would appear to subscribe to the above account and would support the notion that as the nerves and muscles involved appear to be intact and a wide range of movements outside the writing situation which employ these same muscles and nerves are possible, the disorder may be considered to be " functional."

As Pai[2] points out, most neurologists stress excessive writing and the accompanying fatigue as the main cause. Jelliffe[1] is somewhat vague on this point stating the chief factor in the production of the disorder to be frequent and continuous use of certain fine, co-ordinated movements, beyond the capacity of the individual to " stand the strain." Collier (see Culpin[3]) believes that the disorder is unrelated to the neuroses and is simply the result of massive practice. Osler,[4] on the other hand, states that writer's cramp results from disturbance of the area of the brain responsible for writing movements.

* The author is indebted to Dr. Denis Leigh, consultant psychiatrist to Maudsley Hospital, for permission to investigate the patients referred to in this chapter, and also for his interest in the project. This chapter was specially written for this book.

Other writers emphasize their belief that the disorder is largely or entirely due to psychological disturbance. Janet,[5] for example, places writer's cramp unequivocally among a group of neurotic disorders, and Glover[6] believes the symptoms fit in with a picture of conversion hysteria.

Culpin's experience[3] leads him to conclude that the cramp may be associated with severe anxiety and obsessional states, or as part of a pure conversion hysteria in patients presenting no other symptoms whatever. Pai[2] endorses Culpin's findings, noting that writer's cramp *appears* to occur in patients suffering from neuroses whose work does not in fact involve much writing, so that it seems to be a symptom of neurosis rather than an occupational disease.

Jelliffe[1] points out that clinicians have described 4 main types of the disorder, the spasmodic, the tremulous, the neuralgic and the paretic forms. He adds that these categories are not mutually exclusive and that almost all cases show more than one of these symptoms. He believes the tremulous type to be rare in isolation; it simply consists of shaking or tremor in the writing hand when the act of writing is commenced, in some cases the disturbance extending to and involving the whole arm. According to Jelliffe the neuralgic form is antecedent to all forms of writer's cramp and consists of sensations of fatigue, weakness and soreness of the involved muscles. In the paralytic type, also rare in its pure form, the patient may be completely unable to grasp the pen. Usually this type is preceded by fatigue and weakness up to the point at which paresis is reached, the fingers typically becoming stiff and inactive.

Jelliffe states that the spastic form is reported to be most common. This form alone, or in combination with tremors, is said to account for 40 per cent of all cases. He quotes Berger as finding in his analysis of 64 cases that 24 were purely spastic, 10 paralytic, 8 tremulous and 22 had combinations of these basic forms. Over 50 per cent of these cases had spasms. In Remak's 42 cases there were 9 individuals with " true writer's tremor," 32 with spastic symptoms and only one purely paralytic case.

Pai[2] suggests a more detailed classification which embraces two broad categories, psychogenic and physiogenic. The former is further subdivided into 3 types, the tremulous, spastic and ataxic forms. He describes the tremulous form as being manifested in less fluency in execution of contours resulting in a more angular style of writing, and a fine tremor produces minute waves in the script.

The spastic or genuine cramp form according to Pai tends to result in small letters, and the spasm may involve the muscles employed in gripping the pen and those used in moving the hand along during writing. Sometimes, owing to tonic contraction, an individual may be unable to write at all, and occasionally the severity of the spasm results in " locking " where the hand becomes a tightly clenched fist.

Characteristic of Pai's ataxic form are irregularitie in shape and sizes of letters and spacing. Here, exaggerated contraction of extensor muscles results in erratic, jerky and apparently uncontrolled performance.

In the physiogenic category Pai places all those physical disorders in which writing disturbances similar to those seen in the psychogenic groups are found. Among these physical disorders he notes chorea, disseminated sclerosis, paralysis agitans, progressive muscular atrophy, and post-vaccinal encephalomyelitis. Here, because of paralysis or muscle weakness, letters tend to be large, irregular, lacking in contours, and the act of writing may in itself be painful and fatiguing.

Although it is possible to devise a rough classifactory system for writer's cramp it seems possible that this would have few practical implications for treatment. It is also the case, as Culpin points out, that " the vagaries of writer's cramp symptoms and their accompanying manifestations " are many and their variety is infinite. One or more symptoms of the disorder may be present; the disorder may occur in several types of personality; it may or may not be accompanied by vascular disturbances; other motor symptoms, e.g. tics or stammers, may be present or absent; the onset may be sudden or slow in developing. In addition many investigators point out that the symptoms may be found in individuals who have little writing to do. Because of this fact and because actual " cramps " are not always present, Pai prefers to use the term " writing disturbance," and this title certainly seems to be less misleading as it avoids some aetiological and symptomatological difficulties.

TREATMENT

Culpin,[3] who finds that telegraphist's cramp and similar disorders usually occur in conjunction with anxiety states, obsessional states or in an hysterical form, and rarely in the normal individual, advocates a psychotherapeutic approach to treatment. He describes a case of writer's cramp treated successfully by means of uncovering repressed thoughts concerning sexuality, the writing disturbance being the symbolic expression of these repressed thoughts. In this particular case[3] he states that as the symbolism became recognized by the patient it (the symbolism) was rendered ineffective and the patient came to write more and more easily. In essence the cramp symptoms were the expression of unconscious ideation which, when made conscious, became redundant.

Essentially the same theoretical position and treatment are found useful by Glover[6] who considers the disorder to be a typical example of conversion hysteria.

On the other hand, Drews[7] has reported upon the relief of writer's cramp by means of psychodrama after the failure of medical, osteopathic and psychoanalytic forms of treatment.

Pai, who also takes the view that writer's cramp is a symptom of a neurosis, advocates the use of both physical and psychological forms of treatment. For the tremulous types of disorder where, according to Pai, all patients are anxious and highly strung, treatment is directed toward the anxiety state in the form of continual narcosis or heavy sedation for a week or two with modified insulin. He finds that with this therapy there is general improvement in both the somatic disturbances and the writing of the patient.

For the spastic type, who are all said to have predominantly hysterical reactions, the treatment aims at removing the underlying conflict by hypnosis or other means, relief of the spasm by barbiturates or hypnosis, together with supervision and correction of the mechanics of writing. In addition, for the ataxic form, Pai suggests active exercise of flexor muscles together with massage.

Jelliffe[1] finds that, for most patients, benefit is derived from general methods of increasing physical vigour and adds that complete abstinence from writing is a useful preliminary measure. He states that some physicians recommend teaching the patient to write with the non-affected hand, but says that this not infrequently results in " cramps " developing in that hand too, and he feels that this phenomenon may be regarded as presumptive evidence of a " large psychic element."

The above type of reaction is also described by Culpin in stressing the non-specific nature of the disturbance. He cites the case of an individual suffering from telegraphist's cramp who, when transferred to other work, developed writer's cramp. In this individual other forms of employment subsequently taken up led to the development of motor symptoms which interfered with the jobs. Culpin also mentions individuals who, on being transferred from employment as telegraphists (because of telegraphist's cramp) to employment as telephonists, developed laryngitis.

Jelliffe[1] does, however, make an interesting suggestion respecting treatment of writer's cramp which he believes would achieve the best results. He recommends working out in minute detail the sequence of specific cramp movements and then having the patient practice the opposing movements. For example, if extension of the forefinger is one element in the disorder the patient should repeatedly practice contraction of that finger. The patient is, in fact, set the task of learning the entire cramp movement in its opposite form. This suggestion by Jelliffe is mentioned because of its similarity to the " incompatible response " technique which will be discussed later.

Sadler[8] in discussing treatment of tremors, tics and convulsive movements, recommends building up physical health and training in muscle control. He also advocates favourable suggestions being made to the patient. Muncie[9] also supports the value of motor re-education, but argues that tics, cramps and the like should be treated in much the same way as hysterical paralyses, by hypnosis to secure symptomatic relief and by re-adjustment of personality in order to prevent further breakdown.

On the other hand, Radovici[10] recommends atropine and similar drugs for all types of writer's cramp. According to many, however, such treatment would be most unsatisfactory, for example Kihn[11] believes that " mechanical " treatment of any kind simply results in the disturbance becoming latent. Effective treatment, Kihn alleges, demands a knowledge of the psychic origins of the symptoms.

Perhaps the most successful and rapid form of therapy yet reported is that devised by Liversedge and Sylvester.[12] Their work is also interesting in that it suggests that one can work at the symptom level with considerable success and without any evidence for relapse or the production of other symptoms in substitution. Their observations have led them to the " tentative conclusions that, whatever the origin of writer's cramp, its persistence might be explained by the establishment of a conditioned reflex." They then go on to argue that " it might be possible to disturb the reflex by the administration of a sensory counter-stimulus whenever the motor effect took place."

The theoretical position adopted by Liversedge and Sylvester is not developed beyond the above statements and one might reasonably question the mechanisms involved in " disturbing " the reflex. It might also be pointed out that these authors state that their method " really amounts to the extinction of the conditioned reflex " although the procedure which they use would not be described in these terms by the learning theorists from whom they appear to borrow.

Perhaps even more significant is the apparent failure of Liversedge and Sylvester to give any account of the means by which the conditioned reflex continues to operate, i.e. persists in time.*

Nevertheless, the position adopted by them appears to be an extremely fruitful one, especially as it seems to be effective in patients differing greatly " in mental and emotional constitution." The importance of this last point is somewhat obscured by the fact that Liversedge has reported that the majority of their patients had no neurotic traits.

These authors take the trouble to point out that it might be argued that the apparatus used in treatment could be regarded as a symbol for psycho-therapy. This appears to them an unlikely explanation as several of their cases had received psychotherapy without benefit before treatment by the conditioning technique. It is also the present writer's experience that cases may be referred for therapy by " conditioning " methods after the failure of psychotherapy.

---

* These criticisms are based upon the original paper by these authors. A fuller theoretical account is, however, given by them in a chapter which appears in this book.

There seems little doubt that writer's cramp represents the outcome of a learning process and it therefore seems reasonable to attempt to reverse this process either by teaching new response habits or by extinguishing old ones. Three methods suggest themselves as possible useful means of modifying undesirable responses, namely avoidance conditioning, negative practice, and reciprocal inhibition. These three methods have been employed by the author in a study of writer's cramp and the following pages attempt to give a brief account of the theoretical bases of these methods together with an account of how they have been used in the treatment of writing disorders.

Before discussing the theoretical implications of these methods and illustrating their application it is necessary to make clear the nature of the investigations which led to the observations reported. The main interest has not in fact been focused upon curing the patient, but rather upon a demonstration that the symptoms could be changed and modified directly with variations in treatment, and that this correspondence would be predictable from theory.

Avoidance Conditioning

The technique used by Liversedge and Sylvester[12] must be classed as avoidance conditioning. Several pieces of apparatus have been devised by these authors all of which serve the same end, namely to deliver a strong electric shock whenever a particular maladaptive response occurs. It is hoped that under these conditions the subject will learn to avoid making the " shocked " responses, and the results of applying the technique to cases of writer's cramp do seem most encouraging. In this connection we might note that punishment as such has been found to be relatively ineffective in modifying response habits, and seems to merely produce interference with on-going behaviour (Estes, 1944). In the technique used by Liversedge and Sylvester however, the outcome is not simply to punish certain responses but to provide an opportunity for the organism to learn to escape from punishment, the latter being a reinforcing situation. Although only a few cases were included in their preliminary report,[12] Liversedge[13] has recently presented *data* showing impressive results with 27 patients out of whom only 6 failed to respond to this form of therapy. The beneficial results of the training were found, on follow-up, to be maintained over periods up to $2\frac{1}{2}$ years and in no case had other symptoms developed to take the place of the " cramps." Indeed, Liversedge reports that in certain cases there was improvement in psychopathological symptoms other than the one treated.

The general theoretical account of learning under the above conditions in terms of drive reduction theory is fairly explicit. Where shock is the unconditioned stimulus, it is supposed that the total response to that stimulus includes some anxiety reactions. These latter reactions, as well as other response elements, become conditioned to the stimulus which precedes shock. In the case of writer's cramp the stimuli preceding shock would regularly include the maladaptive motor responses. Subsequent instrumental responses which occur and which happen to be successful in avoiding shock, are strengthened by drive reduction, and in this case the drive reduced is the anxiety elicited by the administration of shock. Mowrer[14] was probably the first to hypothesize that anxiety may operate as a drive and anxiety-reduction as a reward. Evidence for the validity of this assumption is found in a number of experiments.[15,16]

However, the present writer's experience of treating writing disturbances by avoidance conditioning has not been entirely favourable. It would appear, in fact, that the outcome of applying the Liversedge and Sylvester method may produce either no results at all or, in some cases, might actually exacerbate the symptoms already present. It is possible to put forward a reasonable explanation of the finding that avoidance training may produce results which are decidedly unfavourable and this explanation appears to fit in with certain apparent differences between the samples collected by Liversedge and Sylvester and the present writer.

The symptoms themselves might be regarded as being avoidance responses to the stimulus situation involved in the act of writing. In certain cases one might suppose that such responses are not simple habits developed as a result of excessive fatigue arising out of massive practice, but are responses which may be accompanied by considerable anxiety. Here it is supposed that, for one reason or another, the act of writing produces anxiety which is only reduced by cessation of writing behaviour. In other cases one might suppose that the anxiety generated in the writing situation is the outcome of certain social influences e.g. the embarrassment caused by other individuals observing the clumsy motor movements made.

However the anxiety comes to be attached to the writing situation, it is possible that the avoidance response of " cramps " would be actually strengthened by the administration of shock when these responses occurred. As the cramps have repeatedly been evoked in the presence of anxiety and as the anticipation of shock might be expected to raise the general level of anxiety, the avoidance responses in the form of cramps could be exacerbated.

We can use this concept of anxiety reduction to account for the preservation of the habit through time, a factor which receives no attention from Liversedge and Sylvester. It would appear from a number of experiments that a conditioned avoidance response is " lost " unless, from time to time, it is reinforced. We might expect that the symptoms of writer's cramp, if we regard them as being conditioned aversive responses, require some form of reinforcement in order to preserve their strength. This general need for reinforcement is shown in an experiment by Sheffield.[17] The persistence of the maladaptive habit in cases where there is little or no anxiety might be accounted for in similar terms, excepting that here the drive might be excessive fatigue, and in such cases " shock " would possibly not produce a significant amount of anxiety.

It is interesting to note that in certain individuals seen by the writer, when the induction coil was only allowed to " buzz " instead of actually delivering a shock to the patient an improvement in performance was effected. However, one might suppose that in some patients even the " buzz " alone might be sufficient to evoke and add to the anxiety already present, and in such individuals a rather different approach to treatment would be necessary.

This general theoretical position adopted here seems to fit in well with certain other facts. Liversedge has reported[13] that, for their samples, investigation as to the presence of psychoneurotic traits revealed that the " . . . majority had no such abnormality." For their sample, where some psychological disorder was present, it was felt that such disorder was not the prime cause of the motor disturbance found in writing. This finding contrasts sharply with cases referred to the present writer, all of whom might be considered to be at least moderately neurotic. In other words, the sample collected by Liversedge and Sylvester might be expected to manifest less anxiety than the sample collected by the present writer and this could account for the apparent difference in efficacy of the shock-avoidance training in the two samples. With patients in whom the anxiety level may be assumed to be low, as in Liversedge and Sylvester's sample, the technique of avoidance conditioning appears to be extremely successful. However, the *data* presented by the present writer suggest that in certain cases avoidance conditioning may fail completely because of the high level of anxiety, while in other cases, even when avoidance conditioning has radically reduced the manifestation of symptoms, there may still be some degree of residual anxiety which requires other forms of treatment.

Negative Practice

There is a wealth of evidence from general experimental psychology which indicates that the strength of a habit, for example in terms of frequency and amplitude of a response, may be diminished by continuous evocation. The facts of spontaneous recovery seem to suggest that some inhibitory process is operative, the effects of which dissipate in time. It is possible to account for the growth of this active preventative process which interferes with the evocation of a habit by supposing that for each evocation of the response there is an increase of inhibition. Another way of stating this is to say that each time the response is elicited there is a lowered probability that the response will occur again. When these increments of inhibition accrue and summate, the inhibitory potential may exceed the excitatory potential and at this point the habit ceases to occur. If a rest pause is allowed between successive evocations of a habit then the response suffers no interference, presumably this is because the inhibition is being allowed to dissipate. Clearly this mechanism cannot in itself account for the fact that habits can be completely eliminated by repeated " extinction " trials.

In Hull's[18] theoretical system permanent decrement in habits is a result of the operation of both reactive or fatigue inhibition and conditioned inhibition. His equation is:

$$_sE_R = {_sH_R} \times D - (I_R + {_sI_R})$$

where $_sH_R$ is the strength of the habit, D is drive (a state of physical or psychological tension impelling action), I_R is reactive inhibition, and $_sI_R$ is conditioned inhibition.

When fatigue-type inhibition accumulates through repeated evocation of a response the stimulus no longer produces response evocation, but one might say that at this point the response of " not responding " is produced. Now fatigue may be regarded as a drive state, and there is a good deal of evidence which suggests that the reduction of drive is reinforcing, so that the response of " not responding " is produced at the time when there is a reduction of drive so that this particular response is being reinforced. With successive extinction trials more increments of habit strength are added to the response of " not responding," and on each trial it becomes easier to obtain extinction of the old response, until at some point the old habit is lost completely and there is no further need for extinction trials.

The first reported use of this technique as a therapeutic measure for eliminating an undesirable habit was by Dunlap.[19] More recently Yates[20] has applied this form of treatment in an attempt to eliminate tics in a female patient.

There is some evidence however which suggests that this method might be relatively ineffective when anxiety is attached to the response which is the subject of extinction trials. Miller,[21] for example, found that a fear-acquired motor response needed very many extinction trials before being " lost." In his experiment rats were set the task of learning to escape from a box in which they had received a shock. When this habit had been learned, they were given repeated escape trials without the reinforcement of shock and it was found that very many trials were required in order to obtain curves of extinction.

One must also take into account the concepts of anxiety conservation and partial irreversibility recently put forward by Solomon and Wynne[22] to account for the apparent failure of extinction to take place in cases of traumatic avoidance learning. According to these authors it seems possible that, in certain instances, the occurrence of an extremely rapid instrumental response to the conditioned stimulus would prevent peripheral anxiety

24

reactions from taking place. In such cases it would be impossible to extinguish the connection between the conditioned stimulus and part of the anxiety reaction as the organism is removed from danger before becoming upset by it. Here, however, anxiety reduction cannot strengthen the instrumental response so that its habit strength will suffer decrement. This decrement is revealed in longer latencies of the avoidance response until the conditioned stimulus once again elicits an anxiety reaction, in which case the avoidance response reduces anxiety and strengthens the habit once more. At the same time, however, the conditioned anxiety reaction is weakened because the unconditioned stimulus has not occurred following the conditioned stimulus. The net result, according to Solomon and Wynne, is that habit strength is weakening while anxiety (drive) is being conserved and extinction should occur even though extremely slowly. Therefore, to account for the apparent failure of extinction procedures in certain cases, these authors postulate the principle of partial irreversibility of classical conditioning of intense anxiety reactions.

The implication of this principle is that an instrumental avoidance reaction originally triggered-off by a severe traumatic event will be unresponsive to ordinary extinction procedures.

Although the evidence for postulating this principle is not clear cut, it does receive a measure of support from certain animal experiments and clinical observations. At this stage of our knowledge it would seem that, as a technique, extinction procedures would be less likely to be effective where there is a clear history of traumatic avoidance learning. The case of Mr. C. D., which is reported later in this chapter, would tend to lend support to his position.

Reciprocal Inhibition

The general theoretical principle involved here is that of primary stimulus generalization (Hull[18]). According to this principle it is not only the original conditioned stimulus which evokes the conditioned reaction, but also a whole series of stimuli which are similar to the original. The greater the similarity to the original stimulus the more closely will the response resemble the original conditioned reaction. If a stimulus is introduced which lies distant from the original along the generalization curve, then the reaction will be of small intensity.

In the situation pictured here, a stimulus is used which is distant from that which produced the original conditioned response, although lying along the same generalization continuum. In theory, the response here will be similar to that elicited by the original stimulus, but will be of reduced intensity and, under such circumstances, it is possible to evoke an alternative response incompatible with the potential minimal reaction. If an incompatible response is conditioned to this stimulus and such a response is progressively strengthened, then the possibility that the stimulus will elicit the old conditioned response will be progressively decreased.

Where an anxiety response is evoked by a particular stimulus complex the general aim would be to attempt to substitute an adaptive normal response incompatible with the manifestation of anxiety. A hierarchy of situations would be devised which were similar to the critical stimulus situations known to evoke intense anxiety reactions, but the former would be so devised as to elicit various lesser degrees of anxiety. The individual is first placed in the situation known to elicit the smallest degree of anxiety and in this situation a response or responses are evoked which are incompatible with anxiety feelings. It is supposed that where a relatively dissimilar stimulus to the one which originally evoked the conditioned anxiety reaction is used, then, in the presence of this stimulus, the incompatible response has the effect of inhibiting the small amount of anxiety produced. The reduction of drive which accompanies the production of the incompatible response is held to reinforce this new reaction and to weaken the habit of responding with anxiety. A graded approach is then employed along the generalization continuum, at each stage the stimulus situation being made more like the one in which the original response was learned, and at each stage substituting the adaptive response incompatible with the evocation of anxiety.

There is a good deal of evidence for the therapeutic efficacy of this type of training. Early reports to this effect were given by Jones,[23] and Jersild and Holmes (1935) the latter authors finding this method superior to others in the elimination of children's fears.

More recently other writers have reported upon the effectiveness of this technique (Meyer[24] and Wolpe[25]). Wolpe[25] has been particularly successful in using this form of treatment and has provided examples of a number of types of response which are incompatible with and may be invoked in the presence of anxiety. One of these forms of response incompatible with anxiety is relaxation. This form of response would appear to be particularly appropriate where cases of writer's cramp are concerned as, in the present writer's experience, undue muscular tension is part of the picture presented in this disorder and indeed such tension appears to be largely responsible for the fatigue sensations which patients often report after fairly short periods of writing.

However, as Solomon and Wynne point out,[22] the actual degree of anxiety should be known as well as its strength in relation to the incompatible response. This ought to be known for each step in the hierarchy of response situations devised. Techniques wrongly applied in the absence of such knowledge might result in the anxiety response being attached to parts of the situations which were previously neutral or even attractive. For example, presentation of food to an animal in the " anxiety " situation could possibly result in the animal coming to fear and refuse food instead of eating and inhibiting anxiety.

The above limitations may have little practical significance, however, as those studies which employ this technique have apparently not specified the degree of anxiety which might be expected to be aroused in any of the steps in the hierarchy of situations, nor has any assessment been made of the relative strengths of anxiety and incompatible responses. Yet these attempts have been extremely successful, Wolpe claiming, for example, that the technique has provided beneficial results in 90 per cent of his cases.

CASE STUDIES
Mr. A. B.

This patient, aged 48 years, had suffered from a writing disturbance over a period of 5 years before coming to the present writer. The treatment which he had received prior to seeing me had extended over $4\frac{1}{2}$ years and had included 1 year of psychoanalysis and infrequent but continuous hypnotherapy for 1 year. The Liversedge and Sylvester treatment by avoidance conditioning had also been attempted unsuccessfully at another hospital, the patient in fact complaining that the training there had been inadequate in a number of respects.

On examination two quite distinct maladaptive motor movements were noted, both affecting the writing hand which was the right hand in this patient. The first of these was a contraction of the index finger which, instead of remaining extended down the barrel of the pen, was retracted by bending it at the joints until the nail of that finger rested against the barrel. The whole movement of this finger in its contraction was a laboured and painful one, which, once completed, was difficult to reverse.

The second clearly identifiable component of the disorder was a spasm which involved the hand as a whole which was turned in toward the body until at an angle of 90° to the arm. To execute this movement the wrist was bent sharply until further movement was impossible, the suddenness of the movement frequently causing pain. It was not surprising to find that the pen was quite often dropped during this hand spasm.

The patient also reported that he experienced painful fatigue whenever he had to write more than a few lines.

An interesting feature of this case was that the patient had successfully taught himself to write with his left hand. No symptoms were discovered related to this change in writing hand although the patient habitually used this hand in the course of his employment.

On testing on the MPI[26] the patient's scores were indicative of high neuroticism and a moderate degree of extraversion. It should be pointed out that the present writer is assuming that high neuroticism is indicative of high anxiety.

Initially, an endeavour was made to confirm the patient's observations concerning the failure of the avoidance conditioning technique. The apparatus was so designed as to administer shock whenever the maladaptive responses occurred and a number of training sessions were devoted exclusively to treatment by this technique.

After a number of sessions using avoidance conditioning it became clear that the technique was not a beneficial one for this patient. This conclusion is made clear by reference to Fig. 1 which presents the results of training on trials 6–10 using apparatus designed to correct the hand spasm. It will be seen that here the number of maladaptive responses (shocks delivered) remains essentially the same, while the speed of performance is slightly lower. This picture simply represents a continuation of trials 1–5. During this time it also appeared that the quality of writing seemed, if anything, to be a little poorer than before treatment began.

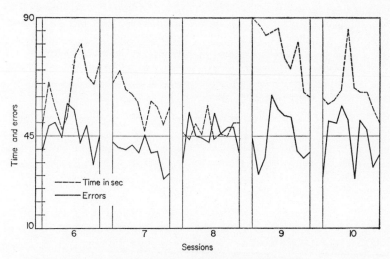

FIG. 1. Graph showing the results of avoidance training for patient A. B. "Errors" refers to the number of hand spasms occurring during tracing the Liversedge and Sylvester maze. Ten trials in each session.

A letter which the patient wrote to the author seems to confirm the view put forward in this paper, namely that avoidance conditioning of this kind may be unsuitable in cases where the instrumental response is mediated by anxiety. The letter stated that "the treatment is very similar to the one which I received a year ago at hospital, and to my great surprise I seemed to feel something not unlike a psychological resistance against resuming it. This was expressed by an attack of palpitations on arrival at the hospital on the last occasion, which continued throughout the morning, and also by excessive perspiration whenever I was actually attached to the apparatus."

Disregarding the interpretation of these symptoms given by the patient, the explanation advanced above does account for his lack of positive response to this form of treatment, although alternative explanations of his reactions to shock are possible.

An alternative method used in an attempt to control the patient's symptoms has been the method of negative practice. So far only one of the symptoms, that of finger retraction, has received detailed attention, and the relevant data for the first few sessions is presented in graph form in Fig. 2. Massed practice of the maladaptive response has, because of certain technical considerations, been conducted in a somewhat artificial situation. The patient has been required to reproduce, as precisely as possible, the finger movement but at the same time weights are attached to the finger making this movement rather difficult and fatiguing. It was hoped that the extra effort involved in the production of the response when weights were attached to the finger would lead to more rapid extinction. An experiment by Mowrer and Jones[27] suggests that in fact the ease of extinction varies directly with the energy expended in making each reaction. Practice takes place up to the point at which the patient reports that he can no longer produce any effective contraction of the index finger.

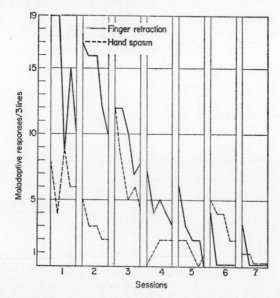

FIG. 2. Graph showing results for treated (finger retraction) and untreated (hand spasm) symptoms for patient A. B. Trials 2, 3, 4 and 5, for the treated symptom were each preceded by " extinction " procedures as described in the text.

In the graph (Fig. 2) the results of 7 separate training sessions are reported. Each session consisted of 5 trials; the first trial was concerned with

" pre-training " responses, i.e. a simple count of the number of manifestations of the symptom before the weight-lifting practice. The subsequent 4 trials were each preceded by weight-lifting practice to " exhaustion." Each of the 5 trials consisted of 3 lines of handwriting to dictation, the frequency of both finger and hand symptoms being noted during these periods.

It would appear from the results presented in Fig. 2 that the training is having the desired effect, and that the progress within any one session and between one session and the next, is that which one would expect from the growth of reactive and conditioned inhibition. It seems also that there is some degree of interdependence of the two symptoms, the untreated hand spasm showing a roughly similar decremental process as the treated symptom although the latter, as might be expected, appears to show a somewhat more irregular decline. In fact, the data suggests also that the treated symptom is tending to " overtake " the untreated in respect of rate of decrement and this too fits in with theoretical considerations.

These results are, of course, obtained only in 7 sessions, and the observations on each of the 5 trials within any session refer only to 3 lines of hand-writing. It may be that more prolonged periods of writing would result in symptom evocation, but it may be noted in this connection that at the end of the eighth session of training the patient was able to write 24 lines with only one hand spasm being manifested. It should also be pointed out that the quality of the writing, presumably as a result of reduction in the symptoms, was very much improved.

If these results are indicative of permanent decrement in the symptoms the results would appear to conflict with previous findings on extinction of responses mediated by anxiety. But at least one might reasonably argue that negative practice could be expected to produce more favourable results in the anxious patient than shock-avoidance training; the former is hardly likely to add to the degree of anxiety which may be implicit in the writing situation, and it may be that the actual act of writing during periods when symptoms are not manifested would be capable of reducing anxiety. Clearly a great deal more work would be required in order to sort out these complexities.

Mr. C. D.

This patient, aged 37, had suffered from " cramps " over a period of several years. He had received little in the way of treatment before coming to the present writer other than some psychotherapy and several psychiatric interviews.

His difficulties involved both hands. The right hand, which he used in handwriting, exerted so much energy in grasping the pen and pressing on its point that he became exhausted after writing a few words. Under such conditions the few words which he did manage to write were quite legible.

On the other hand any relaxation of this vast expenditure of energy resulted in his writing becoming extremely disorganized and so poorly controlled that almost nothing he wrote could be read.

His left hand, which he had habitually used in typing, was now clenched fairly tightly into a fist and he was quite unable to open this hand for more than a few seconds at a time. To prevent the fingernails of this hand digging into the palm, the patient frequently tucked a handkerchief between the two, or, on other occasions, interposed the thumb between palm and fingers.

There was extreme muscular tension in both hands and arms even in a state of " rest." The patient's MPI scores indicated high introversion and high neuroticism.

Attention was first concentrated upon the left hand, the choice of starting point being purely arbitrary. To begin with, the technique of avoidance conditioning was used, electrodes being attached to the palm in such a way that relief from shock could be obtained only by opening the hand. Even fairly severe shock failed to produce evidence of improvement in terms of increased duration of hand opening, and the procedure clearly evoked a fair measure of stress and discomfort. After 10 such training sessions, seeing the patient twice on each successive day, the method was abandoned in favour of negative practice.

Before commencing treatment at all it had been established that the patient was capable of opening his hand for an average duration of 3·5 sec over a series of 10 trials. Having established this base line a training schedule was devised which attempted to overpractise the " hand closure " response. The task chosen was exercise on the dynamometer where closure was achieved only with the expenditure of considerable muscular effort and opening the hand was relatively easy. On the dynamometer, hand opening and closing occur with equal frequency and if one were simply dependent upon this factor in extinction there would be no reason to expect that hand closure should be weakened while hand opening was strengthened. It is here supposed that the habit strength of " hand closing " is so much greater than that of " hand opening " that the latter has little chance of appearing, and the dynamometer exercise is specifically aimed at so weakening " hand closing " that the incompatible response of " hand opening " can occur. This differential weakening is achieved by the different degrees of effortfulness of the dynamometer responses.[27] The patient was given this exercise to " exhaustion," i.e. until he reported being unable to produce further effort in pulling on the dynamometer handle, twice each day on 5 days each week. The length of training actually extended over a period of approximately 8 weeks, the curve of improvement in duration of hand opening being shown in Fig. 3. In fact, after some 8 weeks of training the patient was able to hold open his hand for an indefinite period without feeling the need for closure.

This improvement was not maintained to the same degree outside the testing sessions however, although the patient actually reported that this ability to hold open his left hand was much improved even outside the test situation. It was particularly noticeable that under stress the old habit of involuntary closure was re-evoked almost in its old intensity, e.g. whenever

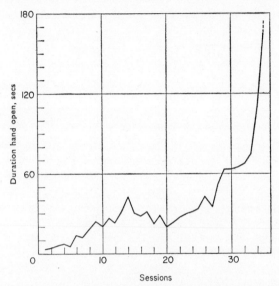

Fig. 3. Graph showing curve of improvement in duration of hand opening for patient C. D. after 33 sessions.

he began to think about or discuss his work, or when there were any difficulties with individuals in his environment, or when presented at a case conference. It appeared to be the case that whenever anxiety was evoked the old habit tended to reappear.

It could be argued that the improvement obtained with dynamometer practice was a response to the permissive nature of the environment in view of the above observations. However, it could be demonstrated that the decrement in the old response was a function of the actual technique, and the graph in Fig. 3 supports this contention. It is also supported by the data presented in graph form in Fig. 4 which illustrates the phenomenon of spontaneous recovery of the " bad " habit over a period of some 20 min after one training session on the dynamometer.

Attention was then turned upon the patient's right hand, again first using avoidance conditioning in an attempt to reduce the intense pressure exerted both in gripping the pen and in pressing its point into the paper. Specially constructed pens were used which delivered a strong electric shock whenever the grip and point pressure became excessive.

The results were again disappointing. Relaxation of pressure exacerbated tremors and spasms with a resultant marked deterioration in quality of writing. An attempt to correct tremor and spasms by avoidance conditioning followed, and in this case the patient simply reverted to the habits of excessive pressure in order to escape shock. No attempt was made to present shock to both types of escape responses at the same time as it became clear that the situation was becoming too stressful for the patient.

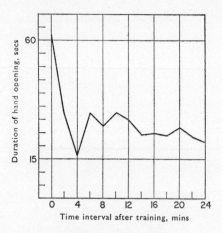

FIG. 4. Curve of recovery of habit of " hand closing " at varying intervals after dynamometer practice. Patient C. D.

At this stage it was decided to utilize the method of reciprocal inhibition as it appeared that the writing situation generated a good deal of anxiety in this patient and it seemed reasonable to conclude that shock was merely adding to his anxiety level and driving him from one maladaptive response to another.

For reasons already given, the incompatible response chosen was relaxation and an attempt was made to form a hierarchy of situations which would culminate in the act of writing. The range of situations covered imagining the act of writing, holding some object other than a pen while imagining the act of writing, holding a pen, writing with chalk on the blackboard, etc.

Training along these lines appeared to effect an improvement and for several days the patient maintained a good performance at the stage of being able to write without undue pressure and without any marked manifestation of tremor or spasm. However, the patient relapsed and the same training programme was re-instigated from the starting point of relaxation while imagining the act of writing. The outcome was virtually the same as before, a gradual improvement up to the stage of writing tolerably well for one or two days, followed by relapse. After a third attempt to train the patient along these lines had also resulted in failure the treatment was abandoned.

It is of course possible that the schedule of training planned was in some way defective, or that the experimenter was in too great a hurry in transferring from one stage to the next. For various reasons it was not possible to pursue these possible defects.

Mr. E. F.

This patient, aged 43, was referred for investigation of a writing disorder which had first troubled him about 17 years previously. He had also suffered from a speech disorder which commenced at about the same time but which had cleared up spontaneously some years before. The difficulty in writing had however continued without relief. He had previously sought treatment and had received this from three different psychiatrists. From one of them he had received psychoanalytic treatment over a period of 15 months without any improvement. From another he had received " hypnotherapy " over 8 sessions without benefit, although it should be added that the patient reported that no trance could be induced.

He described his difficulty as being that of " making the pen do what you want it to do." He tended to grip the pen very tightly and felt a sense of exhaustion after relatively little writing, such sensations occurring " sometimes right at the start, and sometimes after a line or two." The more " jittery and excited " he felt the more pronounced the disorder became. An additional symptom was that of hesitancy which took the form of very marked pauses, especially at the beginning of sentences, during which he found great difficulty in getting the pen down on to the paper. To a lesser extent this hesitancy occurred between words in one sentence.

Testing on the MPI resulted in the patient obtaining a moderate score on neuroticism and a high score on introversion.

As seems to be the case with many patients suffering from a writing disorder Mr. E. F. believed that the excessive pressure used in gripping the pen was the only way to prevent disorganized writing. Accordingly, this notion was tested for this patient by having him write after " exhausting " the writing hand by dynamometer practice. The outcome was clear cut. Before such practice the patient exerted a great deal of pressure, while after practice much less pressure was exerted without any noticeable deterioration in writing quality.

Two lines of treatment were planned, both involving avoidance conditioning. In the treatment of hesitancy, shock was delivered to the non-writing hand whenever hesitancy occurred. Undue pressure was treated by delivering shock whenever the patient's grip of the pen became excessive, a special pen being used for this purpose.

The curves of improvement on both these symptoms are shown in Figs. 5 and 6. The curve for " hesitancy " shows an almost linear decline over 26 sessions, each session occupying about 15 min of training. The symptom was rarely seen to occur after training. The curves for " pressure " show a somewhat more rapid decline, the manifestation of this symptom reaching zero on " shock " trials before doing so on " non-shock " trials

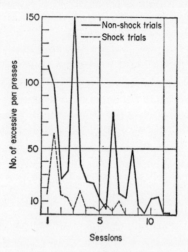

FIG. 5. Comparison of number of times excessive pen pressure used per 10 lines of writing on " shocked " and " non-shocked " trials. Patient E. F.

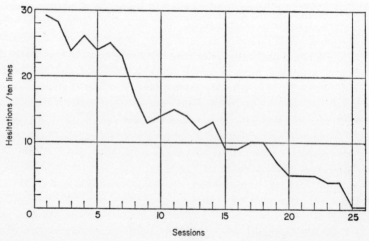

FIG. 6. Curve of improvement for " hesitancy " over 26 sessions. Patient F. F.

as might be expected. However, after 19 sessions, each lasting approximately 15 min, the pen was not squeezed excessively even when no shock was to be presented for this purpose.

Unfortunately the patient still reported sensations of fatigue and vague feelings of discomfort during the act of writing. Behaviourally, his movements in writing still appeared to be stiff and jerky and he perspired freely. In fact no relapse had occurred in the symptoms treated but there were signs of anxiety while writing and the patient did report a sense of strain under these conditions.

It was therefore decided to use relaxation as a response incompatible with the sensations of strain, fatigue, general discomfort, and assumed anxiety. The general plan adopted was very much along the lines previously outlined in the case of Mr. C. D. This method produced favourable results over a fairly lengthy period, actually several months, with the patient being seen once each week for 1 hr. During this time the quality of the patient's handwriting was further improved and he was able to write continuously for periods up to 1 hr without any manifestation of anxiety and without sensations of discomfort and fatigue.

The patient has remained symptom-free up to 1 year after treatment.

Mr. G. H.

This patient, a 36-year-old foreign postgraduate student at a British university, was referred for writing difficulties of long standing which had recently become exacerbated. When interviewed he complained that he had very great difficulty in taking adequate notes in lectures and that he feared he would be unable to sit his examinations because of his disorder. In respect of the latter problem an *amanuensis* had been offered by the university, but the student felt that he would find it difficult to communicate his ideas for others to write down.

As stated above, his present difficulties represented a recent exacerbation of long-standing complaints. The symptoms of which he complained had become intensified one or two years previously in his own country during a period of stress, but had subsided when the stress had been removed. The most recent intensification of the symptoms began some 3 months prior to referral to the present writer and appeared to coincide with his arrival in this country.

The symptoms as presented were excessive fatigue during the act of writing which forced him to rest very frequently, a fairly marked tremor and difficulty in " controlling the pen." The patient's writing was, in fact, barely legible in parts and a more detailed examination revealed that excessive pressure was being exerted by the thumb and index finger of the writing hand.

On testing, the MPI scores indicated high neuroticism with a moderate degree of extraversion. These scores may, of course, be misleading in view of cultural dissimilarities, but it was decided to assume them to be valid and to make a prediction from the former. According to the theoretical position adopted here, it should follow that avoidance conditioning should produce little benefit in the way of establishing a new response to the writing situation.

This prediction was tested by training the patient on the specially constructed pen which delivered shock whenever grip pressure became excessive. In 10 training sessions over a period of 3 weeks the following results were obtained:

Session	1	2	3	4	5	6	7	8	9	10
No. of excessive pressures (shocks)	48	102	110	62	71	69	125	110	98	132

Certainly these results do not provide any evidence that the patient was learning to avoid excessive pressure in gripping the pen. If anything they support the contention that, in the anxious patient, shock may very well exacerbate the symptoms.

It was, therefore, decided to revert to the procedure involving the use of relaxation as the response incompatible with anxiety in the writing situation. The actual techniques employed were essentially the same as those described in the case of Mr. C. D. The two symptoms selected for close scrutiny were tremor and pressure exerted, both responses being easily quantifiable.

The first stage involved maintaining a relaxed state while at the same time imagining the act of writing. Short periods of training were given in each session, each lasting approximately 30 sec, while the session was of approximately 1 hour's duration.

Initially the patient appeared to be slightly disturbed even by this remote imaginal situation. However, after several of these 30-sec trials during the first session he began to report feeling less tense, less fatigued, and had ceased to perspire so freely. These periods were then extended in length during the remainder of that session.

The next stage involved holding a small piece of wood in the manner adopted in holding a pen. A slight tremor and twitching of the fingers appeared under this condition, but this rapidly disappeared, and the patient was then next asked to imagine the act of writing while still holding the stick. Further stages were then passed through successfully until eventually, after 5 sessions the patient was writing with pen on paper in a relaxed manner without producing symptoms.

At this stage, when the patient was reporting excellent progress even when taking fast dictation in the form of class lecture notes, notice of a terminal examination was given which re-evoked the symptoms. In fact the intensity of these symptoms was much less marked than formerly and the most disturbing effect of this relapse was upon the morale of the patient.

It was decided next to deal with the apparently stressful nature of " examinations " in just the same way as before, constructing a hierarchy of situations building up to the real thing. This programme is now in progress, the patient having reached the stage at which he is able to write brief answers to short questions taken from the patient's own university syllabus without manifestation of symptoms.

CONCLUSION

The evidence presented here, although somewhat limited, suggests that one important variable governing the choice of therapeutic technique should be the patient's level of anxiety. In particular, the results presented in this chapter appear at first sight to be at variance with those obtained by Liversedge and Sylvester, but it is believed that this discrepancy can be accounted for in terms of differences in anxiety level of patients treated. Where the general level of anxiety is high the evidence presented would indicate that avoidance conditioning might fail to produce positive results and may even worsen the condition. It is assumed here that the anxiety evoked by shock or anticipation of shock is adding to the level already present. On the other hand, avoidance conditioning might successfully reduce the frequency and amplitude of symptoms where the anxiety level is low, but even here it appears that some alternative technique must be used in order to deal with situations in which the anxiety level may be raised.

Negative practice does appear to produce at least temporary favourable results where avoidance conditioning has failed, although the case of Mr. C. D. indicates that anxiety-producing stimuli may completely or partially negate any improvement so obtained.

Where the response is mediated by anxiety and where that anxiety level is high, the most appropriate treatment would appear to be by reciprocal inhibition. Here the training is specifically directed toward teaching the patient to produce a response or responses incompatible with the anxiety triggered-off by certain stimuli.

One possible difficulty arises in connection with this technique, namely that the therapist should have some awareness of the degree of anxiety evoked by his stimulus hierarchy, and also knowledge of the strength of the anxiety response in relation to the incompatible response. Failure to pay attention to these points may have contributed to the unsatisfactory outcome of treatment of Mr. C. D.

REFERENCES

1. JELLIFFE, S. E. (1910). Migraine, neuralgia, professional spasms, occupation neuroses, tetany. In *A System of Medicine* (ed. by Osler, W. and McCrae, T.). Hodder & Stoughton, London.
2. PAI, M. (1947). The nature and treatment of writer's cramp. *J. Ment. Sci.*, **93**.
3. CULPIN, M. (1931). *Recent Advances in the Study of the Psychoneuroses.* Churchill, London.
4. OSLER, W. (1906). *The Principles and Practice of Medicine.* Appleton, New York.
5. JANET, P. (1925). *Psychological Healing.* Allen & Unwin, London.
6. GLOVER, E. (1949). *Psycho-Analysis.* Staples Press, London.

7. DREWS, R. S. (1952). Psychodrama in private practice. *Group Psychother.*, **5**, 70-72.
8. SADLER, W. S. (1936). *Theory and Practice of Psychiatry.* Henry Kimpton, London.
9. MUNCIE, W. (1948). *Psychobiology and Psychiatry.* Henry Kimpton, London.
10. RADOVICI (1936). Der Schreibkrampf. *Zob. Neurol.*, **82**, 484.
11. KIHN, B. (1937). Uber den Schreibkrampf und seine behandlung. *Nervenarzt.*, **10**, 69-84.
12. LIVERSEDGE, L. A. and SYLVESTER, J. D. (1955). Conditioning techniques in the treatment of writer's cramp. This volume, pp. 327-333.
13. LIVERSEDGE, L. A. (1957). Conditioning treatment of writer's cramp. Paper presented at the Third European Conference on Psychosomatic Research. Copenhagen.
14. MOWRER, O. H. (1939). A stimulus-response analysis of anxiety and its role as a reinforcing agent. *Psychol. Rev.*, **46**, 553-566.
15. MOWRER, O. H. and LAMOREAUX, R. R. (1942). Avoidance conditioning and signal duration—a study of secondary motivation and reward. *Psychol. Monogr.*, **54**, No. 5.
16. MOWRER, O. H. and LAMOREAUX, R. R. (1946). Fear as an intervening variable in avoidance conditioning. *J. Comp. Psychol.*, **39**, 29-50.
17. SHEFFIELD, F. D. (1948). Avoidance training and the contiguity principle. *J. Comp. Physiol. Psychol.*, **41**, 165-177.
18. HULL, C. L. (1943). *Principles of Behavior.* Appleton–Century–Crofts, New York.
19. DUNLAP, K. (1932). *Habits, Their Making and Unmaking.* Liveright, New York.
20. YATES, A. J. (1958). The application of learning theory to the treatment of tics. This volume, pp. 24-27.
21. MILLER, N. E. (1951). Learnable drives and rewards. In *Handbook of Experimental Psychology* (ed. by Stevens, S. S.). Chapman & Hall, London.
22. SOLOMON, R. L. and WYNNE, L. C. (1954). Traumatic avoidance learning: the principles of anxiety conservation and partial irreversibility. *The Psychol. Rev.*, **61**, 353-385.
23. JONES, M. C. (1924). The elimination of children's fear. This volume, pp. 38-44.
24. MEYER, V. (1957). The treatment of two phobic patients on the basis of learning principles. This volume, pp. 135-143.
25. WOLPE, J. (1958). *Psychotherapy by Reciprocal Inhibition.* Stanford Univer. Press, Stanford.
26. EYSENCK, H. J. (1956). The questionnaire measurement of neuroticism and extraversion. *Rev. Psicol.*, **54**, 113-140.
27. MOWRER, O. H. and JONES, H. M. (1943). Extinction and behaviour variability as functions of effortfulness of task. *J. Exp. Psychol.*, **33**, 369-386.
28. JONES, H. G. (1958). Neurosis and experimental psychology. *J. Ment. Sci.*, **104**, 55-62.
29. DUNLAP, K. (1944). An experimental study of punishment. *Psychol. Monogr.*, **57**, No. 263.

PART V

THERAPY BY POSITIVE CONDITIONING AND FEED-BACK CONTROL

INTRODUCTION

MOST neurotic conditions investigated in the clinic or the hospital are characterized by *surplus conditioned reactions* and consequently the extinction of the habits, phobias, anxieties and the like thus acquired has attracted most attention. In certain cases, however, there are *deficient conditioned reactions* and in these conditions other methods may be required. Enuresis is the most obvious example that comes to mind; here clearly a conditioned response is missing which is present in the majority of people and learning theory provides appropriate methods for curing this particular symptom by positive conditioning. So much work has been done in this field, and the results are so important from the theoretical point of view, that a quite extensive review has been specially written for this book by H. Gwynne Jones.

Actually the antithesis between *surplus* and *deficient* conditioned reactions is probably less important than might appear at first sight. We never *abolish* a surplus reaction, but we substitute a positive reaction for it which is in some social or individual sense *better*; similarly, we do not create a new reaction where previously there was lack of one, but we substitute a better reaction for an inadequate one. It is as easy to look upon conditioning treatment for enuresis as the abolition of a bad habit (bed-wetting), as it is to regard it as the acquisition of a new, " good " habit. Similarly, getting rid of such bad habits as phobias, obsessive-compulsive symptoms or anxiety might be regarded as acquiring " good," i.e. more normal habits. It is when the " good " habit is specific, as in using the w.c., that we tend to speak about its absence as a *deficient* conditioned response; when the " good " habit is quite general and simply the absence of a specific bad habit, we tend to speak of *surplus* conditioned reactions being extinguished. Another way of differentiating between these two types of symptoms, again not very fundamental but merely heuristic, is by stressing that in the case of deficient reactions the response in question may never have been acquired in the first place, while in the case of surplus reactions a response specifically acquired has to be extinguished. While on both counts extreme cases are quite easy to classify, there must remain much doubt about others and decisions may be quite arbitrary and subjective in many cases.

One type of deficient conditioned reaction should have been included here but had to be omitted because no adequate accounts of successful treatment could be discovered. In *The Dynamics of Anxiety and Hysteria* attention has been drawn to the possibility that many psychopathic and criminal acts may be due to a failure of the individuals in question to acquire appropriate conditioned anxiety responses to behaviour which is socially undesirable; this was shown to be particularly likely to occur in the case of very extraverted individuals who were shown in general to have considerable difficulties in forming conditioned responses. Here would appear to be a condition somewhat analogous to enuresis, but of considerably greater social importance, where therapy by positive conditioning would appear to be called for. (It might be argued that the treatment of *criminals* is not within the province of the psychiatrist or the clinical psychologist, who deal exclusively with neurotics. It is noteworthy that in our experimental work with criminals, particularly with recidivists, we have throughout found them to have mean neuroticism scores of a size similar to clinical neurotic groups. In terms of questionnaire responses, recidivists were indistinguishable from hysterics on neuroticism and on extraversion.) Experimental work in this field would appear to be as promising as the application of behaviour therapy has shown itself to be in that of the clinical neuroses, and the traditional failure of society to deal with crime may be transformed into success by calling in the aid of modern learning theory. Needless to say, much arduous experimentation and theorizing will be required before any useable form of treatment can emerge; there are no cheap and easy answers to profound and long-standing problems.

THE BEHAVIOURAL TREATMENT OF ENURESIS NOCTURNA*

H. Gwynne Jones

Department of Psychology, Institute of Psychiatry, Maudsley Hospital

PHYSIOLOGY OF MICTURITION

AN ADEQUATE behavioural account of the aetiology and treatment of bed-wetting needs to be based on an adequate analysis of the mechanism of micturition. Contemporary views concerning the physiology of micturition are based on the classic experiments of such workers as Barrington,[1,2,3] Learmonth[4] and Denny-Brown and Robertson,[5] and are well reviewed by Best and Taylor.[6] For the purposes of this paper it is sufficient to present a brief schematic description in functional terms without reference to anatomical detail. Several of the mechanisms described were originally postulated on the basis of the results of experiments with animals, particularly cats: the physiology of human micturition may differ in several respects.

Urine passes from the kidneys to the bladder via the *ureters*. This passage is assisted by peristaltic action of the ureteral walls, the urine entering the bladder in " spurts " rather than a steady flow. Backflow of urine into the ureters is prevented by the oblique extension of the latter into the vesical (bladder) cavity and their consequent closure by back pressure or contraction of the bladder wall.

Urine is voided from the bladder via the *urethra*, a muscular tube passing from the base of the bladder to the exterior. The proximal portion of its wall includes layers of smooth (involuntary) muscle fibres and, at its junction with the bladder, these condense to form the *internal sphincter* which, when contracted, closes the urethral orifice. In the male the distal portion of the urethra is encircled by a striated (voluntary) muscle or *external sphincter*. Though women lack this sphincter, urine is not allowed to escape after paralysis of the internal sphincter owing to contraction of the urethral wall and neighbouring muscles.

The bladder itself is a roughly spherical sac the wall of which includes three layers of smooth muscle fibres constituting the *detrusor* muscle. Owing to the reactions of this muscle, the bladder does not respond to increasing volume of its contents in the manner of an elastic container such as a rubber balloon. Within wide limits the detrusor tone is progressively adjusted to

* Specially written for this book.

allow changes in the volume of stored urine with little alteration in internal pressure.

The tone of the detrusor muscle and internal sphincter is controlled by the co-ordinated but antagonistic activity of the pelvic (parasympathetic) and hypogastric (sympathetic) nerves (see Fig. 1). Parasympathetic stimulation increases the tone of the detrusor and has an inhibitory effect on the internal sphincter; sympathetic stimulation has the reverse effects. Detrusor tone and hence bladder capacity varies according to the type and degree of activity of the organism and with its physiological and emotional state.

Cystometric studies have shown that when additional fluid enters the bladder there is an immediate smooth rise in pressure but, after a brief interval, there occurs an abrupt re-adjustment of tone and the pressure falls sharply to a level little above the original. When the volume of stored fluid exceeds some 200–250 ml further additions of fluid cause larger increases in pressure and the tonal compensation mechanism, though more vigorous than at low volumes, is less effective in restoring the lower pressure. As still more fluid enters the bladder, the detrusor muscle commences to respond with rhythmical contractions and, as the pressure increases still further, the micturition reflex occurs. This consists of strong contraction of the detrusor with relaxation of the internal sphincter followed by the opening of the external sphincter and the emptying of the bladder. There are wide individual differences in the pressure at which this response occurs, a typical value being about 20 ml of water. During urination the pressure exerted by the contraction of the detrusor rises to well over 100 ml of water and evacuation continues until the bladder is practically empty.

Tension in the detrusor is the adequate stimulus for this response and, as the volume of urine in the bladder increases, a human subject is first aware of vague feelings of discomfort in the penis or perineal region. Though micturition is based on a reflex mechanism the normal adult subject can initiate it voluntarily and can inhibit it well beyond the first sensation of urgency. If it is long postponed, there are marked sensations of fullness, discomfort and ultimately pain. It is probable that, at bladder volumes insufficient to arouse conscious sensations of urgency, voluntary mechanisms operate at a sub-conscious level to restrain the reflex. Various postural adjustments, particularly of the abdominal and perineal musculature, are probably important factors in the voluntary control of micturition.[7,8]

Though described as a reflex, micturition is in fact a complex response resulting from the co-ordinated activation of several simple reflex mechanisms. Of these, five are particularly important for normal integrated activity of the urinary apparatus and are described below. The relevant neural pathways are illustrated in Fig. 1.

(1) Contraction of the detrusor muscle and reciprocal relaxation of the internal sphincter is evoked by distension of the bladder. Both afferent and

efferent pathways of the reflex arc consist of parasympathetic fibres of the pelvic nerves. There is evidence that this reflex is normally under the control of a " centre " in the region of the hind-brain.

(2) Contraction of the detrusor muscle is evoked by fluid running through the urethra. The afferent path consists of somatic fibres of the pudic nerve and the efferents lie in the pelvic nerves. This arc is also linked to a " centre " in the hind-brain. This reflex was originally observed in cats by Barrington.

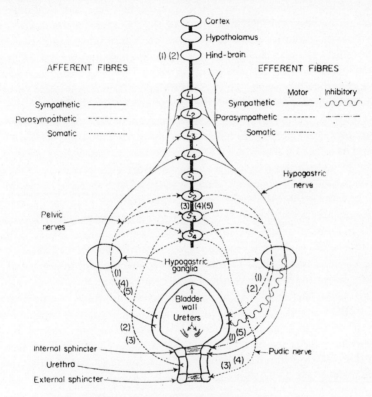

FIG. 1.   Schematic representation of the nervous control of urination responses: afferent fibres shown on left, efferent fibres on right.

S_1 to S_4 = sacral segments of spinal cord
L_1 to L_4 = lumbar segments of spinal cord
(1) to (5) = paths of main micturition reflexes

Nathan[9] found no evidence of such a response to stimulation of the urethra in human subjects but Barrington[1] points out that the effective stimulus may not be the passage of fluid through the urethra but the relaxation of the external sphincter induced by this passage (see (3) below). Certainly in the absence of a reflex of this nature it is difficult to explain how the bladder continues to discharge when the initial pressure is relieved.

(3) The external sphincter relaxes in response to passage of urine along the urethra. Both afferent and efferent limbs lie in the pudic nerves and the " centre " is located in the sacral region of the spinal cord.

(4) Relaxation of the external sphincter is evoked by distension of the bladder. The afferent pathway lies in the pelvic and the efferent pathway in the pudic nerves. Again the " centre " is in the sacral region of the cord.

(5) Relaxation of the involuntary musculature of the proximal portion of the urethra is evoked by distension of the bladder. Both afferent and efferent paths lie in the pelvic nerves and the " centre " in the sacral cord.

In normal micturition the first of these reflexes is sufficient to initiate all the others automatically. The sympathetic (hypogastric) nerves appear to be unimportant for the act of micturition, their role being confined to the maintenance of appropriate tone of the detrusor and proximal urethra.

Apart from nerve centres in the spinal cord, hind-brain and possibly the mid-brain the phenomena of voluntary control of urination indicate the importance of cortical areas. Excitatory and inhibitory effects on the detrusor have been noted when electrical stimulation has been applied to the pre-motor areas of the cortex or to regions of the hypothalamus. Ablations and other experiments suggest that the cortical and hypothalamic centres both tend to inhibit the reflex arcs involved in micturition. Voluntary micturition may then consist in a relaxation of these inhibitory influences.

The hind-brain centre appears to be essential to normal micturition. If the cord is severed above the sacral region, there is recovery—after a period during which urine is retained until overflow—to a condition in which the bladder, under the control of the sacral centres, empties automatically at intervals. Considerable residual urine remains, however, in the bladder, owing to the absence of the first and second reflexes described earlier. Even when the bladder is completely isolated from central nervous control it may partially empty automatically in this manner. The co-ordinate activity of the detrusor and internal sphincter in this condition suggest that purely local reflex arcs run through a vesical plexus.

THE DEVELOPMENT OF VOLUNTARY AND NOCTURNAL CONTROL OF THE BLADDER

Micturition in the infant is an automatic reflex response to moderate bladder tension and similar in many respects to the micturition of mature animal or human subjects in whom disease or surgical intervention isolates the bladder from the control of higher nervous centres.[10] Cortical influences can only operate after a period of post-natal neural maturation. Once connections are established between the cortex and the lower centres there arises, not only the possibility of voluntary initiation and inhibition of micturition, but also the possibility of the development of numerous conditioned reflexes linking this initiation and inhibition with various environmental stimulus situations. Thus, at a later age, the child is able to choose, within fairly broad limits, the time and place at which he will allow micturition to occur and he tends to experience the urge to urinate at relatively low bladder volumes when in a " toilet " environment, or adopting certain postures.

The obvious establishment of such conditioned reflexes during normal development is the stimulus for the widespread adoption of various toilet-training procedures such as " potting " the child when taken up after sleep, after meals, before sleeping and at other times during the day. Though some authorities recommend such schedules of training from the early months, McGraw,[11] in a carefully controlled experiment, found that two male infants trained in this way showed little or no gain in bladder control when compared with their twin brothers who had received no specific training.

McGraw used, as a measure of bladder control, the ratio of the number of positive responses during a daily 7 hr potting schedule to the total number of urinations during the same period. This ratio tended to decline slightly during the early months and was at a minimum between 6 and 10 months. It then increased rapidly up to 1 year, declined again for a month or two and then rose steadily to stabilize at about the 90 per cent value by 2 years. The early relatively high ratio, during a period when the cortex is considered to have no influence on the bladder, might be due, McGraw suggests, to hyper-sensitivity of the reflex mechanism at this stage. The first rise follows the beginning of cortical participation in micturition and, during this period, McGraw observed that the children began to attend and overtly react to the act of micturition and its consequences. The decline following this rise is postulated to relate to a disturbance of the positive conditioned reflexes established during the earlier period which results from the complex patterns of inhibitory conditioned reflexes and discriminations being learned at that time. Stabilization and integration of these patterns are considered to coincide with the final improvement in scores.

The controls for McGraw's data concerning changes in bladder capacity were inadequate for a developmental study of this attribute. She found no evidence, however, of any basic physiological rhythm such as has been frequently postulated and upon which many training schedules are based.

Ultimately, bladder control becomes so well established that the external sphincter may be voluntarily contracted to cut off the flow of urine during the act of micturition: other striated muscles in the perineal region contract simultaneously. Contraction of the external sphincter in this way almost certainly inhibits the contractions of the detrusor[12] though whether this inhibition occurs by simple or conditioned reflex action remains obscure. The sensitivity of the perineal musculature to local skin stimulation indicates how postural stimuli in particular may readily become conditioned stimuli for this chain of responses.

The voluntary initiation of micturition, which is of less interest in the context of this paper, is less well understood in that the external sphincter cannot be opened voluntarily independently of detrusor activity.[13] Voluntary micturition begins with relaxation of the perineal muscles which is immediately followed by strong vesical contractions. Voluntarily induced intra-abdominal pressure is a usual but inessential factor. Thus, voluntary micturition is usually interpreted in terms of a relaxation of voluntary restraint,[5] but the conditioning of vesical contraction to postural stimuli is also likely to be of great importance.

Nocturnal continence is very rarely achieved before bladder-control in the waking state is well established. This suggests strongly that similar mechanisms are involved but that the maintenance of cortical inhibition is more difficult during sleep. Writers on this topic, however, have postulated independent factors of maturation and learning.

Mowrer and Mowrer,[14] while admitting that untrained healthy children will ultimately achieve nocturnal control as do members of other mammalian species, lay great stress on parental training. If a child is wakened consistently when his bladder is at moderate pressure and then urinates, there will develop in time, they suggest, a conditioned response of awakening to the stimulus of sub-threshold bladder pressure. They describe analogous but unintentional training situations common in primitive cultures.

In the writer's view, the Mowrers greatly exaggerate the prevalence of nocturnal training even in western culture. More damaging to their viewpoint, however, is the fact that children, once nocturnal continence is achieved, rapidly acquire the ability to sleep through the night without waking to urinate. As urination immediately follows waking during training, this system would also be likely to reinforce tendencies to urinate at low bladder pressures except that the range of pressures at which waking occurs is likely to be so wide as to prevent any appreciable conditioning to pressure stimuli.

Crosby[15] stresses the development of cortical inhibitory tendencies which, with increasing anatomical capacity of the bladder, ultimately allow the child to remain continent without waking. In a healthy older child or adult these inhibitory tendencies become so potent that he may wake from a deep sleep to the immediate experience of considerable pain from a greatly extended bladder.

Crosby quotes evidence to show that a range of stimulation, particularly if of a startling nature, evokes responses which reciprocally inhibit micturition. He postulates that a naturally occurring stimulus of this nature is the " somatic discomfort " deriving from the " wet urinous state " of the child who has wet his bed. At the onset of micturition this, he suggests, evokes an unconditioned response tending to reflexly inhibit the contraction of the detrusor and the relaxation of the sphincters. Repeated soiling leads to a progressive increase in the inhibitory tone of the bladder and hence to an increase in the volume of urine necessary to initiate urination. A concomitant increase in intra-vesical pressure would tend to disperse sleep. Training procedures, according to Crosby, may well disrupt this developmental trend. Gross extension of the soiling period, as occurs with enuretics, is postulated to lead to adaptation to the somatic discomfort and consequent inefficiency of the reciprocal inhibition.

The outstanding weakness of Crosby's argument lies in his choice of an inhibitory stimulus. If the " wet urinous state " produces an antagonistic response immediately, the infant would never complete the act of micturition. If, however, the " somatic discomfort " does not arise until some time after soiling there is then no appreciable degree of detrusor tension to be inhibited. General observation and systematic observations of the writer's own two children indicate that infants during the period of incontinence present no evidence of aversive reactions to being wet unless the napkins become cold or " stale " or the skin sore. Crosby presents no direct evidence in support of his postulates.

The two children mentioned, one male and one female, were never submitted to any training procedures during their sleeping hours. After napkins had been discarded during the day they were worn at night and removed in the morning until such time as they were consistently unsoiled. In this way both children achieved continence by the age of 3 years which, if rather late by parental " ideal " standards, cannot be considered abnormal.

It appears unnecessary to postulate learning mechanisms operative in the development of nocturnal continence additional to those described in relation to daytime bladder control. Without entering into the vexed question of the physiological nature of sleep it is clear that the sleeping state essentially involves the inactivation of the higher parts of the brain, especially the cerebral cortex. During sleep the threshold for most somatic reflexes is raised but that for most autonomic reflexes is lowered.[6] Despite the general low activity of the cortex certain " sentinel " points involved in the control of vegetative functions remain active[16] and local awakening may occur in response to appropriate stimuli.[17,20]

Sentinel points in the cortex for the inhibitory control of bladder reflexes are established by neural maturation and day-time learning. With further maturation and increased potency of these centres, they are likely to remain locally active during sleep or to " awaken " in response to bladder and postural stimuli. The importance of such cortical influences during sleep is strongly indicated by the prevalence, among enuretics, of the " toilet dreams," described by Mowrer and Mowrer[14] and others, in which the sleeping child dreams that he is in a toilet or secluded place, adopts a suitable posture, and urinates.

The operation of these mechanisms is portrayed schematically in Fig. 2. The unbroken lines represent the course of events at the stage when the child is continent during the day but incontinent at night. Throughout the range of bladder pressures up to the threshold for micturition, the cortical

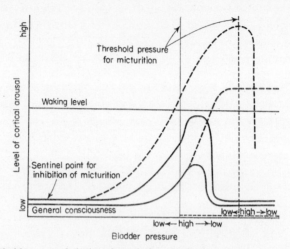

FIG. 2. Bladder control during sleep, before (unbroken lines) and after (broken lines) achievement of continence.

sentinel area is relatively inactive. Though sleep may be somewhat disturbed, the child urinates without waking and sleeps on in a soiled state. When cortical influences have become more potent the sentinel area, as shown by the broken lines, becomes fully active well before the micturition threshold, which now corresponds to a greater volume of urine, is reached. As pressure increases sleep becomes progressively more shallow until the child wakes, experiences the urge to urinate, and goes to the toilet. The increased bladder capacity would be expected from the tonic effects on the detrusor of the cortical inhibitory influences and from anatomical growth. Ultimately, tolerance will be sufficient to enable the child to sleep throughout the night in normal conditions.

NOCTURNAL ENURESIS*

Definition and Incidence

The developmental processes described in the preceding section involve the acquisition of delicately adjusted and finely co-ordinated central nervous

---

* This discussion is confined to nocturnal enuresis unrelated to demonstrable organic pathology or anatomical abnormality. Diurnal enuresis and such disorders as frequency of micturition are not considered though these are frequently associated with nocturnal enuresis.

responses in opposition to a strong natural reflex. Not surprisingly, a proportion of children fail to achieve this adjustment or are retarded in terms of its development. All young infants are bed-wetters and the age beyond which the clinical term *enuresis nocturna* may be applied depends upon the age at which a normal child may be expected to achieve nocturnal continence. In contemporary western culture most parents expect their children to cease bed-wetting during the third year of life: lapses after this age are frequently described as " accidents." In accordance with this criterion many authorities, in defining enuresis, put the borderline at 3 years.[18] Recent authors, employing a statistical criterion of abnormality, have tended to raise the borderline to 4 years[19] or 5.[20] A distinction may be made between children who have never achieved continence and those who revert to bed-wetting after a period of continence. These may be described as suffering from primary and acquired enuresis respectively.[21]

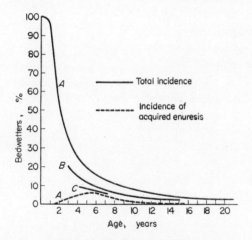

FIG. 3.   Incidence of bed-wetting at different ages:
A—After Crosby[15]
B—From data in Bransby *et al.*[22]
C—From data in Hallgren[19]

As enuresis is a developmental disorder its incidence must be assessed in relation to age. Crosby[15] constructed an age incidence curve for bed-wetting from his own data and available published material. This is included, as curve *A*, in Fig. 3. For comparison, additional data from recent surveys in England and Sweden have also been included. Curve *B* is a plot of smoothed weighted averages of the data from a national survey and studies in York and Birmingham described by Bransby *et al.*[22] Curve *C* is based on a combination of the data for males and females provided by Hallgren[19] from his survey in Stockholm schools. These additional data, while tending to confirm the general shape of Crosby's curve, suggest that his estimates may be too high, though the nature of the later surveys was such as to produce a bias towards underestimation. It is clear, however, that enuresis is among the most widespread of children's disorders. Most authors report a higher incidence for boys than girls and this is confirmed by Hallgren[23] for an unbiased sample. The shape of the curves, while illustrating the high rate of spontaneous recovery to be expected in a developmental disorder, does not support the hypothesis, sometimes advanced, that the period of puberty is especially favourable to recovery.

Aetiology

The literature concerning the aetiology of enuresis is extensive and theories numerous but most of the latter may be subsumed under one or other of the following six categories without gross injustice to the authors' points of view:

(1) Specific Physiological Dysfunction

Some authorities consider that enuresis may not be a symptom of some more general disorder but a specific clinical entity. Crosby[15] uses the term " essential " enuresis and believes that most enuretics fall into this category. He postulates that these children, owing presumably to some specific immaturity, fail to achieve continence before adapting to the " somatic discomfort " he considers instrumental in the acquisition of tonic detrusor inhibition. In a majority of cases complications arise from the conditioning of the act of micturition to various stimuli impinging upon sleep, or to intervals of time. Many of these complicating responses, Crosby suggests, derive from attempts at training by the parents and he reports consistent patterns of nocturnal urination in support of this view.

Mowrer and Mowrer[14] also consider that, in a large proportion of cases, enuresis derives primarily from faulty habit development. Though mention is made of individual differences in response to training, they stress, however, the faultiness of the training rather than the immaturity of the child.

(2) General Immaturity

Enuresis is often described as one aspect of general immaturity which may also be reflected in other spheres of development such as speech, in timid and dependent behaviour and in emotional immaturity.[18] Intelligence, above the " defective " level, is apparently unrelated to enuresis.

(3) Deep Sleep

Another characteristic of a physiological nature, frequently considered to be typical of enuretics, is hypersomnia. Braithwaite,[24] from an extensive clinical study, concludes that, with chronic tension of the detrusor, deep sleep is a fundamental condition in enuresis and psychological factors are secondary. Ström-Olsen[25] reached similar conclusions from the study of a group of adult patients. Depth of sleep was not objectively measured in these studies and two subsidiary factors may contribute to a clinical impression of deep sleep. Enuretics, by reason of their wet beds and parental supervision, are subjected to excessive stimulation during sleep. A protective response of " not waking " may then develop as it does in people living in close proximity to factories or railway stations. Parents frequently attempt to wake their enuretic children at times of maximal sleep but rarely wake their normal children, except in the morning. In this way a false impression of differential " wakeability " may arise.

Ditman and Blinn[26] made electrographic recordings of the sleep-levels and other physiological changes in enuretics during sleep. Some subjects were unresponsive to arousal stimuli at times when their EEG recordings were typical of the waking state and were " physiologically awake " at the time of urination though unaware of the act. Bed-wetting occurred at all stages from deep sleep to wakefulness though the former was more typical of young children. Before and during urination there was increased general autonomic and motor activity.

(4) Behaviour Disorder

Several authors consider that enuresis is but one manifestation of a general behaviour disorder. Michaels, in a long series of papers (see especially Michaels[27]) has particularly elaborated this view. He concludes that enuresis is closely related to delinquency, both being manifestations of a fundamental psychopathic personality. Though his interpretations of this syndrome are largely psychoanalytic in nature, Michaels draws implications of a biological nature and reports positive associations with EEG abnormalities.

(5) Emotional Disturbance

A high incidence of enuresis among children displaying nervous symptoms or emotional disturbance is frequently reported, but it is extremely difficult to establish whether, in these cases, the enuresis is a consequence, a cause or independent of the emotional difficulties.[14] Certainly increased environmental stress, as in war-time conditions, tends to precipitate the disorder[28] and the findings of experimental psychology indicate that anxiety and similar emotional states have a disruptive effect on learned behaviour, especially when the latter involves complex discriminations.[29] Enuresis itself is, however, a source of distress and makes the sufferer a target for parental censure and punishment. In this way it may become the cause of secondary emotional disturbances.

(6) Specific Dynamic Connotation

Several writers, particularly those of a psychoanalytic persuasion, suggest that enuresis may play a specific role in the psychodynamics of neurotic patients.[14] One view, advanced by Freud himself, is that bed-wetting functions as a substitute for sexual gratification. This is a difficult hypothesis to evaluate except by the methods of psychoanalysis.

Others[30] consider that enuretic behaviour often has an aggressive connotation and that, by bed-wetting, the child is able to exercise power over or express his resentment towards his parents. This view is supported by the lack of co-operation shown by some patients during the treatment of their enuresis.

Many of the hypotheses implicit in the above classification were tested by Hallgren[19,23,21] in his recent extensive and carefully controlled investigation in Stockholm. His conclusions include the following:

(a) Diurnal enuresis and frequency of micturition are positively associated with nocturnal enuresis.

(b) The age of onset of acquired enuresis is typically less than 4 years and rarely over 8.

(c) When the lower intelligence ranges are excluded there is no significant relationship between intellectual level and enuresis.

(d) Left-handedness is unrelated to enuresis.

(e) From clinical histories, deep sleep is significantly more common in enuretics than in matched controls. Other evidence, however, suggests that deep sleep is not causally related to enuresis.

(f) Enuresis is associated with a high incidence of emotional disturbance, nervous symptoms and behavioural abnormalities. No differential association with clinical " types " was evident.

(g) Enuresis is associated with speech disorder and other indicators of immaturity. It is probable that both symptoms are concurrent manifestations of a common cause.

(h) Enuresis is more common in lower socio-economic groups and is associated with adverse environmental conditions such as broken homes, maternal psychiatric disorders, mother-child separation, and " unfavourable background." Onset of acquired enuresis may often be related to increased emotional stress.

(i) Aetiologically, nocturnal enuresis is a heterogeneous condition.

(j) Hallgren was particularly concerned to carry out a genetic analysis. The implications of his findings are by no means unequivocal but he concludes, tentatively, that though there are many " non-genetic " cases of nocturnal enuresis, there exists a group in which the condition is primarily genetically determined but the manifestation of the genes is modified by environmental factors.

In general, Hallgren's findings support most of the hypotheses described earlier. He did, however, find significantly more " childhood masturbation " in enuretic children than in their unaffected siblings, a fact difficult to reconcile with the hypothesis that enuresis is a substitute for sexual behaviour.

It is clear that the causation of nocturnal enuresis is heterogeneous and usually multi-factorial. This is consistent with the developmental theory described in the previous section and illustrated in Fig. 2. The course of development would be expected to be affected by abnormalities affecting any one of the interacting functions. Various physiological factors might affect the development of the " sentinel " point, the cortical arousal mechanisms, the waking level and the micturition threshold. Owing to a characteristic high level of " cortical inhibition," individuals of extremely extraverted temperament might develop hypersomnia, while those of neurotic constitution might be expected to have low thresholds for micturition as for other autonomic responses.[31,29] Emotional reactions would have a disruptive effect on the learned " sentinel " functions in the manner already described.

Treatment (Excluding Specific Conditioning)

The methods of treatment which have been applied to enuresis are even more heterogeneous than the aetiological theories as, in addition to those logically indicated by the latter, a host of empirical treatments have been developed at various times but have failed to survive in clinical practice. Some indication of this diversity is provided by Geppert's[32] report on the previous treatments received by 42 enuretic children referred to him for treatment. He gives the following percentages:

Psychiatric treatment	8 per cent	
Punishments	24	„ „
Drugs	30	„ „
Rewards	54	„ „
Arousing at intervals	60	„ „
Restriction of liquids	80	„ „

Davidson and Douglass[33] only employed their conditioning method with patients who had failed to respond to various other methods of treatment. Persuasion, suggestion under relaxation, ephedrine, methyl-ephedrine, amphetamine, placebo and the keeping of a record card are all mentioned.

Most of the reported methods of treatment may be classified under four broad categories:

(1) Avoidance of Bed-wetting

Many physicians recommend the restriction of fluid intake, particularly during the latter part of the day, in order to control enuresis. It is very doubtful that bed-wetting can be avoided in this way as the bladder receptors are sensitive to highly concentrated urine and the enuretic is characteristically prone to micturate at low bladder volumes.[15] One aspect of the therapeutic

26

problem is the development of tolerance for larger volumes of urine and Smith[12] even suggests that deliberate day-time practice of such tolerance may be of benefit.

The awakening of the enuretic child to urinate at intervals throughout the night, whether by alarm clock or by the parents, is similarly intended to prevent the accumulation of sufficient urine for involuntary micturition. In so far as the practice establishes conditioned waking responses to moderate bladder tension or to certain intervals of time, it may also be classed as a conditioning treatment.[14] As such, however, it would tend to reinforce the maintenance of low micturition thresholds. Even so, Davidenkov[16] claims that, by establishing a conditioned waking reflex to a specific time of the night, a colleague successfully treated 70 of 77 enuretic patients so trained. During the conditioning period these patients received a mixture of bromides and caffeine or ephedrine at night.

(2) Pharmacological Treatment

Drugs such as posterior pituitary snuff may also be used to limit the production of urine at night[34] but drug therapy is more usually intended to reduce the depth of sleep or to inhibit micturition by parasympathoparalytic action. Thus, by reducing the depth of sleep with massive doses of amphetamine sulphate, Ström-Olsen claims good therapeutic results with adult enuretics.

Leys[35] carried out a carefully controlled evaluation of the efficacy of propantheline bromide as compared with placebo. The ratio of wet to dry beds was measured for 2 pre-trial weeks, 2 trial weeks and 4 post-trial weeks. While there was a significant decrease in this ratio in the drug group, but not in the placebo group, during the 2 trial weeks, this difference between the groups was not maintained during the post-trial period.

(3) Psychotherapy

All forms of psychotherapy, from the most superficial to full psychoanalysis, are described in the literature on enuresis, the range being too wide to attempt generalization. Several psychotherapists would refrain from any specific attack on the enuresis as such, subscribing to the view, described earlier, that it satisfies some dynamic " need " of the patient and, if removed, would further prejudice the patient's adjustment and be replaced by fresh symptoms.

(4) Suggestion

As many different treatments have, at different times, produced apparently good therapeutic results for some therapists, but these results could not be duplicated by others, it has been considered that enuresis is responsive to suggestion procedures.[14] It has even been claimed that the method employed is of little importance so long as the therapist believes in its efficacy. In line with this reasoning, a number of deliberately suggestive techniques have been employed, ranging from the keeping, by the child, of record cards of his wet and dry nights to the use of hypnosis.

Owing to the multiplicity of the methods of treatment and the inadequacies of many of the reports it is impossible to attempt an assessment of relative efficacy, but the fact that enuresis continues to present an extremely difficult therapeutic problem is evident from data reported by Blomfield and Douglas.[36] They assessed the further progress of children who were regularly wet at the age of 6 and relate this to broad categories of treatment. Their findings are set out in Table 1.

TABLE 1

		Type of treatment (as reported at 6 years)			
		Clinic	Reward or punishment	Other active measures	No treatment
Number of children		41	67	32	26
State at age 7¾ yrs.	Dry	19·5%	20·9%	31·3%	57·7%
	Improved	24·4%	28·4%	28·1%	11·5%
	Unchanged	56·1%	50·7%	40·6%	30·8%

Some 30 per cent of the entire group recovered between the ages of 6 and 7¾ years, a figure approximating equal to that to be expected to spontaneously recover according to the age incidence data plotted in Fig. 3. The recovery rate within the " no-treatment " group is well above the average and that within the " clinic " group is below the average. This does not imply that medical treatment is detrimental to this condition as undoubtedly the " clinic " group included the more complicated disorders. It is clear, however, that contemporary clinical procedures have little effect on enuresis.

SPECIFIC CONDITIONING TREATMENT OF ENURESIS

Rationale

Despite the disappointing results obtained with most methods of treatment of enuresis and the apparent efficiency of the method to be described in this section, the latter has gained little general acceptance during the

20 or so years since the Mowrers'[14] important paper. There is, however, a suggestion of a reversal of this trend in recent publications.

It is likely that clinicians are reluctant to adopt this method because it is highly specific and, as such, violates the clinical *dictum* that " one should treat the disease and not its symptoms." According to this view, symptomatic treatment will inevitably lead to " symptom substitution." Despite the evidence to the contrary, this prejudice dies hard and is very likely important in the genesis of two very common misapprehensions concerning the nature of the technique. It is frequently said that the method is punitive and even that the patient is submitted to electric shocks—though this is only true of Crosby's modification of the method. It is also argued that conditioning cannot be involved as the ringing of the bell occurs last in the sequence of events and backward conditioning is notoriously difficult to establish. In fact, the bell is not employed as a conditioned stimulus. Owing to the prevalence of these false beliefs it is worthwhile to consider the rationale of the method in some detail.

Though earlier European work on similar lines has been described, Mowrer and Mowrer[14] were the first to devise and, for therapeutic purposes, to make systematic use of an efficient apparatus for waking a child immediately following the onset of micturition. Extending their theory of normal bladder training, described earlier, they argued that to awaken the child at this time would have the effect of conditioning the waking response to the stimulus of bladder tension at or near the threshold value for micturition. This could only occur if waking followed the onset of micturition within a very brief span of time. As waking was accompanied by the inhibition of further urination it was also postulated that the latter would become conditioned to threshold bladder tension and therefore raise the threshold on future occasions.

The Mowrers do not state clearly whether they consider that the inhibition of further urination is an involuntary act simultaneous with the response of waking or a voluntary act following waking. If the latter were true, the temporal relationships would probably be such as to prevent the conditioning of the inhibitory response to events preceding waking.

In fact, the response to a waking stimulus such as a bell reciprocally inhibits micturition as, indeed, is shown by the Mowrers' report that urination usually ceases even though the child fails to wake. Thus the bell, an *unconditioned* stimulus, evokes two simultaneous responses, waking and the reflex inhibition of micturition. If it is arranged that the bell rings immediately following the onset of micturition, both these responses occur in appropriate temporal relationship to the stimuli evoking micturition for conditioning to occur. The conditioning paradigm can be schematically represented as follows (UCS = unconditioned stimulus, CS = conditioned stimulus, UCR = unconditioned response, CR = conditioned response):

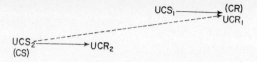

UCS$_1$ is the original stimulus for response UCR$_1$. UCS$_2$ is the original stimulus for response UCR$_2$, which is usually neglected in conditioning experiments. If UCS$_2$ consistently precedes UCS$_1$ by some brief interval of time, a " connection " is established between UCS$_2$ and UCR$_1$ such that UCS$_2$, now termed a conditioned stimulus, if presented alone, will evoke UCR$_1$, now termed a conditioned response. If the stimuli and responses under discussion are substituted for these symbols the following two patterns result:

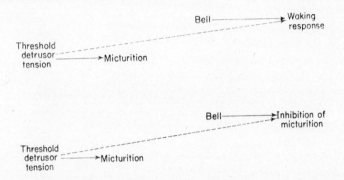

Thus detrusor tension, in addition to being the unconditioned stimulus for micturition, becomes the conditioned stimulus for the inhibition of micturition and for an independent waking response.

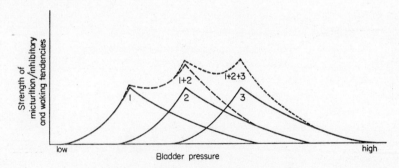

FIG. 4. Summation of generalization gradients for conditioned response tendencies.
1 to 3 = individual generalization gradients
1 + 2 = summation of gradients 1 and 2
1 + 2 + 3 = summation of gradients 1, 2 and 3

According to the principle of stimulus generalization,[37] if conditioning occurs at any one intensity of the conditioned stimulus, the conditioned response tendency, in progressively lesser degree, is also evoked by adjacent stimulus values. This generalization gradient is less steep in the direction of the higher stimulus values. If later reinforcements occur at a stimulus value different from the original the resulting generalization gradients summate with those established earlier. The successive summation of the relevant generalization gradients is schematically presented in Fig. 4.

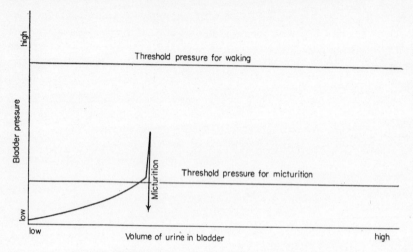

FIG. 5.   Nocturnal urination of enuretic (before training).

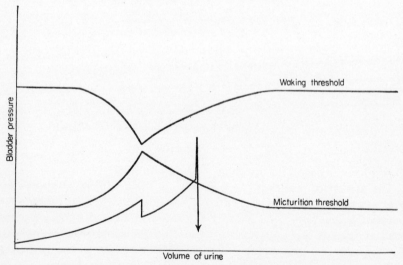

FIG. 6.   Nocturnal urination of enuretic during training—Stage I.

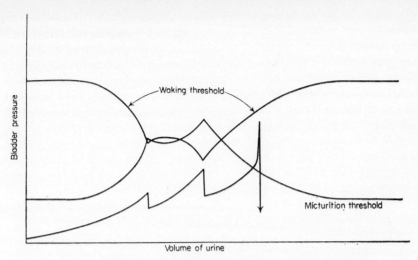

FIG. 7. Nocturnal urination of enuretic during training—Stage II.

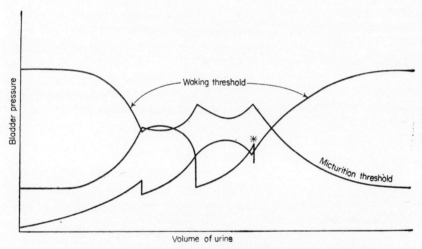

FIG. 8. Nocturnal urination of enuretic during training—Stage III.

* patient awakens.

The postulated sequence of events during the treatment of an enuretic by arranging that he is awakened by a bell immediately after the onset of nocturnal urination is schematically portrayed in Figs. 5–8. On the first occasion (Fig. 5) detrusor tension reaches a threshold value well below that necessary for awakening. The child urinates and as the bell rings conditioning occurs in the manner described. Thus, on the second occasion

(Fig. 6) both the micturition and waking thresholds are distorted by the generalization gradients of the contrary tendencies conditioned on the first. A somewhat greater volume of urine is now tolerated but urination still occurs at a pressure well below the waking threshold and fresh conditioning of the micturition/inhibitory and waking tendencies occurs. On the third occasion (Fig. 7), the thresholds are further distorted by the summated generalization gradients. Still further urine is tolerated but micturition still occurs below the waking threshold and further reinforcement, by the bell, of the conditioned tendencies follows. At this stage, however, there is a range of pressures at which the waking threshold is below that for micturition. At the next stage (Fig. 8.) the thresholds are grossly distorted and the range over which the waking threshold is below the micturition threshold is broad. The patient now awakens spontaneously at a bladder volume at which he previously micturated.

Ultimately, most patients develop the ability to sleep through the night without waking to urinate. This is consistent with the hypothesis that whereas the " waking threshold " remains as portrayed for the " sentinel " activities of the cortex, it progressively rises for general consciousness. Thus, the training process enables the child to reach a stage from which normal development can proceed. Apart from this factor, reinforcement of the desired tendencies would cease at the point where the opposing tendencies are just in balance. A certain number of " relapses " would then be expected but these would in no way prejudice further training. Mowrer and Mowrer deliberately aim to upset this balance by increasing the fluid intake when it is reached. In this way they create the conditions in which " overlearning " of the desired tendencies is possible.

Apparatus and Technique

The Mowrers' apparatus for the presentation of a waking stimulus at the onset of urination was designed with four considerations in mind. They intended to allow the child to sleep in comfort, to grant him liberty of movement, and the freedom to rise from his bed and visit the toilet unaided. The intensity of the waking stimulus was to be so adjusted as to be sufficient to awaken the patient but not so loud as to be traumatic. They constructed a pad, on which the patient slept, consisting of two layers of heavy absorbent cotton fabric separating two pieces of bronze gauze and a third covering layer of cotton, the whole being quilted together. Leads from the two sheets of gauze were connected in series with a small battery and a sensitive relay. When urine struck the pad it rapidly penetrated and, by virtue of its electrolytic properties, completed the circuit and activated the relay. This completed a second circuit which activated an electric bell. The sensitivity of the apparatus was such that the urine voided before the inhibition of micturition was only sufficient to wet the pad over an area some 2 in. or 3 in. in diameter. Thus temporal relationships favourable to conditioning were ensured.

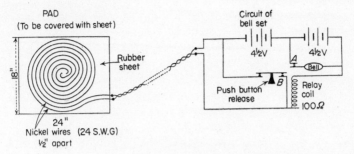

FIG. 9. Apparatus used by Davidson and Douglass.[33]

Later workers have modified the original apparatus in several ways. That designed by Davidson and Douglass[33] is illustrated in Fig. 9. It is superior in that the pad can be easily wiped dry and the inclusion of a holding circuit, which can be released by a push button, ensures that the bell continues to ring after the initial contact at the pad, even if this is subsequently broken. This pad and others of similar construction suffer from one grave defect in that electrolysis of the urine occurs on the surface of the pad and in contact with the child's skin. This is liable to cause sores or rash on the child's buttocks.[38] In the Mowrer apparatus, electrolysis would only occur in the sheets separating the gauzes and these are not in contact with the child's skin. This is also true of recent commercial forms of the apparatus in which the gauze is replaced by sheets of aluminium foil, the upper of which is perforated. In the best of these the relay not only activates the bell and holding circuits but also breaks the circuit through the pad: electrolysis is then minimal.

In certain circumstances the ringing of a bell at night interferes unduly with the sleep of others. The writer has, in one such instance, removed the gong of the bell and included the ear-piece from a hearing-aid in the circuit. Much more convenient and almost as effective is the placing of a buzzer under the pillow, which transmits vibrations to the patient's ear. Such a buzzer is included with some commercial forms of the equipment.

Crosby[15] modified the apparatus to such a degree that, apart from making it considerably more complicated, he violated several of the Mowrers' principles. His patients' freedom was restricted, supervision was necessary and, in that he used electric shock as a stimulus, the procedures were liable to be traumatic. Crosby claims that the earlier method merely establishes conditioned waking reflexes whereas his own, in line with his genetic theories, builds up tonic inhibition of the detrusor. In fact, as shown by the analysis above, this is also a probable consequence of the

Mowrer method. To the writer there appears no essential difference between the two techniques and it seems unlikely that Crosby's modifications will produce therapeutic gains to offset their disadvantages.

In describing the practical application of their method Mowrer and Mowrer recommend that the method be described in detail to the patient and the operation of the mechanism demonstrated with a little salt solution. The patient is instructed to sleep naked below the waist and to awaken fully, jump out of bed, and go to the toilet immediately the bell is heard. He is urged to visit the toilet even if no urge is experienced. If the patient fails to wake, his parents are instructed to rouse him and the loudness of the bell is increased. Thorough awakening is stressed and it seems likely that this will aid the development of " sentinel " activity. After visiting the toilet the patient changes the wet pad for a dry one, wipes the latter, and returns to sleep.

Once a criterion of 7 uninterrupted nights is achieved with normal fluid intake, it is recommended that the latter be increased by one or two cups of water before retiring. Then, when 7 further successive " dry " nights occur, the extra fluid and the use of the apparatus are both discontinued. If a later relapse occurs training is resumed until a similar criterion is again reached. From published reports it appears that the modal length of treatment is between 2 and 3 months but some patients may be treated for as long as a year.

Many authors have modified this procedure in certain respects, especially in relation to the additional fluid and the criterion for discontinuation. Apart from mechanical failures of the apparatus, the main difficulties arise from the lack of co-operation shown by a minority of patients and parents and the difficulties experienced by some patients in waking to the bell. The latter difficulty sometimes leads to involuntary lack of co-operation in that the patient half-wakes, finds some means of disconnecting the apparatus and returns to sleep and a wet bed. Several authors have claimed that the administration of drugs such as amphetamine during training has been effective in facilitating arousal.

Many of the common features and hazards of this method of treatment are illustrated by the treatment of a young man, a chronic and frequent bed-wetter, by the writer. Data from the training period are presented in Fig. 10. The upper frequency polygon represents the number of " dry " nights, i.e. nights on which no involuntary micturition has occurred, in successive 6-day periods. The middle polygon similarly represents the number of nights during which the bell was activated and the training reinforcements occurred. The lower polygon represents " wet " nights, i.e. nights upon which the patient thoroughly wet his bed and failed to wake. Theoretically, wet nights should not occur during treatment and are considered detrimental to the training. Except for the last occasion (B), which resulted from a failure of the apparatus, these were caused by the patient partly wakening to the bell, disconnecting the apparatus from his bed and returning to sleep. Despite strategic placements of the apparatus this continued for some weeks. A longer lead was about to be fitted when this

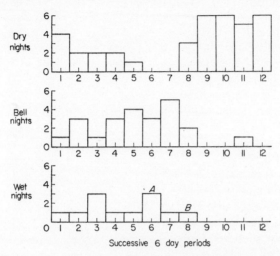

FIG. 10. 72-day treatment of a male patient (for explanation see text).

behaviour ceased. The peak (*A*) on this polygon refers to three successive nights during which the patient suffered a severe cold.

Some authors (e.g. Davidson and Douglass[33]) have commented on the influence of suggestive factors associated with this method. They point out that some patients become dry during the very early stages of treatment, before effective reinforcement of the conditioned responses has been possible. Similarly, the present data include a marked early increase in the frequency of " dry " nights which may well be related to suggestion. In the course of this protracted treatment, however, there was a gradual transition to a period during which reinforcements were maximal and then to the final period when " dry " nights were again typical. Even if the early stages reflect the influence of suggestion the later ones are the products of learning.

Assessment of Results

A sufficient number of reports on the treatment of fairly long series of patients by the specific conditioning method have been published to arrive at a realistic evaluation of its therapeutic efficacy. These reports, data from which are listed in Table 2, are not directly comparable owing to variations in the type of apparatus and technique employed, the severity and complexity of the patients' conditions, the follow-up period and the author's criteria of success.

TABLE 2

Author	No. of cases	Age range	Per cent cured	Per cent markedly improved	Per cent failures
Mowrer and Mowrer[14]	30	3–13	100	100	0
Davidson and Douglass[33]	20	5–15 (+ 2 adults)	75	25	0
Crosby[15]	35	3½–10½	88	3	9
	23	11–28	83	5	12
Sieger[39]	106	3–15 (+ 4 adults)	89	7	4
Geppert[32]	42	5–10	74	16	10
Baller and Schalock[40]	55	Median 9·5	70	30	30
Wickes[41]	100	5–17	50	24	26
Gillison and Skinner[42]	100	3½–21	88	5	7
Freyman[48]	15	5–14	33	40	27
Murray[43]	33	—	75	9	16
* Martin and Kubly[44]	118	3½–18½	56	18	26
* Lowe[45]	322	5–10	88	12	12
	276	10–16	88	12	12
	171	16+	85	15	15

The last two entries, marked with an asterisk in the Table, refer to commercial use of the technique. Martin and Kubly base their figures on the replies to questionnaires issued to those who had purchased conditioning apparatus (in the U.S.A.) over a period of 18 months. Slightly more than 50 per cent of the questionnaires were returned. Lowe's figures, which are considerably more favourable, are those of an unqualified practitioner who offers a personal service in his clients' homes. The great number of cases indicates the size of the demand for such a service in Britain. This sample is selected in that subjects with evidence of neurological or psychiatric disorder and the mentally deficient are excluded.

Kahane[46] criticizes studies included in Table 2 for their lack of control groups. He allotted 59 enuretics to three groups. The 21 members of group (1) were given immediate conditioning treatment, group (2) ($N = 22$) were similarly treated after a delay of several months and group (3) ($N = 16$) received no treatment beyond being placed on a waiting list after the initial paediatric examination. All subjects in group (1) conditioned successfully but 13 relapsed within 1 to 7 months. Ten members of group (2) stopped bed-wetting before being treated and only one of these relapsed. Two members of group (3) ceased bed-wetting. Kahane claims that, though evidence of symptom substitution was minimal, parental reports of behavioural changes indicated that improvement was only significantly related to spontaneous remission.

One weakness of Kahane's study is that the many " relapsers " in the experimental group were not given a second course of training. Though never as many as in this study, a high frequency of relapses is commonly reported. Most, however, respond well to further treatment and the failures are, in the main, those who fail to reach the required criterion during their initial training. Smith,[47] using a rather short training period, finds that almost a quarter of his patients relapse but that the large majority of these respond to a second treatment.

Despite fears of " symptom substitution " deriving from a symptomatic treatment all authors have failed to find any evidence of this mechanism, though special attention has been paid to this question. The reverse is, however, commonly reported, favourable changes of personality and attitude frequently following the remission of this troublesome condition.

The investigations reported throw little light on the question of the nature of the differences between those who respond to this treatment and those who fail. Lack of co-operation, whether voluntary or involuntary, is undoubtedly a factor in some cases and deep sleep in others but these are by no means the only factors. There is little evidence to suggest that " acquired " enuresis is less responsive than " primary " enuresis but this is a hypothesis worthy of further investigation.

Though most of the studies listed in Table 2 did not include control groups it is evident that the degree of success achieved by this method is well in excess of the spontaneous remission rate as indicated by the data in Fig. 3. It is apparent that, if widely adopted, the specific conditioning method of treatment is capable of significantly reducing the incidence of enuresis nocturna at the later ages of childhood.

REFERENCES

1. BARRINGTON, F. J. F. (1928). The central nervous control of micturition. Brain, 51, 209-220.
2. BARRINGTON, F. J. F. (1931). The component reflexes of micturition in the cat. Brain, 54, 177-188.
3. BARRINGTON, F. J. F. (1933). The localization of the paths subserving micturition in the spinal cord of the cat. Brain, 56, 126-128.
4. LEARMONTH, J. R. (1931). A contribution to the neurophysiology of the urinary bladder in man. Brain, 54, 147-176.
5. DENNY-BROWN, D. and ROBERTSON, E. G. (1933). On the physiology of micturition. Brain, 56, 149-190.
6. BEST, C. H. and TAYLOR, N. B. (1950). The Physiological Basis of Medical Practice, 5th edition. Baillière, Tindall & Cox, London.
7. FREEMAN, G. L. (1938). Postural accompaniments of the voluntary inhibition of micturition. J. Exp. Psychol., 23, 45-61.
8. MUELLNER, S. R. and FLEISCHNER, F. G. (1949). Normal and abnormal micturition: A study of bladder behaviour by means of the fluoroscope. J. Urol., 61, 233-241.
9. NATHAN, P. W. (1952). Micturition reflexes in man. J. Neurol. Neurosurg. Psychiat., 15, 148-149.
10. McLELLAN, F. C. (1939). The Neurogenic Bladder. Thomas, Springfield, Ill.

11. McGRAW, M. (1940). Neural maturation as exemplified by the achievement of bladder control. *J. Paediat.*, **16**, 580-590.
12. SMITH, S. (1948). *The Psychological Origin and Treatment of Enuresis.* Univ. of Washington Press, Seattle.
13. FULTON, J. F. (1950). *A Textbook of Physiology*, 16th edition. Saunders, Philadelphia and London.
14. MOWRER, O. H. and MOWRER, W. M. (1938). Enuresis: A method for its study and treatment. *Amer. J. Orthopsychiat.*, **8**, 436-459.
15. CROSBY, N. D. (1950). Essential enuresis: Successful treatment based on physiological concepts. *Med. J. Aust.*, **2**, 533-543.
16. DAVIDENKOV, S. N. (1953). The treatment of neuroses by Pavlovian methods. *S.C.R. U.S.S.R. Med. Bull.*, **2**, No. 7, 1-5 (translated).
17. DELAFRESNAYE, J. F. (1954). *Brain Mechanisms and Consciousness.* Blackwell, Oxford.
18. KANNER, L. (1947). *Child Psychiatry.* Thomas, Springfield, Ill.
19. HALLGREN, B. (1956). Enuresis. I. A study with reference to the morbidity risk and symptomatology. *Acta Psychiat. Neurol. Scand.*, **31**, 379-403.
20. HODGE, R. S. and HUTCHINGS, H. M. (1952). Enuresis: A brief review, a tentative theory and a suggested treatment. *Arch. Dis. Childhood*, **27**, 498-504.
21. HALLGREN, B. (1957). Enuresis: A clinical and genetic study. *Acta Psychiat. Neurol. Scand.*, **32**, Suppl. 114.
22. BRANSBY, E. R., BLOMFIELD, J. M. and DOUGLAS, J. W. B. (1955). The prevalence of bed-wetting. *Medical Officer*, **94**, 5-7.
23. HALLGREN, B. (1956). Enuresis. II. A study with reference to certain physical, mental and social factors possibly associated with enuresis. *Acta Psychiat. Neurol. Scand.*, **31**, 405-436.
24. BRAITHWAITE, J. V. (1950). Enuresis in childhood. *Practitioner*, **165**, 273-281.
25. STRÖM-OLSEN, R. (1950). Enuresis in adults and abnormality of sleep. *Lancet*, **259**, 133-135.
26. DITMAN, K. S. and BLINN, K. A. (1955). Sleep levels in enuresis. *Amer. J. Psychiat.*, **111**, 913-920.
27. MICHAELS, J. J. (1955). *Disorders of Character: Persistent Enuresis, Juvenile Delinquency and Psychopathic Personality.* Thomas, Springfield, Ill.
28. BURT, C. (1940). The incidence of neurotic symptoms among evacuated school children. *Brit. J. Educ. Psychol.*, **10**, 8-15.
29. JONES, H. G. (1960). Learning and abnormal behaviour. In: *Handbook of Abnormal Psychology* (ed. by Eysenck, H. J.). Pitman, London.
30. McGUINESS, A. C. (1935). The treatment of enuresis in childhood. *Med. Clin. N. Amer.*, **19**, 286-294.
31. EYSENCK, H. J. (1957). *The Dynamics of Anxiety and Hysteria.* Routledge & Kegan Paul, London.
32. GEPPERT, T. V. (1953). Management of nocturnal enuresis by conditioned response. *J. Amer. Med. Ass.*, **152**, 381-383.
33. DAVIDSON, J. R. and DOUGLASS, E. (1950). Nocturnal enuresis: A special approach to treatment. *Brit. Med. J.*, **1**, 1345-1350.
34. MARSON, F. G. W. (1955). Posterior pituitary snuff treatment of nocturnal enuresis. *Brit. Med. J.*, **1**, 1194-1195.
35. LEYS, D. (1956). Value of propantheline bromide in the treatment of enuresis. *Brit. Med. J.*, **1**, 549-550.
36. BLOMFIELD, J. M. and DOUGLAS, J. W. B. (1956). Bed-wetting. *Lancet*, **1**, 850-852.
37. HULL, C. L. (1952). *A Behavior System.* Yale Univer. Press, New Haven.
38. WICKES, I. G. (1959). Letter to editor. *Brit. Med. J.*, **1**, 175.
39. SIEGER, H. W. (1952). Treatment of essential nocturnal enuresis. *J. Pediat.*, **40**, 738-749.
40. BALLER, W. and SCHALOCK, H. (1956). Conditioned response treatment of enuresis. *Except. Child.*, **22**, 233-236; 247-248.
41. WICKES, I. G. (1958). Treatment of persistent enuresis with an electric buzzer. *Arch. Disorder of Childhood*, **33**, 160-164.

42. GILLISON, T. H. and SKINNER, J. L. (1958). Treatment of nocturnal enuresis by the electric alarm. *Brit. Med. J.*, **2**, 1268-1272.
43. MURRAY, J. (1959). Personal communication.
44. MARTIN, B. and KUBLY, Delores (1955). Results of treatment of enuresis by a conditioned response method. *J. Consult. Psychol.*, **19**, 71-73.
45. LOWE, K. (1959). Personal communication.
46. KAHANE, M. (1955). An experimental investigation of a conditioning treatment and a preliminary study of the psychoanalytic theory of the etiology of nocturnal enuresis. *Amer. Psychologist*, **10**, 369-370 (Abstract).
47. SMITH, K. C. P. (1959). Personal communication.
48. FREYMAN, R. (1959). Experience with an enuresis bell-apparatus. *Medical Officer*, **101**, 248-250.

HYSTERICAL ANESTHESIA, ANALGESIA
AND ASTEREOGNOSIS*

R. R. SEARS, PH.D.†

and L. H. COHEN, PH.D., M.D.‡

Department of Psychology and Department of Psychiatry, Yale University

EXPERIMENTAL STUDY

IT IS unfortunate that with the realization of the psychic causation of hysterical symptoms there has been a widespread neglect of the study of these phenomena from the physiologic standpoint. Psychoanalysts, in their elaborations of the psychologic mechanisms involved in the production of conversion symptoms, have not questioned seriously the means by which the nervous system is able to build these sudden physiologic manifestations of psychopathologic processes. The existence of the question has not been entirely ignored,§ but with the exception of Hurst,[2] who reported a number of excellent experiments on the frequency and extent of special sense disorders in the war neuroses, there is an astonishing paucity of experimental data bearing on the problem. That this paucity has been a result of a lack of adequate methodologic approach seems possible.

However, within the last decade technics have been developed which should prove fruitful if employed in this connection. One need mention but a few to indicate the possibilities. The study of chronaxia in functional anesthesias and paralyses, the application of Hull's[3] technics for the quantitative analysis of amnesias, the pharmacologic study of vascular changes, globus hystericus and conditions of sleep disturbance should all yield valuable experimental data. Indeed, the majority of technics and methods suggested by Hull for a study of hypnosis should be applicable with profit to hysterical phenomena.

The difficulty of securing adequate experimental controls in pathologic conditions is especially great in the case of hysterical reactions. No observation can be considered valid, however, unless comparable observations

---

* Reprinted by permission of the author and the editor of the *Arch. Neurol. Psychiat.* from (1933) *Arch. Neurol. Psychiat.*, **29**, 260-271.

† Blossom Fellow in Neuro-Anatomy, 1931–2.

‡ Sterling Fellow in Psychology, 1930–1.

§ Ferenczi,[1] in a discussion of this topic, suggests that " . . . in spite of all our satisfaction with what has been achieved, it is more to the purpose to indicate the lacunae in our knowledge of these matters. The 'mysterious leap from mental to bodily' (Freud), for instance, in the symptoms of hysteria is still a problem " (p. 90).

have been made on normal persons or on the patient himself either under controlled conditions or after disappearance of the phenomenon under investigation. Hurst and Symns,[4] among others, have demonstrated the danger of neglecting this type of " normal control." For decades, pharyngeal anesthesia had been accepted by clinicians and textbooks as an unquestioned stigma of hysteria. A seven point rating scale was devised by these investigators and the excitability of the pharyngeal reflexes examined in three groups of subjects: 170 persons who were normal; 64 who had hysteria, and 34 who had hysterical mutism and aphonia. The excitability of the pharyngeal reflexes proved to be as great in the two hysterical groups as in the normal group, and in all three the distribution conformed to that of the normal probability curve. The writers drew the obvious conclusion that pharyngeal anesthesia is not an hysterical stigma.

Present knowledge of the physiology of hysterical symptoms is derived mainly from the results of the work of Hurst and his collaborators and the experiments of Levine.[5] Hurst limited himself to a study of hysterical anesthesia and areflexia. His theoretical conclusion was that functional anesthesias are a result of inattention to the sensory input from the anesthetic area. This inattention, it is suggested, may consist of " a throwing out of dendrites, or it may depend on some biochemical change in the material which occupies the space between the dendritic terminations of adjacent neurones. Whatever it may be, the increased resistance which is present when attention is very deficient results in anesthesia, and at the same time a block is produced in the reflex arc which results in diminution or abolition of the reflex."

Rosanoff,[6] on the other hand, believed that hysterical symptoms are similar to those manifested in deliberate malingering, and are thus on a purely verbal and conscious level of behavior. It might be noted in support of this conception that Levine obtained the galvanic skin reaction to pain in two cases of hysterical analgesia and in two cases of hypnotically induced analgesia. The reaction was not measured quantitatively, however, and one of us (Dr. Sears)[7] showed recently that, though the galvanic skin reaction to pain is indubitably present in cases of hypnotic analgesia it is considerably reduced in strength. Possibly this same reaction, though present, may also be reduced under hysterical analgesia in comparison to normal reactions. Technical difficulties with the galvanometer have prevented a study of this problem in the present case.

The purpose of the present study has been to determine, in three types of sensory dysfunction, the extent to which the normal reactions to stimuli affecting these modalities are modified by the functional sensory losses. More specifically, the problem has been to investigate some of the fundamental physiologic reactions concomitant with such phenomena.

It is unfortunate that only one patient has been immediately available for this study, but it is believed that the relatively large number of observations and their comparison with control experiments under normal conditions may compensate to some extent for the lack of a larger number of subjects.

Mrs. I. B., aged 45, whose complete case history, physical and mental examinations are not relevant for present purposes, developed symptoms 8 months before admission to the psychiatric clinic.

The left hand was completely anesthetic to superficial touch as produced with cotton-wool and by brushing of the hairs; it was analgesic to superficial pain and to deep pain except that produced by flexion of the fingers, which were partially paralysed (probably a functional paralysis). Thermal sensitivity was normal. There was complete astereognosis. The right hand was entirely normal except that the thumb was " numb."

The following diagnosis was made: psychopathic personality, with hysterical anesthesia to superficial touch, analgesia to superficial and deep pain and astereognosis.

ANALGESIA

In a recent study,[7] it was shown that when normal persons are hypnotized and by the process of suggestion are rendered anesthetic or analgesic in one leg, painful stimulation of that member will not produce the normal respiratory reaction to pain evoked by stimulation of the normal or control leg. In an attempt to determine whether hysterical analgesia modifies this reaction in a similar way, the technic used in the former study was applied to an investigation of the present case.

Two types of painful stimuli were utilized: (1) that produced by an algesimeter, and (2) that produced by electric shock from a high frequency induction coil.

Technic

The algesimeter* consists of a sharp steel point inserted at an angle of 45° in the end of a small metal rod. The rod slides easily within a sleeve and rests against a small coil spring held in place by a transverse pin at the upper end of the sleeve. The sharp steel point, which presses against the skin at an angle of 45°, exerts a pressure of 20 oz against the skin surface when the coil spring is completely depressed. Depression of the spring produces an increased air pressure in a tube leading from the upper end of the sleeve to a recording tambour on the kymograph. Incidence of the stimulus is thus recorded automatically. Comparable areas, 5 cm square, on the dorsum of each hand were used for stimulation. Respiration was recorded by a Sumner pneumograph placed over the region of the eighth rib.

The patient was blindfolded during each of the four experimental periods, the first three of which were devoted to stimulation with the algesimeter and the last with electric shock. Stimuli were presented in the *A B B A* order, beginning with the anesthetic arm, and were from 50 to 80 sec apart. A

* For a more comprehensive description of the apparatus, methods of measurement and technic, see Sears, R. R.[7]

definite rhythm was avoided in order that temporal conditioning might not be a source of error.

Measurement of the respiratory records was made with the Hull oscillometer,[8] an instrument which summates the vertical oscillation of a wavy line. One inch of vertical tracing is equivalent to 39 oscillometer units. Periods of 20 sec duration were marked off before and after each stimulus. The total amount of oscillation in each of these two periods was measured and the algebraic difference (increase, $+$; decrease, $-$) in amount of breathing following stimulation noted. Normally the total oscillation is markedly increased following stimulation. The reliability of this method of measuring the respiratory reaction to pain has been amply demonstrated in the studies of one of us (Dr. Sears)[7] and of Garvey.*

Results

Table 1 shows the number of stimuli presented to each arm, the normal and anesthetic and the mean amount of oscillation in the respiratory tracing both before and after the stimulus. These values are in terms of oscillometer units. The normal reaction to pain produced by the algesimeter is an increase of 10·73 units over the prestimulus amount of respiration. The probable error of this mean is 1·56. The reaction to pain presented to the anesthetic area, however, is an increase of only 2·85 units, with a probable error of 1·5. The difference between the sensitivity of the two arms, as measured by respiratory response, is 7·88 units. This difference is 3·63 times as great as its probable error. The difference between the sensitivity of the two arms as measured by reaction to shock is 2·87 times its probable error.

In the earlier experiments on hypnotic analgesia, a control series was run in which 6 subjects were instructed to pretend that they felt no pain when the left leg was stimulated but to react normally when the right was stimulated. No difference was found between the respiratory reactions to pain on the respective legs. In other words, voluntary inhibition, the verbal level of behavior described by Rosanoff, does not produce the same type of modification of this reaction to pain that is produced by true hypnotic analgesia. The present data indicate that hysterical analgesia modifies the normal reaction to pain in substantially the same way as hypnotic analgesia. It seems probable, therefore, that the loss of sensitivity is on a lower level of physiologic activity than that implied by Rosanoff.

---

* One exception may be noted. One of us (Dr. Sears), in collaboration with Mrs. Helen Hope Dibbell, attempted to apply the foregoing technic to a patient at Bellevue Hospital, New York, who suffered from a complete hemilateral functional analgesia. Although a hundred stimuli were presented on each leg, measurement of records shows that no reaction to pain was obtained from either the normal or the anesthetic side. Whether the cause lay in faulty recording or in the patient has not been discovered. It is possible that a complete bilateral analgesia was spontaneously developed during experimental periods as a defense against the pain. Garvey, G. R.: *J. Exper. Psychol.*, to be published.

TABLE 1

Stimuli presented to the normal and anesthetic hand and the mean amount of respiratory oscillation

	Cutaneous pain (algesimeter)			
Hand stimulated	Number of stimuli	Mean before stimulus	Mean after stimulus	Mean difference
Normal	49	81·73	92·46	+ 10·73 ± 1·56
Anesthetic	47	86·76	89·61	+ 2·85 ± 1·50
Difference between normal and anesthetic			7·88 ± 2·17	
D / P.E.D.			3·63	

	Electric shock			
Hand stimulated	Number of stimuli	Mean before stimulus	Mean after stimulus	Mean difference
Normal	25	67·04	69·04	2·00 ± 0·86
Anesthetic	23	70·65	69·13	− 1·52 ± 0·89
Difference between normal and anesthetic			3·25 ± 1·22	
D / P.E.D.			2·87	

The differences between the two arms in this respect, with the probable error of difference and the critical ratio, are given at the foot of the table.

This abolition of the normal respiratory response to pain is consonant with the results of tests made by Schilder[9] on a patient with a hemilateral functional analgesia. Application of pin pricks to the normal arm raised the blood pressure to 140 mm from its normal level of 130 mm, but similar stimulation of the analgesic arm failed to elicit any change in pressure. Schilder referred to some experiments of Lowenstein, which gave results that conflict with these findings, however; in these, no modification of pain responses by the analgesia was demonstrated. Unfortunately, the original reports of Lowenstein's work have not been available to us.

The point in the nervous system at which this modification occurs cannot yet be ascertained. In consideration of Levine's results, one must surmise that it is neither in the sense organ proper nor in the afferent-pathway to the thalamus.

It may be concluded, then, that hysterical analgesia consists of a blocking of at least two of the normal reactions to pain, viz., verbal report and increased respiration. This blocking is not simply a voluntary inhibition of verbal report (simulation), but its position in the nervous system can be defined only in a negative fashion; i.e., it lies neither in the sense organs nor in the afferent-pathways to the thalamus.

ASTEREOGNOSIS

Stereognosis, unlike pain, pressure, touch and temperature, is not a simple cutaneous sense. It belongs to that class of psychologic acts termed perceptions rather than sensations. It is an act mediated by the fundamental senses and is, essentially, a correlation of the data derived through those senses. The question arises in a study of the hysterical loss of stereognosis as to whether the loss is confined to the perceptual level or whether there is a concomitant loss of the fundamental sense modalities underlying the perceptual act.

Campora,[10] from an analysis of a large number of cases of astereognosis in which the organic foundations were subsequently verified by autopsy, concludes that the sense data which are of primary significance in the stereognostic act are those of two point discrimination. Deep sensibility was often but not uniformly impaired and superficial touch was occasionally destroyed in this series of cases, but the two point limen was invariably raised no matter what the other sensory losses were.

An examination of the efficiency of two point discrimination was therefore made in this case of hysterical astereognosis. Since the right hand, except for the thumb, was perfectly normal, it was used as a control for the measurements obtained from the left hand (astereognostic).

Technic

Twelve separate areas were chosen on the left hand at which to determine the two point threshold, and exactly comparable positions were marked on the right hand. In this way differences in the thresholds of the left hand were made immediately discernible by reference to the values obtained from the comparable positions of the right, or normal, hand.

The 12 positions chosen for the examination were: (1) the tip of the thumb; (2) the tip of the first finger; (3) the tip of the second finger; (4) the tip of the third finger; (5) the tip of the fourth finger; (6) a line drawn horizontally across the center of the palm; (7) a line drawn vertically across the center of the palm; (8) the inner phalangeal margin of the thumb; (9) the ball of the thumb (palmar surface of the distal phalanx); (10) the palmar surface of the second phalanx of the first finger; (11) the palmar surface of the second phalanx of the second finger; and (12) the palmar surface of the second phalanx of the third finger.

The thresholds were obtained in the usual manner. The determination by descending order was made first; the limen was found and passed, and the determination by ascending order followed promptly. This process was repeated 3 or 4 times and the lowest reading obtained for each order of stimulation recorded on the chart, as indicated in Table 2. The values are in terms of sixty-fourths of an inch. Thus, on the tip of the index finger of the right hand the distance necessary between two points simultaneously presented, if they were to be discriminated as two separate points, was found on ascending order to be $\frac{6}{64}$ in., and on descending order, $\frac{5}{64}$ in. The threshold values obtained by ascending and descending order have been averaged for each area, and the means thus derived are considered to be the " true " threshold of discrimination.

TABLE 2

Thresholds for two point discrimination determined by ascending and descending order at twelve comparable positions on the normal (right) and astereognostic (left) hands

Position	Right (normal)			Left (astereognostic)			Per cent increase
	Ascending	Descending	Mean	Ascending	Descending	Mean	
Thumb tip	9	7	8·0	10	8	9·0	12·5
	9	*8*		*9*	*6*		
First finger tip	6	5	5·5	10	8	9·0	63·6
Second finger tip	6	4	5·0	10	8	9·0	80·0
	8	*6*		*10*	*10*		
Third finger tip	7	4	5·5	11	10	10·5	90·9
Fourth finger tip	9	7	8·0	10	10	10·0	25·0
	7	*8*		*7*	*6*		
Palm: horizontal	22	21	21·5	23	23	23·0	7·0
Palm: vertical	32	28	30·0	29	27	28·0	−6·7
Thumb: phalanx	18	15	16·5	30	20	25·0	51·5
Thumb: ball	27	27	27·0	54	32	43·0	59·2
First finger: phalanx	14	13	13·5	48	44	46·0	240·8
Second finger: phalanx	13	11	12·0	22	22	22·0	83·3
Third finger: phalanx	14	14	14·0	40	18	29·0	107·7
Mean			13·834			21·950	+67·9
Difference between hands				8·116 ± 1·772			
Critical ratio				4·58			

Values in italics are for re-tests. All values are in terms of sixty-fourths of an inch.

Results

Table 2, giving comparable measurements on the two hands, indicates that in all but one of the 12 positions the threshold was higher on the astereognostic hand. However, the tip of the thumb and the tip of the fourth finger were given re-tests, since the patient reported that the thumb on the right (normal) hand was in a condition similar to that of the left hand; i.e., it was " no good, feels numb and is stiff," and the little finger on the left (astereognostic) hand was normal.

Little difference between the thumbs was found originally, and on the re-test (values in italics) the ascending order gave the same value for each hand while the descending order seems to have demonstrated a lower threshold for the left hand. The patient's uncertainty during stimulation of this area renders doubtful the reliability of all values obtained for the thumb tips.

This ambiguity is not present in the re-test results for the fourth finger. The criteria were quickly and easily satisfied, and the outcome was a reversal, again in favor of the astereognostic hand.

A re-test on the two second fingers, done as a control because of the equivocal results obtained from the other two re-tests, showed that here, where there was no question as to the relative conditions of the fingers, there was no reversal of the limens, although the actual values have changed. This is not an unusual phenomenon. The two point threshold, like other physiologic processes, varies somewhat from day to day, although the limens obtained within any one hour may be considered fairly reliable.

TABLE 2

Two point thresholds at twelve comparable positions on the right and left hands after the spontaneous disappearance of the astereognosis in the left hand

Position	Right			Left (formerly astereognostic)			Per cent increase
	Ascending	Descending	Mean	Ascending	Descending	Mean	
Thumb tip	6	6	6·0	5	4	4·5	−25·0
First finger tip	6	5	5·5	6	3	4·5	−18·1
Second finger tip	6	6	6·0	5	5	5·0	−16·7
Third finger tip	6	5	5·5	6	5	5·5	0
Fourth finger tip	6	6	6·0	6	5	5·5	− 8·3
Palm: horizontal	11	10	10·5	14	10	12·0	+14·3
Palm: vertical	16	15	15·5	18	16	17·0	+ 9·0
Thumb: phalanx	14	12	13·0	20	8	14·0	+ 7·8
Thumb: ball	8	7	7·5	7	6	6·5	−13·3
First finger: phalanx	15	15	15·0	13	12	12·5	−16·7
Second finger: phalanx	15	13	14·0	18	18	18·0	+28·5
Third finger: phalanx	14	13	13·5	17	17	17·0	+20·6
Mean			9·78			10·12	− 1·5
Difference between hands					0·34 ± 0·38		
Critical ratio					0·89		

The means of the 12 values for each hand have been calculated. The difference between the two is 8·116, and the probable error of that difference*

* The two columns of means were correlated and the *r* used in the following formula for determining the probable error of the difference between the means:

$$\sqrt{P.E._{A^2} + P.E._{B^2} - 2r\,P.E._{A}P.E._{B}}$$

is 1·772. There is little question as to the reliability of the difference, the critical ratio being 4·58.

Six weeks after this series of determinations, an examination showed that there had been a spontaneous recovery of the stereognostic ability. This fact presented an opportunity to discover whether the loss of two point discrimination had been directly correlated with the astereognosis. The former procedure was repeated in every detail, and the results of this second series of determinations are given in Table 3.

It will be seen that there is now practically no difference between the thresholds of the two hands. The left hand (formerly astereognostic) has a slightly higher mean threshold value, but the difference is only 0·89 of the probable error of the difference. This indicates no more than a normal variation. The difference between the thresholds of the normal hand on the two series of determinations is not of significance in the present study; it may be accounted for by normal daily variability and the fact that a different pair of compasses was used in the second series.

It may be concluded that if Campora is correct in his assumption that two point discrimination is fundamental to cutaneous spatial perception, there is, in functional astereognosis, a dropping out of the fundamental processes concerned with this activity. The astereognosis is not, as might be expected *a priori*, simply a loss of discrimination between commonsense objects such as knives and keys or velvet and wood, but involves the deeper and more fundamental physiologic mechanisms that are involved in this type of perception. With return of the higher function, moreover, we find a concomitant return to normal of the underlying discriminatory ability.

ANESTHESIA

Although, as was demonstrated in the experiment on analgesia, the innate unconditioned reaction to a stimulus acting on a functionally anesthetic sense may be greatly modified, the question arises as to how effective the sensory block is if the anesthetic sense is used as the medium for the conditioned stimulus in the process of establishing a conditioned reaction. As early as 1912, this method suggested itself to von Bechterew[11] as a technic for differentiating organic from functional anesthesias. He said, in part (p. 188): " While in organic lesions of cutaneous sensibility the associative-motor-reflex method clearly shows the presence or absence of an anesthesia, it cannot be employed with security in the case of hysterical anesthesia. In a case of hysteria with anesthesia and paralysis of the lower extremities, we were unable to set up an associative-motor-reflex, although Kunjajew (1911) succeeded in establishing an a.-m.-r. in a patient with total hysterical anesthesia but retention of voluntary movement. The stimulation was associated with a bell-active finger retraction serving as the response."

More recently, Myasishchev,[12] in an extensive study of hysterical and hypnotic symptoms, was able to repeat Kunjajew's reported success.

An attempt was made in the present instance to establish a conditioned reaction to cotton-wool stimulation of the dorsum of the left hand; this, it will be remembered, is an area anesthetic to superficial touch. The unconditioned stimulus was an electric shock applied to the normal (right) hand, the reaction being a quick withdrawal movement. Although a severe shock was used, this withdrawal was not, initially, great enough to be accurately observed.* The patient was therefore requested to withdraw her hand voluntarily as quickly as possible each time she felt the shock. In conditioned reflex terminology this verbal instruction amounts to an externally induced but internally maintained constant facilitation of the unconditioned reaction.

Experiment 1

The hands were placed palm down on a table before the patient, the right resting on a simple electric grid. A bandage was placed across the eyes, and every effort was made to eliminate slight sounds of movement as the stimulations were given. No attempt was made to record the reactions mechanically. The conditioned stimulus consisted of a quick brush of a wisp of cotton across the back of the left hand (anesthetic). Preliminary examination proved this to be an entirely insensible stimulus. The unconditioned stimulus (shock) acting on the right (normal) hand followed the cotton stimulus by approximately one second.

Fifty re-enforcements of the cotton stimulus were given with the shock, but no conditioned reaction was evoked.

Experiment 2

The fingers of the right hand were placed on the electrodes of a delicate recording apparatus† and the procedure of experiment 1 repeated for ten further re-enforcements. The graphic record showed clearly the failure of the cotton stimulus to evoke even a minimal reaction.

In the belief that the phenomenon of irradiation, as described by Anrep,[14] might be invoked to elicit a conditioned reaction, the conditioned stimulus was transferred to the right (normal) hand. A conditioned reaction appeared after 2 re-enforcements. In consideration of some preliminary work carried out by Mr. Shipley, we believe this to be fewer re-enforcements than are necessary in the average normal subject with this technic. It seems not improbable that some type of association had already been established between the cotton stimulation and the finger reaction by the previous

---

* This restriction of defense behavior to a relatively small portion of the available reactive mechanism is in accordance with the observations of Schilder[9] and Bender and Schilder[13] on the pain reactions of hysterical and catatonic patients.

† Designed and constructed by Walter C. Shipley, who assisted in this experiment.

stimulation of the anesthetic hand; even if this is true, the reaction tendency had not yet reached the threshold at which an overt reaction would appear.

Ten further re-enforcements were given to the cotton stimulus acting on the right hand. A return of the stimulus to the anesthetic hand did not evoke a response. In the course of the experiment, six more cotton stimuli were presented to the left hand interspersed in a series of 25 cotton stimuli presented to the right. No conditioned response was established in the left hand, however, although the normal hand provided consistent reactions.

Experiment 3

Although there was no irradiation from one part of the body to another within the same sense modality, it seemed possible that there might be an irradiation from one sense modality to another within the same part of the body. In order to test this hypothesis, a sharp rap with a pencil was used as the conditioned stimulus, the pressure sense being normal in the otherwise anesthetic hand.

The conditioned response appeared after one re-enforcement on the left hand and remained strong through 10 trials. On the twelfth re-enforcement the cotton stimulus was substituted for the pencil rap and evoked a similarly strong response. The cotton was repeated, but no reaction occurred. Six further re-enforcements were given to the pencil rap stimulus and again the cotton was interspersed in the series. The result was the same positive response as before. Another series of 6 re-enforcements of the pencil rap was given, and a third time the cotton was presented. Reactions this time appeared to two successive stimulations before extinction of the response.

Experiment 4

Forty-eight hours later the patient was brought to the laboratory and tested for retention of the conditioned response to the tap of the pencil and the cotton. Both responses had suffered spontaneous extinction. After one re-enforcement, however, the response to the cotton stimulus reappeared.

The patient was asked why she withdrew her hand before receiving a shock. She replied that she " didn't know " and, to questioning, denied that she felt the cotton on this day or at the session 2 days previously. The two succeeding stimuli were not felt and failed to evoke reactions, but the third evoked not only a finger withdrawal but an exclamation of surprise. The patient reported that she had felt the cotton. Twenty further stimulations were given, and 15 of these were felt by the patient and reacted to by withdrawal of the hand. The cotton stimulus had become frankly sensible to her and thereafter served as an easily perceptible warning signal. It is worthy of note that the anesthesia disappeared completely at this time and that there was no evidence of its return 6 months later.

In conclusion, it may be said that although neither simple re-enforcement nor the ordinary process of irradiation (within the same sense, but from one anatomic area to another) was adequate to develop a conditioned response to a stimulus affecting a functionally anesthetic sense modality, irradiation from a normal sense to the anesthetic sense within the same anatomic area was shown to be a usable mechanism. This conclusion is valid, however, only on the supposition that the pencil rap actually affected the deep pressure sense and did not bring about its conditioned response simply by supraliminal stimulation of the superficial touch sense. This possibility must not be ignored; the problem is one which can be settled only by further experiment.

SUMMARY

(1) Hysterical analgesia modifies the normal reaction to pain in much the same way as hypnotic anesthesia if the reduced respiratory response to pain found in these two conditions be accepted as the criterion.

(2) Hysterical astereognosis presents a concomitant heightening of the two point threshold; spontaneous recovery of the astereognosis is concomitant with a return to the normal two point discrimination threshold.

(3) A conditioned response to a stimulus affecting an hysterically anesthetic sense modality can be established by utilizing the principle of irradiation from one sense modality (normal) to another (anesthetic) within the same area of the body, but cannot be established either by simple re-enforcement or by irradiation within the same sense modality from one part of the body (normal) to another part (anesthetic).

With the modern development of psychologic and physiologic methods, a few of which are illustrated, the subjection of the physical manifestations of functional nervous disease to rigorously controlled investigation and measurement becomes feasible. The value of such study lies not only in the clinical realm but in the information it may give to an understanding of certain principles of endogenic control of nervous activity. Hysterical reactions may be considered as limiting cases of the action of these principles and, as such, should provide valuable laboratory material for their discovery and examination.

REFERENCES

1. FERENCZI (1927). *Theory and Technique of Psychoanalysis.* Boni & Liveright, New York.
2. HURST, A. F. (1930). *Croonian Lectures: The Psychology of the Special Senses and their Functional Disorders.* Oxford University Press, New York.
3. HULL, C. L. (1930). Quantitative methods of investigating hypnotic suggestion. *J. Abnorm. and Soc. Psychol.*, **25**, 200 and 390.
4. HURST, A. F. and SYMNS, J. L. M. (1918). Seale Hayne Neurol. Studies, **1**, 43.
5. LEVINE, M. (1930). Psychogalvanic reaction to painful stimuli in hypnotic and hysterical anesthesia. *Bull. Johns Hopkins Hosp.*, **46**, 331.
6. ROSANOFF, A. J. (1920). *Manual of Psychiatry.* Wiley, New York.

7. SEARS, R. R. (1932). An experimental study of hypnotic anesthesia. *J. Exper. Psychol.*, **15**, 1.

8. HULL, C. L. (1929). An instrument for summating the oscillations of a line. *J. Exper. Psychol.*, **12**, 259.

9. SCHILDER, P. (1931). Notes on the psychopathology of pain in neuroses and psychoses. *Psychoanalyt. Rev.*, **18**, 1.

10. CAMPORA, G. (1925). Astereognosis: Its causes and mechanisms. *Brain*, **48**, 65.

11. von BECHTEREW, W. (1912). Die Anwendung der Methode der motorischen Assozi- ations reflexe zur Aufdeckung der Simulation. *Z. ges. neurol. Psychiat.*, **13**, 183.

12. MYASISHCHEV, V. (1929). Experimental evidence on the problem of objective indices. in sensory disorders. *Nov. refl. fiziol. nerv. Sist.*, **3**, 458; *Psychol. Abst.*, **4**, 4349 (1930)

13. BENDER and SCHILDER, P. (1930). *Amer. J. Psychiat.*, **10**, 365.

14. ANREP, G. V. (1923). The irradiation of conditioned reflexes. *Proc. Roy. Soc. B.*, **94**. 404.

TOTAL HYSTERICAL DEAFNESS :
AN EXPERIMENTAL CASE STUDY*

R. B. MALMO, J. F. DAVIS and S. BARZA

Allan Memorial Institute of Psychiatry, McGill University, Montreal, Canada

THE PROBLEM

TOTAL hysterical deafness is a rare phenomenon[1] and we have been unable to find a detailed account of a single case which has been carefully investigated with conditioning and allied techniques. However, as early as 1912, Bechterev[2,3] claimed to have successfully treated hysterical deafness with conditioning techniques, and Hilgard and Marquis's[4] summary of the literature dealing with successful CR treatment of hysterical conversions led us to attempt CR therapy with a patient who had failed to respond to other treatments, including narcosynthesis and psychotherapy. Electromyographic studies were planned in connection with this therapy.

SUBJECT

The patient, whom we shall call Anne, is an attractive 19-year-old unmarried girl of middle-class Scottish parentage. She attended school until the age of 16, completing the tenth grade and since then has been employed as office worker. She is the youngest of 3 daughters. The eldest, age 32, is married and no longer lives at home. The other sister, Kay, age 24, lives at home.

About 6 weeks prior to admission, the patient awoke in the morning to find herself totally deaf. Two weeks earlier she had left home following an altercation with her mother and stayed with a girl friend. However, she returned home 2 days prior to the onset of deafness, complaining of spells of faintness and dizziness. She consulted the family physician, who prescribed some pills, but after taking them for 2 days she perceived a buzzing in the ears and the next morning became deaf. In the opinion of Anne's therapist, her tinnitus was not due to the medication.

When she became deaf, all the other symptoms of faintness, dizziness,

* This research was carried out under Contract No. DA-49-007-MD-70 between the Office of the Surgeon General, U.S. Department of the Army, and McGill University. Grateful acknowledgment is made to Professor D. O. Hebb and Dr. T. J. Boag for critical reading of the manuscript, and to Mr. A. K. Bartoshuk for his assistance in statistical analysis of the data.

Reprinted by permission of the author and the editor of the *J. Personal.* from (1952) *J. Personal.*, **21**, 188-204.

and tinnitus disappeared. The deafness forced her to give up her job. However, she did acquire considerable proficiency in lip reading, which made it possible for her to carry on conversations with others. She was examined by an otolaryngologist* who could detect no organic basis for the deafness and referred her to the psychiatric clinic.

She was treated in the Day Hospital for $2\frac{1}{2}$ months. In her therapist's opinion, her deafness was related to the wish that she could be freed from hearing her mother's nagging voice. Anne felt that her mother favored her sister, Kay. The sibling rivalry and hostility toward the mother came out very clearly during a sodium-amytal interview in which the patient expressed death wishes against her mother.

In May, 1949, Anne had given birth to an illegitimate child, and at that time it was discovered that she had syphilis. Friction between the patient and her mother had centered largely around this. Anne blamed her mother for failing to inform her adequately about sexual matters and objected to her mother's giving the baby up for adoption. The mother frequently mentioned the trouble Anne had caused and the money it had cost.

It is of interest to note that Abely and Dupont[5] reported a case of long-standing hysterical deafness in which the explanation offered was " an irremediable trouble of the attention " to avoid hearing the taunts of her parents because of the birth of an illegitimate child. In this case deafness dated back 28 years.

OUTLINE OF EXPERIMENTAL PROCEDURES

Two experiments were performed: Experiment (1): strong auditory stimulation, and Experiment (2): auditory conditioning. Each experiment was performed twice: first, when the patient was deaf, and later, after she had recovered her hearing. The dates of experimental procedures are listed on the following page.

* We are indebted to Dr. H. Caplan, who made the report of his examination available to us. We quote from his findings: " *Ears*: Canals clear, drums intact. All normal landmarks present. *Nose:* Airways clear. No purulent discharge in any meati. *Throat:* Tonsils cleanly removed. Pharynx healthy. Nasal pharynx clear. *Vestibular tests:* Brisk nystagmatic response on both sides producing 3rd degree phenomena to 10 ml of cold water in each ear. *Audiometric test:* An audiogram was attempted but standard responses were not obtained and the patient answered only to high intensity stimulation at 125 and 250 cycles per sec." Dr. Caplan reported that the patient described a feeling of vibration rather than actual hearing with stimulation at 125 and 250 cycles (70 to 75 decibels on a standard A.D.C. audiometer). It may be noted that these particular stimuli were close to the threshold of feeling (19, pp. 59 ff). The patient wept during the test, and later reported no sensation with repetition of the 125 and 250 cycle tones. These clinical findings resemble our own test findings (Experiment (1)). But it is unlikely that threshold of feeling was reached in our experiment.

We have employed the term " total " hysterical deafness to distinguish this patient from cases of partial hysterical deafness, which are much less rare (18, p. 5). The distinction is an operational one and does not imply identity of functional loss with organic cases in which essential parts of the auditory system have been destroyed.

Dates (1950)	Procedure or event
June 14	Admission to Day Hospital
July 31	Strong auditory stimulation, Session No. 1
August 22	Conditioning, Session No. 1
August 23	Hearing recovered
August 25	Conditioning, Session No. 2
August 30	Strong auditory stimulation, Session No. 2

EXPERIMENT (1): PRESENTATION OF LOUD TONE IN EARPHONES

Method

During the experiment the subject lay on a hospital bed. Muscle potentials were recorded by means of surface leads from the following parts of the body: forehead, right neck, right sternomastoid muscle, left extensor and right extensor muscles of both forearms. The auditory stimuli were 700-cycle tones approximately 90 db. above auditory threshold. There were 10 stimulus presentations in the first test (deaf state) and 14 stimulus presentations in the second test (after Anne had recovered her hearing). Stimuli were transmitted to the subject through binaural earphones. It should be mentioned that a constant feature of the stimulus was a sharp " on effect," which gave the impression of a click of very brief duration.

One observer sat with the subject. Others, including the therapist, viewed the patient through the one-way-vision window in the control room.

Results

Deaf state—The first stimulus produced a startle reaction (see Fig. 1). The observer in the room with Anne noted a slight movement at the time of stimulation. This observer also noted trembling which began with the head and spread to the rest of the body. A few seconds following her startle reaction, Anne displayed a marked emotional reaction, with crying. This reaction alarmed the therapist to the extent that he risked spoiling the test by hurrying into the room to give reassurance to the patient.

When asked whether she had heard the sound, Anne replied that she had heard nothing, but that she had felt pain in her head " as if something hit me on the head." Later, after the test, she added: " It felt as if the top of my head were going to blow off."

The second stimulus, which came 1 min following the first, failed to elicit any reaction, nor did any of the subsequent stimuli produce any reaction which could be detected in the EMG records (see Fig. 1)* or by the observer.

---

* Blinks were not recorded, and because of their frequency, the observer's notes on this point are not conclusive. But it is possible that blinks were produced by stimulation. This would correspond to Landis and Hunt's[6] finding that the blink component of the startle pattern was the only one to occur in hypnotized subjects, who were instructed either not to hear the stimulus or not to react to it.

Each time the observer heard the stimulus, she asked the subject if she had felt anything. The reply, each time, was that she had felt nothing and heard nothing.

Anne's therapist remained until after the third stimulus, when he left her room and resumed his observation through the one-way-vision window. Sobbing had stopped at this time. Anne complained that her eyes " were smarting," and the observer noted frequent blinking. After the seventh stimulus the subject complained of a little pain in her right forehead (where EMG leads were placed), and she also said that her teeth had begun to ache.

The therapist's suggestion to the patient (before the session) that the " machine " would cure her deafness produced no lasting clinical result which could be detected at this time.

Hearing recovered—In the repeat test, 1 week after Anne had recovered her hearing, she reacted to every stimulus. The most constant feature of

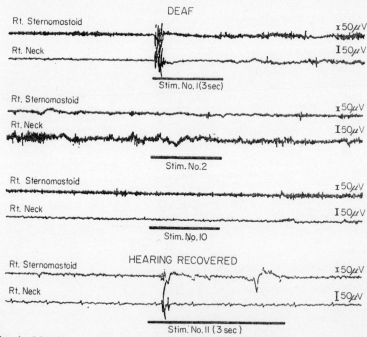

FIG. 1. Muscle potential reaction to strong auditory stimulation. Compare startle reaction to stimulus 1, deaf state, with complete absence of reaction to stimulus 2.

her reaction was frowning, which occurred on every stimulus, with a latency of the order of 0·3 to 0·4 sec. To stimuli 11, 12 and 13 there were reactions which appeared more like startle (see stimulus number 11, Fig. 1). On these stimulations the observer noted twitching of the shoulder and slight arm movements.

Heart rate—The EKG artifact from the neck lead provided heart-rate data for parts of both sessions. These data were examined with respect to resting level of heart rate before auditory stimulation and specific effect of auditory stimulation upon heart rate. In the 3-min. rest period preceding stimulation in the first session (deaf subject), heart rates for successive 2-sec periods ranged from 94 to 102 beats per min. In the second session, after recovery of hearing, the range was from 71 to 76. The high heart rates in the first session showed the subject's apprehensiveness about the test.

Emotion accompanying the startle reaction to the first stimulus during the first session, when the subject's symptom of deafness was present, was reflected in an immediate rise in heart rate of 13 beats per min. During the period of crying heart rate was above the resting level, gradually returning to this level as the emotional disturbance subsided. No rise in heart rate was noted on any other stimulus in the first session, when the EKG tracing could be measured (stimuli 5, 6, 7, 8 and 9). These data were carefully examined in order to determine whether significant fall in heart rate was associated with stimulation. This examination proved negative. Similar examination of the heart rate data for the second session (hearing recovered) also failed to reveal any consistent relationship between stimulation and change in beat rates, which, in this session, never rose above 81 beats per min.

Discussion

In the first place, it is important to satisfy ourselves that this is a case of hysteria rather than one of malingering. There were a number of things which made it appear extremely unlikely that this was a simple case of malingering. Anne had actually become quite proficient at lip reading. Her therapist was able to determine this by tests in which he formed words with his lips, without actually speaking. The results of sodium-amytal sessions provided further evidence against the malingering explanation. It is typical of malingerers that they fight the effects of barbiturates, showing resistive behavior and a highly defensive reaction under amytal.[7] Hysterics, on the other hand, seldom show this behavior, but usually lose their symptom while under the influence of the drug.[7,1] Under amytal Anne behaved in the typical hysterical way. As long as the effects of the amytal persisted, she could hear perfectly, but lost her hearing when the effects wore off and had amnesia for the whole episode.

In the auditory test Anne's symptom-defense was broken through by means of intense auditory stimulation. The penetration of the symptom barrier, which occurred in our test, was probably due to the novel character of the stimulus and of the stimulating situation.* Startling noises in everyday

* It is important to state that Anne had been undergoing a course of ECT. The dates of treatment were July 19, 21, 22, 24, 29 and 31. On July 31 Anne had ECT in the morning, and our auditory test in the afternoon. No post-ECT confusion was noted at the time of testing. It would obviously have been more satisfactory if no ECT had been used in this case, but there is nothing in our present knowledge of its mode of action to suggest that it affected the experimental results.

life situations were ineffective. For example, the therapist's attempt to produce a startle reaction by clapping his hands behind Anne's back had failed to elicit any reaction.

She reacted to the novel stimulation in our test with emotional disturbance, had a brief fit of crying which subsided when her therapist came into the room and reassured her. Then—and this is the most remarkable thing—in the 60 sec which elapsed between stimulus 1 and stimulus 2, her defense against sound somehow strengthened so that it was now *completely* effective against the same stimulation upon repetition (stimulus 2).

Somehow, the impulses coming in over auditory pathways (which had in the first instance effectively carried through to the skeletal-motor pathways) were blocked centrally upon repetition of the stimulus. This must mean that central reorganization took place, and that it happened in a remarkably short space of time. An understanding of the neural mechanisms involved in such rapid alteration of central nervous system action would seem to lead to basic explanation of typical hysterical phenomena, such as sudden onset and disappearance of conversion symptoms, and repression of certain thought sequences.

These observations lead us to consider the matter of central inhibition in relation to the phenomena of muscle reaction. The following analysis does not presume to handle all the possible interrelationships; it is intended merely as a useful reference point for the subsequent discussion. We list three conditions of central inhibition in one column and the corresponding feature of muscle reaction in the other.

Central event	*Muscle reaction*
1. Complete inhibition	1. No reaction
2. Partial or incomplete inhibition	2. Reduced reaction
3. No inhibition	3. Unaltered response

The reference experiments for all three categories of inhibition are found in an important paper by Magoun and Rhines.[8] While it seems likely that the diffuse projection systems[9] may be involved in many inhibitory phenomena important for behavior, it is not an essential assumption in our analysis.*

Present data indicate that following reaction to the first stimulus, central reorganization led to the complete form of inhibition which remained in

---

* Actually, a case can be made for implicating the brain stem inhibitory system in the present instance. This part of the brain stem stands in close topographical relationship with the cochlear nucleus of the auditory system. Functional connection between motor cortex and this inhibitory area in the brain stem is known.[10] The sequence of action in our case could be something like this: Conflicting phase sequences[11] would lead to disorganized cortical firing; impulses to diffuse projection system would bring these regulatory mechanisms into action (reducing reaction). If we posit a localized disturbance primarily in auditory areas, specific activitation of that part of the brain stem associated with the auditory system could occur.

force throughout all succeeding auditory stimulations. EMG data were necessary to distinguish between the complete and partial forms of central inhibition. The available EKG data were also in line with the conclusion of complete inhibition.

The second experiment was carried out with therapeutic aims, and also to obtain further data bearing on the question of inhibitory mechanisms.

EXPERIMENT (2): CONDITIONED FINGER WITHDRAWAL TO SOUND STIMULUS
Method

Conditioning was carried out in the same duplex suite which was used in Experiment (1). One observer stayed in the same room with the subject. In the instrument room two other observers watched the subject through a one-way-vision window.

Instructions to the subject were as follows: " You are to sit on this chair as comfortably as you can and place your right middle finger on this button, with the underpart, not the end of the finger, in contact with this silver electrode. Now, this is how the shock will feel (shock presented). When the shock comes, lift your finger and put it right down again, because the shock will be over very quickly. Try the shock once more (shock presented second time). The next thing I am going to do is sound a tone from the other room just to see if it is working properly. During the session this tone will sound before every shock. Now, if your finger should tend to lift up just before the shock comes along, don't worry about it—just let it come up, and then put it right down again. There will be quite a long series of shocks, so try to keep our instructions always in mind."

A finger button covered with a nickel silver disc 1·7 cm in diameter served the dual purpose of one shock electrode and of a pick-up for recording finger movement.[12] The other shock electrode was a nickel silver plate (2·5 cm × 3·5 cm) attached just above the right wrist. The conditioned stimulus was a clearly audible 1,000-cycle tone of 0·22 sec duration which came from a 10-in. 4-ohm loudspeaker placed near the subject. The shock consisted of the charge of a 2 mfd. condenser discharging through the subject's electrode resistance (never over 50,000 ohms under these conditions and usually of the order of 10,000 ohms); thus practically all of the condenser charge reached the subject within 0·10 sec. Voltage used to charge the condenser was progressively increased during each session in order to compensate for adaptation to shock.[13] Increments in voltage were of the order of 3 to 5 V and were introduced whenever an increase in latency of the voluntary response time was observed. Initial strength of shock was set near the upper limit of S's tolerance, i.e., as great as she could be persuaded to endure. The range for the first session was from 60 V to 100 V; that for the second session was from 40 V to 55 V.

Shock followed onset of tone at an interval of 0·5 sec. Interval between pairings was varied (8, 10 or 12 sec in randomized order) to avoid temporal conditioning. Test trials (tone without shock) were presented on trial numbers 150, 159, 165, 169, 174, 179, 183, 189, 193, 198 and 202 in Session 1;

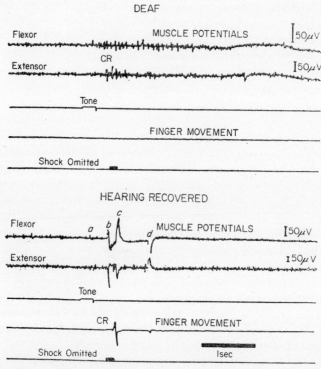

FIG. 2. CR's on first test trial, in Session 1 when S was deaf, and in corresponding test trial, Session 2, after hearing had been recovered. Electrical artifacts in muscle lines of lower record are (a) relay switching artifact, (b) closing shock circuit connected to S (who felt nothing because shock voltage was zero), (c) artifact due to S's removing finger from electrode which was ground, and (d) artifact caused by return of finger to button electrode.

and on trial numbers 149, 157, 163, 167, 172, 177, 181, 187, 191, 196 and 200 in Session 2.*

Muscle potentials were recorded continuously from the flexors and extensors of the right forearm (see Fig. 2). We employed closely spaced leads now standard, in our laboratory, for experiments in which independent

* In Session 1, 26 pairings of tone and shock were given before the main block of 202 trials. These 26 trials were omitted from consideration because the shocks were not eliciting finger retractions. In Session 2 there were 19 trials preceding the main block of 200 trials. On the nineteenth trial of this pre-series, procedure was halted to remove 60-cycle interference. These 19 trials were omitted from consideration.

recording of flexor and extensor activity is desired. It should be stated, however, that with surface leads, one cannot assume *absolutely complete* independence in such recording.

Therapist's Suggestion

Before the first CR session the therapist suggested to the patient that the " machine " could cure her deafness: that she must not expect it to come back during the procedure, but that—in his opinion—she would be able to hear again on the following morning (August 23). As we shall see, this suggestion in combination with the procedure and other factors proved effective in restoring the patient's hearing.

Results

(*1*) *Test trials (unreinforced)*—During her first session, when deaf, Anne's record showed a CR on the first test trial (without shock). This CR was restricted to increased muscular tension, without any detectable finger movement (see Fig. 2). Anne's record for the corresponding test trial in the second session (2 days after she had recovered her hearing) showed the reverse of that shown in the record for the deaf state. The CR consisted in overt withdrawal of her finger from the button *without* the large tensional (muscle potential) component observed in the first session (see Fig. 2). During initial conditioning (deaf state) 2 observers noted a tensing of the right forearm muscles, associated with the recorded muscle potential CR's. These reactions which were clearly visible, through the observation window, appeared to involve a tightening of forearm muscles near the wrist. The same observers watched for this tensing reaction during the second conditioning session (hearing state) but failed to see it on any trials.

A comparison of the record for the 11 test trials in Session 1 (deaf state) with those for the 11 test trials in Session 2 (hearing recovered) showed a preponderance of muscle potential CR's in the first session, and mainly finger movement CR's in the second session. In all test trials, both sessions, actual withdrawal of the finger from the button occurred only once, in the first test trial, in Session 2 (see Fig. 2). In the test trials, Session 1, the finger movement line on the record showed only 1 deflection, of 1 mm* (trial No. 11). During test trials in the *second* session, after hearing was recovered, deflections on the finger line were as follows: 8 mm, trial 1; 3 mm, trial 2; 3 mm, trial 3; 7 mm, trial 6; 2 mm, trial 8.

In the first session muscle potential increments were scored as CR's on 7 of 11 test trials.† Except for test trial 1, in which both flexor and extensor muscle lines were scored positively, reactions were all recorded from the

---

* On the finger button line, deflections less than 1 mm were not scored as CR's.
† Clear increments in muscle potential following tone were scored positive. Small or doubtful increments were scored negative.

extensor leads. Muscle potential reactions were scored as CR's on test trial numbers 1, 3, 7, 8, 9, 10 and 11. For the second session only trial numbers 6 and 8 were scored positive (both from extensor leads). The increments in muscle potential on these two trials were smaller than those in the record for the first session.

(2) *Reinforced trials*—The same scoring methods were applied to the records for all reinforced trials, in both sessions. For these trials the section of record between onset of the CS (tone) and onset of US (shock) was examined for CR's on the two muscle potential lines and the finger button line. Clear increments* in muscle potential were scored as CR's. Deflections in the finger button line were measured to the nearest millimeter. A distinction was made between *positive* deflections on the finger movement line, indicating *less* pressure on the button (in the direction of *extension* or *withdrawal*) and *negative* deflection indicating *more* pressure on the button (flexion, or the opposite of withdrawal).

Table 1 summarizes the analysis for frequency of finger movement and muscle potential CR's. The table shows that muscle potential CR's were significantly more frequent in Session 1 (during deafness), and that finger movement CR's were significantly more frequent in Session 2 (after recovery). In Session 1, two of the nine deflections in the finger button line, scored as CR's, were minus in sign, indicating *pressure* on the button. In Session 2 none of the finger movement CR's were of this kind.

TABLE 1

Per cent frequency of CR's on reinforced trials

	Deaf	Hearing recovered	Difference	P
		Muscle potentials		
Flexor	20·9	3·3	17·6	< ·001
Extensor	17·3	1·7	15·6	< ·001
N	191·0	180·0		
		Finger movement		
	4·7	17·5	12·8	< ·001
N	191·0	189·0		

Table 2 presents data related to acquisition and extinction of CR's. Note the fairly close correspondence between the flexor values for Session 1 (in third column) and finger movement values for Session 2 (in fourth column). Zero values for extinction trials appeared in finger movement, Session 1, and in muscle potentials, Session 2. Note that in Session 2, four flexor CR's

* Increments scored on CR's were larger than spontaneous variations in muscle potential noted in the sections of record preceding and following trials.

appeared in the first 20 trials and that this reaction seemed to extinguish in succeeding trials.

Flexor-extensor relationships—Several lines of evidence indicated that flexor-extensor opposition was stronger in the deaf than in the hearing state. Pooling data from reinforced and non-reinforced trials, in the " deaf" session there were 16 trials in which definite bursts appeared nearly simultaneously in both flexors and extensors in the interval between tone and shock. In the " hearing " session there was only one instance of this. When deaf, two of Anne's ten finger movement CR's were *pressures on the button* (i.e., movements *opposing* finger withdrawal). With hearing recovered, in the second session, Anne gave 38 reactions without a single instance of pressure on the button in the interval between onset of tone and shock. Seven of these reactions were full finger withdrawals. When deaf, Anne did not raise her finger off the button at any time, preceding shock.

TABLE 2

Acquisition and extinction of CR's

Trials	Session 1 Deaf				Session 2 Hearing recovered		
	No. test trials	Number of conditioned responses					
		Finger movement	Extensor	Flexor	Finger movement	Extensor	Flexor
		Acquisition					
1–20	—	0	0	1	1	0	4
21–40	—	0	0	4	5	0	0
41–60	—	2*	4	4	3	0	0
61–80	—	1	4	3	2	1	0
81–100	—	1	7	8	1	1	1
101–120	—	3*	4	2	3	0	1
121–140	—	2	5	9	11	1	0
		Extinction†					
141–160	2	0	3	7	5	0	0
161–180	4	0	0	1	1	0	0
181–200	5	0	4	2	1	0	0

* One reaction was pressure *on* the button.   † Test trials not included.

Therapeutic results—Following Session 1 the patient smilingly asserted that she still could not hear. The therapist then repeated his suggestion that hearing would return on the following morning, after a night's sleep.

The therapist made certain that the patient read his lips correctly. On the next morning Anne was crossing a busy street, on her way to the Institute, when a driver who had narrowly avoided hitting her, blasted his horn and shouted at her. Her hearing suddenly returned, and has remained intact.* This was the first time since her deafness that the patient had attempted crossing a busy street alone.

A week following Anne's return home, her sister, Kay, left home and did not return. The patient has been steadily employed since her discharge and has made a satisfactory adjustment. She has been getting along well with her mother, whose fright over Anne's deafness seemed to produce a shift in her attitude from one of criticism to one of solicitousness.

DISCUSSION

The hysterically deaf subject was conditioned to an auditory stimulus. This is what might have been expected on the basis of previous conditioning experiments carried out with hysterical subjects.[4] The remarkable thing about our CR data was the evidence for discontinuity in the conditioning from Session 1 (deaf) to Session 2 (hearing). CR's in Session 1 were muscle potential reactions with *higher* amplitudes than those associated with the finger movement CR's in Session 2. Comparison of these data with those of Hilden[14] from normal subjects reveals the discontinuity of conditioning in our subject. In Hilden's study, as conditioning progressed from muscle potential reactions to actual overt finger withdrawal, the muscle potential component of the CR typically showed continuous increment, such that amplitudes of the muscle potential CR's were *lower* early in conditioning than they were later.†

Analysis of the CR data from the deaf subject revealed a flexor-extensor opposition which was not a feature of the CR, after recovery of hearing. The extensor component is easily identified with finger withdrawal in the familiar avoidance conditioning. What is the origin of flexion, the antagonistic reaction? It seemed clear from the data analysis that flexion was identified somehow with the hysterical symptom of deafness. According to the interpretation of Dollard and Miller,[15] hysterical symptoms are drive reducing. If drive is the learned one of anxiety, interruption of the symptom would have the effect of raising the level of anxiety. In the present case there was a good example of this phenomenon in the elicitation of anxiety following the subject's reaction to the auditory stimulus in Experiment (1).

Now finger extension in *anticipation* of shock would actually represent symptom interruption because it would imply ability to hear. It follows

---

* In April, 1952, it was learned that the patient's hearing was still intact, that she was apparently symptom free and that she was about to be married.
† Another evidence of discontinuity in conditioning was the observation of tensing in forearm muscles, associated with CR's *in the deaf state only*.

then that extending the finger or even the initiation of finger extension might be anxiety arousing. Here anxiety assumes the status of drive.[15] It thus appears that, when the symptom was present, there were two coexisting and interrelated mechanisms of conditioning, leading to conflict. These mechanisms may be outlined as follows:

Conditioning	Drive	Cue	Response	Reinforcement
A	pain	tone	finger withdrawal (extension)	avoidance of pain
B	anxiety	motor cue (lifting finger to tone, in anticipation of shock, signifies hearing)	movement opposed to finger withdrawal (flexion)	avoidance of anxiety

It should be pointed out that the motor cue in Conditioning B need not be confined to actual *muscular* reaction. It *could* be an activation of phase sequences[11] in the central nervous system *without* discharge into muscular activity. In fact, the conflict could be resolved at a central level, with *complete* inhibition of the extensor reaction (CR A). This inhibition would be like that seen in Experiment (1).

The muscle potential data in Experiment (2), however, indicated that inhibition was of the *incomplete* kind, in which conflict between central mechanisms was reflected in overflow of impulses to the muscles.

According to this interpretation, these EMG increments were not CR's of the usual kind, but were actually the peripheral evidence of partial central inhibition. From our data it appears that such an overflow phenomenon is associated with EMG increments which are larger than those preceding uninhibited extension of the finger, as in the second session when hearing was recovered.

We may raise the question why inhibition was complete in Experiment (1) and incomplete in Experiment (2). The chief difference between the two experimental situations lies in the use of shock in the second experiment. This introduced a strong drive, that of pain, setting the stage for conflict. Conflict of this sort was not a feature of Experiment (1) in which pain was not involved.

Freud[16] believed that hysterical and hypnotic phenomena of sensory exclusion involved the same basic mechanism of suggestion. We are now in a position to put this to a test. Erickson[17,18] was successful in producing total deafness hypnotically. In one study[18] he employed a conditioning technique similar to ours in studying two hypnotized subjects. He reported a failure to produce auditory conditioning in his subjects when they were deaf. In control test trials introduced in the same hypnotic session, but with hearing temporarily restored, conditioned responses were promptly elicited. Since Erickson did not record muscle potentials, it is not possible to make direct comparison of his data with ours. If we compare our measure of finger *withdrawal* with his motor measure, however, there is essential agreement. The crucial point, which remains to be assessed, is whether the hypnotically deaf subject will, like our hysterical subject, show the phenomenon of incomplete inhibition in conditioning. In order to answer this question it seems necessary to record muscle potentials from hypnotized subjects, under the experimental conditions employed in the present investigation of hysterical deafness.

Landis and Hunt's[6] finding that all components of the startle pattern, except blink, were usually abolished by inhibitory instructions under hypnosis is also very relevant here. In the first place, voluntary inhibition in the waking state never abolished the pattern to this extent. This practically rules out any explanation of our finding in terms of malingering. In the second place, their work raises another question for further investigation: whether under deeper hypnosis and with complete hysterical deafness, even the blink might be abolished.

SUMMARY

This paper reports the results of a special case study. The subject was a 19-year-old girl with complete hysterical deafness. The main points of interest in this study were (1) the patient's electromyographic reaction to novel and intense auditory stimulation, (2) auditory conditioning, and (3) " CR therapy."

The first auditory stimulation produced a startle reaction followed by marked emotional disturbance. Repetition of the same stimulus 1 min. later produced no reaction and no change in the patient's EMG record. Auditory conditioning was obtained in the deaf state and the procedure appeared useful therapeutically, since the patient recovered her hearing on the day following the CR session. In the deaf state CR's were mainly confined to muscle potentials. In the hearing state the large muscle potential components were significantly less frequent in the CR's which were mainly responses of finger movement.

Results are interpreted in terms of CR and neuropsychological theory.

REFERENCES

1. SEMENOV, H. (1947). Deafness of psychic origin and its response to narcosynthesis. *Trans. Amer. Acad. Ophthal. Otol.*, **51**, 326-348.
2. BECHTEREV, V. M. (1933). *General Principles of Human Reflexology. An Introduction to the Objective Study of Personality.* P. 401. Jarrolds, London.
3. BECHTEREV, V. M. (1912). Die Anwendung der Methode der motorischen Assoziations reflexe zur Aufdeckung der Simulation. *Z. ges. neurol. Psychiat.*, **13**, 183-191.
4. HILGARD, E. R. and MARQUIS, D. G. (1940). *Conditioning and Learning.* Pp. 296-299. Appleton-Century, New York.

5. ABELY, X. and DUPONT, A. (1928). Un cas de surdité hystérique datant de 28 ans. *Ann. Med.-Psychol.*, **86**, 227-236.

6. LANDIS, C. and HUNT, W. A. (1939). *The Startle Pattern.* Farrar & Rinehart, New York.

7. MENNINGER, W. C. (1948). *Psychiatry in a Troubled World.* P. 214. Macmillan, New York.

8. MAGOUN, H. W. and RHINES, R. (1946). An inhibitory mechanism in the bulbar reticular formation. *J. Neurophysiol.*, **9**, 165-171.

9. JASPER, H. H. (1949). Diffuse projection systems: The integrative action of the thalamic reticular system. *EEG Clin. Neurophysiol.*, **1**, 405-420.

10. RUCH, T. C. (1951). Motor systems. In *Handbook of Experimental Psychology* (by Stevens, S. S.), Pp. 186-187. Wiley, New York.

11. HEBB, D. O. (1949). *The Organization of Behavior.* Wiley, New York.

12. MALMO, R. B. and SHAGASS, C. (1949). Physiologic studies of reaction to stress in anxiety and early schizophrenia. *Psychosom. Med.*, **11**, 9-24.

13. WOLFLE, H. M. (1930). Time factors in conditioning finger-withdrawal. *J. gen. Psychol.*, **4**, 372-378.

14. HILDEN, A. H. (1937). An action current study of the conditioned hand withdrawal. *Psychol. Monogr.*, **49**, No. 217, 173-204.

15. DOLLARD, J. and MILLER, N. E. (1950). *Personality and Psychotherapy.* McGraw-Hill, New York.

16. FREUD, S. (1950). *Collected Papers,* Volume II, pp. 105-110. Hogarth, London.

17. ERICKSON, M. H. (1938). A study of clinical and experimental findings on hypnotic deafness: I. Clinical experimentation and findings. *J. gen. Psychol.*, **19**, 127-150.

18. ERICKSON, M. H. (1938). A study of clinical and experimental findings on hypnotic deafness: II. Experimental findings with a conditioned response technique. *J. gen. Psychol.*, **19**, 151-167.

19. STEVENS, S. S. and DAVIS, H. (1938). *Hearing. Its Psychology and Physiology.* Wiley, New York.

20. ROSENBERGER, A. I. and MOORE, J. H. (1946). The treatment of hysterical deafness at Hoff General Hospital. *Amer. J. Psychiat.*, **102**, 666-669.

THE APPLICATION OF CONDITIONING AND LEARNING TECHNIQUES TO THE TREATMENT OF A PSYCHIATRIC PATIENT*

H. GWYNNE JONES

Institute of Psychiatry (Maudsley Hospital), University of London

AN EXPERIMENTAL approach to the diagnostic investigation of psychiatric patients has been advocated for some time.[1,2,3] Experimental techniques applying the findings of experimental psychology, particularly those pertaining to learning processes, are equally relevant to the *treatment* of psychiatric symptoms. This paper is presented in illustration of such application.

SUMMARY OF THE CASE HISTORY

The patient, a young woman of 23 years, was admitted to the hospital on a day-patient basis for investigation and treatment.† She complained of frequency of micturition with associated secondary fears and general lack of confidence. One instance of psychiatric disorder was reported in the family history, a sister being described as suffering from an " hysterical" paralysis. At the age of 14, the patient left school, where she had been an above average scholar and athlete. She was described as quiet and timid but no other abnormalities were reported. During the next 4 years she enjoyed a successful and progressive career as a " soubrette dancer " with various theatrical companies. She was described as a quiet and timid person off the stage but self-assured on it. Her feelings were easily hurt and she " took everything to heart." She complained that she disliked the lax moral tone of stage life.

The patient's sexual history was thought to be relevant to her illness. At 17 she met and became engaged to a young man of 23. They had sexual intercourse, practicing *coitus interruptus*, which caused her some anxiety. She submitted but found it unpleasant. After a year, discovering her fiance's

* This article is based upon a paper presented to the British Psychological Society at Durham in April, 1955.

Reprinted by permission of the author and the *Amer. Psychol. Ass.* from (1956) *J. Abnorm. and Soc. Psychol.*, **52**, 414-420.

† This patient was under the care of Dr. A. Harris, consultant psychiatrist to the Bethlem Royal and Maudsley Hospitals. Without the permission, co-operation and medical supervision of Dr. Harris and his registrar, Dr. P. M. Middleton, this experiment could not have been carried out. Their encouragement and assistance are gratefully acknowledged.

infidelity, she broke off the engagement but retained some affection for him. Before this, she discovered that he had suffered from gonorrhea but claimed to be cured. She later developed a vaginal discharge, but medical investigation failed to indicate venereal disease. Some 2 years later, she entered into a relationship with an older man. This gave her more pleasure, but it terminated with her discovery of the man's concurrent engagement to another woman.

The urinary frequency started when the patient was 17 at about the time she met her first fiance and, within a year, became a serious embarrassment. By the time she was 19 it made much stage work impossible, but she continued to work sporadically for a further 2 years. She then lived for a year with her mother, during which time the frequency remained unchanged with steadily increasing anxiety symptoms. She complained of a pain in her abdomen after urinating which persisted for from 5 to 10 min. As an example of her anxious state, she described a shopping expedition after a morning indoors during which she felt well. As soon as she reached the door, she experienced what she described as a " panic " that she might pass urine. Her legs shook, the traffic sounded very loud, and she became out of breath. In fact she has never been incontinent out of doors, but, on one occasion, she became so immediately after entering the house. After a year with her mother, she made a final attempt to return to the stage but failed to start work. This shortly preceded her admission to hospital.

On examination when admitted to hospital the patient was described in the following terms.

Physically—Passes urine approximately every $\frac{1}{2}$ hr with abdominal pains. Evidence of autonomic imbalance in that her limbs are at times very cold, at other times warm, and she sweats copiously. Slightly enlarged vascular thyroid.

Mentally—Friendly, quiet, and serious with no histrionics. Easily embarrassed. Talks frankly and to the point. Not depressed but somewhat hopeless and low spirited. Sleep moderate. Appetite fair.

Extensive specialist gynaecological, urological and neurological examinations failed to reveal any local or general physical abnormality, nor was there evidence of venereal disease. Psychiatric investigation indicated that the illness was of the nature of an anxiety reaction with hysterical urinary frequency. Psychotherapy and general day-hospital treatment over a period of 5 weeks produced very little change in her condition. At the end of this period it was suggested that she be discharged from the day-hospital, advised to give up her stage career to which she had shown ambivalent attitudes, and advised to take up such employment as secretarial work in which toilet facilities were always available. In this way it was hoped that the symptoms would improve gradually. The patient reacted very strongly and negatively to these suggestions and was unwilling to contemplate the relinquishment of her stage ambitions. At this stage the psychologist was consulted as to the possibilities of applying learning techniques to the symptomatic treatment of the urinary frequency.

SYMPTOMATIC TREATMENT OF THE URINARY FREQUENCY

The work of Mowrer[4] and others on the treatment of enuresis indicates that the bladder is an organ susceptible to training and conditioning procedures. More relevant to the present problem is experimental work described by Bykov.[5] In these studies, warm water was introduced into the bladders of human Ss, the pressure changes being recorded graphically and displayed on a manometer placed before the S. This manometer could be disconnected without the S's knowledge. Since the urge to urinate tends to occur at a definite pressure for each individual, the Ss rapidly developed a " connection "* between the manometer reading equivalent to this pressure

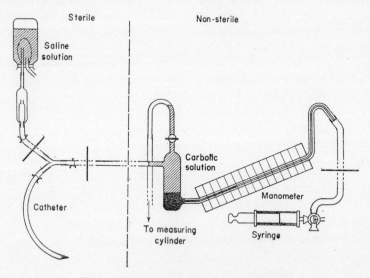

FIG. 1. Cystometric apparatus (not to scale).

and the urge to urinate. An intense urinary urge and an associated galvanic skin response could be elicited merely by calling out, via a microphone and loud-speaker, the figure of the critical manometer reading. This response occurred even when the bladder contained practically no fluid. Conversely, and of more direct interest, if the manometer, disconnected without S's

---

* Bykov describes this experiment in terms of " conditioning." Others may prefer to class it with experiments on " suggestion " in that the phenomenon observed has much in common with such well-known effects as the " heat illusion," generally described in terms of suggestion.

knowledge, registered zero, it was possible to introduce far greater quantities of fluid than normally produced urination without evoking the urgency response.

In the light of this report an apparatus was constructed as illustrated in Fig. 1. The manometer was fitted with a scale in arbitary units and, by means of an inconspicuous tap, could be connected to a syringe, thus creating a back pressure and decreasing the reading on the scale. By means of this apparatus, with appropriate arrangements of the clips and taps, varying volumes of sterile saline solution could be introduced into the patient's bladder, true or decreased pressure readings could be taken at any stage, and the patient's bladder could be voluntarily evacuated, the outflow being measured in a cylinder. In use the manometer was placed at bladder height and immediately before the *S* where she could read the scale.

The patient was given elementary instruction in the physiology of urination, the nature of the apparatus (except for the function of the syringe) was explained, and she was told that, after the apparatus had demonstrated the nature of her malfunctioning, she would be trained to achieve normal reactions. The apparatus was then set up and saline was introduced into

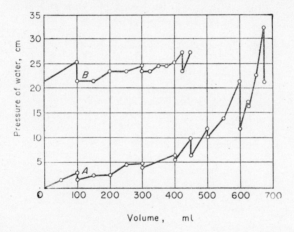

Fig. 2. Cystometrograms. *A*. Normative data; *B*. Patient's responses d ring the first trial.

the bladder, true pressure readings being taken at intervals. The results are shown in Fig. 2. For comparison the graph includes data reported by Denny-Brown,[6] illustrating the reaction of a " normal " bladder. Each curve ends where the urge to urinate became imperative.

From these data, the patient's bladder responses may be described as abnormal in three respects: (1) The urge to urinate occurred at relatively low bladder volumes and pressures. The threshold pressure, equivalent to about 27 cm of water, corresponded to the figure 7 on the arbitrary scale.

(2) The patient's detrusor muscle responses to changes in bladder volume were abnormally sluggish. Normally the bladder wall reacts to increased fluid with increased tension followed by an adaptive relaxation producing a zigzag effect on a graph. (3) The bladder musculature maintained abnormally high bladder pressure at low bladder volumes. In the graph shown, the pressure was in fact only just subliminal throughout, and the patient reported urgency at a volume of 300 ml.

Of these abnormalities the first was expected to respond to the conditioning technique, and it was hoped that the others would improve with practice and attempts at voluntary relaxation.

Three further trials were carried out on the first day of treatment. During the first two, the manometer was left open to the atmosphere and, when the bladder contained some 300 ml of fluid, attempts were made by the patient to lower the manometric reading by voluntary relaxation. Tension of various body muscles, as would be expected, increased the pressure, but relaxation had no effect. These two trials showed a little improvement over the first in that 550 ml of fluid were retained, and the pressure during the earlier part of the curve was slightly lower at about 20 cm of water. The threshold for urgency remained at the arbitrary figure of 7. For the last trial, the manometer was connected to the syringe, thus artificially lowering the

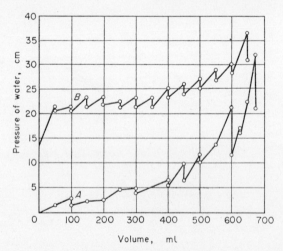

FIG. 3. Cystometrograms. *A*. Normative data; *B*. Patient's responses during the third trial of the second session.

manometric readings. This technique had the expected effect in that the patient now retained over 600 ml of fluid, but the " true " threshold pressure was little if any higher than previously. On this and later occasions when the back pressure was utilised, the patient was encouraged, when she reported urgency, to accept a little more fluid. While it was being introduced, the syringe was disconnected, allowing a final " true " pressure reading. This modified procedure was adopted in order to demonstrate to the patient that she was able to tolerate increased pressures as well as increased volumes and because she was aware of the nature of her abnormalities.

The apparatus was again used 2 days later. The first trial, with the manometer open, was generally similar to the middle trials of the first session as was the second, during which the patient was standing instead of sitting as previously. For the third and last trial of this day, the manometer was connected to the syringe. The results are shown in Fig. 3 where it may be seen that the first abnormality, relating to the pressure and volume at the

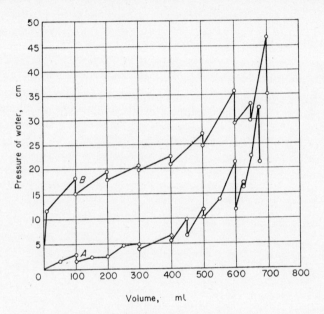

FIG. 4. Cystometrograms. *A*. Normative data; *B*. Patient's responses during the first trial of the fourth session.

outset of urgency, was more or less eliminated and, most strikingly, the adaptive contractions and relaxations of the bladder wall were clearly evident. This change apparently resulted from the repeated stimulation. The third abnormality, relating to high pressures at low volumes, was essentially unmodified.

Similar use of the apparatus was made on two further occasions at intervals of 3 and 2 days. Figure 4 refers to a trial on the fourth occasion and illustrates considerable modification of the original bladder reactions. The pressure at low volume was less but still abnormally high. There was, however, a considerable range of pressure below the threshold value. The fifth and final session, 2 days later, was devoted to an unsuccessful attempt at modifying the lower end of the curve. Immediately after bladder evacuating, the pressure fell to a value lower than 2 cm of water, but invariably, after a period between about 2 sec and 30 sec, the pressure suddenly rose to about 14 cm of water. This rise seemed to be precipitated by any activity such as a laugh or cough, or by the addition of a small volume of fluid to the bladder; but even in the absence of such specific stimuli, the rise invariably occurred.

After the first day's treatment the patient reported that she felt " easier and more confident " and appeared to derive satisfaction from the knowledge that she could retain a fairly large volume of fluid in her bladder. After the third session she became markedly cheerful and optimistic. At this stage she successfully completed a game of tennis, whereas she had previously been unwilling to embark on any strenuous activity, fearing that it would precipitate urination. This confidence, optimism, and enterprise increased during the remaining sessions. She now intended to seek employment, possibly as a telephone operator, and to make a gradual return to the stage via evening engagements. A week after the cessation of the laboratory treatment, her urinary frequency had practically disappeared and no other symptoms were evident in the setting of the day-hospital. The prospect of venturing into the streets, however, induced a strong anxiety reaction. Thus, she reported spending " about an hour thinking about it " before leaving for home in the evening. She would not accompany E outside the gates of the hospital, claiming that she would require time for mental preparation. It was therefore decided to devise a training program aimed at the elimination of this anxiety reaction.

TREATMENT OF THE ANXIETY REACTION

The therapeutic problem may be described in terms of substituting for the original dominant (anxiety) reaction an alternative (normal) reaction to the stimulus of being placed in a public situation. Guthrie[7] suggests that one way of achieving such a substitution is to present the stimulus at reduced intensity so that the accustomed response is not elicited. Presumably, the presentation of a stimulus qualitatively remote from the original, but occupying a position on the generalization curve of the latter, would operate in the same way as a reduction in stimulus intensity. On the basis of such a theoretical formulation, a graded re-education program was devised, concentrating, in order to maximize the motivation related to the alternative reaction, on the stage situation. Wolpe[8] has reported animal experimentation which would serve as a paradigm for such a technique and quotes[9] the successful treatment of many psychiatric conditions by somewhat similar methods.

The treatment involved a daily program in several stages. In a secluded garden, the patient first embarked alone on a training course of limbering-up exercises to make her physically fit for dancing. She then devised and rehearsed a dance routine, first concentrating on the movements and then on acting as if before an audience. She was encouraged to imagine such an audience and to " live the part " as actively as possible. She then gave a " private showing " to the *E*, and, finally, she performed successfully in a public non-professional stage show. In this way the normal response was gradually shifted along the stimulus generalization continuum until it superseded the original anxiety reaction. Parallel with this training, the patient made unrehearsed and progressively more extensive outdoor expeditions.

A fortnight after the commencement of this treatment the patient was discharged from the day-hospital. The public stage appearance took place a short time after discharge. Though it was intended that she should attend the hospital at intervals as an outpatient, she only attended one follow-up clinic 1 month after discharge. She then reported that her urinary frequency and general condition were greatly improved. She still experienced some anxiety about travelling in the rush hour and suffered occasional brief depressed moods but felt better able to combat them. She had obtained a job in a shoe shop but hoped to change to a better one in a theatrical agency and ultimately to return to the stage. Fifteen months after her discharge, her private physician reported that she had remained free of symptoms and had recently married with apparent success.

DISCUSSION

During the course of the treatments described, the patient's long-standing symptoms improved considerably. That this amelioration resulted from the treatment cannot be asserted with confidence. Large-scale controlled studies involving such treatments would be necessary to establish their efficacy. It is hoped, however, that this paper demonstrates that it is possible to devise rational symptomatic treatment for psychiatric symptoms, whether physical or emotional in nature. That such treatment is symptomatic is, in the writer's view, no handicap. Much evidence points to the fact that neuroticism is largely a constitutional defect for which no effective radical therapy is yet available. The individual of neurotic constitution in certain environmental circumstances develops certain symptoms. The rational therapeutic approach is then to treat the symptoms and to modify the environment so as to avoid their recrudescence or the development of fresh symptoms. The more specific the treatment, the more likely may be its success.

SUMMARY

The treatment is described of a psychiatric patient who, in the framework of an emotional disorder, presented a disabling somatic symptom in the form of abnormal frequency of micturition, especially evident when she was in public places or engaged in her profession of dancing. Intensive investigation failed to reveal any organic basis for this symptom, and psychotherapy during a period of hospitalization failed to produce any amelioration. Since bladder responses are susceptible to conditioning procedures, a plan of treatment including a conditioning situation and a graded training program was designed and executed.

It was shown that the patient's bladder responses were abnormal in three aspects: (1) Urgency occurred at abnormally low bladder pressures and volumes. (2) The muscular responses to changes in bladder volume were abnormally sluggish. (3) The bladder musculature maintained abnormally high bladder pressures at low bladder volume.

The first abnormality responded rapidly to the conditioning technique employed. The second disappeared, apparently as a result of exercise. The third was partially modified. After the laboratory treatment, considerable improvement in the patient's general condition was evident in a non-stressful environment, but a graded re-education program was necessary before effective relief from the symptoms in normal life situations was achieved.

REFERENCES

1. EYSENCK, H. J. (1952). The role of the psychologist in psychiatric practice. *Proc. Roy. Soc. Med.*, **45**, 447-449.
2. PAYNE, R. W. (1953). The role of the clinical psychologist at the Institute of Psychiatry. *Rev. Psychol. Appl.*, **3**, 150-160.
3. SHAPIRO, M. B. (1951). An experimental approach to diagnostic psychological testing. *J. Ment. Sci.*, **97**, 748-764.
4. MOWRER, O. H. and MOWRER, W. M. (1938). Enuresis: A method for its study and treatment. *Amer. J. Orthopsychiat.*, **8**, 436-459.
5. BYKOV, K. M. (1953). New data on the physiology and pathology of the cerebral cortex. Communication at the 19th International Physiological Congress, Montreal.
6. DENNY-BROWN, D. and GRAEME-ROBERTSON, E. (1933). On the physiology of micturition. *Brain*, **56**, 149-190.
7. GUTHRIE, E. R. (1935). *The Psychology of Learning*. Harper, New York.
8. WOLPE, J. (1952). Experimental neuroses as learned behaviour. *Brit. J. Psychol.*, **43**, 243-628.
9. WOLPE, J. (1954). Reciprocal inhibition as the main basis of psychotherapeutic effects. *Arch. Neurol. Psychiat.*, **72**, 205-226.

EXPERIMENTS UPON THE TOTAL INHIBITION OF STAMMERING BY EXTERNAL CONTROL, AND SOME CLINICAL RESULTS*

C. CHERRY, D.SC. and B. McA. SAYERS, B.SC.

Imperial College, London, S.W.7

Clinical Notes in Appendix by

PAULINE M. MARLAND

St. Mary's Hospital, London, W.2

SYNTHETICALLY PRODUCED " STAMMERING "

THE METHOD by which people of normal speech habits may have their speech-behaviour seriously disturbed was reported some years ago by Lee.[1] These results are now well known and have been widely demonstrated. The method, usually known as a delayed-playback speech, consists of recording a speaker's speech on a magnetic-tape machine and playing this record back to him whilst he is speaking, through well-fitting headphones, but delayed by approximately $\frac{1}{10} - \frac{1}{5}$ sec. As a result the subject hears his own speech in an unnatural time relationship with his voice production; his perceptual habits and self-monitoring of speech are disturbed, the consequence being an excessive drawling of vowels, repetition of words, stuttering of syllables and other defects. We are not here intending to suggest that true stammering behaviour is an analogous phenomenon, but rather to assume the moral that the production of speech involves a closed-cycle feedback action, by which means a speaker continually monitors and checks his own voice production.

We are extending this hypothesis, and suggesting that stammering (functionally) represents a type of relaxation oscillation, caused by instability of the feedback loop. This is a hypothesis, but with no pretence to formal theory; to check it, various experiments have been designed to break the closed-cycle feedback loop, by interfering with a speaker's perceptions, using individuals having chronic stammering habits. The results have been surprising, both as regards their universality over a very wide range of cases, and as regards their extent; the stammering habits can be almost totally inhibited and normal speech induced, suggesting that the determining defects are perceptual rather than motor.

* Reprinted by permission of the author and editor of the *J. Psychosom. Res.* from (1956) *J. Psychosom. Res.*, **1**, 233-246.

The suggestion that speech and aural perception are closely integrated into a self-monitoring feedback activity is by no means new. Sikorski called attention to the importance of " self-awareness " in speech behaviour as early as 1892, and Freund[2] emphasized that many psychic phenomena suggest the wide use of feedback reinforcement. Kern[3] stressed the need for examining the feedback actions provided by auditory perception, and their significance to the phenomenon of stammering. He writes: " The last 10 years have seen studies concentrated on motor behaviour . . . effort should perhaps now be focused on taking away the *attention* from the vocal actions." He proceeds to describe what happens when stammerers read from books, whilst they are partially deafened by the sound of a Barany drum.

The experiments described here, carried out in collaboration with Mrs. P. M. Marland, are closely related to this earlier work by Kern; we would appear to have rediscovered his main findings independently but, as might be expected from the use of more modern techniques, to have made these findings much more precise and consistent, and in a very enhanced form.*

There are two ways in which the self-monitoring (feedback) actions due to auditory perception may be prevented, in order that their effects upon speech behaviour may be observed:

(1) By deafening—suppressing both air- and bone-conducted hearing, in ways more extreme than that used by Kern.

(2) By compelling transference of the speaker's perceptions to a source of sound other than his own speech.

It is this latter means which provided our own approach to the pheno-menon of stammering, though we have been led to conclusions wholly in agreement with those of Kern. However, this diametrically opposite approach may itself be not without value; for whilst we are inclined to agree with Kern that the inhibition of stammering by temporary deafening may have no therapeutic value (and may even involve risk) we would suggest, tentatively and cautiously, that inhibition of stammering by transference of the auditory perceptions may provide valuable means for the clinical treatment of stammerers.

THE NATURAL READINESS FOR IMITATIVE ACTION — THE SPEECH-SHADOWING TECHNIQUE

The starting point of our experiments is the technique we have termed shadowing, a means for compelling at least a partial transference of a speaker's auditory perceptions away from his own voice to that of another speaker, as reported earlier by one of the writers.[4] This concerned the great ease with which we can speak at the same time as someone else, if we copy what they are saying. One speaker (the *control*) reads from a book and a second (the *subject*) shadows him without seeing the text. The subject may have

* We are indebted to Dr. E. Froeschels for calling our attention to this earlier work.

only a vague idea of the content of the words he utters, perhaps none if the text is difficult. This shadowing is an imitative motor action accomplished with surprising ease; the subject's perceptions are transferred, to a large extent, away from his own voice, to the control speaker's voice. It is as though the subject's deeply engrained speech habits are readily stimulated into action, by his perceptions of sounds conforming fairly closely to these habits. Using an English control speaker and an American subject, it has been found that the latter lapses into common Americanisms (like *gotten*, rail-*road*, etc.), these being his own speech habits.

It is this speech-shadowing technique which had been put to clinical use, with most encouraging results; a short report is appended.

(1) Intention Movements; Imitative Behaviour

This readiness for shadowing, or imitative speech behaviour, may perhaps be allied to the so-called *intention movements* of animals (as in flocking, or swarming, where one creature is stimulated into imitating the behaviour of others in a group). There are other similar infectious actions in humans— as yawning, or giggling—and there are certain, almost unavoidable, imitative actions which are very common—such as marching in step, or in time to a tune, or singing in a choir (in true, or imagined, tune). There are endless examples and we suggest that speech may be a kind of activity which is in a closely related class, but no more.

The question then arises: in view of the naturalness and readiness of such speech shadowing, might we not expect stammerers to show similar behaviour? During our experiments a number of subjects reported that they had no difficulty in singing in a choir, or in reciting the Lord's prayer in church, in unison. This is not quite identical with shadowing, because the utterances are learned beforehand and so provide a lessened stimulus; such actions merely emphasize their readiness for imitation, no more.

Numerous "speech shadowing" tests have been carried out, with a variety of adult stammerers as subjects and they have shown an ability to speak coherently, with little or no difference from normal people. It was decided to investigate this technique further, for although different people experience varying difficulties at first, they all show improvement with practice; that is, speech shadowing seems to represent a marked learning situation.

(2) Simultaneous Reading

A somewhat similar external control is provided by simultaneous reading; in this, the subject and the control read together from the same seen text. It has been found that stammerers, of all the types studied, and unable to read alone could do this almost immediately with no more than a few seconds practice. Again, such a technique has the effect of partially transferring the subject's perceptions away from his own speech-sounds to those of the control.

It might be objected here, that the results of such highly personal experiments would depend upon other factors in the sufferer's environment, or upon his emotional state. But it has been found that both the shadowing and the simultaneous reading techniques were always successful with a very wide sample of sufferers, under varied conditions and on a number of different occasions. There were no negative results. For example, the experiments were carried out with one sympathetic person watching, with a few sympathetic persons and with a dozen strangers. The stammering subjects came from many walks of life, and they had very different histories, educations and personal environments.

The simultaneous reading technique has led to a number of secondary but important observations. The first was the distinction between the success of control in the steady-state condition, when the subject had settled down to fluent utterance and was steadily following the control speaker, and that in the initial launching or starting condition. In this latter, it was found that some stammerers have difficulty in commencing utterance, when the control speaker first starts reading the text. Consequently, further investigation into the distinction between the steady-state and the starting conditions was required.

(3) Control by Independent Vocal Stimuli

(a) Using different texts—A second observation has more profound implications. We found that during the simultaneous reading tests the control speaker could switch his reading to another paragraph, without warning, whilst the subject continued to read without stammering through the original paragraph. We then had the spectacle of the two people reading different material simultaneously, with the implication that it is not the words, their interpretation, or their semantic content, which exercises control over the stammerer; rather, it is the physical sounds of the control speaker's voice which are significant, or some elements of these sounds. Further investigation has been made to determine what elements of voice-sounds are of importance.

(b) Using gibberish—The conclusion is further strengthened by another test, in which the control speaker commences by reading from a text, with the subject reading simultaneously and with no stammering; later, the control speaker changes without warning to speaking complete gibberish. It is extremely easy, with a little self-training, to mouth gibberish-sounds without using any true words of one's language; nevertheless, the sounds uttered will undoubtedly conform to the *phonetic* structure of the language, through the constraints operating by virtue of deeply engrained speech habits. Such gibberish is essentially speech-like.

Again, under such control (and steady-state) conditions, stammering was completely inhibited in all cases, on all occasions.

(c) *Using reversed speech*—Another form of control, giving similar results and illustrating similar points, arose from playing a vocal recording backwards, through headphones, to the subject (reversed speech). What, then, are the acoustic elements of the phonetic sounds which exercise such strong influence over the subject's perceptions?

The various experiments described above have all employed vocal stimuli, to place inhibitory control upon a stammerer's voice, resulting in nearly normal speech behaviour. The qualification " nearly " is stressed. For the results of such methods of control, using external speech or speech-like stimuli, have not been absolutely certain and regular; there has been some degree of variation between the various subjects used depending, *inter alia*, upon the difficulty of the text used for the shadowing tests and upon the extent of the stammerer's experience with the technique. Some stammerers can shadow immediately, at first trial; others work up to fluency more or less quickly. Indeed, it is this very personal variation, with the suggestion that learning is taking place, which underlines the therapeutic possibilities of the shadowing technique. As a technique it is fairly natural-istic, having relation to the normal processes of learning to speak and hear during infancy. The hope is that with continued shadowing exercises, using suitable texts, a sufferer's perceptual habits might be changed; this is being borne out well by the first clinical experiments, as reported in the Appendix.

These first experiments used speech and speech-like stimuli and, as already mentioned, carried the implication that it is purely acoustic elements which exercise control over the attention, rather than interpretation or meaning. But in real life, when one is speaking, the speech is controlled by feedback mediated through both air-conduction and bone-conduction path-ways. Is there any significant difference then, to a stammerer, between perceiving the purely air-conducted sounds of the control speaker's voice while shadowing and perceiving his own voice-sounds through both pathways when he speaks alone?

The air-conduction and bone-conduction pathways differ very much in their acoustic properties. In order to investigate more closely the nature of the sounds which exercise control, some further experiments were made using, not speech stimuli, but instrumental means.

STAMMERING AS A PERCEPTUAL DEFECT

(1) External Control of Perception

Our previous results have given indications that control of the acoustic environment of speech and speech-like sounds perceived by the subject may provide at least a partial control of his speech difficulty. It is clearly important to determine what components the subject perceives out of his own voice whilst self-monitoring, and to determine which of the components of the speech stimulus take control in the perceptual habits which appear to give rise to stammering. That is, we should not assume that all components of the speech sounds exercise such controlling influence. The fact that a normal individual hears and monitors his own voice through both air conduction and bone conduction is widely realized. Subjectively these two stimuli are comparable in loudness. We set out to separate these two stimuli by interfering with the feedback channels which transmit them to the ears.

(2) Separation of Air-Conduction and Bone-Conduction Pathways

Elimination of air-conducted sound alone is readily achieved by blocking the ears. The results with this method of interference were neither striking nor consistent. Elimination of both air- and bone-conducted voice sounds was effected by playing a loud masking tone into both ears of the subject through headphones. The loudness of the tone used approached pain level and complete masking of the subject's awareness of his own speech sound was achieved. The results of this experiment were immediate and consistent. Control of both steady-state speech and of the ability to make immediate starts in speaking was rapidly established. In general, virtually complete elimination of stammering resulted during the experiment. The ability of each subject to make an immediate start in speaking improved to a very considerable extent.

Thus we have found that elimination of air-conducted feedback of the monitored sounds has little effect on the performance of a stammering subject, whereas blocking both air-conduction and bone-conduction pathways of speech feedback results generally in a virtually complete suppression of stammering. Such a method of interference with the appropriate feedback pathways results in virtually complete control of both steady-state and starting-condition utterance of the stammerers we have studied.

(3) The Importance of the Pitch of the Perceived, Monitored Sounds

The exact pitch of the masking tone is not critical within the approximate range: 120–180 c/s. However, more detailed inspection has shown that it is essential to mask the *very-low*-frequency tones of the stammerer's voice, if he is to be controlled. A more elaborate masking technique is reported later, which demonstrates that if he hears the very lowest tones of his own voice, stammering will remain. No conjecture will be made here as to the physiological significance of these results. Clearly, a general difference in pitch of sounds transmitted by bone-conduction and by air-conduction pathways can be admitted (as can be demonstrated subjectively by listening to the difference in quality of one's own speech sounds, first while speaking, and second when hearing a high-quality gramophone or tape recording of the same utterances). It is well understood that bone-conducted sounds manifest a strong low-frequency emphasis which is not evident for air-conducted sounds.[5]

On the basis of the results we cannot verify whether perception of bone-conducted sounds alone is significant in stammering, or whether any feedback, whatever the channel, is adequate to set up the perceptual difficulty. But there is fortunately one clue to this problem in another connection. We have observed that in the case of artificially induced " stammering " in normal individuals (Section 1) using delayed playback speech, an interesting feature arises. The effect of sounds impressed on the ear through a bone-conduction channel is considerably more severe than that of a correspondingly loud sound impressed through telephones by air conduction. (A simple bone-conduction channel is provided by an adapted electrical headphone pressed on the subject's temples.) The experience of such a bone-conducted " delayed playback " speech can be described as more than irritating; it can be quite distressing.

Finally we have attempted to assess the significance of the bone-conduction pathway in another way. We have required the subjects to read a standard text, without voicing (i.e. in a whisper). Despite the extraordinary fact that few of our subjects seem to have had occasion to whisper and that indeed by no means all could be induced to do so, we have obtained some results.

Of 15 cases who were able to whisper only 3 showed any significant tendency to stammer whilst doing so. In 12 cases of the 15, the total breakdown duration averaged 3 sec during the whispered reading of a 120-word text; the maximum observed was 5 sec. In normal voiced reading, the total breakdown duration for these cases averaged 24 sec, the maximum being 59 sec. In one of the three exceptions the total breakdown interval during usual (voicing) performance was 15 sec, reducing to 9 sec whilst whispering. In another of the exceptions, the subject repeatedly broke into voicing but achieved a total breakdown duration of 32 sec compared with 200 sec for that during usual speaking (voicing) performance. In the other case no improvement was observed during whispering compared with the usual performance of relatively mild speech difficulty (total breakdown time 14 sec).

It is evident that in some cases the elimination of bone-conducted sounds by whispering in this way is also highly rewarding in control of stammering. It seems likely therefore that the low-pitched components of the speech (monitored through a bone-conduction pathway) are of primary significance in mediating the perceptual abnormality which we associate with stammering. It remains to consider the stimuli preferentially transmitted by this pathway. The most important of such stimuli are undoubtedly the larynx tones of the speaker. Hence we are tentatively associating stammering with an abnormality in perception of the low-frequency components of the larynx tones of the stammerer. This, of course, is not the same thing as saying that such abnormality is a *cause*.

STATISTICAL RESULTS

It is proposed to report here the details of our experiments using stammerers, under the influence of acoustic masking and also with the technique of speech shadowing.

A series of 54 cases has now been studied. In conformity with current English usage of the term " stammering," we have not attempted to sub-divide or otherwise classify the cases we have seen. It is believed that to say this is to imply that each case is different. Our cases demonstrated a range of speech defects; namely, repetition of sounds, words or phrases, and hesitations and pauses of duration varying from $\frac{1}{2}$ sec up to severe blockages of some 30–60 sec. In each case pauses and repetitions were accompanied by evidence of psychological tension such as facial grimacing, shuffling of the feet and often temporary interference with respiration. For a test, each subject was given a standard text of 120 words to read aloud. The textual material was taken from contemporary non-fiction magazine

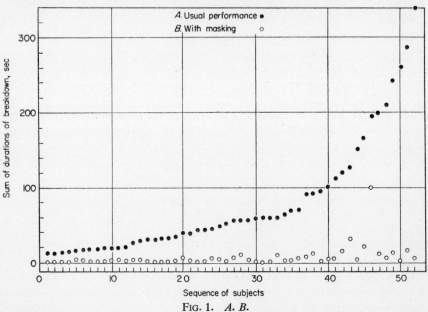

Fig. 1. *A. B.*

articles. The time taken to read the text, the number of repetitions, hesitations and breakdowns, and the duration of each breakdown was assessed. Usng a new text, we determined the ability of each subject to make immediate starts in utterance when new parts of the text were pointed out, in quick succession.

The experiment was then repeated in entirety, using new textual material, whilst the subject was wearing a pair of neatly-fitting telephones activated by high-energy 140-c/s tone. Complete masking of the subject's aural awareness of his own voice was achieved by using a masking-tone loudness close to the threshold of pain. The whole experiment was then repeated.

The results are summarized in the figures. Figure 1A shows the usual performance of each stammerer measured by average results before and after the masking experiment; Fig. 1B shows the performance under the influence of the masking tone. The parameter recorded is the total duration due to hesitations, blockages and repetitions while reading the standard text.

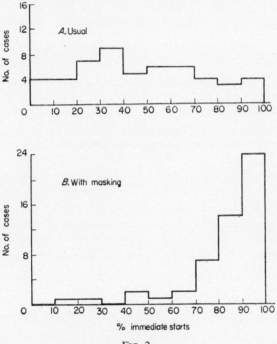

FIG. 2.

(The time to read the text by a number of normal (non-stammering) individuals averaged 58 sec.) The average duration of breakdowns, in the case of stammerers unassisted by masking, averaged 55 sec.

The improvement observed in ability to make immediate starts in utterance is illustrated in a different way in Fig. 2, which gives the frequency distribution of cases showing given percentages of immediate. unhesitant starts. The improvement is again clearly demonstrated.

Another observation of interest concerns the temporal distribution of breakdown, both in the usual performance of stammerers and in the case of their tonally masked performance (to the small degree in which breakdowns remain). Discounting the one exception to the general result we have described above, a rough estimate of the distribution in both situations can be made. This indicates that 90 per cent of all (the relatively few) breakdowns under masking occur within the first 5 or 6 sec. Under conditions of usual (non-masked) performance, only some 10 per cent of the much greater number of breakdowns occur within the same period. It is clear that control of both starting and steady-state conditions has been established, if not immediately, then within the first few seconds.

We have measured also the ability of the subjects to shadow, concurrently and continuously, a message read aloud by a control speaker. In 39 cases of the 51 with whom we have tried this test, the stammerer was able to shadow a 120-word message, read by a tutor at the rate of 50–100 words per min, with relatively few breakdowns, and without missing more than 5 words. In these cases the total duration of breakdowns for the worst case, whilst shadowing, was 4 sec. In a further 8 cases of the 51, breakdowns of up to 15 sec caused several phrases (6–20 words) to be missed. In the remaining 4 cases of the 51, the stammerer demonstrated an inferior ability in shadowing and was unable to complete the message successfully. Thus in at least 75 per cent of the stammerers we have seen, relatively little difficulty was experienced by subjects in carrying out this shadowing technique, particularly when the subjects were reassured before the attempt.

It should be emphasized that these results were obtained at virtually the first trial of the experiment in each case, with only elementary instructions and without any previous learning. Later investigation has led us to observe that this technique appears to establish what might be called a marked learning situation. People seemed to improve with practice. This improvement appeared to be maintained to various degrees, so much so that it seemed essential to suggest clinical trial. A very preliminary account of some early clinical trials is reported in the Appendix. In view of the known fact that stammering appears to be habit forming, it seemed possible that normal speaking also might be habit forming for a stammerer. We consider therefore that this last technique offers some possibility of treating stammering by controlling acoustic environment and training a sufferer in new habits of perception—namely those associated with normal patterns of speaking.

SOME ALTERNATIVE HYPOTHESES

Three main alternative hypotheses could perhaps be postulated to explain the results we have observed.

First, it might be argued that what we have found are distraction techniques for the inhibition of stammering behaviour. We would not deny this but would emphasize the generality, reproducibility and completeness of results from the particular techniques we use. Thus the shadowing technique, by its very nature, compels the stammerer to listen to the control speaker; whilst under the influence of this control, transference of at least part of his aural perceptions is ensured. Many other distraction techniques (e.g. rhythmic movement of the arms) might also exercise such control, but the present techniques appear (from their very generality) to mediate control of a primary quality. Secondly, it may be suggested that the apparent environmental isolation produced by the use of a loud masking noise, might induce an improvement in a stammerer's speech habits just because a new situation has been created and because the stammerer has the impression of isolation. The features of our experiments relevant to the previous hypothesis are also relevant to this. Furthermore we find no evidence that familiarity with the changed subjective situation causes a deterioration of the stammerer's speech behaviour while reading aloud.

These two hypotheses are expressed in subjective psychological terms; words such as distraction, attention, isolation, are used. But it is rather the experimental conditions and the resulting overt behaviour changes which we wish to emphasize in our own statement, in objective terms—not their correlates in sensations.

Thirdly, it is known that some stammerers show improved performance under normal conditions when speaking very loudly. Since the masking technique induced some subjects to speak loudly, might this not be a significant factor in the improvement which has been observed? Each of the last 30 subjects in our series was instructed, for reasons which were not explained to them, to speak very quietly for a 30-sec period while the masking tone was applied. We have found no deterioration of the subject's performance, whilst reading, due to quiet speaking (at or below normal levels) in any case. Under the influence of the masking noise, some subjects spontaneously spoke at normal or less than normal levels. It is therefore evident that the loudness of speaking was not a significant factor in these experiments.

PARTIAL PERCEPTION; EFFECTS UPON STAMMERERS OF HEARING LOW-PITCH VOICE TONES

The masking tone used in the experiments so far described resulted from sinusoidal excitation of a pair of headphones, at about 140 c/s; the sound waves produced are such as to set the basilar membrane into vibration and so to obliterate all hearing, over the whole range of pitch of the human voice. We considered it of interest to observe what happens if the sound is changed in character in such a way as to permit the listener to hear only the very-low-frequency sounds of his voice. That is, how low in pitch must the obliteration extend for control of stammering?

Rather than use a pure-tone masking sound (with its highly concentrated energy), we have chosen to work with a white-noise masking sound,* which

* White noise is the technical term for a sound which has its frequency energy uniformly spread over all frequencies. It can very readily be generated electronically.

has its energy widely spread over the whole aural spectrum; then this sound is passed through one of two filters which effectively concentrate the energy into frequency components lying: (*a*) below about 500 c/s or (*b*) above about 500 c/s.

The first of these filtered white noises (low-frequency) is far more pleasant to listen to than a loud low-frequency pure tone, but is as effective in obliterating hearing of low-frequency sounds; such a masking sound has been found to be equally effective in inhibiting stammering behaviour. The results are again consistent and virtually complete.

The second of these filtered white noises (high-frequency) obliterates all hearing expect that of the extreme-low-frequency voice sounds. The listener then has some awareness of these components of his own voice. The results of such tests have been interesting and, we believe, significant, because they have been found to be very varied indeed compared with the results obtained with the low-frequency masking noise. Fourteen cases were examined for this comparison; details are given in Table 1.

TABLE 1

The effects of filtered-white-noise masking upon stammering behaviour
(Total breakdown time during reading of a 120-word text)

Case	(*a*) Noise through Low-pass filter. Breakdown duration (sec)		Per cent Reduction	(*b*) Noise through High-pass filter. Breakdown duration (sec)		Per cent Reduction
	Usual	Masked		Usual	Masked	
a	260	2	100	220	150	32
b	200	10	95	180	25	86
c	150	10	93	162	110	32
d	125	15	88	105	82	22
e	93	11	88	80	30	63
f	90	7	92	81	10	88
g	56	3	95	70	75	−7
h	48	4	90	44	64	−45
i	44	1	98	31	15	52
j	38	5	87	43	25	42
k	31	0	100	24	4	83
l	22	1	95	22	18	18
m	19	0	100	26	22	15
n	18	0	100	15	14	6

Average reduction with low-frequency-noise masking $= 94 \pm 5$ per cent.
Average reduction with high-frequency-noise masking $= 35 \pm 37$ per cent.
　　The *t*-test on the difference in means of the two samples shows that the difference is very significant, i.e. at the $p = 0.1$ per cent level ($t = 6.0$; d.f. $= 26$).

From these figures we make two observations: (1) Under the condition of high-frequency-noise masking (when the subject is aware of his low-frequency voice tones) stammering is by no means generally suppressed and may even be made worse. Consequently we conclude that total masking of the extreme-low-frequency sounds of his voice is essential in such experiments for the control of a stammerer's speech. (2) We notice the very great variability of behaviour, when using high-frequency-noise masking. This scatter seems to us to be of significance. Thus, on our hypothesis that stammering is mediated by (note: not *caused* by) the subject's perceptions of his own low-frequency-voice sounds, one cannot set a universal threshold on the frequency of instability, that is upon a threshold of frequency below which a speaker's perceptions of his own voice should not pass. Rather, the safe threshold would seem to vary from individual to individual; then his potential for stammering behaviour is a function of the extent to which his aural perceptions are allowed to exceed his particular threshold by the conditions of his environment.

SUMMARY

A series of experiments is described, carried out on 54 widely varied adult patients suffering from forms of chronic stammering. Different external acoustic stimuli were used, which resulted generally in almost total inhibition of stammering behaviour. This demonstrates that, in all these varied cases, stammering is a perceptual rather than a motor abnormality. Under control, the sufferers were induced to speak and read at normal rates.

An interesting feature of these results is their universal nature, since the cases were drawn from a wide field. Some of the experiments have suggested methods for training, and show some therapeutic promise.

APPENDIX

Notes on some Preliminary Clinical Trials

The object of these first trials has been to determine whether our findings may have any clinical value and to gather experience of various methods of organizing and executing the shadowing technique, in children and adults. Briefly, the aim has been to train the stammerers into new habits of aural perception.

For very young children two types of recordings of simple stories were made. In the first, pauses occurred after each phrase; in the second no pauses occurred. The first record was played and the child asked to repeat each phrase aloud, during the subsequent interval (copying). The second record was then played, after it had been explained to the child that he should continue talking, since no pauses would occur (shadowing). Whilst young children appear to be able to carry out the first task, with the help of some unison speaking, more practice seems to be required before they can shadow really adequately. Disc records were given to them for daily home practice; later, stories were read to them by their parents for shadowing, though this was avoided when the parents were of nervous temperament.

With older school children, shadowing was understood at once, though their early performances suffered due to losing the (spoken) place, and to missing phrases. The use of headphones for relaying either disc-recorded speech, or the voice of the therapist reading into a microphone, has proved useful in teaching shadowing. Instructing the patient to face away from the therapist has also been found helpful. In several cases the voice was initially very monotonous, with the speech jerky and arhythmic; there were some stammering breakdowns, mainly on unfamiliar or misheard words, or, if the subject was conscious of his accent, on words which he usually pronounced differently. Breakdowns soon became less frequent, but the defects in rhythm took longer to correct. One common fault was as follows; the child paused to listen and followed this by a rush of words to catch up when the end of the phrase had been heard. As the quality and the speed of shadowing improved, so did the quality of conversational speech. In those who found difficulty in shadowing, practice of two-text reading (in which the therapist reads one text and the stammerer another) led to an improvement in shadowing. It is well known that stammering can build up rapidly when confidence is lost, whether in conversation or reading, and in a few cases this has also applied in shadowing. In all these situations when patients found themselves unable to complete a particular phrase, several repetitions of this phrase by the therapist, with out-of-phase shadowing by the stammerer, has been found useful in helping them to pick up normal rhythm again. (This is no doubt related psychologically to the " cancelling out of blocks," van Riper.[6]) As soon as the patient had acquired the normal rhythm of the phrase in question, the therapist stopped repeating it and either continued reading (in shadowing) or left him to continue (in conversation and solo reading). Some individuals who found difficulty in shadowing showed an improvement in this ability when merely reminded " to attend to the rhythm."

Practice in shadowing appeared to lose efficacy when the textual passage used had been memorized by frequent repetition (as with gramophone records). It seemed necessary to use very simple texts at the start and to read them in a smooth manner, although only *normal* rhythm and intonation were used throughout. Some cases showed a strong tendency to try to speak in unison at first. Whispering was used with other cases who were unable to shadow voiced speech at the start.

With adults, observations were similar to those with older school children. In severe cases, they were often initially unable to copy phrase by phrase (in contrast to very young children) but learned to shadow fairly easily and at gradually increasing speed. Once able to shadow, they learned copying much more easily. One or two adults and older children with very severe stammering were able to shadow rapid speech only. In this type of shadowing the individual automatically falls much further behind and hears whole phrases before beginning to shadow them. These patients derived benefit from being taught to shadow slow speech.

At whatever point on the scale a stammerer began, the aim was to lead him up through these forms of training, gradually increasing the difficulty of the task until he was able to retain stable rhythm in conversation without any aids and to maintain a high threshold of tolerance to environmental stimulation.

Psychological considerations have not been overlooked and it is not suggested that methods of retraining aural perception would be sufficient without any psychological help except in certain cases, but that these methods may prove to be a useful contribution to the treatment of stammering.

No general conclusions can be reached from the few cases summarized below; they illustrate the technique with which experiments have been started, the types of case, and the time intervals involved.

Case 1—A boy, aged $2\frac{1}{2}$ years, had stammered for 4 months before treatment by standard methods was given (advice to parents). The difficulty then disappeared for 9 months but recurred in a more severe form on his entering nursery school. After 8 months (at age 4 years), shadowing practice was instituted as a form of play. The child apparently did not connect this with his stammer. After daily practice for 10 days the stammer disappeared and has not recurred during the following 5 months, including the upheaval of family migration to another country. At such times of strain the mother resorted to daily shadowing practice with the child again.

A school report stated that a year ago the child " was stammering so badly we were hardly able to understand him. His speech is now perfectly normal."

Case 2—A girl, aged 6 years, while being treated for an articulation defect, developed a stammer which became extremely severe. A number of forms of treatment for the stammer proved valueless. Practice with copying and shadowing was then started and improvement was noticed within a week. Of the two, she strongly preferred copying, probably because of the immaturity of her speech generally. After several weeks' practice the stammer had disappeared except for very occasional lengthened vowel sounds. Treatment of the articulation defect was then resumed and had no deleterious effect on fluency. The child was discharged (for follow-up) with only occasional vowel prolongations and articulation within normal limits for her age.

CASE 3—A schoolboy, aged 16 years, had a very severe stammer, with word-blockages of up to $3\frac{1}{2}$ min duration. Standard methods of treatment over a period of 5 months resulted in slight temporary improvements. At the end of this time he was in a bad phase; long blocks with violent grimacing virtually prohibited conversation. Shadowing practice was then started and resulted in immediate improvement. The boy continued it alone using gramophone records at home, daily for 5 months, with weekly visits to the therapist for correction of his current faults in technique. Subsequently, practice once every 2–3 days was found adequate. His speech was then nearly normal, and he was able to make telephone calls, entertain his parents' friends, and speak freely in class. Except for three brief very mild set-backs (of which the cause was unknown) the improvement has been steady and maintained over a period of a year. In a professional interview 3 months ago the boy did not stammer and only slight abnormal rhythm was evident.

CASE 4—A boy, 6 years old, was treated in 1954 over several months for his stammer. Standard methods of treatment produced a gradual improvement. In 1955 the child had a recurrence of the stammer in a severe form. Standard methods of treatment were not successful. Shadowing was then taught and practised daily. The child showed strain in the form of wriggling, kicking, frowning and jerky speech while shadowing for the first 3 weeks, but he then mastered the technique (at his third treatment) and the stammer had disappeared 1 week later, except for a very infrequent momentary catch in his breathing. In the next 5 months the improvement has been maintained except for a single brief set-back from which the boy quickly recovered after resuming home practice of shadowing for a few days.

CASE 5—A Singhalese student, aged 20, had jerky speech and a " gulping " type of stammer with grimacing. After daily shadowing practice for 6 weeks, his speech became smooth and of virtually normal rhythm and the grimacing had disappeared. The stammer occurred occasionally in a very much milder form.

CASE 6—A man of 59 years, with a violently explosive stammer of 51 years' duration, had made unsuccessful attempts to improve his speech (by various methods) since 1920. In shadowing practice he was at first only able to follow rapid speech. For a time he practised only occasionally, but when daily practice of slow shadowing was employed his speech improvement accelerated.

While he has still a comparatively severe stammer, it is very much less explosive and, measured by the methods used in the present paper, had been reduced by some 60–66 per cent in 4 months, and is still improving.

CASE 7—A man of 39 had a very severe, constant, violently explosive stammer, of tono-clonic type, of 34 years' duration. During speaking, showers of saliva were produced. The stammer had improved several years ago but recurred after a family bereavement. After explanation and brief practice this man was able to shadow very slow reading at his first treatment. No helper was available for practice at home, and the slowest disc-recorded speech available (for a heavy-weight pick-up) was still too fast for him until he was familiar with the content. In spite of these handicaps, striking improvement was observed after 4 visits (treatment once weekly).

In general, after 2 months, this man's speech is now slower, much freer, with much less tension and no spitting; he already reports the ability to make long phone calls without noticeable difficulty. He is occasionally disturbed by stammering spasms which are habit-forming in one conversation if not taken in hand. This may be done by directing attention to the correct rhythm of an incorrectly spoken sentence. If this fails, an immediate improvement in his conversational speech follows a period of shadowing.

CASE 8—A girl of 17, in whose family most of the females have stammered for several generations, has an inspiratory stammer mainly on voiceless consonants. She has improved with daily shadowing practice but only very slowly as compared with the previous cases. She still stammers while shadowing; does so less if using headphones.

CASE 9—A boy of 12 has stammered for 7 years, particularly on voiceless consonants. A psychiatrist had pronounced him normal except that he was over-emotional when frustrated. He was unusual in that he stammered most on totally unimportant sentences.

All forms of speech therapy tried had failed and any discussion of his speech caused his eyes to fill with tears. This occurred if he blocked badly in shadowing. Although this boy did learn to shadow well there was no noticeable improvement in his daily speech.

CASE 10—A boy of 16 with the most severe form of stammering, complete freezing into immobility on attempting to speak, said that his stammer had taken that form since it began at the age of 7. He was unable even to make single consonant sounds on request. The attempt to teach shadowing produced further anxiety and was abandoned.

The use of brief periods of filtered white noise (low frequencies) played through headphones under strict supervision, is now being tried clinically for conversational speech as well as reading, in school children and adults. Some school children react unfavourably by flushing of the face and increased stammering, in spite of being forewarned. One child asked for a second trial and was then no longer worried by it and showed some improvement in speech. Case 3 responds in a striking manner and experiences pleasure in the smooth conversational speech which he can produce under these conditions. This is so also for Case 6, but at present his fluency in conversational speech masked by white noise deteriorates after about a minute and has to be brought out anew by starting again after a pause. Deteroration during a long conversation is one of the unvarying characteristics of his stammer uinder normal conditions.

REFERENCES

1. LEE, B. S. (1950). Effects of delayed speech feedback. *J. Acoust. Soc. Amer.*, **22**, 824-826. See also **22**, 639.
2. FREUND, H. (1932). Der Induktive Vorgang im Stottern und Seine Therapeutische Verwertung. *Z. Gesamte Neurol. u. Psychiat.*, **141**, 180-192.
3. KERN, A. (1932). Der Einflusz des Horens auf das Stottern. *Arch. Psychiat.*, **97**, 429-449.
4. CHERRY, E. C. (1953). Some experiments on the recognition of speech, with one and with two ears. *J. Acoust. Soc. Amer.*, **25**, No. 5, pp. 975-979.
5. BEKESY, G. VON and ROSENBLITH, W. A. (1951). The mechanical properties of the ear. Ch. 27 in *Handbook of Experimental Psychology*, S. S. Stevens, Wiley, N.Y.
6. VAN RIPER, C. (1947). *Speech Correction*. 3rd edition, p. 423. Prentice Hall, New York.
7. HAAS, H. (1951). Uber den Einfluss eines Einfachechos auf die Horsankeit von Sprache. *Acustica*, **1**, 49.
8. CHERRY, E. C., SAYERS, B. McA. and MARLAND, P. M. (1955). Some experiments upon the total suppression of stammering. *Nature, Lond.*, **176**, 874.

THE TREATMENT OF STAMMERING BY THE CHERRY–SAYERS METHOD : CLINICAL IMPRESSIONS*

J. MACLAREN

St. Mary's Hospital

IT IS now 3 years since experiments were started at St. Mary's Hospital, London, in treating stammering by new techniques suggested by the experiments of Cherry, Sayers and Marland. I give below some of the observations which have been made in the clinic during this period.

A very young child listens to speech patterns with a quality of attention which becomes unnecessary when he can reproduce these patterns himself. Once he attains this skill he ceases to listen in the same way; he does a kind of " shorthand " listening which is really a quick referring back to his own remembered speech patterns. He now speaks—not from an external pattern but from an internal one; a memory of how he said it before—a legitimate and labour-saving process on which, of course, the skill of normal speech is built but the very efficiency of which can quickly create a vicious circle where habit is abnormal.

It has been interesting to observe in our work at the clinic how rapidly speech habits are formed and, once formed, how obstinately they persist. Often some gross error is made by a patient while copying a simple passage; on repetition of the same passage the mistake will be repeated over and over again, though the patient may protest that he is " really listening." Sometimes with heightened attention the passage will finally be copied correctly— often without the subject being aware of any alteration.

An intelligent 6-year-old copying simple phrases substituted " we *shall* be going " for a very clearly spoken " we'll be going." He was asked to listen more carefully and say it back just as he heard it, but each time the passage was repeated he made exactly the same substitution. His attention was diverted for some minutes and then he was again presented with the phrase and again repeated his original version.

An adult patient somehow managed to substitute the word " beautiful " for " lovely " while shadowing, and persisted in the same error when taken back repeatedly over the passage, until he was told that he was actually changing a word. He was incredulous, but, shocked into heightened attention, *listened* and shadowed correctly.

* Specially written for this book.

The observation of such phenomena, common to all speakers, shows clearly to what extent we become imprisoned in our own habits, speaking as it were in a closed circuit of our own way of saying it.

When, as with the stammerers, abnormal speech habits are associated with anxiety, the subject reacts to his difficulty in his own individual way and other abnormal patterns of behaviour are added, these also being caught up and perpetuated in a vicious circle of compulsive habit. Our task is to break through this vicious circle; to free the attention from its compulsive attachment to defective patterns and set it on normal ones.

With our young patients the heightened attention to listening which is required is gained by various methods—we play sound games of " follow-my-leader " checking back on the tape recorder to see how faithfully the leader is being followed. Headphones help to cut out distractions, give speech a more direct impact on the attention and are enjoyed by the children. Usually it is not long before the child is copying normal phrases without difficulty. Then stories can be followed in something between copying and shadowing—what we call " coming in on your heels." Sometimes the child follows, in this way, a text relayed through headphones from a disc and we are able to record the child's natural fluent speech on the tape recorder and play it back to him. Hearing his own voice speaking normally and experiencing the feeling of normal speech movement help to detach him from the defective patterns.

Obviously the environment of the patient, particularly that of the young child, must be most carefully studied for causes of anxiety.

Recently a little girl of 3¾ years with a marked secondary stammer was brought to the clinic. It was noticeable that when the child blocked she flushed and looked apprehensively at her mother, though at all other times their relationship appeared very happy. A history of her case brought out the following facts: The stammer had only developed in the previous 2 months. The child was a slow starter in speech development and her speech was still immature with many childish substitutes and poorly articulated sounds. There was only one other child in the family, a sister 5 years older whose speech development had been unusually forward. The parents had suddenly become anxious about the younger one's speech, comparing it with the older girl's at the same age, as a result of which our little patient had been subjected to 2 months constant checking and correction, well meant and kindly administered but entirely frustrating to the child's intense desire to communicate.

The parents were extremely co-operative and once they understood the position they refrained entirely from criticism. After 2 months auditory retraining the stammer was entirely eliminated.

It might be argued that, once the anxiety factor had been eliminated, this patient's speech would have reverted to normal without further treatment and it is impossible to prove anything either way, but from our knowledge of the self-perpetrating character of stammering it seems likely that this would not have been so. It should be added that in the process of the more careful listening required in treatment many of the child's articulatory weaknesses cleared up without any direct attention being focused on them.

With most older stammerers their anxieties spring from *mal* attitudes connected with their handicap and it is most interesting to observe how these subjective reactions, often the cause of so much trouble in their lives, are gradually brought to light and seen in a different perspective as the patient begins to observe during the treatment what it is that prevents him hearing and holding in his attention the normal pattern of speech.

With the more mature patient we usually start with shadowing—recording by tape and playing back to check accuracy. Usually a fair degree of fluency is obtained without difficulty—but with gross inaccuracy in speed and rhythm. Our patient is shown how such inaccuracies predominate in passages containing feared sounds. He begins to appreciate that at such times his attention is switched back to his own patterns—he is " reacting." He is encouraged to try to keep attention on the external pattern presented to him—to listen " all along the line of sound." As he becomes more successful in this he experiences a pleasant sense of freedom and normality and he is beginning to exert a necessary inhibition on the old defective habits and to build up normal ones. Even in this apparently simple and very practical exercise our patient can be brought to see something of the reasons for his enslavement to his stammer, and the possibilities, on a small scale at least, of something different.

When he has begun to give relaxed attention to the text, and to resist the switch back to his own defective pattern, we make the exercise more difficult in various ways; by interruption, change of speed and volume and so on. Again we use our technique with a dual purpose. Not only does the patient have to give increased auditory attention to surmount the disturbance but certain attitudes common to stammerers become apparent under these conditions and can be observed and gradually discarded. The stammerer is habitually on the defensive about speech—over-eager to justify himself for failure; and even intelligent and co-operative patients very often find extreme difficulty in accepting external interruptions without irritation and embarrassment. A good step forward has been taken when such interruptions and disturbances can be accepted without subjective reactions—the patient shadowing when he can hear the test and remaining passive and unmoved when he cannot.

New techniques designed to sharpen the stammerer's appreciation of the phrase as the natural unit of speech play an important part in treatment.

By frequent and varied exercises in phrase-copying, building up resistance to subjective reactions in similar ways to those used in shadowing, the patient's attention is gradually drawn away from his disintegrating pre-occupation with the individual sound and back on to the sensible unit of the phrase.

One exercise required of our patients in this connection is to add a loose repetitive " faked " stammer to the beginning of each phrase, still keeping attention on the pattern presented to them in the rest of the phrase and looking the therapist calmly in the eyes as they speak. On one occasion a group of students visited the clinic and watched a 9-year-old boy stammerer go through this test without flinching. The students were then put through a similar test. Only one of the 7 managed the assignment successfully; the others all showed obvious embarrassment, turning away their eyes on the faked stammer, completely changing the original rhythm of the phrase and, in two cases, actually producing an involuntary stammer—much to the amusement of our young patient. When one realises how sensitive even the normal speaker is to this type of speech situation the value of such an exercise in developing a more objective attitude in the stammerer is clear.

The problem of stammering is not one of speech, but of *speech in the act of communication*. It is a problem of human relationships and, as such, is infinitely complex. No one approach can be said to be " the " approach—there must be many ways of helping the stammerer. But we have found it possible in our work at St. Mary's during these last 3 years to build up on this perceptual approach a dynamic and interesting technique which can be adapted to all ages and types of stammerers.

The young patient—provided that environmental stresses can be relieved—responds well to direct auditory retraining.

With the older patient the anxiety attached to the speech situation itself often spreads its tentacles through the whole pattern of life. It would be absurd to expect that auditory retraining alone could bring any real relief to such patients. But here our technique has been found of great value, for it not only serves to strengthen and reinforce the memory of normality but it can be used as an instrument by which, in a very practical way, the stammerer can be brought to realise in actual experience the nature of his difficulties and the principles which must be followed if he is to free himself from them.

SUMMARY AND CONCLUSIONS

THE PAPERS presented in this book must, of course, speak for themselves; nothing that can be said in these few concluding remarks is likely to alter the judgment which the reader will have formed of the present studies of behaviour therapy. Nevertheless, it may be useful to repeat concisely some of the main points made in these papers and to indicate some of the possible conclusions that may be drawn from all the work reviewed here.

(1) It will have become clear that the group of techniques discussed here presents a genuine alternative, both on the theoretical and on the practical level, to current psychoanalytic theories and methods of psychotherapy based upon them. Both what the therapist does and the reasons why he does it, differentiate behaviour therapy from psychoanalytic therapy; indeed the very aims of the two techniques are different, centering on the removal of symptoms in the case of behaviour therapy and regarding such removal of symptoms as relatively unimportant in the case of psychotherapy.

(2) There is ample evidence in these pages that treatment based upon behaviour therapy produces results not inferior and often superior to those produced by psychotherapy. It is important that this statement should not be misunderstood. I have always argued that evidence for therapeutic effectiveness must come from *properly controlled experiments contrasting different types of treatment or a treatment and no-treatment group*; without experiments of this type, we shall never be able to make any definitive statements about the efficacy of any type of treatment. No such properly controlled study of either psychotherapy or behaviour therapy has yet appeared and certainly there is none comparing the two techniques in a proper experimental setting.

Granted that no definitive statement can be made about the efficacy of these different types of treatment, we may nevertheless note that there are certain data which are suggestive, although admittedly the conclusions to be drawn from them are still subject to argument. The data quoted in the paper by Gwynne Jones on enuresis very strongly suggest the greater efficacy of behaviour therapy as compared with psychotherapy. The same is true of the comparative figures given by Wolpe in comparing his method of treatment with orthodox psychoanalysis. Indeed, wherever comparisons are possible, they seem to indicate that behaviour therapy as a method of treatment shows considerable promise and deserves to be followed up and studied in much greater detail than has hitherto been done. It would also seem to be desirable to run properly controlled comparative studies in order

461

to analyse the relative efficiency of behaviour therapy and psychotherapy in carefully de-limited groups of patients. This would seem to be particularly valuable where symptoms can be quantified and measured with accuracy, as in the case of enuresis, tics, stammering, alcohol addiction and so forth. In view of the fact that claims for " cures " have been made and apparently substantiated for methods of treatment ranging from cold baths to the extraction of teeth, it would obviously be absurd at this stage to make any greater claims than this for the curative powers of behaviour therapy; it must be left to future research of a much more rigorous character to assess the precise possibilities and limitations of this new approach.

(3)   It should be noted, however, that behaviour therapy is not limited in its method of proof to a simple actuarial count of actual cures. The methods described in these pages are derived deductively from a general set of theories which was not, like the Freudian theory, created *ad hoc*, but owes its existence to a large body of rigorous experimental evidence accumulated over many years. The applicability of this body of knowledge can be tested in other ways than by the simple fact of a " cure " being achieved or not and attention has throughout been drawn to tests of this kind. When we are treating a patient for a series of tics, say, then the simple fact of the disappearance of these tics after many months of treatment may or may not be indicative of the value of the method employed; the frequency of spontaneous remission in cases of this kind makes it impossible to draw any firm conclusions from a single case or even a whole series of cases. Learning theory and behaviour therapy, however, enable us to treat the symptom in a quantitative manner as a dependent variable in an experimental design in which the treatment is the independent variable and if we can show, as was done by Yates for instance, that we can at will alter the dependent variable by making changes in the independent variable, then even a single case becomes a strong argument in support of the theory in question. At the present time, it would perhaps be true to say that it may be more important to look for evidence of the correctness of the general principles of behaviour therapy in the strict, rigorous and quantitative relationship between symptom and experimental treatment, than to concentrate on actuarial comparisons of treatment efficacy between what are often, if not always, non-comparable groups.

(4)   I would like to draw attention again to one crucial point on which the two theories differ most profoundly. Psychoanalysis predicts quite definitely that symptom removal by means of such methods as those advocated here must result in the formation of new symptoms or the recrudescence of the old. Behaviour therapy equally definitely makes the opposite prediction and asserts that symptoms once removed will not recur, nor will new symptoms arise in their stead. Admittedly, there are certain points which mitigate against the clear-cut nature of this dichotomy. As pointed out previously, symptom removal means removal of *autonomic* as well as *motor* symptoms and

if an investigator should claim a " cure " without having removed the autonomic symptom, there may be an apparent symptom revival which might be
erroneously interpreted as supporting the Freudian theory. Again, neurotic
symptoms tend to appear most frequently in people who may be supposed
to be endowed genetically with an over-reactive autonomic system, i.e.
people who are high on " neuroticism "; such people may be cured of a
particular conditioned motor or autonomic response, but they will nevertheless remain liable to form new conditioned responses in appropriate conditions. This again might be misinterpreted as a " symptom revival "
whereas in reality it would be more appropriate to consider it as a new
reaction to a new situation.

However, even without bearing these cautionary arguments in mind,
it is noticeable, and perhaps surprising to many orthodox psychoanalysts,
that writer after writer is able to say that cures, once accomplished, are *not*
followed by symptom revival or the growth of alternative symptoms. Even
if we were to assume that behaviour therapy has little to do with these cures
and that they were all spontaneous remissions, this failure of symptom
revival would still speak very strongly against the Freudian hypothesis.
The whole notion of symptom revival is a *shibboleth* which has never
received the critical scrutiny it deserves; the notion has been accepted
without proof in the first place, and has been perpetuated through indoctrina-
tion. It is high time that a more experimental and empirical outlook
supplemented this reliance on authoritative *obiter dicta*.

(5) It will have been noted in the chapter by Shoben that many of the
procedures of psychotherapy can be interpreted with respect of their
effectiveness in terms of learning theory. Thus, psychiatrists and clinical
psychologists, who have in the past concentrated almost entirely on methods
of this type and who accept the general argument of this book, do not
necessarily have to give up all or most of their favourite techniques. Many
procedures admittedly have been widely used, not because of their proven
effectiveness, but because they are derived from Freudian theory. In so far
as this is their only justification, it is difficult to believe that it will suffice
for ever as a sign of legitimacy. Many others, however, have a long history
of at least suggestive effectiveness, such as, for instance, the Roman Catholic
confessional, and it must be a matter of empirical research combined with
rigid logical deduction from learning theory to decide whether these methods
do or do not produce genuine therapeutic effects. Shoben's pioneering
article does not seem to have led to the re-thinking and experimental
re-examination of this field which is so urgently necessary; until more is
known about this aspect of treatment it will be idle to speculate further.

(6) It will have struck many readers that some at least of the procedures
and methods used are extremely primitive. This, together with the very
mechanical nature of some of the procedures gives rise in many psychiatrists

to a strong feeling of aversion which makes them less receptive to the theoretical arguments or the experimental results obtained with these procedures. This is unfortunate, because no *a priori* feelings or attitudes should be allowed to stand in the way of an objective appraisal of the facts such as they are.

Nevertheless, it must be agreed that considerable improvements should be possible in the procedures and methods used. It is curious, for instance, that in connection with aversion therapies the device of making the patient vomit in connection with a stimulus to be extinguished has been so widely used. Many of the disadvantages of this technique will be obvious; from the point of view of the psychologist its main disadvantage is perhaps the difficulty of *exact timing* of its onset and the *needless prolongation* of its duration. Electric shock would seem a very much better choice and it seems likely that experiments such as those by Freund would have had more favourable effects if shock had been used.

On the whole, of course, it is inevitable that at the beginning methods should be crude, mechanical and even brutal. It is only constant and long-continued experimentation, together with theoretical advances and progress in fundamental research, that will gradually lead us to procedures which are at the same time more elegant and more certain in their working. The fact that the present procedures, crude as they are, yet appear to have some effect is the best justification for believing that the time spent in seeking for improvements will be well spent.

Some of these improvements will undoubtedly be related to better apparatus design. The efficacy of the enuresis pad and the writer's cramp shocking devices, for instance, are almost certainly a direct function of their sheer physical efficiency in producing the desired effect *promptly*, *invariably* and at the *correct intensity*. Greater familiarity with modern electronic devices or even with simple workshop practices, would undoubtedly suggest many appropriate devices to psychologists and psychiatrists engaged upon behaviour therapy. Mechanical improvements of existing devices may have an equally beneficial effect upon therapeutic practice.

(7) Some adherents of learning theory do not find the notion of " personality " and " types " useful and claim that the laws of learning theory are universal laws which apply to everyone and that consequently the therapist who wishes to apply these laws need only be familiar with the general body of learning theory. I find it difficult to believe that such a stand can be justified on theoretical grounds, or that experience bears it out. General laws only apply to objects which are *homogeneous in all relevant parameters;* this is patently not true of organisms which differ profoundly in such traits as autonomic reactivity, conditionability and so forth. This is implicitly recognised by learning theorists who introduce special constants into their equations to take account of the varying properties of their subjects.

No individual predictions can be made without knowing and taking into account these individual constants.

Exactly the same is true when deductions are made from learning theory in the field of behaviour therapy. A good example of this is contained in the paper by R. Beech. He points out that the original aversion-type deconditioning methods used by Liversedge and Sylvester for the treatment of writer's cramp were very successful with their subjects, but failed with other groups. The explanation apparently is that the original subjects were *low* on neuroticism, whereas the latter ones were *high* on neuroticism. Thus, the anxiety generated by the electric shock, which constituted the aversion stimulus, produced quite different behavioural effects on these two groups, deconditioning the cramp reaction in the first place and increasing it in the other. Quite obviously the same symptom may require different techniques of treatment, depending on the autonomic reactivity and the condition-ability of a patient. This point is also made by V. Meyer in his paper where he demonstrates the different reactions to a similar mode of treatment made by relatively extraverted and relatively introverted subjects. D. Walton also stresses this point.

These considerations indicate two things. In the first place they suggest the importance of *diagnostic testing* in planning a course of behaviour therapy. The type of diagnostic testing envisaged, of course, is very different from the usual categorical disposal of patients in diagnostic groups having little meaning in terms of fundamental theory and having little relevance to actual methods of treatment. The diagnostic system envisaged here is one which grows directly from the same set of theories as does the treatment and is linked intimately with the method of treatment chosen. What is required is a *rational* system of diagnosis to set besides a *rational* system of treatment; I have argued this point in some detail in the *Dynamics of Anxiety and Hysteria* and will not pursue it here.

In the second place it is clear that the personality characteristics of a person which lead him to acquire the particular habit we wish to extinguish may militate against such a process of extinction. Under those conditions, use may be made of the relationships established between personality dimensions, as used in diagnosis, and drug effects. We can shift a person's position on the extraversion-introversion and the neuroticism dimensions temporarily by the use of suitable drugs and it seems likely that much greater use could be made of this fact in the treatment of neurotic responses. In view of the established relation between personality dimensions and drug effects, it is to be hoped that further research will be directed at this very important problem. Again the papers by V. Meyer and D. Walton may be used as an illustration of this.

(8) The last point to be made is one which underlies most of the others and is probably the most important of all. The treatment of neurosis and

behaviour disorders, if it is to be anything but a simple custodial type of treatment relying on spontaneous remission, lucky accidents and haphazard " insights," must be an *applied science*. Until relatively recently the science in question existed only in such an imperfect state that no application could be made with any great degree of confidence. Due to the work of Pavlov, Hull, Tolman, Guthrie, Thorndike and many others this position has changed, and we now have available a set of principles which constitute at least the beginnings of a properly formulated learning theory. It would be a dis-service to learning theory to pretend that it has advanced further than a certain very limited distance; it obviously cannot and does not rival the physical sciences in precision, in rigour or in interconnectedness. Quantifica-tion, although of the rudimentary kind only, has been achieved in certain aspects, although not in others. The field is a rapidly growing one and theories are constantly being improved or discarded. There is no uniformity of opinion and no general established theory to which everyone subscribes. This is often interpreted by outsiders as meaning that learning theory for practical purposes is useless. Nothing could be further from the truth, and no one with any knowledge of the place of theory in the physical sciences would make such a suggestion. The position in psychology very closely resembles that in sub-atomic physics in the period between the wars, when a new theory of the atom was being brought out almost every year. This creative period has not produced a universal theoretical framework com-parable to the Newtonian one; yet who could doubt the great value to applied research of all these very imperfect theories? Scientific theories seldom resemble the Newtonian one in degree of inclusiveness and length of life; it is probably unfortunate that books on the history and logic of science and scientific method should so much concentrate on this particular theory to the exclusion of the far more typical short-term, small-scale theories which are so much more characteristic of the day-to-day work of the scientist.

We have, then, the beginnings of a genuinely scientific system of learning theory from which we can deduce certain methods of treatment for behavioural disorders. The contents of this book have illustrated some of these deductions and the kind of effects which can be obtained by calling in learning theory to help us deal with these pressing and difficult problems. It should be noted, however, that these are mere skirmishes, small-scale investigations of one or two cases carried out to illustrate a method or to learn a little more about its possibilities. If behaviour therapy is to be used widely and effectively, then research will have to be done on a very much greater scale than anything hitherto contemplated. It is a commonplace in science that there is a great gap between pure research and applied research in the sense that fundamental advances cannot be immediately translated into applied projects. What is required is special research into the *methods of application* of fundamental advances, and such research is usually just as time consuming, expensive and complex as is fundamental research; often, it is far more so. Rutherford's work on the splitting of the atom did not begin to compare in point of expenditure of money, time and energy with the applied work that produced the atom bomb and the modern nuclear reactor. In psychology there has unfortunately usually been a hiatus between pure and applied work. The applied psychologist often considers the academic psychologist unpractical, remote from life and a prisoner of his " ivory tower " attitude; the academic psychologist often feels contempt for workers in applied fields whom he considers ignorant of fundamental facts and uninterested in theoretical problems. This gap must be bridged if our treatment of neurotic disorders is to emerge from its present highly unsatisfactory state. We must insist that those who carry out the applied work should be familiar with the facts ascertained by fundamental research; we must carry on applied research which will improve our knowledge of the applicability of such methods as those here discussed and which will give us information about their relative value with certain types of symptoms and certain types of patients. We must, above all, try to interest the academic psychologist in the fact that applied work is not in any sense inferior, but can and should be done in as rigorously an experimental fashion as any other kind of research. Indeed, many predictions of learning theory can be studied better in the clinic than in the laboratory. If this book has done anything to bring together these different bodies of workers and to kindle their interest in methods and applications which they may not previously have considered, it will have been eminently worth the effort.

AUTHOR INDEX

SUBJECT INDEX